Organization and Evolution in Plants

Organization and Evolution in Plants

C. W. WARDLAW

Department of Botany,
University of
Manchester

LONGMANS

LONGMANS, GREEN AND CO LTD
48 Grosvenor Street, London W.1
Associated companies, branches and representatives
throughout the world

© *C. W. Wardlaw 1965*

First published 1965

Printed in Great Britain in the
City of Oxford at the
Alden Press

To Alastair and Norman

Contents

Plates

A*

Acknowledgements

We are grateful to the following for permission to reproduce copyright material:

George Allen & Unwin Ltd for material from *Evolution as a Process* by R. A. Fisher (ed. Huxley, Hardy and Ford); The American Journal of Botany for material from an article by R. H. Wetmore and J. P. Rier, published in *The American Journal of Botany*, 1963; The American Naturalist for material from 'Genes as Physiological Agents' by S. Wright, published in *The American Naturalist*, 1945; British Association for the Advancement of Science for material from W. H. Lang's Presidential Address in 1915; Cambridge University Press for material from *Growth and Form* by D'Arcy W. Thompson and *The Course of Evolution* by J. C. Willis; Cambridge University Press and The Macmillan Company, New York, for material from *Science and the Modern World* by Alfred North Whitehead; Columbia University Press for material from *New Patterns in Genetics and Development* by C. H. Waddington; the author for material from *Symposium of Eigenschaften and Wirkungen der Gibberelline* by Dr F. Lona, published by Springer-Verlag, Berlin; Manchester University Press for material from *Lamarck and Modern Genetics* by H. G. Cannon; the Council of the Royal Society for material from 'The Chemical Basis of Morphogenesis' by A. M. Turing, 1952, published in *Philosophical Transactions Royal Society*, *B*.237; the author and Munksgaard A.S. for material from an article by H. Waris, published in *Physiologia Plantarum* 12, 1959, and C. A. Watts & Co. Ltd for material from *Problems of Life* by L. Bertalanffy.

Preface

When the late D'Arcy Thompson launched his now classic book *On Growth and Form*, he wrote that there was little need of a preface, since it was 'all preface from beginning to end'. The present volume, although it has been long in the making, is likewise no more than an unfinished discussion: in biological science we always seem to be at new beginnings and seldom do we see the fruits of our visions, hopes and labours brought to completion or finality. In this book, which is essentially concerned with *plants* and their *constituent processes*, I have discussed the central and integrating theme of organization in some of its many aspects. In attempting to cover such a wide field I am well aware that I have laid myself open to the criticisms of those with specialized and up-to-date information on particular aspects of the subject. This danger is accepted: an author cannot do greater honour to his readers than to set forth, fairly and fearlessly, what he believes to be true, recognizing the many inadequacies of his scholarship and the fallibility from which even the most distinguished biologists have not been immune. There are, moreover, parts of the book of which adherents of particular schools of thought may not approve. However, it has not been my aim either to placate or to please such categories of readers. But neither have I set out to displease or provoke them. Quite simply, my aim has been to discuss, as objectively and constructively as possible, what has been thought and written about organization and evolution in plants. This has not been an easy task: more often than not the truths which we think are within our grasp prove to be elusive; and commonly accepted views are seen to be less well-founded and considerably more conjectural than is usually assumed. But this is a common experience in biological inquiry. Nature is so complex, multifarious and enigmatic!

Contemporary botanists differ widely in their views as to where the broad highways to a fuller understanding of organisms lie and how they should be approached and traversed. Quite understandably, innovations and the so-called 'break-throughs' usually attract considerably more attention and publicity than the sustained scholarly work which is necessary to bring the new discoveries into a proper relationship with the central corpus of knowledge, shaped, reshaped and refined over the years. But both contributions are essential. The

Plant Kingdom affords abundant and wonderful opportunities for all kinds of investigations, both general and specialized. For my part, I have tried to indicate one avenue along which an *integrated* and *comprehensive* botanical science might well advance.

I wish to express sincere thanks to the many whose scholarly works have contributed to this volume. All borrowed illustrations are acknowledged and here I take the opportunity of thanking authors, publishers and those who have assisted me in the preparation of original illustrations for their ready assistance. For untiring secretarial assistance I am indebted to Mrs J. Birkett, Mrs O. Davison, Miss J. Shore and Miss S. Sullivan; and to Dr E. G. Cutter and Miss A. Walton for assistance with illustrations and proof-reading. I would also like to record my appreciation of the courteous assistance and encouragement in all matters relevant to the production of this book which I have invariably received from my publishers, Messrs Longmans, Green & Company Ltd. Not least, the book owes much to the unfailing patience and sympathetic interest shown by my wife.

C. W. WARDLAW

Manchester
4 February 1964

Caveat

'He that will pass over the sea to go to the city of Jerusalem may go many ways, both by sea and land, according to the country that he cometh from: many ways come to one end. But you must not expect that I will tell you all the towns, and cities, and castles, that men shall go by; for then I should make too long a tale.'

The Voyages and Travels of
Sir John Maundeville, 1356.

'The realization among biologists that the characteristic properties of living things are not dependent upon the presence of a special "living substance" — protoplasm — or a special ingredient, but upon ordinary chemical substances organized in extraordinary ways, brought about a great deal of speculation about the "nature" of organization. Many biologists have endowed organization with all the mysteries of life itself, and have indeed seen in organization a magical agent. Woodger collects and presents a number of passages in which biologists speak of organization as if it has "to be 'postulated,' 'recognized', 'ascribed', 'assumed', etc." The wide use of the term "organizing relation" is a residue of this tendency: the term seems to imply that these relations do something — something inscrutable, perhaps — in the way that a union organizer does something. But a relation is just a relation, not an agent. The bare recognition that there are relations between things that obtain only in virtue of the way they are organized provides neither a science nor the foundation of one. Put another way, we can say that the concept of organization itself plays no role within a science. The same can be said also for the concepts "whole," "organic unity," "hierarchial organization", etc.

'Nevertheless, there is a "problem of organization". This is the problem of subjecting to scientific treatment systems which are highly complex with respect to any of a set of theories which are known to be applicable to the systems. The problem for philosophy of science is to understand and formulate whatever special methods, e.g., of concept formation or explanation, are developed in the pursuit of this task. This seems to me the only final way to show that the organismic biologist is correct in his insistence on the right to a "free biology, with concepts and laws of its own".'

Morton Beckner, *The Biological*
Way of Thought, 1959

CHAPTER 1

The Concept of Organization

That being then one Plant, which has such an Organization of Parts in one coherent Body.   LOCKE

The challenge was, and still is, formidable, namely to anatomize total metabolism
into its individual partial reactions, to isolate the components of specific enzyme
systems responsible for each reaction, and to determine how these systems integrate
to confer the inherited vital activity shown by a tissue usually in the service of the
organism as a whole. The word organization appears to have replaced the old term,
vital principle, or still older, the vegetable soul.

MEIRION THOMAS, 1961

INTRODUCTION

The purpose of this book is to examine two closely related phenomena
that lie at the centre of botanical science, namely, the *organization* and
the *evolution* of plants. The origin of species, each with its distinctive
organization evolved during descent, still presents itself as one of the
major themes in biology. A considerable part of the contemporary
botanical effort is, however, being directed to the specialized investigation of individual biological processes, e.g. as in the new 'molecular
biology' (*see* p. 78). Such investigations are, of course, quite essential
to our better understanding of plants and to the advancement of
botanical science; and their results become specially valuable when they
can be related to other processes and integrated with the corpus of
knowledge. All too often, however, this does not happen. Accordingly,
it may also be recognized that one of the more immediate effects of
specialized investigations is that they tend to deflect our attention from
organisms as organisms. Also, although the isolation of particular
factors for special study is in the classical tradition of science, and
although many biochemical reactions can now be carried out *in vitro*,
reactions in the living organism can rarely take place in isolation. They
take place as components of a whole system of processes and always in
relation to an organization that is already present.* Hence the importance, especially at this time, of examining the comprehensive theme of

---

* This was written several years ago. The writer was pleased to note that, recently,
Sonneborn (1963), a distinguished geneticist, has expressed very similar views. Also,

organization in plants; for it connotes the summation and integration of many processes that are, and have been, involved in the formation, functioning, survival and evolution of species.

DEFINITIONS

In biology, the term *organization** connotes an organized body or structure. If we examine any plant throughout its development, noting the characteristic and harmonious changes in its size and shape, the diversification of its cells, organs and tissues, and the mutual relationships of parts; and if we have in mind that all these distinctive features have come into being from a single cell with specific hereditary properties, and that regular sequences of physiological-genetical activities and environmental factors are involved at all stages, then we may be said to be concerned with its organization. When we recognize two plants as belonging to different species, we are, in fact, distinguishing between two specific organizations; and even in closely related species it may be possible to distinguish differences in their organizations at an early stage in ontogenesis. When we refer to a plant as an organization, we imply that its characteristic form, structure and related functional activities have come into being as a result of a sequence of orderly processes. Moreover, we are forced to recognize that some basis for the specific organization is present from the outset, i.e. in the protoplasm of the zygote or generating cell, and that the ontogenetic process is essentially the expression or manifestation and elaboration of that organization. The phenomena of organization are thus held to be comprehensive, pervasive, progressive and ever present, both in the individual development and the evolution of the race.

---

since this book went to press, many botanists have expressed concern at the contemporary tendency towards over-emphasis of particular aspects of what is evidently a very comprehensive subject.

* *Organism* 1. Organic structure; organization. Now rare. 2. An organized or organic system; a whole consisting of dependent and interdependent parts, compared to a living being. 1768. 3. An organized body, consisting of mutually connected and dependent parts constituted to share a common life; the material structure of an individual animal or plant. 1842.

Organization 1. The action of organizing, or condition of being organized, as a living being; also, the way in which a living being is organized; the structure of an organized body (animal or plant), or of any part of one; bodily (*rarely* mental) constitution.

The Shorter Oxford English Dictionary, 1933

In a critical study, Beckner (1959) has stated that: 'Many biologists have endowed organization with all the mysteries of life itself, and have indeed seen in organization a magical agent.' But he admits that there is 'a problem of organization'. In the present writer's view, organization need not be endowed with magical properties: it is undoubtedly very complex but it has a physico-chemical basis. And the many mysteries of plant life – the unexpected and often surprising functional and adaptive features, the commonplace but still remarkable fact that, during development, 'the right things happen at the right time' and in the proper sequence, and so on – are envisaged as being necessarily related to, and based on, the evolution of organization. But the mysteries are still great and wonderful mysteries and, even allowing for accelerated technical advance, they will assuredly keep botanists occupied for a long time to come.

SPECIFIC ORGANIZATION AND THE EVOLUTIONARY PROCESS

Since each species is a unique or specific organization, the evolution of plants, which has been characterized by the appearance of large numbers of new entities, usually showing increasing structural complexity and refinements in their physiological and morphological mechanisms as compared with their ancestral forms, is essentially a *progressive elaboration of organization*. This process is fundamentally due to permanent changes in the hereditary constitution, since, in any individual plant, it is the genetical factors, operating in an orderly fashion in conjunction with environmental factors and certain other factors (*see* pp. 25, 133), which determine the distinctive morphology of the species.

Important as the specific chemical properties and activities of individual genes undoubtedly are, physical factors which determine or affect their disposition and mutual relationships in the individual protoplast, and environmental and organismal factors which affect their serial evocation, are also closely involved in organization. The action of genes in every aspect of development is a subject on which contemporary geneticists have much to say (*see* Chapter 4); but it is salutary to reflect on how very different, and in some respects far apart, are the accounts, for example, of protoplasmic organization and functioning, as given by contemporary geneticists and by physiologists.

As embryonic cells and tissues, e.g. a spore, a zygote, a young embryo, a bud, or a shoot apical meristem, are the sites or loci of growth, they are also the loci in which the higher manifestations of organization have their origin. Now the entity which is formed from a developing zygote, or from a shoot apical meristem, has an evident unity and harmony of development. This is exemplified by any leafy shoot. It is therefore a reasonable assumption, or working hypothesis, that this entity is the product of a single though complex *reaction system*, the components of which are intrinsic (genetical) and extrinsic (non-genetical) factors. If this be accepted, then the basic or essential features of evolution could be ascribed to *the evolution of specific organismal reaction systems*. How these reaction systems may be constituted, and how they may become modified, with consequential effects on the organization of the adult plant, is still very hypothetical (*see* Chapter 7); for, as Weiss (1939) has said, an organism, as compared with inorganic aggregates of different kinds, 'does not have merely some pattern; it has a *definite* and typical pattern ... which is *essentially identical* for all members of a species ... This order according to which *every part is put into its proper place, and into specific relationships with* other parts, and according to which *the activities of every part are made to comply with the plan of the* whole *system* to which it belongs, is called organization'.

The evolution of plants, which has usually been characterized by a progressive elaboration of form, has not taken place solely along one sustained line of advance. On the contrary, closely comparable innovations and elaborations of form have seemingly taken place independently along several lines of descent, i.e. in groups of plants or phyla not considered to be closely related genetically. These *parallelisms* or *convergences* are of very wide generality in the evolution of plants (*see* Chapter 4): they are, indeed, a substantial part of the process. Accordingly, close consideration must be given to the phenomena aptly and comprehensively described as *homologies of organization*.

Much of the evidence of organization with which we shall be concerned is visual. This is true whether we are concerned with the appearance or shape of an organelle as disclosed by the electron microscope, or with a megascopic organ. In this connection Needham (1944) recognized *form* (presumably in its original, wider connotation – *see* p. 8; and Arber, 1950) and *organization* as being synonymous. Also, since there is evidence of organization even at the atomic level, we can, according to Needham, disregard the old concept of *form* and *matter* and replace it by one of *organization* and *energy*.

LEVELS OF ORGANIZATION

As Needham (1942, 1944) stated, the universe may be envisaged as a series of *levels of organization and complexity*, ranging from the sub-

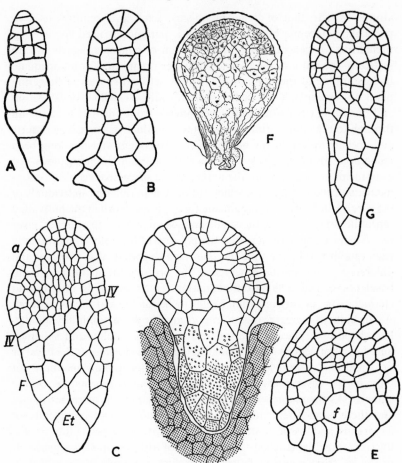

Fig.1.1 Embryos in different major groups of plants have many developmental features in common. These include the inception of polarity in the dividing zygote (or earlier), an orderly sequence of cell divisions resulting in a characteristic tissue pattern, the organization of a distal apical meristem, and an acropetal gradient in cell size.

A, *Delesseria ruscifolia*, a red alga, germling (after Nienburg). B, *Notothylas* sp., Anthocerotales, young sporophyte (after Lang). C, *Lycopodium selago*; young embryo: *et*, suspensor, *F*, foot, *a*, apex (after Bruchmann). D, *Lycopodium cernuum*, young embryo: the enlarged cells of the foot in contact with the prothallus contain starch grains (after Treub). E, *Osmunda cinnamomea*, showing the large cells of the foot, *f*, and the smaller cells of the embryonic distal region (after Cross). F, *Ginkgo biloba*, young embryo (after Lyon). G, *Zea mays*, young embryo (after Randolph). (From C. W. Wardlaw, *Embryogenesis in Plants*, 1955.)

atomic level to that of living organisms. Each level requires its own particular concepts, but there is also a paramount need for a comprehensive, or general, concept, or system of concepts, which will do justice to the unity of the individual higher organism. For an adequate understanding of the organization of any selected species of flowering plant, for example, it will be necessary to study its cellular organization and its form, structure and development from the fertilized ovum through to the culmination of the adult reproductive stage. The orderly and specific nature of the entire process is evident and has long been recognized. In the zygote and in the early stages of embryogenesis, for example of an angiosperm, the nature of the successive visible developments, and the fidelity with which they occur in different individuals of the species, indicate that 'organizing forces' are at work in the individual reproductive cell and in the small multicellular body to which it gives rise. The evidence indicates that the polarity of the embryo has already been established by the time the zygote undergoes its first division, and differences can often be observed in the protoplasm at the apical and basal poles. The cellular differentiation which ensues is orderly and characteristic, i.e. organization begins to be manifest at the tissue level. As the embryo increases in size, important changes in its initially spindle-like shape take place: the distal region becomes bulky and spherical and, later, cotyledons and a shoot apex are formed while, at the basal or proximal end, a radicle is formed. Organization is now manifest not only in the several organs but in the overall conformation of the embryo. As the embryo develops into the seedling, it increases in size and there is an attendant increase in the number and complexity of its organs and tissue systems until the fully-developed adult, reproductive stage is reached. The whole of this complex sequence of processes, from zygote to flowering, is thus characterized by a distinctive unity of development. In brief, a fuller understanding of an organism requires a knowledge of its protoplasmic constitution and reactivity and of the factors and relationships that are involved in its ontogenetic development, the organizational phenomena at the several levels being brought into a unified system. This, indeed, has long been accepted as one of the central aims in biological science (Figs. 1.1, 1.2).

Plant populations also yield evidence of organization, though this does not come within the purview of this book. For a discussion of this and some other more general aspects of organization, the reader is referred to Mather (1955).

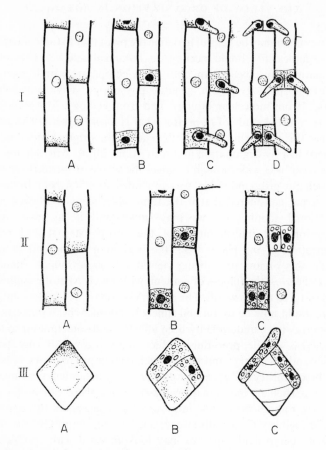

Fig.1.2 Polarity and the differentiation of tissues.

I. Formation of root hairs, monocotyledonous type. *A*, Gradient of protoplasmic density, due to polarity; *B*, Unequal division, origin of trichoblasts. *C*, Development of root hairs. *D*, Division of trichoblasts, occurring in several species by the formation of a wall in the direction of the polarity gradient, giving rise to two equal cells, both forming root hairs.

II. Formation of stomata, monocotyledonous type. (Notice similarity to root hair formation.)

III. Unequal divisions in the leaf cells of *Sphagnum*. The stippling again indicates a protoplasmic gradient.
(After E. Bünning, from *Survey of Biological Progress*, 1952.)

THE STUDY OF ORGANIZATION IN BOTANICAL SCIENCE

At this point it may be helpful to define the place that a study of organization occupies, or should occupy, in botanical science. The relevant information must be drawn both from comparative and general (or causal) morphology, from general physiology, from physiological genetics, from molecular biology, and from ecology. Morphology, by definition, is the study of *form*. But what is *form*? Arber (1950) pointed out that this is a term of which, in general, the original wider meaning has been lost by degradation and restriction. But to Aristotle the scope of the term 'was wide enough to cover the whole of the intrinsic nature of which any given individual was a manifestation' (Arber). In the same vein, Arber considered that if the term *morphology* is allowed its full derivational significance, we may understand it 'as involving the description and interpretation of the entire external and internal organization of the plant, from the beginning to the end of its life history, this organization being viewed *sub specie formae* – under the aspect of *form* – the fulness of content, with which Aristotle endowed it, being restored to this word'. The author (Wardlaw, 1961a) has suggested that it would now be useful and timely to adopt Arber's suggestion.

Botanists have undoubtedly been affected and sometimes inspired by the success of the procedures which have proved so successful in physics and chemistry; and hence much contemporary work in physiology, biochemistry and genetics is concerned with the analytical investigation of particular, individual processes. Now, there can be no doubt whatsoever about the merits, importance and success of this approach: it is the highway to new discovery; and, in fact, important discoveries are daily being made and we may look forward with confidence to further considerable accessions of new information. The observations on organelles, cellular organization and so on, made possible by the electron microscope, have their place in this context. Nevertheless, as the central aim in biology is to understand organisms as organisms – though it is appreciated that there may be those who dissent from this view – it may well be doubted if the analytical, or physico-chemical, approach is in itself likely to yield an adequate account of specific organization. In brief, botanists must formulate their own concepts.

CAUSATION IN BIOLOGY

The whole question of causation in biology, as in other branches of science, is one of acute difficulty. Aristotle had pondered the subject and distinguished four kinds of primary cause, namely, the material, the efficient, the formal and the final cause. The material and efficient causes, i.e. involving physico-chemical processes, lend themselves to investigation by the accepted methods of science – observation, analysis and experiment. The formal and final causes, i.e. the teleological* causes, are not amenable to investigation by these methods and their introduction into discussions of biological phenomena is regarded with suspicion as being unscientific and as making for facile 'explanations' which are neither susceptible of detailed investigation nor of experimental proof (*see* following section). But, as Arber (1950) said: 'The exclusively mechanistic view of the organism, which was fostered by the physics and chemistry of the nineteenth century, is far narrower than the outlook of Aristotle, who, though assigning the fuller significance to the Final Cause, also recognized the importance of the Efficient Cause.' Francis Bacon maintained that physical and final causes were true and compatible. Kant held that they were irreducible, and D'Arcy Thompson described them as being 'interwoven together'. Contemporary thinkers, such as Bertalanffy (1952), while agreeing that biology is based on physics and chemistry, and that these disciplines are indispensable in the investigation of the phenomena of life, nevertheless pointed out that biology has its own particular problems, such as those of organic form, purposiveness and phylogeny, which do not lend themselves to solution by the methods and concepts of physics and chemistry. He would, indeed, place biology rather than physics and chemistry in the centre of the sciences and considered that it should have its own autonomous development. In brief, he has advocated what he described as the *organismic conception*, one of the aims of which is to develop laws of organic systems.

Readers who wish to examine more closely such topics as 'organismic biology', logical aspects of the philosophy of biology, the use of various terms and concepts often used in a rather general way by biologists, e.g. organization, organizing relations, etc., are referred to Woodger (1929, 1930, 1945, 1948) and Beckner (1959).

Here, too, we may note that Whitehead (1926, 1938), in his theory of organic mechanism, stated that:

the whole concept of materialism only applies to very abstract entities, the products of logical discernment. The concrete enduring entities are organisms, so that the

---

Teleology. Teleology is the doctrine, or the study, of ends or final causes. It is sometimes used in biology in the sense that the course followed in development is determined by some useful, or essential, aim or end to be attained.

plan of the *whole* influences the very characters of the various subordinate organisms which enter into it. . . . Thus an electron within a living body is different from an electron outside it, by reason of the plan of the body. The electron blindly runs either within or without the body; but it runs within the body in accordance with its character within the body; that is to say, in accordance with the general plan of the body. . . . But the principle of modification is perfectly general throughout nature, and represents no property peculiar to living bodies . . . this doctrine involves the abandonment of the traditional scientific materialism, and the substitution of an alternative doctrine of organism (p. 99).

According to this theory the evolution of laws of nature is concurrent with the evolution of enduring pattern. For the general state of the universe, as it now is, partly determines the very essences of the entities whose modes of functioning these laws express. The general principle is that in a new environment there is an evolution of the old entities into new forms (pp. 133-4).

TELEOLOGY IN BIOLOGY

It is really not surprising that teleological interpretations of biological phenomena have often appeared, sometimes unintentionally, in the literature. Some aspects of teleological interpretation have, indeed, been justified (*see* below).

The numerous specialized structures and organs in plants appear to the observer to function with a high degree of efficiency, almost as if some element of purpose – working towards a necessary goal – had directed their development. However, such teleological conceptions are usually quite unacceptable to contemporary biologists. This was not always the case; and there are those who detect teleological implications in neo-Darwinian evolutionary interpretations. To the teleologist and, indeed, to others, examples of seemingly purposeful developments occur everywhere in the Plant Kingdom and may be selected at random: e.g. the scaly protection of over-wintering or resting buds; tuberous storage developments in perennial species; the shape, distribution and disposition of leaves in relation to photosynthesis; the horizontally-disposed zygomorphic flower in relation to insect visitation, and other floral mechanisms; the distribution of fibrous tissues in relation to mechanical requirements; the devices in pitcher plants, and other insectivorous plants, in relation to the attracting and trapping of insects; and so on. All of these, which illustrate specialized organizational features and integrated functional activities, may well present themselves to some minds as developments appropriate, or indeed essential, to the life, economy and survival of the individual species. And the matter is made still more mysterious, perplexing and intriguing by the fact that the primary pattern of the adult organ or mature tissue under consideration is determined, or established, in a minute embryonic region, e.g. the apical meristem, well in advance of the functional activity to be performed later; i.e. teleologically speaking, and as Bower (1921) wrote as a *jeu d'esprit*, the primary embryonic pattern is an 'intelligent anticipation' of what will be required later for efficient functioning in the adult organ or mature tissue. The basis of these remarkable properties is inherent in the zygote.

Since the time of Darwin, the pervasiveness of adaptation in virtually every phase of development has become generally accepted (Huxley, 1942), the occurrence of specialized organs and tissues being explained in terms of heritable evolutionary change, adaptation and selection. When examined closely, however, explanations or interpretations along these lines are seldom as full, adequate and free from assumptions as they might be. Some assertions that certain organs or structures are closely adaptive, that they have, or have had, selective value and have therefore persisted, may well seem to the cautious observer to be facile, untested, and open to doubt. That adaptation and natural selection are of great importance as pervasive general phenomena is beyond dispute and is not disputed. Nevertheless, there are many examples of formal or structural elaboration making, as it seems, for functional efficiency, in which it is doubtful if competition and selection have played a major part. D'Arcy Thompson (1917, 1942), for example, showed that many organizational features can probably be explained without direct reference to the action of selective forces. There are also many structural features in plants, often seemingly adaptive, for which no comprehensive, validated explanations have yet been advanced. It is salutary to reflect that Haberlandt's *Physiological Plant Anatomy*, which in its day was a classic – as indeed it still is – is now a rather neglected work. In it the author illustrated cell types and tissue systems and attempted to explain their function, adaptive nature, and the part which they played in the economy of the plant. Moreover, where it was available, relevant experimental evidence was discussed. Today, many of Haberlandt's views, e.g. on the efficacy of the seemingly effective water-conserving features in xeromorphs, are disputed, denied or disproven.

Of course, the foregoing reflections are not to be taken as meaning that, in considering organization, we should have recourse to teleological explanations. But they do indicate that, even with our now considerable resources of evolutionary fact and theory, there are still many biological phenomena in which we have not yet got to the root of the matter: we are still unable to account in detail for the organization and related functional efficiency of plants and their parts. The crux of the matter seems to be that while the concepts and methods of mathematics, physics and chemistry have enabled botanists to make considerable progress in the investigation of particular processes, they have their limitations; and there is little in contemporary physical or chemical theory that reveals the way to the next step, namely, how physico-chemical processes become so integrated as to yield the distinctive organization of a living cell, organ or tissue, or of the organism in its entirety, each part functioning in such a way as, seemingly, to fulfil the needs of the organism at different stages of its development.

The use of teleological explanation in biology is, of course, under-standable, since so many aspects of human conduct tend to be explained by reference to the ends pursued, or thought to be pursued. The explanation of biological phenomena by reference to ends was formally and explicitly recognized by Aristotle who, in fact, dealt with the whole question of causation in a manner that, in some respects, has probably never been bettered. But teleological views, once regarded as self-evident, are now very much discounted, though probably many botanists would be willing to admit that some element of teleology is hard to exclude, especially where explanations of some of the more compre-hensive life relationships are involved.

The contemporary attitude is that the more biologists have moved away from metaphysical explanations towards explanation in terms of physics and chemistry, the more scientific and fruitful has their work become. Nevertheless, there are still biologists who hold that full or adequate explanations of certain biological phenomena are impossible without the introduction of some element of teleology, e.g. Agar (1943, 1951), Sinnott (1954); and philosophers, of high authority, both past and present, have supported this view. Indeed, many 'explanations' in biology, e.g. of adaptation along purely mechanistic lines, seem to the uncommitted observer to be inadequate. Moreover, it is perhaps worth noting that, among biologists, there is a detectable tendency to think teleologically about phenomena, e.g. in devising a 'working model' of a process; but, having arrived at a seemingly satisfying explanation, they take care that it is couched in non-teleological terms!

A major problem of 'explanation' in biology seems to be that while the mechanistic or physico-chemical approach has yielded much new infor-mation, it has proved inadequate in attempts to account for organisms as organisms, with their appropriately regulated, overall development and the formation of their adaptively functional organs and tissues.

Many philosophers, including some recent and contemporary ones, who have been actively interested in the general problem of design in Nature, have either accepted the need for teleological interpretations or have argued that they are not necessarily incompatible with attempted explanations along other lines. On the other hand, progress in the detailed investigation of biological phenomena, including the formulation of new ideas, and of new techniques to test these ideas, has been almost entirely due to those who have advocated and adopted the mechanistic approach. Somewhere between these two extremes it may be that there is a place for teleology. Certainly it will be no bad thing in analytical biology if investigators remind themselves from time to time of the inherent limitations of their approach and of the inadequacy and incompleteness of the 'explanations', or interpretations, which they offer of the wider phenomena of living organisms.

Reference should here be made to the writings of some contemporary thinkers, such as Sommerhoff (1950), Braithwaite (1953), Nagel (1953) and Beckner (1959). In different ways, and for various reasons, these authors do not consider that all teleological explanations are necessarily anthropomorphic and unacceptable; nor do they think that, in such explanations, a metaphysical doctrine of final causes is necessarily assumed. On the contrary they hold that teleological language may have legitimate scientific uses; and they are in agreement with biologists in general in the view that 'no non-physical agents or causes need to be active in teleological behaviour and that no unique method of treatment is required in its explanation' (Beckner, 1959, p. 132). Sommerhoff, for example, has argued that 'purposive' biological phenomena, which might be regarded as subjects for explanation along teleological lines, can be analysed in the ordinary way as instances of *directively correlated behaviour*. (For a useful contemporary discussion of teleology, *see* Beckner, 1959).

INTERPRETATION OF EXPERIMENTAL OBSERVATIONS

Experimental investigators have shown that distinctive features of the normal development may be promoted or modified by particular treatments. For example, applications of gibberellic acid to rosette plants may result in stem elongation and the promotion, or even induction, of flowering. But although these developments are more or less directly related to the chemical treatment applied, and even where it has been shown that a particular substance must be present before some particular development can take place, the underlying specific organization is always the major factor in the situation; and the observed chemical reactions, as it were, fall into place in that context. Holmes (1948) pointed out that although the laws that determine biological processes appear to be unique, with no counterpart in physics and chemistry, that does not mean that a mechanistic approach need be ruled out. And, following Roux (1895), he stated: 'The question of paramount interest to the mechanist is whether these laws may be regarded as resultants of simpler uniformities which in turn are capable of final analysis in terms of the laws of physics and chemistry.'* The hope implied in this view will, of course, be disappointed if, on the evidence, the organismic whole proves to be greater than the sum of its parts – as is maintained by adherents of the concept of emergent evolution (*see* p. 324).

IMPORTANCE OF THE STUDY OF ORGANIZATION

Enough has perhaps been said to indicate how important an enquiry into organization is for botanical science. The analytical, mechanistic approach, for all its merits, is limited and seems unlikely in itself to explain phenomena that are of paramount interest to botanists: the teleological approach is unlikely to commend itself unless some particular aspect of it can be urged with new cogency. Meanwhile, what has been described as the 'inward directiveness' of the organism, manifesting itself in the distinctive organization and adaptiveness of the species during ontogenesis, presents itself as an ever-present challenge. Perhaps the methods by which we may hope to advance are less obscure than is sometimes thought. Oppenheimer (1955), for example, in a

---

* Polanyi (1957), in criticizing statements of Lashley (1951) to the effect that the phenomena of behaviour and of the mind are ultimately referable to mathematical and physical concepts, and of Gerard (1957) that higher types of organization are understandable in terms of their component units and their relationships, has pointed out that in no process known to conform to the present laws of physics and chemistry is there evidence of consciousness. Accordingly, he has suggested that a future enlargement of physics and chemistry 'might account for the sentience of certain material structures'. He has followed this by reminding us that, in Nature, action is usually accompanied by reaction, and he has concluded that it would be reasonable 'to expect that the new physics and chemistry, which would account for the production of consciousness by material processes, would also allow for the *reverse* action, that is, of conscious processes acting on their material substrate'.

Somewhat along the same lines, Schrödinger (1944) stated that while living matter cannot escape the laws of physics, as presently understood, other laws of physics, still unknown, are likely to be involved. And when once those have been discovered, they, too, will take their place as an integral part of physical science.

survey of the problems and concepts of embryology, has noted that progress, as in all developing science, has been marked by a gradual transition from the metaphysical to the physical. The significant advances have been made by those who have derived their ideas and intuitions from the direct observation of embryos, rather than by those whose approach has been from the philosophical side and whose paramount interest has been in ideas. Also, in considering the view (*see* Parpart, 1949) that contemporary biochemistry may prove inadequate to solve the fundamental problems of organization, Oppenheimer has suggested that there may be a biological level at which work might be done without reverting to the vitalistic position.

ENVOI

No apology, other than an acknowledgment of the author's limitations, need be made for urging the study proposed here; for all science is concerned with order and organized systems, and it may well be that the study of organization in plants and animals will be one of the major philosophic as well as biological preoccupations during the latter part of the present century. The task that lies ahead is difficult and complex. For whereas physicists and chemists encounter the phenomena of organization at the molecular, atomic and subatomic levels, biologists have to deal with them, not only at these and at much higher levels, but also with the interdependence of the organizational states characteristic of different levels. But whatever the difficulties, the author believes that the problems should be tackled and he has conviction that progress can be made by more intensive investigations of (a) the fundamental organization of cells, (b) the factors which determine the *primary pattern* in embryonic regions, (c) the factors which *elaborate and modify* the primary pattern, and (d) the organizing effects of specific factors in the hereditary constitution and, in particular, the serial evocation and action of genes. In short, however intangible and enigmatic the theme of organization in plants may appear to be, at least some of the major contributory factors are knowable and lend themselves to observation, analysis and experiment.

The proposed study should also have other advantages. Since certain major organizational features appear to be common to many plants, not necessarily closely related genetically, the study may in time enable us to formulate simplifying general truths regarding the numerous and highly varied members of the Plant Kingdom. So, as we embark on our studies, we should try to liberate our minds: for example, instead of being overwhelmed, as we tend to be, by the seemingly endless physiological, morphological and structural diversity of plants, we should maintain a lively awareness of these phenomena and we should constantly search for major common factors. The quest for similitude in diversity is almost certain to bring its own rewards, for it is in the great tradition of scientific advancement. Another important attitude of mind will relate to the emphasis which we place on, and the detachment with which we view, the facts derived from different branches of the subject. For example, the importance of genetical factors in morphogenesis is undeniable; but so also is the importance of non-genetical factors. Our task is to understand each of these aspects as fully as may be, to see them in proper perspective, and to perceive their mutual relationships. This attitude should also apply to our assessment of such complementary phenomena as the physical and chemical properties of metabolic substances, of organism and environment, and so on. An open-minded general knowledge of botanical materials, as well as analysis and synthesis, is clearly essential to the investigation of organization.

CHAPTER 2

Theories of Organization

DIVERSITY OF THEORIES

How formidable is the task of understanding organization in plants is apparent when one considers how incomplete, heterogeneous, and sometimes naïve, are the ideas and theories that have been advanced (*see* Wardlaw, 1951, 1952b; Sinnott, 1960). These may now be briefly reviewed. Some of them cannot be narrowly confined under any one heading but, broadly speaking, they are of the following kinds: (a) holistic, (b) morphological, (c) physiological, (d) physical and mathematical, (e) protoplasmic, (f) genetical and (g) epigenetic, multi-aspect or integrative. As Roux (1895) recognized, theories of form must, of necessity, be concerned in the first instance with 'complex components', most of the morphological theories being of this kind.

ENTELECHY AND HOLISM

The old controversy between the vitalistic and mechanistic conceptions of organisms need not be revived here, but mention should be made of the views of Driesch (1908). From long and intimate contact with the developmental processes in animals, Driesch concluded that purely mechanistic conceptions do not, and can not, adequately account for the orderly development and integrated wholeness of organisms; in other words, for their organization. Some other ordering or controlling principle, described as an *entelechy*, which is independent of physico-chemical laws, though these admittedly are involved, is at work. Driesch defined *entelechy* as that which gives form or perfection to anything; or, as Aristotle used the term, it is that which makes actual what is otherwise merely potential; it is an inner activity without which the mere matter of the organism would not become organized into a living entity at all.

In a book of a philosophical rather than a biological character, entitled *Holism and Evolution*, Smuts (1922), too, came to the conclusion that plants and animals cannot be comprehensively understood along purely mechanistic lines. Mechanistic concepts, he maintained, have their place and justification only within the wider framework of the integrated unity of the organism. The process of evolution (he said) is characterized by a fundamental tendency towards the creation of *wholes*, *holism* being a causal factor, with a real existence, which works towards the creation of wholes in the universe. This holistic tendency becomes more marked at progressively higher levels of organic development. Smuts's conception is valuable in that it emphasizes the essential unity of organisms – for botanists, the importance of studying the whole plant – but, like the theory of entelechy, it does not lend itself to experimental validation; nor does it actively stimulate new investigations.

All comprehensive theories of organization, by their very nature, contain a more or less considerable element of holism, even though this may not be explicitly stated; for, as Holmes (1948) said, continuous integration is one of the most outstanding features of living things.* Sachs's (1875) view that the terms *stem* and *leaf* are merely indicative of 'certain relationships of the parts of a whole – the shoot', is essentially holistic; and so, too, is the conception of the leaf as a partial shoot (de Candolle, 1868; Arber, 1950). Arber's view that form, including both its organizational and *Gestalt* aspects, is 'the inherent directiveness of the organism made manifest' (1950, p. 208), is also holistic.

According to the *principle of entropy* (the second law of thermodynamics) all matter tends to pass from certain less probable states to certain more probable states or configurations. In other words, a physical or chemical system tends to attain a state of equilibrium, or of minimum free energy; i.e. of maximum disorder, or of *maximum entropy*. As a plant reaches its permanent adult state, it tends to attain a state of equilibrium; but if the organism is a physico-chemical reaction system, this tendency will be present at every stage of development. The equilibrium attained in growing biological systems is a dynamic equilibrium; or, in terms of open system theory in physical chemistry, the tendency is towards a steady state. However, as Schrödinger (1944) pointed out, the unique feature of organisms, as compared with purely physico-chemical systems, is that they avoid 'the rapid decay into the inert state of "equilibrium" '. On the contrary, during growth, they form more highly organized entities; or, in Schrödinger's words, they feed on 'negative entropy'. It will be seen that this view of organisms is

---

* One is tempted to draw the moral that if botanical science is to remain 'a living thing', it, too, must be continuously integrated.

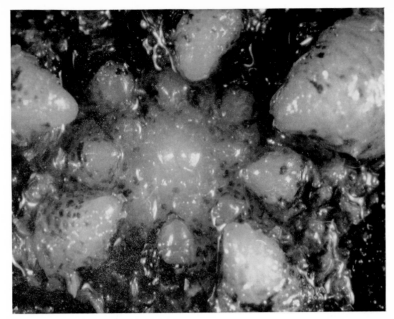

1A. Evidence of organization: the apex of *Dryopteris dilatata* as seen from above, showing the apical meristem in the centre, surrounded by a sequence of evenly spaced enlarging leaf primordia (× 20). (Photo: Dr. E. G. Cutter.)

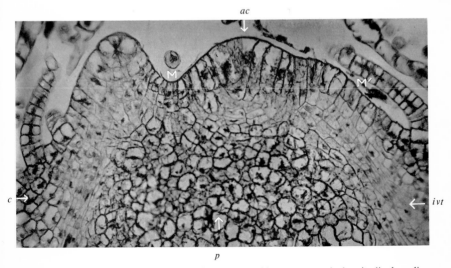

1B. Evidence of organization: the apex of *Dryopteris dilatata* as seen in longitudinal median section, showing the apical cell (*ac*), the prism-shaped cells of the apical meristem (*m-m¹*), the incipient vascular tissue (*ivt*), and developing pith (*p*) and cortex (*c*) (× 160).

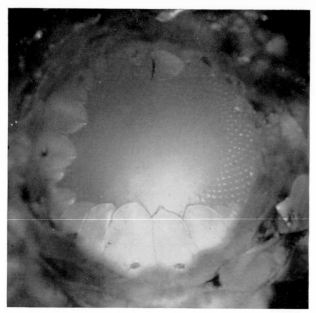

2A. Evidence of organization: the developing capitulum of *Cardunculus* sp. as seen from above; many of the involucral bracts have been dissected off; floret primordia are developing in acropetal sequence from the periphery of the capitulum, but the central region is still undifferentiated (× 17).

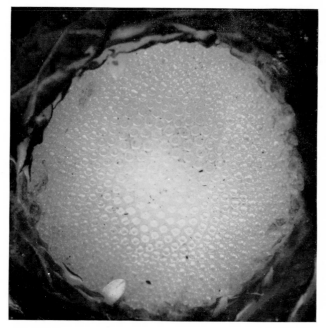

2B. A later stage: the whole of the capitulum is now occupied by an orderly sequence of young florets (× 17).

essentially a holistic one. Moreover, the facts of evolution, as ascertained by biologists, indicate a continuous and progressive increase of organization. Smuts's holism – the tendency towards the creation of wholes at all levels – is thus in general accord with contemporary thought.

MORPHOLOGICAL THEORIES

It is characteristic of these theories that some pre-existing morphological unit, considered to be basic or fundamental, is taken as a starting point, i.e. is treated *as given*. Yet, as early as 1759, Kaspar Wolff had stated that he saw nothing in the plant but leaves and stem, these proceeding from the growth of an undifferentiated *punctum vegetationis* – an essentially epigenetic conception. This was in sharp contradistinction to prevailing preformation theories in which development was attributed to the unfolding of pre-existing rudiments.

In Goethe's Theory of Metamorphosis (1790), the stem is taken for granted and is regarded as being little more than an axis on which the really important organs, the leaves in their several manifestations, are arranged. According to Goethe, all the diverse appendages of the shoot of a higher plant are due to the metamorphosis, or transformation, of a single fundamental organ, the 'ideal' leaf – *das Blatt*. Here, again, a morphological unit – albeit an ideal one – was taken for granted. So, too, in the fundamental categories of parts, including caulome, phyllome, trichome and rhizome, as envisaged by Sachs (1875); and in the Telome Theory of Zimmermann (1930, 1938), pre-existing morphological units are taken as the starting point (Fig.2.1).

In Phytonic Theories of the leafy shoot (Gaudichaud, 1841; Chauveaud, 1921; Bertrand, 1947), the existence of the stem or axis as an independent member is more or less explicitly denied or excluded, the plant being envisaged as a construction of phytons, or segments, of which the leaf-bases, or extensions thereof, are accepted as the fundamental units. Supporters of Axial or Strobilar Theories, on the other hand, regard the stem or axis as the fundamental and pre-existent unit from which microphyllous leaves may have originated by enation and megaphylls by dichotomy passing over to monopodial branching (Bower, 1935; Wardlaw, 1952b) (Fig.2.2).

The point need not be laboured. Nor need one enter into the details of the Pericaulome, Caulome, or Telome Theories (*see* Bertrand, 1947, and Majumdar, 1957, for reviews). In general, theories of organization in plants which are essentially morphological in their inception tend

B

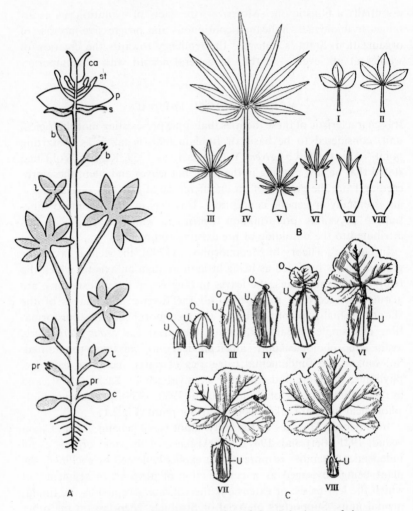

Fig.2.1 A Diagrammatic representation of Goethe's theory of shoot organization and leaf metamorphosis: the plant is envisaged as an axis on which foliar organs, in their various modifications, i.e. metamorphosed forms of *das Blatt* – an idealized leaf – are present.

B. *Helleborus foetidus*. Leaf sequence. I–III, Primary leaves. IV, Fully grown adult leaf. V–VIII, Sequence of leaves in the transition to flowering.

C. *Ribes sanguineum*. I–IV, Scale-leaves of a bud. VII, VIII, Foliage leaves. V, VI, Transition leaves. *U*, flattened petiole base; *O*, lamina rudiment.

(B, C. After W. Troll, *Vergleichende Anatomie der höheren Pflanzen*).

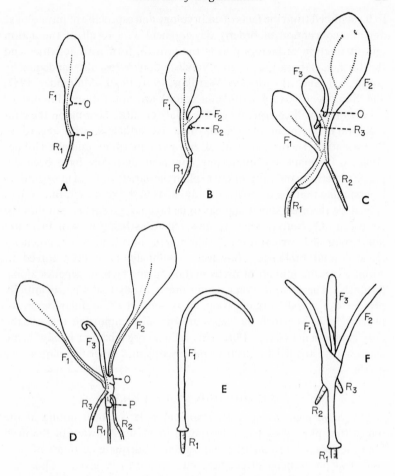

Fig.2.2 Diagrams illustrating Chauveaud's Phyllorhize Theory of shoot organization: the leafy axis is regarded as being composed of morphological units, each consisting of a leaf, a stem segment and a root.

A, B, C, *Ceratopteris thalictroides*, showing the initial and later stages in the organization of a fern by the conjunction of phyllorhizes.

F_1, the first leaf with its root R_1; O, massive initial; P, point of conjunction of young sporophyte and prothallus.

D, *Polypodium vulgare*: the young sporophyte can be analysed in terms of three phyllorhizes.

E, F, *Alisma plantago*: the phyllorhize concept as applied to seedlings of a monocotyledon (After G. Chauveaud).

to be divorced from the facts of embryology and especially of physiology; and the conception of orderly development as a result of the action and interaction of factors during the growth, formative activities and the further elaboration of embryonic regions is usually inadequately considered. Such theories (*see* Wardlaw, 1951, 1952b, Majumdar, 1957, and Sinnott, 1960, for a fuller account) are not without interest or value but, as will emerge, they have relatively little bearing on the contemporary treatment of organization. Nevertheless, with regard to Preformation Theories in general, but particularly in animals, Holmes (1948, p. 8) made the interesting comment that they have been deprecated because they attempt to explain the variety of form in organisms by assuming that the diversity already exists in the germ cell. But even in epigenetic theories, something has to be taken as given, i.e. 'put into the germ cell'. Of course, what we now regard as being present there are not preformed structures but 'developmental factors or potencies (genes)'; and biologists, 'however unwillingly, have been forced to adopt a certain amount of preformation by the facts of genetics alone' (Holmes). The present writer would prefer to say that what is initially present is a specific organization, or system, at the cellular or protoplasmic level, of which the genes are the most important but not the only components (*see* p. 130). This cellular organization is now being actively investigated by electron microscopy and other techniques (*see* p. 25).

PHYSIOLOGICAL THEORIES

Organization and Physiological Phenomena. It is worth noting at the outset that physiologists are becoming increasingly aware of the need for introducing concepts of organization if adequate accounts of physiological phenomena of classical interest are to be given.* Thus in a brief survey of recent trends in plant physiology, including nutrition in relation to growth, the physiology, growth and division of cells, metabolism and synthesis, growth, development and morphogenesis, and molecular biology, Steward (1961) has emphasized that, in every instance, phenomena of organization are involved; and he has recognized that the attempted explanations of the several phenomena are incomplete, largely because of inadequate information on organization. As Vöchting (1877, 1878, 1908) and others have long since pointed out,

---

* *Organization in Plants* by W. M. M. Baron (1963) is a text-book on plant physiology.

two embryonic daughter cells, with the same genetical constitution and basic organization, may differentiate into very different adult cells, the relative position of the cell in the tissue mass, and nutritional and other factors, being important determiners or regulators of the actual course of events; i.e. the same basic organization is capable of very different manifestations, and biochemical factors take their place as only one set of components in a complex reaction system.

In this connection Steward has cogently written: 'who could contemplate the dramatic events of photoperiodism upon the form, the function and reproduction of plants without recognizing the underlying problem of morphogenesis which is to determine how such a complex organization responds by its growth in so dramatic a fashion to such direct and apparently simple stimuli?' While the importance of chemical factors as regulators or modulators of the basic genetic pattern, or 'code', during development may be duly emphasized, Steward has pointed out that although recent and contemporary studies of molecular biology have added greatly to our knowledge of metabolism, they have 'taught us virtually nothing about the problems of organization'; and that 'such problems begin where "molecular biology" ends'. (The last statement is scarcely acceptable, at least to the author: organizational phenomena are present and are important at all levels in the organism.)

Steward's general outlook may be indicated by saying that the future of cell physiology and of other contemporary trends in plant physiology will largely depend on combining a knowledge of biochemical and other factors with a closer understanding of organization at the cellular and higher levels. As to what determines or constitutes organization, at any of the levels under consideration, Steward has made no new pronouncement; but his contribution is of particular interest in that, after a long and varied personal experience as a physiologist and biochemist, he has reached the conclusion that new advances will be made 'by combining the experimental techniques of physiology and biochemistry with an appreciation of, and respect for, the organization of the cells and organism upon which they act'.

In a similar vein, H. Stern (1960) has noted that recent advances in the study of subcellular organelles, biochemical genetics and virology are leading away from the earlier idea that cell organization is a resultant effect of specific catalysis. The emphasis now is on the structural order in catalytical aggregates and how such aggregates are perpetuated. 'Biologists have, of course, long understood that structural order at any organizational level is a cumulative product of evolution. But not until recently has this understanding become general among biochemists, *who now look to order as a basis of effective enzyme action rather than to enzyme action as a source of order'* (Stern: my italics, C. W. W.).

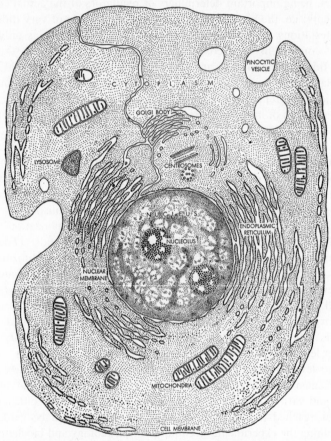

Fig.2.3 Diagram of a typical cell (plant or animal) based on electron micrographs, showing the nucleus and nucleoli, the nuclear membrane, the endoplasmic reticulum with its numerous superficial ribosomes (small dots), centrosomes, Golgi bodies, a lysosome and the cytoplasm which contains various minute organelles and particles still unspecified (After J. Brachet, *Scientific American*, 1961).

Different Aspects of Cellular Organization. In this book, which can claim to be no more than an introductory discussion, it is not proposed to dwell in detail on the very comprehensive theme of the organization of cells. That topic has recently been treated at considerable length by Picken (1960), his stated intention being to give a 'synthetic picture of the organization of cells in terms of macromolecular structure and texture'. Here one may note how very different are the accounts of protoplasmic organization as given by cytologists, physiologists and geneticists. Manton (1961), for example, in a review of plant cell structure, has pointed out that, with the wider use of the electron microscope, new information is accruing so quickly that no final summary is possible at this time. The principal aim of some investigators is the demonstration and interpretation of such structures as may be discerned at the high magnifications afforded by the electron microscope. This approach, in fact, is a kind of new micromorphology. Some physiologists and biochemists, on the other hand, are attempting to combine a study of some particular metabolic process, e.g. an enzymatic process, with observations made by electron microscopy (Simon and Chapman, 1961; James 1962). In such studies, an attempt is made to relate a particular biochemical activity with one or other of the several protoplasmic organelles, regions, or membranes; and where it has been possible to follow up, or envisage, a chain of processes, concepts of protoplasmic organization, in keeping with the physiological observations, tend to be formulated. Although there are evident points of contact, such ideas are still very far apart in many respects from those which have been formulated in recent years by geneticists in their attempts to explain the timely and ordered actions of nuclear and cytoplasmic genes (e.g. Mather, 1948, 1955, 1961). And this is still largely the case even though, as Picken (1960, p. 101) has noted, 'models of chromosome structure and genic activity are now, in a physical sense at least, molecular models'. To bring into a satisfying relationship, in terms of organization, the chains of processes and the coupling of reactions as envisaged by biochemists, the serial or successive evocation and action of genes as envisaged by geneticists, and the microcosm of structural features revealed by electron microscopists, presents itself as a formidable task (Fig.2.3 and Plate 3).

Waddington (1962) has discussed in some detail what constitutes and maintains the morphological organization within cells and has suggested that the positioning of the organelles is not based on the presence of a rigid framework but rather is determined by continuously acting forces; i.e. the micromorphology of protoplasm is dynamic, not static. Botanists, too, are familiar with various active movements within cells, e.g. the circulation of the protoplasm in cells in which the polarity, or the position of major organelles, remains unchanged. However, very little is known of the nature of the forces which determine and maintain the characteristic organization within cells, but biophysical investigations of macromolecules and organelles seem likely to be important. Organelles may undergo spontaneous changes in shape and Waddington has tentatively suggested (*ibid.*, p. 156) that possibly all the macromolecules in cells may be capable of undergoing some spontaneous change in configuration, with concomitant generation of energy. In unicellular organisms it is known that relatively small changes in the external environment can induce extensive changes in the intracellular organization.

Chemical Theories. Physiological theories of organization tend to be general rather than specific. Sachs (1887), in what is now known as the Theory of Chemical Correlation, was the first to formulate views which, in broad outline, covered the facts of correlation and morphogenesis. Differences between organs, he said, are due to differences in the chemical, i.e. metabolic, situation at their inception. His theory, in which the existence of growth-regulating substances and their movement in particular directions through the plant were assumed, not only afforded at least a partial explanation of many morphogenetic developments but also provided a basis for interpreting the integrated unity of the organism. That certain specific organic substances are profoundly important in growth and morphogenesis has now been widely demonstrated, the effects of growth-regulating substances having been detected in practically every phase of development. Such are the auxins, the kinins and the gibberellins. They may indeed be regarded as 'morphogenetic substances' in the sense that they are essential metabolites in certain formative processes. So, also, some common substances, such as sucrose, are essential in morphogenesis. Nevertheless, one may ask if contemporary biochemical concepts and facts alone are likely to afford an adequate account of organization. Sinnott (1946) urged caution in the acceptance of an all-out biochemical explanation of morphogenesis. Certainly, Sachs's view that specific substances, some of which are now known to be gene-controlled, are essential factors in growth and morphogenesis has become increasingly validated. In animal biology, the 'organizer' of Spemann and his school owes its effects to such substances. One trend of thought is that 'the basis for the control of organic development is a series of chemical substances, each with a specific rôle, produced by genes and entering in orderly fashion into the ontogenetic cycle' (Sinnott, 1946); and the central feature in organic development 'is a series of chemical reactions which result in the mobilization, from materials in the environment, of a mass of living stuff which we call an organism. The specific character of this organism and the form and relationships of its parts are to be attributed to the activity of the specific chemical substances which enter into these reactions'. But, as Sinnott also stated, a knowledge of the successive biochemical changes does not enable us to explain the underlying organization, of which organic form is the external manifestation, an organization which persists even when the chemical entities of which the individual is composed are replaced from time to time. Holmes (1948), commenting on the observation that developmental and other processes in organisms seem to be automatically regulatory, emphasized that a theory of development must primarily be a theory of regulation; the regulated activity perceived at any stage being due to the functional interdependence of parts of the organism.

That metabolism must be a potent factor in organization is evident and beyond doubt, but how it is to be closely related to this phenomenon is by no means apparent. For example, growth, organogenesis and histogenesis involve enzyme formation and activity, chains of reactions, linked reactions, and so on; but, as Steinbach and Moog (1955) have noted, these processes also include the mechanisms whereby appropriate newly-formed enzymes take part in the orderly ontogenesis. Accordingly, they have drawn a distinction between enzymes as an *aspect* and as a *cause* of development, and they consider that while 'chemogenetic events' may, in some instances, be causally related to morphogenetic processes, attempts to establish the chain of causality are unlikely to succeed in the present state of knowledge. Like Holmes, they have emphasized the importance of biochemical studies of regulating mechanisms. Moog (1952) established a fact that may be important in explaining the progressive manifestation of organization, namely that, as in the chick embryo, each stage in development is characterized by the activity of particular enzymes.

Gradient Theories. In this Gradient Theory of organization, Child (1941) stated (a) that polarity exists in a majority of organisms, (b) that metabolism is the effective factor in morphogenesis, and (c) that physiological gradients are part of the essential mechanism. He defined *physiological gradients* as 'spatial patterns in living organisms characterized by a gradual progressive differential in certain expressions of physiological condition' (p. 272). The primary gradients in the eggs of some animals are considered to be axial *substance gradients*, and *quantitative* metabolic differences along the axis of the developing organism are held to be major factors in morphogenesis. In the eggs of other animals in which an axial substance gradient cannot be demonstrated, it is thought that a basipetal gradient of metabolic activity may determine morphogenesis. Child did not consider that *specific* or *qualitative* differences in different regions are involved in the initial stages of morphogenesis, though they become important in later stages. According to this theory – the outcome of extensive investigations – organ formation and the development of symmetrical or asymmetrical structures are all referable to gradients (p. 273).

That the specific constitution of the protoplasm, the factors which activate it, and its physiological state, are primary and fundamental in morphogenetic processes, and that *gradients are secondary and consequential*, were emphasized by Child. But he also stated (1941, p. 281) that even if the organization of the egg originates in the orientation of elongate, dipolar and symmetrical or asymmetrical protein molecules, as Harrison (1936) and others suggested, this orientation must occur in relation to metabolism. And although structural changes may also be involved and affect metabolism, metabolism is the effective agent.

The organismal system as envisaged by Child is a dynamic one, the foundation of unity residing in the transmission of dynamic change. Transmitted changes, which will normally decrease in intensity from the locus of activity, are considered to originate in regions of high metabolic rate – the growth centres of other writers – these being attributed to the action of external factors. Child's theory lends itself to experimental investigation, for it is possible to control and alter the spatial arrangements of parts in an organism by altering the length of the metabolic gradient and so the range of dominance.

Prat (1945, 1948, 1954), has elaborated the gradient concept of organization as it may be applied to plants, and has attempted to relate the observed developments in different instances to physico-chemical, physiological and anatomical-histological gradients. Although individual gradients may be distinguished for purposes of analysis, they are all expressions of the progressive changes that take place in the cellular masses during growth and development; and they are all directly or indirectly interdependent. The physiological gradients are related to the polarity of the organism and are evident from the beginning of the embryonic development: but local or organic gradients originate with the formation of the several organs, e.g. lateral buds, leaves, etc.

The reality of physiological gradients is undeniable: they pervade all growth and development; but whether they are among the primary factors in organization is still conjectural. Physiological gradients are necessarily established in regions of high metabolic activity. Such regions, in Prat's view, will give rise to physico-chemical gradients, and these in turn will induce local modifications in cells whereby histological and anatomical gradations will become manifest. 'Finally these histological differences react on the functions of the maturing tissues and the circle is closed, all the gradients being parts of a coherent system, whose parts are all interdependent.' This analysis necessarily involves a consideration of the origin, or inception, of metabolic centres, e.g. the apical and basal poles and the cotyledon loci in a developing embryo, the inception of organs in the apical meristems of shoots, and so on. In many respects Prat's views are essentially similar to those of Child: gradients are held to be major factors in organogenesis. 'Organogenesis in its entirety can be considered as the establishment in a tissue mass, initially homogeneous, of a system of interdependent gradients. The several gradients affect the destiny of each individual cell, in particular its orientation and differentiation. Local conditions determine which of the total potentialities of a cell become manifest and which remain latent or are lost during specialization.' Anatomical and histological gradations are expressions of the physiological and auxetic gradients established during embryogenesis. Once a cell is differentiated in a particular way, it has a particular chemical activity, which in turn affects the system of functional gradients in proximity. This system of relations thus constitutes a closed cycle of interdependent gradients.

According to Prat, it is the constant interdependence of the several categories of gradients which 'constitutes the vital equilibrium or the economy of vegetable organism'. Hence, if the system is modified by injury, it tends to reconstitute itself; but where the injurious factor is persistent, as in galls, new forms develop which are not closely related to the normal form, i.e. a new equilibrium is established. Much of what Prat has incorporated in his general theory bears the stamp of truth. But important as gradients undoubtedly are, the inception of organization must, in the writer's view, be sought in still earlier events (in which, admittedly, gradients are also involved), namely, *those which relate to the establishment, in an initially homogeneous embryonic tissue mass, of active metabolic centres on which the setting-up of gradients depends.* This aspect is considered on p. 33.

Growth Centres and Morphogenetic Fields. A question that is left unanswered in gradient theories of organization is how centres of active metabolism, or *growth centres*, originate. The *field concept*, which has been elaborated in great detail by zoologists, has been adopted to a relatively minor extent only by botanists. The 'organizing' factors in animal development which, in the words of Weiss (1939), cause the individual parts of a germ to become definite and specific in compliance with a typical pattern, are present in sites described as fields. In discussing the 'organizer' effect, Spemann (1921) referred to 'a field or organization'; Gurwitsch (1922, 1927) advanced a somewhat similar idea, and in 1923 Weiss established the field character of organization and subsequently extended the idea to include ontogeny. The notion has been used extensively in discussions of animal embryogenesis.

Weiss (1939) described a field as 'the condition to which a living system owes its typical organization and its specific activities'; i.e. the basic or essential character of a formation is determined by the field. As fields give rise to orderly development, they themselves are deemed to possess order. Each field has a focal point of maximal activity: with increasing distance from this centre the intensity diminishes and hence the conception of field gradients. Of the latter Weiss says that they are merely convenient symbols and are non-existent as physical entities. 'The field concept is an abstraction trying to give expression to a group of phenomena observed in living systems. . . . Its analytical and explanatory value is nil. Its utilitarian value, however, is considerable. It permits us to bring a certain, if only temporary, order into the observed facts.' However, as practically all phenomena of development yield evidence of field-like characters, and as many field properties and activities can be specified, it would appear that the concept may also express physical reality.

According to Weiss – and there is botanical evidence which supports his views – a field is able to maintain its pattern when its mass is reduced or increased, and it can perpetuate its pattern when it is divided into two or more pieces. Gradients, which are all-important in the theory of Child and Prat, are held to be no more than indicators of developmental activity; the latter is to be referred to latent formative tendencies or morphogenetic fields.

In a review of the field concept in biology, J. S. Huxley (1935) described fields as the units of biological organization, the activities of cells, tissues and even organs being on occasion subordinated to the activity of the field. It is not difficult to think of supporting evidence from the Plant Kingdom.

As applied to organization in plants, comparatively little use has so

far been made of the field concept, but it is evident that field properties
might be ascribed not only to the shoot apices of vascular plants in
particular but, indeed, to all apices, including the primordia of the
organs to which they give rise. For the shoot apex has a characteristic
organization and is histologically distinctive. It is a region of active
growth and is the principal formative or morphogenetic region, exercising physiological dominance over other regions and giving rise to

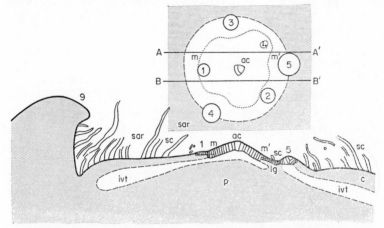

Fig.2.4 *Dryopteris dilatata*: the morphological and histological organization of a fern apex; the apical cone as seen from above and in
median vertical section (AA'–BB'). The interrupted line separates the
base of the cone from the subapical region (stippled). Leaf primordia,
1, 2, 3 etc. in order of increasing age; I_1, position of next primordium
to be formed; *ac*, apical cell; the apical meristem (*m-m'*) does not cover
the whole surface of the apical cone but extends a variable distance
down its sides; *ivt*, incipient vascular tissue below apex and primordia;
sar, subapical region; *c*, cortex; *p*, pith; *sc*, scales; *lg*, leaf gap. (Semi-
diagrammatic) (× 20) (*Phil. Trans. Roy. Soc.*)

physiological gradients (for reviews, *see* Wardlaw, 1952, 1964). (*See also*
Plates 1, 2, 7 and Figs. 2.4, 2.5).

Schoute (1913) and Richards (1948, 1951) have applied what is
virtually the field concept to the problems of leaf determination and
phyllotaxis in flowering plants. Thus, in the shoot apex, Schoute held
that a growth centre is formed first, the leaf being later formed round
this centre; he also suggested that a leaf primordium produced a
specific substance which inhibits the inception of other growth centres in
proximity, with the consequence that new primordia only arise between

older ones when the space has become sufficiently large. The new centre is typically situated at the point of intersection of equal circles drawn round the two adjacent primordia (Fig.2.5). The inhibition of growth

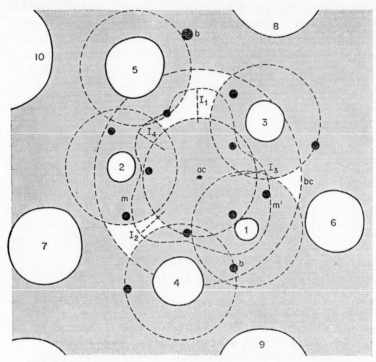

Fig.2.5 *Dryopteris dilatata*. Diagrammatic representation of a large apex as seen from above. The physiological fields of the top cycle of leaf primordia (labelled *1–5* in order of increasing age) and of the apical cell group (*ac*) are indicated by the stippled circles. The next leaf primordium will be formed in the position marked I_1, the next again at I_2; positions I_3 and I_4 are also indicated. Bud positions (b) are indicated by black spots: *m-m′* indicates the lower limit of the apical meristem, which reaches a variable distance down the sides of the apical cone; the approximate outline of the base of the latter, i.e. where it widens out into the broad subapical region is indicated by the broken circular line *bc*. (× 30). (*Proc. Linn. Soc.*)

centres by the shoot apex was also postulated. Richards (1948), in supporting this conception, referred to a new leaf primordium as arising 'round a centre determined as a peak of potential in a field dependent on older primordia, etc.' In his view, a field theory was to be preferred to a purely geometrical theory of phyllotaxis. In experiments, the writer (Wardlaw, 1949, 1952b) showed that, with modifications, Schoute's idea of growth centres affords a basis for a unifying and comprehensive conception of morphogenetic processes at the shoot apex and for the regulated and harmonious formation of the leafy-shoot. The problem then becomes one of envisaging some coherent system which is capable of giving rise to an orderly sequence of growth centres (*see* below). (*See* Figs. 2.4, 2.5).

Of morphogenetic fields and their regulation, Schmitt (1955), following Weiss (1947), stated that intimate contact between cells is a necessary condition for induction and that the idea 'that a few hypothetical diffusible substances, perhaps occurring in gradients of concentration, may trigger off the complex field and regulatory processes, seems to have been abandoned as fruitless'. But how a morphogenetic field is induced is not apparent. Holtfreter (1951), too, concluded that contemporary biochemical methods have not yet provided an explanation of the phenomena of induction and that the task of elucidating them is more a matter for the analytical morphologist than for the biochemist. Schmitt (1955) suggested that the answers are mainly to be sought at the molecular level of organization.

Bünning (1948, 1952) supported the concept of growth centres in morphogenesis and ascribed their regular, or patternized (or patterned), distribution to the mutual incompatibility of regions of vigorous protoplasmic growth. Competition for general nutrients cannot, in his view, be the decisive factor determining their distribution; rather it is that 'a certain type of embryonic growth will not allow the same type of growth to take place nearby'; but a different type of embryonic growth may proceed unimpeded. The processes in question are probably enzymatical, i.e. in the inception and development of a growth centre, a particular enzyme may become quantitatively predominant and this will lead to a diminution of the corresponding substrate in the surrounding field (Fig.2.6).

Turing's Diffusion Reaction Theory. While Bünning's ideas may be applicable to the shoot apex or other regions in which the pattern of organs has already been established, they do not explain how a patternized distribution of metabolites could be brought about in an approximately homogeneous, embryonic region, e.g. a bud rudiment, in which no organs or tissue systems have yet been formed or differentiated. This, indeed, is the basic problem in morphogenesis. In this connection Turing's (1952) Diffusion Reaction Theory of Morphogenesis is of

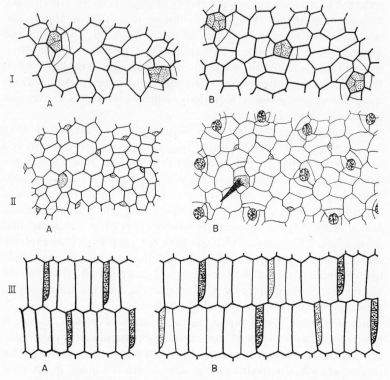

Fig.2.6 Bünning's concept of the inception of regular pattern, due to the 'principle of mutual incompatibility of loci of embryonal growth'.

I. In several plants, procambium strands develop spontaneously in the tissue. *A*, each strand induces new divisions in its vicinity and tolerates new strands only at some distance. *B*, a new strand may develop between the first ones as soon as the distance between them has increased sufficiently.

II. *A*, patterns of stomatal mother cells in the leaf, as in many dicotyledons. The big initial is a hair mother cell; *B*, due to the growth of the leaf surface, these initials have moved away from each other and developed into stomata. The enlarged gaps between them allow the formation of new stomatal initials.

III. *A*, pattern of pith ray initials in the cambium in tangential section; *B*, these initials have moved away from each other during the growth of the stem, and new initials develop in the enlarged gaps.

(After E. Bünning, from *Survey of Biological Progress*, 1952).

special interest and importance, for he has indicated that an initially homogeneous physico-chemical reaction system, in an embryonic region or tissue, may become heterogeneous and give rise to a regular, patternized distribution of metabolites, and thus provide the basis for an orderly morphological or histological developmental pattern. The writer (Wardlaw, 1953b, 1955, 1961, 1964) has pointed out that this theory, or some other theory also resting on a physico-chemical basis, is of the kind that could have a wide and general application to the phenomena of organogenesis and histogenesis (*see* Chapter 7).

PHYSICAL AND MATHEMATICAL THEORIES

Already, in the nineteenth century, Naegeli, Hofmeister, Sachs and others had attempted to relate the development of form and structure in organisms to physical and mathematical laws. With many fascinating examples, D'Arcy Thompson, in his classical work *On Growth and Form* (1917, 1942), showed how a knowledge of physics and mathematics may contribute to our understanding of the development of form and structure. The growth of every organism is characterized by an accumulation of material arranged in a particular way; and it is 'in obedience to the laws of physics that their particles have been moved, moulded and conformed'. In this view, the problems of form in plants are fundamentally mathematical and physical problems; the shape of any portion of matter, or changes in its shape, are due to the forces acting on it. These forces include gravity, cohesion, surface-tension, mechanical pressure, molecular diffusion, and chemical, electrical and thermal forces. Mathematical conceptions and techniques are essential in the analysis of such phenomena as differential growth, the size-structure correlation, and cell division by walls of minimal surface area. Theories of phyllotaxis unavoidably have a mathematical aspect, while Vöchting's theory of cell differentiation involves a consideration of position. All this may be admitted. Physical factors may be the proximate causes of form. But while the use of mathematics or physics may enable us to analyse a biological situation in which differential growth occurs, it cannot explain why it occurs. Nor can it account for specific organization. Indeed, as Northrop and Burr (1937) pointed out, the problem of organization has always been a crucial difficulty in bringing biology and physics into some acceptable relationship: ' ... living creatures possess physico-chemical constituents, but it has not been so certain that the organization of these constituents could be understood in physico-chemical terms'. Hence the introduction of such biological concepts as entelechy and organizer. These investigators suggested that living organisms are complex electrical fields with a definite pattern of ˋpotential distribution as a whole.

This section may perhaps be summarized by saying that we shall arrive at a better understanding of form, structure and organization to the extent that we can apply physical concepts to the processes and events involved in growth and metabolism.

PROTOPLASMIC THEORIES

These, it need hardly be said, are also physiological and genetical theories though their physiological content is sometimes tenuous. The study of embryos teaches us that, if we are to understand the higher manifestations of organization, it is essential to have the fullest possible knowledge of it at the level of the individual cell. Here, at the very outset, we encounter a difficulty: the evidence that cells possess organization is as abundant as the underlying causes are elusive, even though the new techniques of biochemistry, biophysics and electron microscopy add daily to our knowledge (*see* Bourne, 1951). In a survey of the techniques and findings of analytical cytology, Schmitt (1955) noted that the properties of the various kinds of cell components depend on their intimate chemical and structural interrelationships, and that the normal functioning of the cell is dependent on the organization of the system as a whole. The fibrous system of the cytoplasm, as revealed by X-ray diffraction and electron microscopy, may in time be shown to be the molecular framework to which major aspects of cell organization can be attributed. How varied and extensive these problems are may be seen in Picken's large volume on *Organization of Cells* (1960).

The distinctive organization of a species is primarily due to its hereditary constitution, i.e. to specific properties of the zygote or generative cell from which the individual develops; and, as Holmes (1948) said, it is difficult to avoid the postulate of an 'organized aggregate of elements in the germ plasm'. Since the protoplast of the generating cell comprises both nucleus and cytoplasm, there has been much discussion concerning the respective contributions which the two components make to the inception of the specific pattern and to the overall organization of the resulting adult organism. That they are constantly inter-related may be accepted.

Although the nucleus has its own organization, its relation to the differentiation and functioning of the cell is indirect. According to Sinnott (1942, 1946, 1958), genes may modify the developmental pattern but 'they seem quite unable to establish the basis of it. The fact that every cell is genetically equivalent to every other one itself precludes the idea of a control of differentiation by the nuclear apparatus alone. Only one possibility remains – the cytoplasm.' The 'integrating patternizing mechanism which parcels out to every cell its share in the organization of the whole' resides in the cytoplasm; and while the nucleus determines what kind of differentiation pattern shall be produced, e.g. by the action of gene-determined substances, the characteristic, specific cellular pattern is essentially the result of cytoplasmic activity. In this view, the organization of the cytoplasm in embryonic cells is basic to all subsequent manifestations of organization (*see also* further refs. to Sinnott's views on p. 52).

Other investigators have reached somewhat similar conclusions. According to Bünning (1948, 1952), when polarity is induced in a developing zygote or spore, chemical gradients, or gradients of electrical potential, may be directly involved, and may indeed be demonstrable. But it is to some specific protoplasmic structure, to some physical asymmetry, that the ultimate determination of polarity must be attributed. Polar structure in the cytoplasm is held to be the ultimate cause of polarity: without it there can be no differentiation. Polarity may be due to a polar orientation of the submicroscopic protein skeleton on the surface of the protoplasm. Polar molecules in the peripheral strata may be forced by external factors such as light and gravity to orient themselves in a particular direction. If these molecules then become firmly established in this orientation pattern, the attendant asymmetry may lead to differences in electrical potential and to chemical gradients; and these in turn will contribute to the anatomical and morphological differentiation (Bünning, 1952) (*see* Figs. 1.1, 1.2, 2.6, 2.7, 2.8).

That protoplasm may justly be regarded as an organized though heterogeneous system is supported by experimental and other evidence, but the nature of the organization has yet to be defined. Although protein is a main component, it is not the only one in the system. Studies of the effects of centrifuging have indicated that the ovum contains a framework of viscid protoplasm which can recover its usual form after distortion; and it is known that the eggs of some species may develop normally after their movable ingredients have been stratified. In some eggs, however, the cytoplasm is apparently very fluid and may flow like a liquid. Needham (1942) envisaged the protein chains of the protoplasmic lattice as being 'connected at many points by residual valencies and relatively loose attachments' and as being capable of springing back

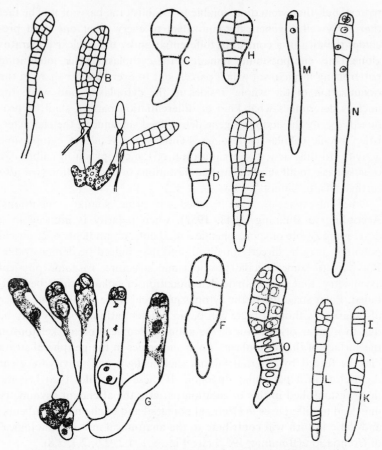

Fig.2.7 Early stages in the development of embryos in different major groups illustrating (i) the filamentous or polarized development of the young plant and (ii) Errera's principle of cell division by walls of minimal area.

A, *Fritschiella tuberosa* (a green alga; after M. O. P. Iyengar). B, *Laminaria digitata* (a brown alga, young sporophytes still attached to oogonia; after F. Oltmanns). C, *Fucus vesiculosus* (a brown alga; after G. Thuret and F. Oltmanns). D, E, *Radula complanata* (*Hepaticae*: *Jungermanniales*; after H. Leitgeb). F, *Selaginella spinulosa* ((*Lycopodiales*; after H. Bruchmann). G, *Sequoia sempervirens* (a gymnosperm; after J. T. Buchholz): several embryos. H, *Poa annua* (a monocotyledon; after R. Souèges). I, K, *Goodyera discolor*; L, *Orchis latifolia* (*Orchidaceae*; after M. Treub). M, N, *Cardamine pratensis* (a dicotyledon; after A. Lebègue). O, *Daucus carota* (a dicotyledon; after H. A. Borthwick).

(From C. W. Wardlaw, *Embryogenesis in Plants*, 1955).

into position after disarrangement. This he referred to as *dynamic structure* in protoplasm. Schleip (1929) noted that in every attempt to explain the polarity and symmetry of eggs 'some as yet unknown property of the protoplasm has to be introduced'. He therefore used the term *intimate structure* to indicate the basis of this protoplasmic property. In this connection Needham suggested that liquid crystals,

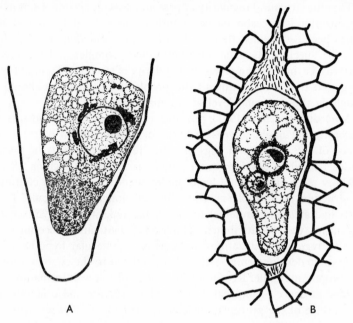

Fig.2.8 *Fegatella conica* (*Conocephalum conicum*). Examples of ova showing differentiation in the protoplasm. A, an unfertilized ovum. B, a fertilized ovum; the male and female nuclei have not yet fused ($\times$ 670).
(After K. L. Meyer, *Planta*, 1929).

i.e. substances in the paracrystalline state, may be important, because (he says) 'living systems actually are liquid crystals, or, it would be more correct to say, the paracrystalline state undoubtedly exists in living cells' (1942, p. 661). Paracrystalline substances have elongated molecules which can be distributed or arranged in different ways, regular and irregular, according to the conditions in which they exist: the molecules may be completely at random as in the true isotropic liquid state, or they may be disposed in different patterns with a high degree of regularity in the crystalline solid state. The paracrystalline state is apparently well suited to biological functions, in that it 'combines the fluidity and diffusibility of liquids while preserving the possibilities of internal structure characteristic of crystalline solids'. Schmitt (1955) has also discussed the probable importance of the paracrystalline state in the microstructure of protoplasm and therefore in cell organization.

That the structural regularity of protein molecules is important in cell organization is a reasonable conjecture. From X-ray diffraction studies it has been ascertained that the fibrous proteins in animal cells, which may be specified as giant macromolecular complexes, have precise patterns, i.e. involving a repetitive regularity of structure. Schmitt (1955) suggested that the solution to the problems of induction should be sought at the molecular level of organization.

According to Child (1941), protoplasts in general do not possess any structure that might serve as a basis for developmental pattern: 'evidence of the presence in eggs or other reproductive cells of a space lattice related to developmental pattern is at present lacking'. Seifriz (1935 *et seq.*), on the other hand, maintained that there is a continuity of structure in protoplasm, consisting of elongated molecules (as in carbohydrates and proteins) to which the polarity and symmetry of organisms can be attributed. Harrison (1936), also, accounted for specific regional localizations in terms of a molecular hypothesis, the embryonic developmental pattern being related to the configuration of the protein molecule. Recent investigations of cell wall formation have yielded evidence of molecular or micellar structure and orientation in the surface of the protoplast in contact with the wall (Frey-Wyssling, 1948; Weiss, 1950).

This brief survey of earlier work indicates that, in the investigation of cellular and ontogenetic organization, certain working hypotheses are necessary. These include: (i) that metabolism enters into virtually all aspects of organization; (ii) that the cytoplasm is essentially heterogeneous in nature, that (iii) centres of special metabolic activity are present in the cytoplasm, and that there is specific molecular orientation in relation to surfaces and interfaces.

Protoplasmic Organization as Disclosed by Electron Microscopy. New accessions of fact about the structures which are present in protoplasm are accruing so rapidly that any summary attempted now will soon be out of date (*see* Whaley *et al.*, 1960; Manton, 1961). Among points of direct relevance here are the following: (i) Many of the protoplasmic arrangements and components, e.g. mitochondria, in higher animals and higher plants, are closely comparable. (ii) Closed cytoplasmic membrane-systems are very general in plants above the level of the blue-green algae, these including plasmalemma (outer cytoplasmic membrane), plastids, mitochondria, Golgi bodies and tubular and vesicular derivatives thereof, vacuoles, including some with special contents, various other tubular and reticulate structures, and the nuclear envelope (Manton, 1961). (iii) There are also various non-membranous systems, e.g. granules, fibres, fat bodies and 'the unanalysable continuum', i.e. the cytoplasmic matrix. So, if the individual protoplast is deemed to exemplify some definite and specific organization, these are some of the components which we have to envisage as participating in the orderly structural arrangement. This organization, moreover, has to be understood in its functional aspect, i.e. as the apparatus, or vehicle, for physiological-genetical activity, with all the functional flexibility that we associate with an embryonic cell during its growth and differentiation, or with a differentiated parenchymatous cell during dedifferentiation and the ensuing regenerative phase. The various organelles may or may not be obligatorily associated with each other, but they are not evidently disposed in the cytoplasm in what one would describe as a characteristic orderly manner, i.e. constituting a recognizable pattern. It may accordingly be asked if electron microscopy has revealed a cytoplasmic reticulum, or some other structural system, which might be the basis of order in the cell, e.g. determining polarity by the prevailing orientation of its fibrils, strands or membranes, as suggested by earlier cytologists.

Manton (1961) has treated the question of the presence of an endoplasmic reticulum in plants with considerable reserve, but, in animal cells, the presence of such a microstructure has been conclusively demonstrated, the reticulum, in some cells at least, being membranous rather than consisting of tubular structures (summary in Picken, 1960). In plant cells, equivalent demonstrations have now been obtained (*see* Whaley *et al.*, 1960, for illustrations and earlier references; Buvat, 1958; Hodge *et al.*, 1956). But whether or not a pliable yet relatively stable endoplasmic reticulum is the main basis of cell organization has yet to be demonstrated. Studies of cytoplasm by Crick and Hughes suggest that there is no clear evidence of a definite structural spatial relationship between the several specific components of the cytoplasm, though, as Picken (1960) has noted, individual components may have mechanical properties which give them a considerable measure of structural coherence, e.g. chromosomes. Cytoplasmic processes undoubtedly appear to be co-ordinated, but whether this is based on some fixed microstructural framework has yet to be demonstrated. Indeed, in Picken's view, the evidence to date, including that from electron microscopy, is against this interpretation; and Crick and Hughes have asked if the evidence of co-ordinated chemical activities necessarily implies the presence of an organized and relatively stable, or persistent, 'cytoskeleton' (Fig.2.3 and Plate 3).

Weiss (1949, 1955), outlined a 'molecular ecology' theory of organization. This postulates that a minimum number of sites, differing in physical properties and chemical activities, are distributed throughout the protoplast; and development results from the interaction between 'the relatively stable, spatially differentiated, absorbing and orienting surfaces, and a population of molecules of all sizes, endowed with specific affinities for each other and for the relatively stable surfaces' (Picken, 1960). As this author has pointed out, a theory of this kind comprises both a preformationist and an epigenetic content – 'epigenesis on a preformed basis'; but, with qualifications, he considers that a theory along these lines may prove to be acceptable.

Studies of animal protoplasts are providing increasing evidence of regional differentiation in the ovum and the zygote. In plants, although the visual evidence from classical embryological studies is scanty, there are nevertheless some useful indications that encapsulated ova and zygotes have protoplasts which are regionally differentiated, i.e. with a distinction of apex and base (Wardlaw, 1955a). This finding is supported by the fact that polarity, irreversibly established, is one of the earliest phenomena manifested by the developing zygote in all classes of plants, from algae to angiosperms. In the free-floating ova and zygotes of certain marine algae, the spherical zygote is initially non-polarized; but polarity is soon established and is then irreversible. Parallel situations have been observed in animals and, as Picken (1960, p. 501) has stated, 'there is reason to believe that structural organization along the animal-vegetal axis comes into being progressively and at different rates in different kinds of eggs. . . .' This organization affords a basis for future differentiation and would, hypothetically, seem to be required, and to depend on, the presence of a definitely orientated reticulum or equivalent structural feature in the cytoplasm. As already noted, this relatively stable structure does not become displaced during centrifugation, even though other ingredients of the cytoplasm may have become stratified. If the encapsulated ovum in plants possesses incipient polar organization, as the evidence indicates, the presence of a relatively stable and characteristically orientated cytoplasmic microstructure is perhaps to be expected, though other explanations of polarity cannot yet be excluded. The application of electron microscopy to zygotes and very young embryos thus seems likely to yield interesting and important information (Figs. 2.7, 2.8).

GENETICAL THEORIES

Closely related to protoplasmic theories of organization, but with a different emphasis and approach, are the genetical theories; for they are directly concerned with individual cells as the sites of gene-determined metabolic processes. The generally accepted contemporary view is that hereditary factors pervade, determine and control every phase and aspect of development, though some biologists consider that this is going too far and claiming too much. The effective units, or factors, are the genes – large protein molecules, or molecular systems, capable of self-reproduction and of mutation – which are arranged in a particular sequence in the chromosomes. Other kinds of gene may be present in the cytoplasm. The genes are combined and redistributed at syngamy and meiosis and their mode of action is chemical. Important metabolic substances, e.g. auxins and enzymes, or their precursors, are now known to be gene-controlled. Certain genes become active at particular times as determined by the physiological condition of the cytoplasm, this condition having been induced by the action of other genes under particular environmental conditions. Sewell Wright (1945), Mather (1948, 1955) and Waddington (1948) have suggested by diagrammatic schemes how morphogenetic processes could be determined and controlled by successive, or serial, genic action (Wardlaw, 1952b). The details are complex and, in the present state of knowledge, the conceptions are necessarily speculative and of a general character.

Fig. 2.9 illustrates Mather's conception of the relation of nucleus and cytoplasm in differentiation. The nuclear genes receive the raw materials for their reproduction and metabolism from the cytoplasm and supply the latter with gene products. These have enzymic properties and are persistent and self-reproducing to an extent determined by the constitution of the cytoplasm as a whole.

To quote Mather (1948):

We can see that while the cytoplasm is the environment in which the nucleus works, it is also the product of the action of the nucleus. The action of a gene will become effective only when the cytoplasm is of the composition necessary for the immediate gene product to reproduce and to multiply, and so to impress its stamp on the cytoplasm. This multiplication then, in its turn, changes the cytoplasm in such a way as to

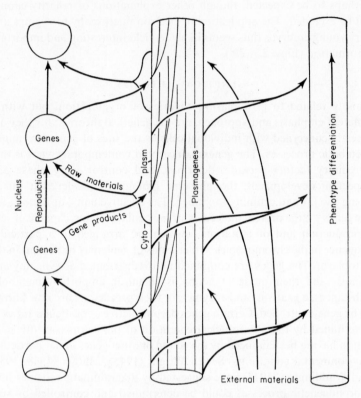

Fig.2.9 The nucleus and cytoplasm in differentiation (diagrammatic). The cytoplasm provides the nucleus with the raw materials for gene production and action. The products of gene action pass back into the cytoplasm where they each persist and multiply (as indicated by lines of varying lengths in the cytoplasm) to an extent conditioned by the constitution of the cytoplasm as a whole. This constitution is itself changed by the persistence and multiplication of the gene products, so that the fate of any gene product (and with it the effective action of the gene) both depends on the earlier action of the genotype and helps to determine the later action of the genotype. Reproduction of the plasmagenes is less limited and they persist throughout the history of the cytoplasm. The phenotype is governed by the constitution of the cytoplasm as a whole, and its development and differentiation reflect the changes of the cytoplasm as they occur in different cells. In this way the cytoplasm can change, and differentiation proceed, even though the nucleus is constant. (After K. Mather, *Growth*, S.E.B. Symp. 2, 1948.)

affect the consequences of the action of other genes. We thus have a basis on which we can understand both why genes have characteristic times of effective action (Haldane, 1932), and also how this time of effective action can be controlled by other genes. Indeed, we have more. We can see how a constant nucleus can be associated with changing cytoplasm and hence changing behaviour of the cell, and how these changes can themselves be determined by the constant nucleus. In other words, we have a genetical basis for differentiation.

The action of genes must be taken in conjunction with other factors. As Sewell Wright (1945) emphasized:

Genes can be thought to act directly only on the metabolic processes in the protoplasm immediately surrounding their positions in the cells which contain them. They can affect morphological characters only by determining one or another reaction of cells to local conditions. The relation of genes to organic structure does not differ essentially from that to hereditary extra-organic structure as of webs of spiders, nests of termites, wasps, birds, etc. A gene is related to a character through a chain of processes to which behaviour at each level determines structure at the next, while this in turn gives a secure basis for behaviour at the higher level.

Another fundamental physiological process, the relations of which to genetics remain to be clarified, is growth. We must distinguish two very different possibilities for gene action. Most of the many genes, known to differentiate large and small varieties, doubtless act mainly by modifying conditions which affect the rate of growth. But growth, as the multiplication of proteins, specific to the species and individual, is a process of the same essential nature as heredity itself. Again, we have the question whether the protein molecules are produced by step-by-step synthesis by specific polypeptidases or are produced as wholes on a model already present.

In fact, each character is always affected by many genes as well as by environmental factors, and each gene in general has multiple effects. No qualitative distinction can be made between abnormalities due to gene replacement and ones due to special environmental treatment (the phenocopies of Goldschmidt, 1938). Organs and, after a mosaic phase of development, the organism as a whole, have very considerable self-regulatory power.

*Gene and environment are alike modifiers of a pattern residing in the whole.** But the genes, while individually mere modifiers, constitute an array of physiological agents, selected through a long evolutionary history, that somehow determines the self-regulatory pattern of the whole.

Spiegelman (1948) indicated that differentiation may be due to the gene-controlled production of unique enzyme patterns. There is evidence that the several different tissues (in mice) are each characterized by a unique pattern of enzyme content. Concomitantly with the differentiation of an embryonic tissue, which has its own enzymic pattern, there is a progressive change in the quantitative distribution of the various enzymes. His hypothesis makes use of the concept of enzymic adaptation (for which there is supporting evidence), i.e. that cells

---

* My italics, C. W. W.

placed in contact with a new substrate after a time acquire the enzymes necessary to metabolize it. Such a process results in a real modification of the enzymic pattern of the cell, and it implies that 'the mechanism of gene control over enzymatic constitution, far from being rigid, is extremely flexible'. Hence Spiegelman's conclusion that genes do not control enzymes, but rather they determine the potentiality of enzyme formation. His general idea is that nuclear genes give rise to self-duplicating cytoplasmic plasmagenes – which are nucleoprotein in nature – and that these mediate enzyme synthesis. The plasmagenes compete with each other for protein and energy, and this, together with the nature of the substrate, determines the enzymic constitution of the cytoplasm. If such cytoplasmic differences constitute the basis of cellular differentiation, then phenotypic changes need not necessarily be preceded by genotypic changes, and certain environmental factors may affect differentiation.

In a discussion of biological organization, largely from the geneticist's standpoint, Mather (1955) noted (i) that genetical study affords evidence of the interlocking and interdependence of all the levels of organization; (ii) that certain genes may govern or control the nuclear mechanism, i.e. 'the genotype governs its own means of propagation'; (iii) that the organization of the cytoplasm is more varied than that of the nucleus, some components of the system, though gene-dependent, being as permanent as genes, while others, which are formed initially as nuclear products, are subsequently self-maintaining in suitable environments; (iv) that although the various cytoplasmic entities of special interest to the geneticist all have particular functional activities, 'little can yet be said as to how they are organized to keep in step with one another and to do their work'; (v) that nucleus and cytoplasm are complementary, the former ensuring steady control, the latter affording the 'flexibility required for adjusted action'; (vi) that the division of functional labour, which is a concomitant of development and differentiation, has been found to be under genetic control in those materials in which the phenomenon has been investigated; (vii) that the essential needs in organization at all levels for successful adaptation and evolution include (a) the property of continuation by faithful reproduction of the hereditary materials, i.e. the nucleus, genes etc., (b) division of labour ensuring continuity and stability on the one hand, and plasticity and a capacity for change and adjustment on the other: 'Upon this initial differentiation all later organization has been built.' Mather's conclusion is that the genetical evidence 'is unanimous that all the complexity of biological organization and its control has arisen in just this Darwinian fashion, though many of the intricacies, especially of gene action and adjustment and of the selective processes, remain to be elucidated'.

Although in genetical theories of development and organization the hereditary potentialities of the generative cell are taken as given, the theories are otherwise essentially epigenetic in nature (*see* p. 22). Thus, at critical stages of development, new metabolic substances enter the reaction system in an embryonic region and certain genes, hitherto passive, become active; their products, in turn, modify the system and thus enable yet other genes to become active; and so on. Some such chain of reactions, together with other aspects of the specific organization, could account for the inception of flowering and for the orderly and characteristic formation of the successive groups of floral organs (Wardlaw, 1957e); and, indeed, for differential processes in general (*see* Chapter 11). Stern (1955) has indicated that gene-substrate, or gene-cytoplasm, interactions could account for the differentiation of cells that are genetically equivalent, and has considered how such views of gene action can be applied to the concept of embryonic fields. Recent work, chiefly on animal cells, indicates that the nucleus and the cytoplasm may both undergo irreversible changes as development proceeds. (For a fuller consideration of genetical aspects, *see* Chapter 4).

EPIGENETIC, MULTI-ASPECT AND INTEGRATIVE THEORIES

The several theories of organization in plants already considered all contain some element of comprehensiveness, but the extent to which different authors have succeeded in bringing together and integrating the diverse and abundant facts of innate constitution, development, etc., varies greatly from one to another. It is in Epigenetic Theories that we encounter the most comprehensive and, in the writer's view, most informed approach to the phenomena of organization; for, in them, although the structure and specific genetic constitution of the generative cell are taken for granted for some purposes, these features are themselves also regarded as being subjects for special study. In epigenetic theories, organization is considered at all levels; as far as possible, nothing is taken for granted; and no single factor, relationship or morphogenetic development is taken for granted as having an overriding or special importance without full consideration of the whole situation. That, at least, is the ideal. Yet, it is salutary to note, as Holmes (1948) has done, that epigenesis, no more than preformation, really explains why a developing organism does what seems to us to be 'the right thing' at the right time. The phenomena of evolution are almost certainly involved; and hence the author's attempt to combine aspects of both organization and evolution in this volume.

As a zygote develops, it changes in a characteristic and orderly manner, each successive stage of embryogenesis being determined or affected by the antecedent stages. This serial or sequential development, known as *epigenesis*,* in which the specific organization becomes progressively manifest, could, in general terms, be referred to the zygote's inherent potentialities for growth and development, to changes in its initial reaction system under the impact of genetical and environmental factors, and to various regulatory relationships that become incident during development. Changes in the reaction system would also account for the competence of embryonic cells to react to particular morphogenetic and other stimuli, whether inherent or external, at particular stages of development. Any purely biochemical theory of ontogenesis, however precisely individual component processes may have been ascertained, will unavoidably be a vast over-simplification of the actual developmental process, characterized as it is by order, sequence, unity and functional activity. To know how different metabolites react and how they become distributed so as to constitute a functional pattern is of fundamental importance; but, even so, this information alone will not enable us to describe comprehensively the morphogenetic process; for the reactions are taking place in embryonic cells which possess the distinctive cellular organization of the species. Given this organization, the evidence is consistent with the view that gene-determined metabolism and differential growth, and various organismal factors, e.g. polarity, correlation, are basic factors in morphogenesis, and that physical factors, such as the forces of cohesion, surface tension, gravity and so on, and spatial relationships, are the proximate causes in the determination of form and structure. An epigenetic view, as published by the author in 1951, is presented schematically in Table 1. The diagram outlines the successive processes which may take place under the influence of the numerous contributory factors and relationships; but the actual *integration* of all the processes, as distinct from merely assembling them, so as to yield an adequate conception of the progressive ontogenetic

---

* Epigenesis: from *epi*, upon, after; and *genesis*, born. '1807. The formation of an organic germ as a new product.'

Shorter Oxford English Dictionary

organization, is a matter that is as difficult as it is elusive. The factors at work during ontogenesis are broadly speaking of two kinds, namely, intrinsic, inherent, or genetic factors, and extrinsic, external, or non-

Table 1. *Generalized Scheme of Morphogenesis*

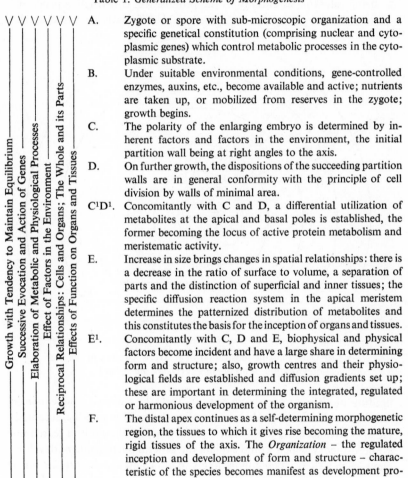

A.   Zygote or spore with sub-microscopic organization and a specific genetical constitution (comprising nuclear and cytoplasmic genes) which control metabolic processes in the cytoplasmic substrate.

B.   Under suitable environmental conditions, gene-controlled enzymes, auxins, etc., become available and active; nutrients are taken up, or mobilized from reserves in the zygote; growth begins.

C.   The polarity of the enlarging embryo is determined by inherent factors and factors in the environment, the initial partition wall being at right angles to the axis.

D.   On further growth, the dispositions of the succeeding partition walls are in general conformity with the principle of cell division by walls of minimal area.

C^1D^1.   Concomitantly with C and D, a differential utilization of metabolites at the apical and basal poles is established, the former becoming the locus of active protein metabolism and meristematic activity.

E.   Increase in size brings changes in spatial relationships: there is a decrease in the ratio of surface to volume, a separation of parts and the distinction of superficial and inner tissues; the specific diffusion reaction system in the apical meristem determines the patternized distribution of metabolites and this constitutes the basis for the inception of organs and tissues.

E^1.   Concomitantly with C, D and E, biophysical and physical factors become incident and have a large share in determining form and structure; also, growth centres and their physiological fields are established and diffusion gradients set up; these are important in determining the integrated, regulated or harmonious development of the organism.

F.   The distal apex continues as a self-determining morphogenetic region, the tissues to which it gives rise becoming the mature, rigid tissues of the axis. The *Organization* – the regulated inception and development of form and structure – characteristic of the species becomes manifest as development proceeds.

genetic factors. Waddington (1957) has referred to the latter group as 'epigenetic' factors. However, this usage tends to limit, or narrow, the scope of the concept.

The scheme presented in Table 1, as also Weiss' hierarchical concept

E

of organization (Fig.2.10), or Waddington's view of the epigenetic system of a cell (Fig.2.11), indicates that it is improbable that there can be any simple or unitary theory of organization. J. T. Bonner (1952) envisaged morphogenesis, or the emergence of an organismal pattern, as being referable essentially to the progressive, constructive processes of growth, morphogenetic movement and differentiation: and to the

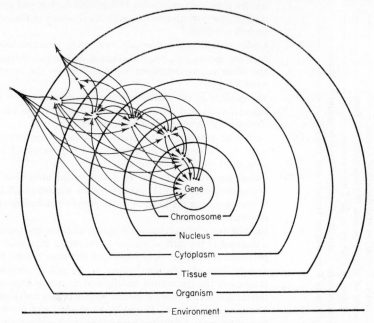

Gene

Chromosome

Nucleus

Cytoplasm

Tissue

Organism

Environment

Fig.2.10 Diagrammatic illustration of P. Weiss' concept of the hierarchical organization of an organism. (*Quart. Rev. Biol.*)

limiting of these processes in various ways by intrinsic and extrinsic factors which check, guide and canalize them. This may be accepted. He also advanced the thesis that a sustaining aim should be a search for a micro-theory which would explain the general phenomena of development, such a theory being more likely to afford an insight into the inner mechanism of the relevant phenomena than any other kind of theory. By a micro-theory he did not imply that all the phenomena of biology are to be brought down to physics and chemistry: some kind of intermediate micro-theory might prove satisfactory. Bonner did not advance any micro-theory, but he indicated that the kind that would be satisfying would be one in which, as in crystal structure, the organism could be

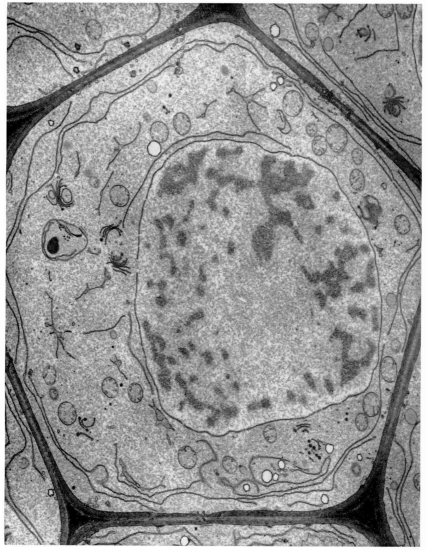

3. Evidence of organization: the pattern of organelles in a meristematic cell of an angiosperm—from a maize root-tip—as revealed by the electron microscope. (After W. G. Whaley, H. H. Mollenhauer and J. H. Leech. *Amer. Jour. Bot.*) (× 6720).

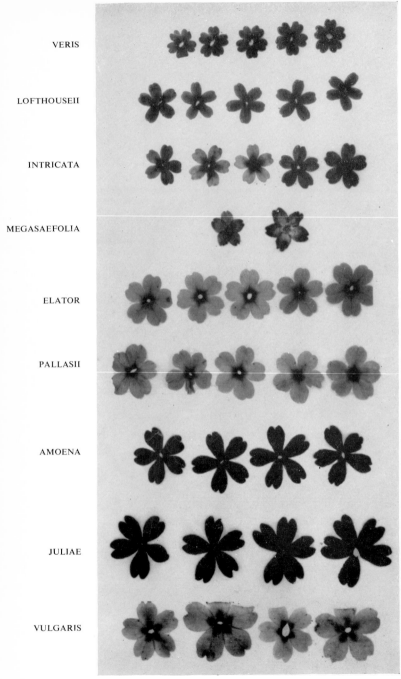

VERIS

LOFTHOUSEII

INTRICATA

MEGASAEFOLIA

ELATOR

PALLASII

AMOENA

JULIAE

VULGARIS

4. Differences in the corolla development in intercrossable species of *Primula* (mean diam. = 14 mm). (After D. H. Valentine, 1961.)

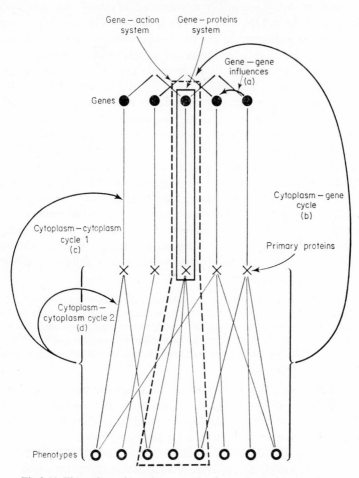

Fig.2.11 The epigenetic action system of a cell. Each gene determines the character of a primary protein, probably through the intermediate steps of RNA and microsomal particles; the primary proteins interact with one another to produce the final phenotype. The whole set of processes connecting a gene with phenotypic character is the gene-action system; the smaller set connecting it with its primary protein is the gene-protein system. Feedback reactions may be from (a) gene to gene, (b) cytoplasm to gene, (c) cytoplasm to gene-protein system, (d) cytoplasm to the primary-protein to the phenotype processes. (After C. H. Waddington, *New Patterns in Genetics and Development*, 1962.)

C

envisaged as being essentially constructed of small repetitive units. When one considers the complex nexus of factors involved in embryogenesis and morphogenesis, and the diverse manifestations of organization at different levels, it seems improbable that a theory of this kind can be adequate. On the other hand, Turing's theory of morphogenesis contributes effectively to an epigenetic scheme. If we envisage an embryonic region, e.g. a shoot apex, as being the site of a reaction system, then, during ontogenesis, the unitary reaction system will change in characteristic ways, each biochemical pattern being based on, and partly determined by, the preceding ones, and in turn effecting changes in those that follow. (This is more fully discussed in Chapter 7.)

'*Morphogenetic Components*' *of Organization.* In a recent summation of his views on organization Sinnott (1960) has recognized that several morphogenetic 'components' are of very wide occurrence in the Plant Kingdom and contribute fundamentally to the general phenomenon of organization. These components – polarity, differential gradients, symmetry and spirality – are also described as 'inherent or basic tendencies'. They

seem to be distinct characteristics and may have different bases in protoplasm . . . All of them, or their rudiments, seem to be present in all plants. They provide the basic ingredients, so to speak, out of which the developmental norm is produced. Just what a specific norm will be depends on the interaction between these inherent protoplasmic traits and two other factors: the genetic constitution of the individual and the environment in which it develops.

The genes, in a particular environment, act on these protoplasmic traits to produce the specific form of the organism. But, as the author has pointed out, how genes control developmental relationships, and thus the production of organic form, is largely unexplored.

Sinnott has also discussed what gives unity and the self-regulatory character to an organism, and has concluded that ontogenetic unity, and also regenerative developments, are not so much due to the unchanging genetic constitution but to the 'developmental norm, immanent in the organism from the first and often reached over different routes'. In brief, the elucidation of self-regulatory, 'normative development' is regarded as the central problem in the phenomenon of organization. The difficulty of the task is indicated by the numerous workers, cited by Sinnott, who have ventured into this field of enquiry. A synthesis of evidence from many different sources is, of course, essential; but what will come out of the attempted synthesis will largely depend on the attitude and philosophic outlook of the investigator. After discussing some of the more interesting and relevant ideas that have been proposed to account for biological organization, Sinnott concluded quite simply by saying that, after all, we still have no idea of what the underlying physical basis really is. But he was not unhopeful, though he recognized that the phenomenon of self-regulatory organization may well involve principles as yet undiscovered. These may prove to be distinctively biological and different from those at present available from the physical sciences – a conclusion which is not unlike that of some other contemporary exponents.

Sinnott's views need not be more fully discussed at this stage. It is, however, cogent to point out that his four basic and ever-present components of organization, i.e. polarity, differential gradients, symmetry and spirality, are capable of being analysed or more fully investigated in one way or another. Differential gradients, for example, must originate in some more or less direct relationship with centres of active metabolism, and the nature of such centres may eventually be discovered.

The Task. The whole question of organization in plants bristles with difficulties and is beset with seemingly endless complexities. It is true that scientific writers of the nineteenth century were well aware of the microcosmic attributes of the living cell but they would assuredly have been amazed at the diversity of detail in nucleus and cytoplasm already revealed by electron microscopy. To understand the basis of organization in an individual cell is clearly a formidable undertaking. Yet our task is no less than to understand the integrated unity or organization of higher plants. However, even though advances are likely to be of a piecemeal character for some considerable time to come, progress will undoubtedly be made, especially if botanists keep their eye on the main biological targets, i.e. the study of the whole plant, and the diversity of plant life.

Since (a) organization is manifested at the cell, tissue, organ, and organism levels, (b) the genetical constitution of even the simplest organism is not simple and not all genes are in action at the same time, and (c) many different factors and relationships are involved in growth and the assumption of form, the concept of organization may well require new and comprehensive, yet sufficiently simple, modes of statement.

CHAPTER 3

Homologies of Organization

Botanists have long been aware that closely comparable formal and structural features may occur in species that are quite unrelated genetically. Further significance is thus given to the phenomena of organization and it becomes increasingly apparent that they must be examined in detail and on the widest possible basis (Figs. 3.1–3.7).

EVOLUTION AND THE COMPARISON OF RELATED FORMS

The conception of evolution in plants and animals is based on the comparison of related forms in living species and in those preserved as fossils. Similarities in the form, structure, reproduction and life history of plants provided the evidence which botanists of the post-Darwinian periods used in attempts to indicate the natural affinities, or 'blood' relationships, of plants and the changes which plant life has undergone during the course of descent. In more recent times the techniques and findings of cytology and genetics, necessarily confined to living species, have played an increasing part in the interpretation of evolutionary processes.

The principal results of extensive morphological and geological investigations have been to establish the fact that, during vast spans of time and from simple beginnings, plant life has undergone a long and remarkable series of changes. Some lines of descent, or phyletic lines, have persisted with but little change at relatively low levels of organization; others have advanced and flourished only to become extinct; but, in general, there has been a sustained upgrade trend, from small, unspecialized, simple organisms to larger, more complex and more highly differentiated ones. Palaeontological studies have thus established both the reality and the probable course of evolution. The very important contributions which taxonomic investigators have made, and are making, to evolutionary theory should also be noted. Since the time of Linnaeus, travellers, collectors and systematists had been at work, studying and classifying the floras all over the known world, with important results. By the middle of the nineteenth century, the formulation of what were described as *natural systems* had reached a considerable degree of fullness, if not completeness; and, as Sachs has told us, no fewer than twenty-four such systems, based on the seeming natural affinities of genera and species, made their appearance during the years 1825–45. The latter part of this period also saw the publication, e.g. by Sir Joseph Hooker, of some remarkable essays on the distribution of plants and the factors involved in this phenomenon. It was from such observations, together with detailed studies of the variability of species, that Darwin and Wallace formulated the theory that organic evolution is a gradual process, that species give rise to small, heritable physiological and morphological variations and occasionally to larger ones, and that natural selection determines which variations and entities will persist or survive. With various modifications in presentation, and vast new accessions of fact, Darwin's conclusions have been substantially supported by the genetical studies of recent decades.

Morphological studies during the post-Darwinian era – the so-called Phyletic Period – yielded reasonable though still incomplete indications of the main trends of evolving plant life. The importance of heritable variations and mutations, intercrossing, natural selection, biological advantage, adaptation, and opportunities for new development, were recognized and accepted, as also were the relative success and persistence, over vast stretches of time, of some phyletic lines, and the partial or complete eclipse of other groups and their replacement by new ones. It is understandable that in the period following the publication of the *Origin of Species*, many of the leading botanists became devoted adherents of comparative morphology, the sustaining aim of which was to construct a unified, comprehensive phylogenetic system – nothing less than a complete 'genealogical tree' of the Plant Kingdom. This, indeed, presented itself as *the* task of paramount importance, satisfying on scientific grounds and affording a great centralizing philosophic theme.

A vast literature has accumulated round the topic of evolution. Nevertheless, after a hundred years, our knowledge of many aspects of plant evolution is still inadequate, not to say meagre. A scrutiny of the various phylogenetic systems (or genealogical or family trees) of the Plant Kingdom that have been proposed shows how incomplete and sketchy they mostly are. Genetical conceptions, it is true, have been advanced to explain, or explain away, some of the difficulties. But however plausible these 'explanations' may be, they are still very incomplete. We still do not know – and, indeed, there appears to be no firm opinion among botanists – whether the Plant Kingdom should rightly

be envisaged as a monophyletic or a polyphyletic system. Nor do we
know how to relate the more advanced groups to their presumed simpler
progenitors, e.g. the bryophytes or pteridophytes to their presumed
green algal ancestors; the pteridophytes to the bryophytes; the gymnosperms to the pteridophytes; or the flowering plants to the gymnosperms
or the pteridophytes. As to the great contemporary group of the flowering plants, we know virtually nothing of its origin, or origins, and little
more of the mutual relationships of its major subdivisions. An increasing awareness of these difficulties, and a growing recognition of *the
prevalence of parallelisms and convergences in evolution,* have led many
botanists to discard the original monophyletic conception of the Plant
Kingdom and to replace it by a polyphyletic one. Although the latter
interpretation may be more in keeping with the facts as presently understood, it tends to raise new problems rather than to solve old ones.

The existence of closely comparable morphological characters,
e.g. in the flowers of *Ranunculus* spp., or of *Viola* spp., is the principal
evidence of the assumed affinity between species. These characters, both
vegetative and reproductive, are the materials which the systematic
botanist uses in his work. However, as a result of parallel or convergent
evolution, more or less closely comparable morphological and structural
features may also occur in plants which are not closely related, or are
even quite unrelated. Such developments in genetically unrelated
organisms are described as being *homoplastic,* or as exemplifying
homology of organization. The relevance of these phenomena to the
present study needs no emphasis.

PARALLELISM AND CONVERGENCE IN EVOLUTION AND HOMOLOGY OF ORGANIZATION

Observation of close similarities in the development, form and structure
of genetically unrelated organisms raises the questions: To what evolutionary processes, and to what ontogenetic factors, are the comparable
developments to be ascribed? Although the scope of the two questions is
different, they overlap in that both involve a consideration of the
genetical constitution; for genetical factors are primary determiners in
the individual development, while heritable modifications of the genetical constitution underlie the observed evolutionary parallelisms and
convergences, just as, in many other instances, they are responsible for
divergences.

The reality of parallel and convergent evolution, sometimes resulting in a close homology of organization, rests on a wide basis of

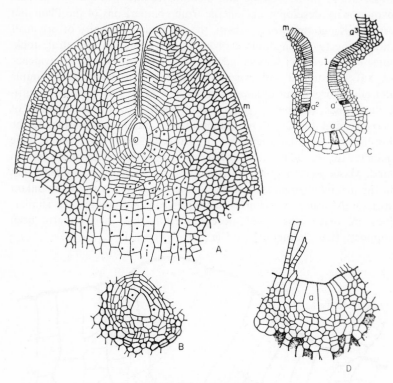

Fig.3.1 Apices of Fucales.

A, B, *Halidrys siliquosa* as seen in longitudinal and transverse section: a distinctive apical cell gives rise to an apical meristem consisting of characteristic prism-shaped cells; some interesting features of sub-apical cell-division and differentiation can also be seen. *m*, meristoderm; *c*, cortex; *i*, inner medulla; *r*, elongated, or prism-shaped cells (in the furrow), formed from the apical cell (× 240, after F. E. Fritsch, *New Phytologist*).

C, *Seirococcus axillaris*: longitudinal section of apical depression, showing meristematic cells, and apical cell *a*; *a¹*, *a²*, *a³*, apical cells of lateral lobes; *m*, meristoderm cells; *l*, a lateral lobe (after Grüber).

D, *Fucus furcatus*: apex of a young plant in l.s., showing *a*, apical cell and its segments. (After F. Oltmanns, *Morphologie und Biologie der Algen*.)

observation. Some striking and incontrovertible examples of parallel evolutionary developments emerge from comparisons of the Plant and Animal Kingdoms; for, in them, the original community of origin, if indeed the two Kingdoms evolved from a common ancestral stock, must have been very remote indeed. Yet the two groups afford evidence of: (a) a sustained and progressive development from small, simple unicellular organisms to large, complicated and highly organized multicellular ones; (b) the inception and elaboration of the mechanisms of heredity and of sexual reproduction, the latter culminating in the fertilization of a large encased or protected ovum by a small male gamete; (c) the adaptation of originally aquatic organisms to life on land. Many other parallelisms could also be enumerated, not least that in the details of organization in the individual cell, with the abundant structural features now known from electron microscopy, the similarities are much closer and more numerous than had hitherto been supposed (*see* Chapter 6; also Fig.2.3 and Plate 3).

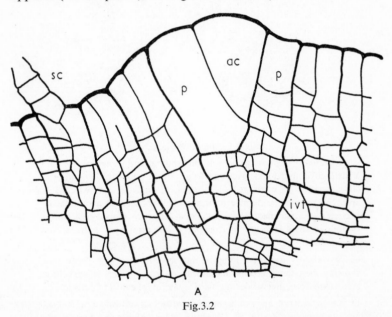

A

Fig.3.2

The major groups of the Algae, which are now regarded as being so distinct from each other as to be ranked taxonomically as *classes*, and which probably originated from flagellate, unicellular, ancestral forms, illustrate evolutionary parallelisms and afford many striking examples

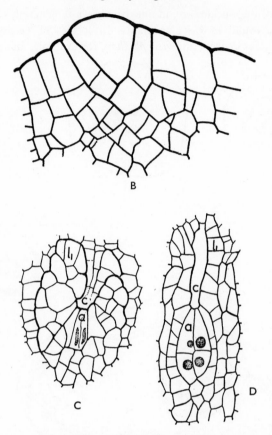

Fig.3.2 A, B, Shoot apices of *Asplenium nidus* (Bird's nest fern) in longitudinal section showing histological organization (× 180). C, D, *Ophioglossum vulgatum*, a eusporangiate fern. The shoot apex, with its apical cell (*a*) and first leaf (*l₁*) are situated at the base of a cavity (*c*) (× 225). (*Annals of Botany.*)

of homology of organization, e.g. the Palmella-condition, the colonial habit, the filamentous and heterotrichous habits, growth by an apical cell, multi-axial somatic development, the trend from isogamy to oogamy, the establishment of similarly constituted alternation of generations, and so on. The similarity in the balance of the life cycle in brown algae such as species of *Laminaria* and in ferns, both remarkable for the somatic advance of the sporophyte, may also be noted. Moreover, the morphogenetic developments in some of the larger parenchymatous

c*

members of the Fucales are, in unexpected ways, generally comparable with those found in vascular plants. In species of *Fucus*, *Halidrys*, *Sargassum*, *Seirococcus* and *Ascophyllum*, for example, an apical cell is

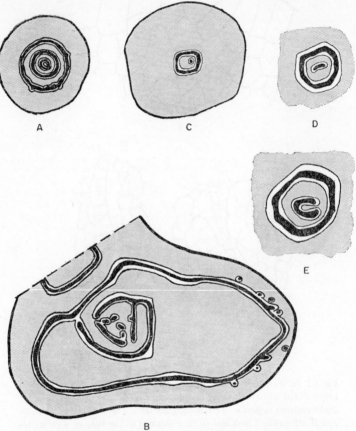

Fig.3.3 Homology of organization in polycyclic solenosteles.
A, Transverse section of a rhizome of a primitive fern, *Matonia pectinata*, and B, of a more advanced fern, *Pteris podophylla*. C–E, steles of a lycopod, *Selaginella lyallii*, in the ontogenesis of which, as in A and B, the size-structure correlation is exemplified. Diagrammatic representations, with xylem black, phloem clear, and endodermis a continuous line (A, × 2; B × 4; C–E × 25).

present at the growing tip of the thallus. This cell gives rise to a distinctive and well-defined apical meristem which is generally comparable with that of a fern; and just as the lateral buds in ferns originate from detached meristems, i.e. from a group of meristematic cells which at one time formed part of the apical meristem, so, too, in *Ascophyllum*, the side branches originate from essentially similar detached portions of the distal meristem. Again, in *Sargassum*, there are complex lateral members which, morphologically, are generally comparable with the axillant-leaf-and-branch of vascular plants. The Fucales, in short, have several organizational features that we usually associate with the higher plants (Figs. 3.1, 3.2).

Axial development, which follows the establishment of polarity in the zygote, is found in many classes of plants and may, accordingly, be regarded as one of the most general homologies of organization. We may also note that comparable phyllotactic and branching systems are found in the gametophytes of bryophytes and in the sporophytes of pteridophytes and seed plants; and, as Wardlaw (1957) indicated, the origin and histological constitution of leaf primordia in the apical meristem are generally comparable in all classes of plants. In vascular plants, now considered to be polyphyletic, the roots are nevertheless closely comparable in their endogenous origin, mode of growth, vascular pattern, and physiological activity. Shoot steles also afford many remarkable parallelisms, including the independent origin of secondary thickening in different phyletic lines. The development of a solenostele from a protostele is generally associated in the minds of students with the ferns; but a closely comparable development can be observed in *Selaginella lyallii*, in which, as in certain fern species, e.g. *Matonia pectinata*, the stele may become polycyclic; and somewhat similar stelar developments are known in the flowering plants. Reference may also be made to the investigations of Bailey (1954) and Metcalfe (1954) who have shown that the evolution of the diverse elements in the conducting systems of vascular plants has proceeded independently, but along parallel lines, in taxonomically unrelated groups. Among vegetative characters, developments such as the succulent, climbing, epiphytic, parasitic, aquatic, herbaceous and arborescent habits are present in different phyletic lines and afford yet further evidence of homologies of organization attributed to parallel or convergent evolution (Figs. 3.3–3.6). Dichotomous leaf venation, which is a commonplace in the ferns, has also been demonstrated by Foster (1961) in a number of dicotyledons (Fig.3.7).

In the angiosperms the evidence of parallel and convergent developments is such that some observers consider that all the major trends in floral evolution, e.g. polypetaly to gamopetaly, actinomorphy to zygomorphy, hypogyny to epigyny, meiomery and pleiomery, have probably originated and developed independently in different families.

While no complete account of the homologies or organization in the Plant Kingdom need be attempted here, mention should be made of such striking examples of similar but apparently independent evolu-

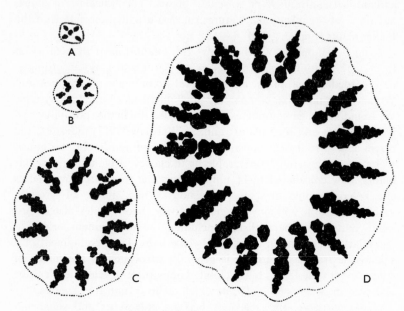

Fig.3.4 *Gunnera chilensis* (Haloragidaceae). Transverse sections of the steles of small and large roots of a dicotyledon, showing diagrammatically the distribution of tissues (xylem, black; the endodermis is indicated by a broken line). Similar series, demonstrating a size-structure correlation, have been obtained from ferns, other dicotyledons and monocotyledons (*see* Fig.3.5): the larger steles show essentially the same kind of histological organization as the smaller ones, but the pattern is considerably more elaborate ($\times$ *c.* 35). (*Trans. Roy. Soc. Edin.*)

tionary innovations as the heterosporous condition in Equiseta, Lycopodiales, Filicales, and Spermatophyta; the Polypodioid and Acrostichoid soral conditions in different phyletic lines in the ferns; the presence of an archegonium in bryophytes, pteridophytes, and gymnosperms; polyembryony in different families of gymnosperms and angiosperms; and apogamy and apospory in various groups.

HOMOLOGY OF ORGANIZATION IN EMBRYOS

Evidence of the prevalence of homology of organization emerges from a study of the embryos in all the major classes of plants (Wardlaw, 1955). In the zygotic development, in species selected from algae to

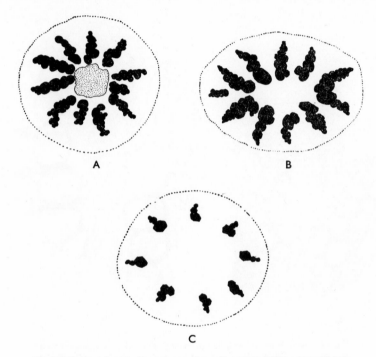

Fig.3.5 Steles of roots, in cross-section, of species which are not closely related taxonomically, but which show closely comparable organization (xylem, black; endodermis, a broken line; sclerotic tissue at centre, stippled).

A, *Danaea nodosa* (a primitive fern; Marattiaceae; × 50) B, *Nuphar polysepalum* (Nymphaeaceae) (×50). C, *Eryngium serra* (Umbelliferae (× 80). (*Trans. Roy. Soc. Edin.*)

angiosperms, the following phenomena are of general occurrence. (i) In the mature or newly fertilized ovum, the distribution of metabolites may initially be relatively homogeneous – though this is probably rare in encapsulated ova – but it quickly becomes heterogeneous: and with or without an attendant elongation of the zygote, an accumulation of different metabolites takes place at diametrically opposite points, the polarity of the new organism being thereby established. (Bonner (1952) noted that polarity may have different physical bases in different instances.) Where the ovum is enclosed, the physiological activity of the surrounding tissue is probably important in determining its polarity.

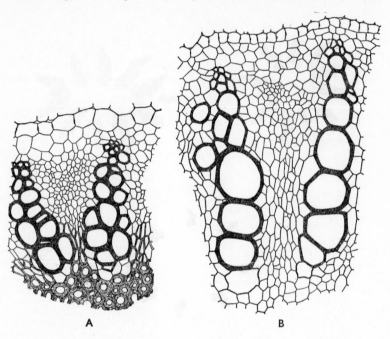

A   B

Fig.3.6 Homology of organization as illustrated by the detailed structure of root steles as seen in cross-section.

A, *Danaea nodosa*. B, *Gunnera chilensis* (both × *c*. 100). The two root sectors show a close similarity in the distribution of pith, xylem, phloem, pericycle and endodermis. (*Trans. Roy. Soc. Edin.*)

In the free-floating zygotes of algae, factors in the environment may induce the reactions which lead to the establishment of polarity. (ii) In the polarized zygote, the apical or distal pole becomes the principal locus of protein synthesis, growth and morphogenesis, whereas the basal or proximal pole is usually characterized by the accumulation of osmotically active substances, its cells becoming vacuolated and distended. (iii) The first division of the zygote is typically by a wall at right-angles to the axis, cell division being possibly stimulated by the increase in size (though this is not invariable in embryos) and the instability associated with the drift to cytoplasmic or metabolic heterogeneity. As cell division tends to restore equilibrium in the system

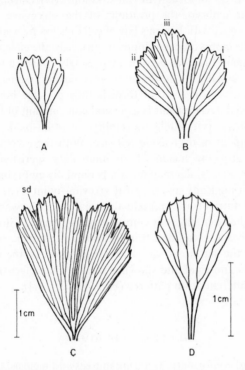

Fig.3.7 Homology of organization as exemplified by the leaves of ferns and of some flowering plants.

A, B, *Aneimia adiantifolia*: juvenile leaves showing the open dichotomous venation characteristic of many ferns (× 4). (After F. O. Bower, *Trans. Roy. Soc. Edin.*)

C, *Kingdonia uniflora*: segment of a lamina. D, *Circaeaster agrestis*: total venation of a leaf. A number of other flowering plants also show dichotomous venation. (After A. S. Foster, from *Recent Advances in Botany*, 1961.)

(D'Arcy Thompson, 1917, 1942), the position of the partition wall will be such that the forces present in, or associated with, the two daughter cells will be balanced. According to the nature and distribution of the forces involved, the zygote may be more or less equally divided, or it may be divided into a small, densely protoplasmic distal cell and a larger basal cell. The nature of this division is thus ultimately determined by the specific metabolism of the zygote. (Changes in the nucleus itself may also be important in cell division.) (iv) During the further growth of the embryo, the positions of the successive walls are in general conformity with Errera's law of cell division by walls of minimal area. (v) As the embryonic development proceeds, the effects of genetical and environmental factors become increasingly conspicuous, and, as a result of differential growth, the embryo begins to assume a distinctive form. An immense diversity of form is thus possible but, with some exceptions, axial development is a general concomitant of the establishment of polarity. (vi) While the embryo is still small, it shows an acropetal gradient of decreasing cell size. With the exception of those algae which grow by means of an intercalary meristem, the distal region of the axis, which may remain perennially embryonic, becomes organized histologically as an apical growing point. (vii) Though the absorption of nutrients may initially take place over the whole surface of the embryo, the later stages of embryogenesis appear to involve uptake by the more basal tissues and translocation to the apex. (viii) Primary growth is in the nature of an accretionary process, the older tissues becoming firm and rigid and showing various characteristic concentric and radiate differentiation patterns (Figs. 1.1, 2.7, 8.4).

NUCLEAR PHENOMENA

The events and conformations during mitosis and meiosis, the construction of chromosomes, and the genic mechanism, show close similarities in organisms which are widely separated taxonomically, or even completely unrelated. Hence many cytologists and geneticists regard themselves as biologists rather than as botanists or zoologists.

INTRA-CLASS PARALLELISMS

Within well-defined taxonomic groups, such as the ferns or flowering plants, parallelisms of development may also be discerned in the evolution of the constituent phyletic lines: hence structural features which are truly homoplastic in origin may be mistakenly regarded as being homogenous.

HOMOLOGY AND HOMOGENY

Homology,* in biology, means correspondence in type of structure. The term *homogeny* indicates 'correspondence in structure due to common descent' (*The Shorter Oxford English Dictionary*, 1870). Organs which are comparable in position of origin, development, form and structure are said to be homologous. Species with homologous members were regarded by post-Darwinian morphologists as being related to a common ancestor. The conception of homology in comparative morphological studies has been clearly defined by Bower (1947, p. 344). In his view, the classification of parts

must be based upon their origin, and upon the place which they take relatively to other parts at the time when they first appear . . . *those parts of the individual or of different individuals, species or genera, are distinguished as homologous which have the same relation to the whole plant body, whatever their function or external conditions may be.* The strictest conception of homology is that designated as *homogeny*. Lankester defined as homogenous those structures which are genetically related in so far as they have a single representative in a common ancestor.

It was the anatomist Owen who, in 1843, described as *homologous* those organs which have the same fundamental structure, even though they may differ in a more or less marked degree in their appearance and function. The phenomenon, however, was known to much earlier observers, e.g. Aristotle; in 1555 Belon identified the homologous bones in birds and man; and Goethe's theory of metamorphosis implies the *serial homology* of leaves on the same axis and the special homology of the leaves of different species. As Dobzhansky (1955) pointed out, homology does not prove, but rather suggests, evolution, i.e. the

---

* Definitions from *The Shorter Oxford English Dictionary*.

Homogen.   A part or organ homogenetic with another.

Homogenetic. Having a common descent or origin, applied to organs or parts of different organisms which show a correspondence of structure, due to derivation from a common ancestor.

Homologous.   (Biol). Having the same relations, proportion, relative position, etc. Having the same relation to a fundamental type; corresponding in type of structure.

Homoplastic   (Biol.). An organ or part homoplastic with another; opp. to *Homogen*. Having a similarity of structure without community of origin.

Homoplasy   (Biol.). 1870. Homoplastic condition; similarity of structure produced independently by similar external circumstances. opp. to *Homology*.

presence of comparable organs in different species because they have been derived from a common ancestral stock; and, conversely, evolution affords the best explanation of the abundant instances of homology. Again, Dobzhansky (1955, p. 242) noted that it is 'the developmental system as a whole which is preserved or modified by natural selection', Haeckel's biogenetic law – that ontogeny is a recapitulation of phylogeny – being 'simply an expression of the unity and of a relative stability of the developmental system in evolution'. The developmental system is, of course, simply another way of describing the specific organization or the manifestation of the underlying reaction system.

HOMOPLASY AND HOMOLOGY OF ORGANIZATION

Botanists of the post-Darwinian 'phyletic period' who believed in a monophyletic genealogy* of the Plant Kingdom, worked on the basic assumptions that all plants shared a common ancestry and that the major subdivisions were offshoots from a main stem. In this conception similar formal and structural characters in different species, genera and higher systematic units were accepted as being homologous. Later, as already noted, contemplation of the accumulating morphological evidence brought the realization that comparable developments were to be observed in species that could not be regarded as being closely related genetically. This led to a recognition of the fact that parallel evolution must have been very general in both the Plant and Animal

---

* The monophyletic system, or 'family tree', was held to have had its origin in a green algal ancestor; the tips of its 'branches' indicated the various levels of organization attained in the several classes, the flowering plants over-topping all others. All amphibious and land plants, from bryophytes to flowering plants, were thought to exemplify a single, sustained, upgrade evolutionary trend: the filamentous and parenchymatous algae were thought to have originated from autotrophic, unicellular organisms; the bryophytes were held to have arisen from the more advanced green algae which had managed to secure a foothold on the land; pteridophytes, which shared the archegoniate and motile spermatozoid characters with the bryophytes, were held to have evolved from the latter; and finally seed plants had evolved from the pteridophytes. The confidence of the early phylogenists in such conclusions, e.g. Haeckel, is clearly indicated by the completeness with which their diagrams of the 'family tree' were executed; and not dissimilar views were still held by some botanists well into the present century. That there were gaps in the system, and that the fossil evidence was fragmentary and incomplete, was realized; but confidence in the methods of comparative morphology was such that at least a provisional acceptance of the monophyletic scheme seemed to be justified by the facts. It afforded, moreover, a unified conception of the Plant Kingdom that was undoubtedly pleasing and satisfying to some minds (*see* Wardlaw: *Phylogeny and Morphogenesis*, 1952).

Kingdoms. The more the evidence was critically examined, the more important these parallel or *homoplastic developments*, or homologies of organization, were seen to be. This view has prevailed until the present time. Since these similar developments in unrelated species can not be attributed to homogeny, it has long been recognized that it is a matter of the first importance, both in evolutionary theory and in morphogenesis, to ascertain to what factors they can be referred.

Not all botanists were able to accept the monophyletic conception of evolution in plants and, during the latter part of the nineteenth century, doubts as to its validity had already taken root and begun to grow. The notion of homoplastic development, or *homoplasy*, introduced in the first instance by Lankester (1870) to zoology, and slowly taken up by botanists, played an important part in this critical stage. In the words of Bower: 'His short paper went far towards clearing up the ideas that surrounded the term "homology" in the minds of early evolutionists.' Lankester also introduced the idea of *homogeny*, the term *homogenetic* being applied to organs or parts which were similar because they were developed in plants of common ancestry. We also owe the term *homoplasy* to him:

Under the term *homology* belonging to another philosophy (Platonic philosophy), evolutionists have described and do describe two kinds of agreement – the one, now proposed to be called *homogeny*, depending simply on the inheritance of a common part, the other, proposed to be called *homoplasy*, depending on a common action of evoking causes or moulding environment on such homogenous plants, or on parts which for other reasons offer a likeness of material to begin with. In distinguishing these two factors of a common result we are only recognizing the principle of a plurality of causes tending to a common end, which is elsewhere recognizable and has been pointed out in biological phenomena.

Lankester considered that the term *homology* should be dropped, but that the term *analogy* should be retained and should not be regarded as equivalent to *homoplasy*. Thus, any two organs having the same function are analogous, whether they closely resemble each other in their structure and relation to other parts or not; but homoplasy includes all cases of 'close resemblance of form which are not traceable to homogeny, all details of agreement not homogenous in structures which are broadly homogenous as well as in structures having no genetic affinity'.

According to Lankester, if a similar organ is present in two plants which are both related to a common ancestor also possessing it, the organs would be described as being homogenous. But two related organisms may show comparable structural features which were not present in the common ancestor. In such a case the structural features would not, in Lankester's view, be homogenous: they would be homoplastic. Some homoplastic developments may be very closely comparable in form, even identical. This was explained by Lankester as follows:

> When identical or nearly similar forces, or environments, act on two or more parts of an organism which are exactly alike, the resulting modifications of the various parts will be exactly or nearly alike. Further, if, instead of similar parts in the same organisms, we suppose the same forces to act on parts in two organisms, which parts are exactly or nearly alike and sometimes homogenetic, the resulting correspondences called forth in the several parts of the two organisms will be nearly or exactly alike. There will be . . . no kind of difficulty to the evolutionist . . . in admitting the above propositions; and it is in accordance with the principles they set forth that serial homologies and much else which, together with what is here distinguished as homogeny, has been included under homology may be explained. I propose to call this kind of agreement *homoplasis* or *homoplasy*.

Lang (1915) commented on Lankester's view of homogeny, which can be traced to the influence of Haeckel, as follows:

> . . . nothing shows the consistency of phyletic morphology to its clear but somewhat narrow ideal so plainly as the repeated attempts to introduce into practice a sharp distinction between homogeny and homoplasis. . . . Many of the homologies that exist between series of parallel development are what have been happily termed homologies of organization; these are sometimes so close as to result in practical identity, at other times so distinct as to be evident homoplasis. The critical study of homologies of organization over as wide an area as possible becomes of primary interest and importance.

EFFECTS OF ACCEPTANCE OF HOMOPLASY

As recognition of homoplastic developments increased, it was inevitable that confidence in some of the assumed genetical relationships would decline; and as the evidence for parallel and convergent evolution accumulated, the monophyletic tree became progressively dismembered, till the point was reached when cautious morphologists were reluctant to do more than indicate possible phyletic relationships between different major groups. Some botanists, indeed, advocated the replacement of the monophyletic system by one consisting of a number of parallel lines of descent originating from unspecified thallophyte sources. Thus Church (1919) not only held that the Pteridophyta shared no common ancestors with the other large subdivisions of the Plant Kingdom, but that its several component classes, Filicineae, Lycopodineae, Equisetineae, and so on, were separate and distinct lines which had originated from different algal ancestors in remote geological times.

Among botanists who upheld the Darwinian position, but who recognized the prevalence of homoplasy, there was an important change of emphasis, the reconstruction of a complete genealogical tree being replaced by studies of the methods of evolutionary advance in individual phyletic lines. Bower's work on the ferns, for example, and much of the recent work on gymnosperms, is essentially of this kind.

The problems raised by the recognition of homologies of organization have been viewed in very different ways by different thinkers. Bower (1914), for example, regarded the prevalence of parallel evolution as an 'obstacle to success' in phylogenetic studies, whereas Lang (1915) maintained that the 'demonstration of parallel developments constitutes a positive result of great value', and that it pointed the way to new and important investigations. Since parallel evolutionary developments and trends are so general, both in unrelated groups and in groups of close systematic affinity, there is clearly a case for making a close examination of them. The particular value of such investigations is that they lead to a search for common causes that may underlie major features in the organization of plants.

At this point, some of the assumptions that underlie monophyletic and polyphyletic conceptions may be re-examined in the interests of organization theory. In the monophyletic view, it is assumed or implied that one ancestral type of organismal reaction-system, or genetical system – that of an unspecified, primitive green alga – gave rise to all green plants at and above the thallophyte level of organization. In the extreme polyphyletic view, on the other hand, it is assumed or implied that several, sufficiently different, unspecified, ancestral green algae were involved, these having given rise to distinct phyletic lines.

In some schemata, which are in the main polyphyletic, the several phyla of vascular plants are nevertheless indicated as stemming from a Psilopsid ancestral group; i.e. the scheme is initially monophyletic.

Surveys of the morphology and anatomy of vascular plants have, quite understandably, led some botanists to conclude that the major classes, or groups, are so different and distinctive that they must have been polyphyletic in origin and that, accordingly, they have differently constituted genetical systems. Adherents of these views may well be right. Neverthless, we may note that the species in these groups have major organizational features in common. Thus, whether the individual plant be a fern, a lycopod, a gymnosperm or a dicotyledon, it consists essentially of a vascularized axis, with lateral foliar and branch members and a root system, the whole of the primary leaf-shoot development resulting from the morphogenetic activity of an apical meristem. Further-more, in all of these several kinds of plants, major features of the life cycle and of the reproductive processes are also generally comparable. If we view these facts with some detachment, and if we avoid the obscuring effects of over-attention to details, vascular plants from the several different classes appear to be much more alike than they are unlike in their main organizational features. It is therefore appropriate to enquire to what extent these important homologies of organization may be attributed

i. to genetical factors that are common to all vascular plants, implying a common ancestry and a more or less considerable measure of genetical homology (*see* Chapters 4 and 5);

ii. to dissimilar genetical constitutions which nevertheless determine or admit of comparable morphogenetic and organizational developments (*see* Chapter 7); or

iii. mainly to factors which are either non-genetical or not closely and specifically genetical (*see* Chapter 7).

SIMILITUDE AND DIVERSITY

The number of plant species, fossil and living, is so large and their form and structure so diverse that it is not surprising that we tend to be more impressed by their evident differences than by their sometimes less evident similarities. Yet similitude in the Plant Kingdom is a very general phenomenon, while much of the diversity is often no more than variations on a theme. Green plants of all classes, for example, have common features in their metabolism. Their photosynthetic and res-piratory processes may differ in details but, in their more fundamental aspects, they are very similar, if not identical. Closely comparable assemblages of aminoacids involved in protein synthesis are found in all green plants though, as we now know, there are also many other aminoacids, not involved in protein synthesis, of less general occurrence (Fowden, 1962). Similar observations could be made regarding carbo-hydrates, nucleoproteins, enzymes, growth-regulating substances (e.g. indoleacetic acid, the gibberellins etc.), and so on. Moreover, during growth and differentiation, the embryonic cells of green plants develop comparable osmotic and other physiological activities, become vacuo-lated and deposit cellulose walls, to mention only some of the more general phenomena. Not least, the constitution of the nucleus and the mechanism of its division appear to be closely comparable in green plants at large. In brief, in respect of their principal cell components and physiological activities, plants in all the major phyletic lines, some of which have persisted for vast spans of time, have a great deal in common: at the cell organizational level, and notwithstanding their many specific gene-determined differences in metabolism, they are more alike than they are unlike. Thus, while it is accepted that genetical factors are involved in every aspect of development, these common metabolic processes, physical factors and organismal relationships, must also be given due weight in the study of organization. It is also pertinent to note that major organizational phenomena, such as polarity, the inception of a distal meristem, axial development, the formation, symmetry and positioning of leaves and buds, have not so far been explicitly related to genic action. To obtain a balanced view, it is therefore necessary to enquire to what extent certain prevalent homologies of organization can be accounted for in terms of genetical factors, on the one hand, and of what, for convenience, may be described as common, extrinsic, or not specifically genetical, factors, on the other.

In concluding this chapter it may be recalled that, almost one hundred years ago, in a 'lay sermon', T. H. Huxley (*Collected Essays*, 1901) described 'protoplasm' as 'the physical basis of life' and affirmed that life had but one physical basis. Constitutionally and functionally (he said) protoplasm was substantially the same over the whole range of living organisms – a generalization that still holds good.

CHAPTER 4

The Nature of Genetical Systems

INTRODUCTION

In this chapter, views on the action of genes in development, especially as they contribute to our understanding of organization, are briefly outlined. The subject has been treated abstractly, i.e. in terms of the 'principles' of genetic constitution and activity; but readers will have no difficulty in finding illustrative examples of the various points discussed in the many standard texts now available. It is appreciated that, because of the contemporary rapid elaboration of genetical theory, some of the views considered here may be out of date, or even discounted, by the time this book is published; they are, nevertheless, views which have been explicitly stated by leading geneticists in recent years.

In view of (a) the abundant evidence of parallel evolutionary developments in plants, (b) the importance of genes in morphogenesis, and (c) recent and contemporary elaborations of genetical theory, it is somewhat surprising to find so little information on, or discussion of, genetical aspects of homology and related topics in standard genetical works, e.g. Darlington (1939, 1958), Darlington and Mather (1949), Waddington (1939, 1940, 1957), Sinnott, Dunn and Dobzhansky (1950), Dunn (1951), Huxley, Hardy and Ford (1954) and Willier, Weiss and Hamburger (1955). References to these topics are, however, made in Vavilov (1922), Haldane (1927, 1952), Harland (1933, 1936), Huxley (1942), Stebbins (1950), de Beer (1951) and Dobzhansky (1955).

The evolution of plants, from the simple and primitive forms that existed in remote geological times to the highly organized members of the contemporary flora, is the result of changes in the hereditary constitution in stable or changing environments. For reasons that are more fully considered in Chapter 6, the *hereditary constitution* is here regarded not merely as comprising and being equivalent to the *genotype*, i.e. the total assemblage of all the categories of genes, but as *the genotype together with the other permanent features of cell organization.*

EVOLUTIONARY MECHANISMS

According to contemporary ideas, evolution proceeds by several different but related mechanisms. These include gene mutation, changes in the constitution and organization of individual chromosomes and therefore in the mutual relationships of genes, hybridization, polyploidy and aneuploidy, together with natural selection in stable or changing environments. According to Stebbins (1950), Huxley *et al.* (1954), Waddington (1957) and others, the processes of mutation, recombination, selection, isolation and extinction, which yielded the subspecies and species of flowering plants, could also account for the higher taxonomic categories and for the 'gaps' which separate them, the element of time being of great importance.

THE NATURE OF GENES

In contemporary genetics, *all* heritable characters are considered to be controlled by hereditary factors or genes. Though the genes are mainly located in the chromosomes, some of them are present in the cytoplasm, and all are transmissible in heredity. Offspring resemble their parents because the genes of the former are normally precise replicates of those of the latter, i.e. genes are formed only from genes. When a nucleus divides mitotically, all its component genes reproduce themselves, the fidelity of the hereditary process being attributed to the precision of genic self-duplication. Thus, during somatic division, all the cells of a tissue usually receive the same genes, though some exceptions are known. Some aspects of the relationships of chromosomes, genes and the manifestation of heritable characters are illustrated in Fig.4.1.

Genes are envisaged as large organic molecules, in fact, as aperiodic linear polymers, consisting mainly, if not wholly, of nucleoproteins; and their composition and constitution, and the way in which they are synthesized and reproduced in the chromosomes, are now beginning to be known. Furthermore, new information is almost daily being obtained. However, genes are not all of one kind: in attempting to interpret their experimental observations, geneticists have had to postulate the existence of plastogenes (associated with the plastids) and plasmagenes in the cytoplasm, and genes, major genes, supergenes and polygenes in the chromosomes. A supergene is the name given to a group of genes acting as a mechanical unit in particular allelomorphic combinations (Darlington and Mather, 1949); major genes are such that their differences or mutations are large enough to be identified by the individual effects which they produce in organisms; polygenes are genes whose differences and mutations produce only very small effects in the development of

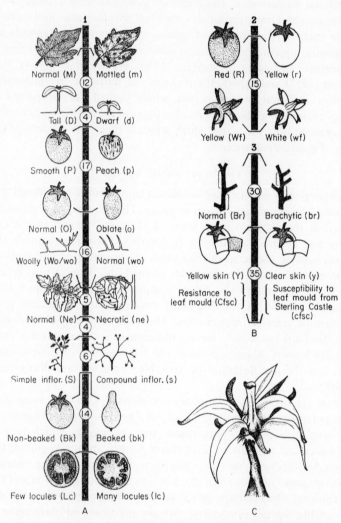

Fig.4.1 *Lycopersicum esculentum.* Genes and morphological development in the tomato. A, Map of *Chromosome 1*: two genes, which can be specified, affect fruit shape; and other genes affect other structural features. B, The genes, and associated characters, on other chromosomes. (After L. Butler, *Jour. Hered.*) C, The flower of a stamenless mutant (Redrawn from L. Butler, *Canadian Jour. Bot.*, 1963.)

an organism. Other important conceptions are those of gene frequency and of the gene pool, i.e. the totality of genes present in a Mendelian population of a species and therefore available for various recombinations.

Although each gene is considered to have a specific chemical activity and, therefore, by inference, a specific chemical structure (but *see* below), some of them must be closely comparable in composition and structure in that they are apparently capable of giving rise to one another by small mutational changes (Darlington, 1939, 1958). Most normal or 'wild type' genes are stable and change very infrequently, but some are subject to mutation. The mutant gene usually shares the stability of the original gene, but it may mutate back to it, or it may undergo further mutation. Some genes are said to mutate to a state of inertness. Gene mutation implies a constitutional change in the gene-molecule, i.e. in its chemical composition, structure and action, a high degree of randomness being held to be a general and important feature of the phenomenon. Conditions within cells at particular stages of development, the presence of certain other genes, exposure to higher temperatures than normal, subjection of chromosomes to ionizing radiations of all kinds and to certain chemicals, are among the conditions known to predispose genes to mutation. Gene mutations may occur from time to time with statistically definable frequencies, but no individual mutation is predictable. The cause of any particular gene mutation is highly localized in the chromosome, i.e. in the gene locus. The so-called mutable genes mutate frequently, and their frequency of mutation may differ in different tissues. On evidence from many sources, most mutations tend to be recessive; they are often downgrade and harmful, or even lethal; and, in homozygous combinations, they tend to be eliminated by natural selection. Mutant genes need not be selected, or selectable, in the generation in which they arise: they may be carried on as recessives, exercising very slight effects on the genetical constitution; but, at some later time, they may have selective value because of some useful property which they manifest in a new environment or in a different genetical combination.

One result of recent cytogenetical investigations of a widening range of organisms, including bacteria, bacteriophage, and so on, has been to raise the difficulty that no single definition of the gene now adequately covers all cases. At least four different definitions have been proposed, namely, (a) that the gene is the ultimate unit of recombination; (b) that it is the ultimate unit of mutation; (c) that it is a unit of physiological activity; and (d) that it is the ultimate unit of self-reproduction. As Swanson (1958) noted, these definitions are inconsistent with each other to a varying extent, each 'being meaningful within the limits of the techniques used in studying the gene'; and he has cited Stadler's (1954) distinction between the hypothetical gene of classical genetics, i.e. the gene as a discrete particle, and the operational gene which 'can be defined only as the smallest segment of the gene-string that can be shown to be consistently associated with the occurrence of a specific genetic effect'. The gene, in short, is much better understood in terms of its function and behaviour than of its actual physical constitution. Goldschmidt (1946, 1951) denied the existence of genes as particulate structures, mutations in his view being due to rearrangements of parts of the chromosomes. What appears to be agreed is that a gene is part of a *continuum* on the chromosome and that its properties are not entirely inherent in itself but are affected to a varying degree by neighbouring genes. It is evident that many points still await clarification. In recent studies of the so-called 'lamp-brush' chromosomes, it has been shown that 'loops' of different sizes and configurations may occur along the length of the chromosome and that these loops may become modified at different phases of cellular activity (*see* Fischberg and Blackler, 1961, for review).

MOLECULAR BIOLOGY AND THE CONTEMPORARY GENE

The macromolecular gene is no longer the particulate, discrete entity of classical genetics: we need not 'assume discreteness in the structural organization because we find discreteness of function . . . the genes are units of function arising from an aperiodic sequence of structural elements . . . we can get crossing-over between parts of genes, as well as between genes' (Pontecorvo, in Waddington, 1959, p. 22). As now envisaged, genes can combine in practically any linear sequence or order, and hence they have great physico-chemical flexibility. They may also have many common activities as well as more specific ones. A new genetical terminology has been devised to describe these discoveries (*see* Benzer, 1959; Sonneborn, 1963).

Investigations of the physico-chemical nature of chromosomes and genes, i.e. of the long-chain molecules of which they are composed, have revealed an order of complexity undreamt of a few decades ago. The centre of the picture is, of course, occupied by deoxyribonucleic acid (DNA), ribonucleic acid (RNA) and the proteins. The DNA molecules have been shown to be the most important components of the chromosomes. Although the greatly elongated DNA molecules in a chromosome are all different, they all share the same general construction. The contemporary view (Crick *et al.*, 1961; Benzer, 1959; Sonneborn, 1963) is that the 'genetic code', inherent in the DNA molecules, is fundamentally determined by the arrangement of the four bases (normally adenine, cytosine, thymine and guanine) attached to the DNA chain. The sequence of these bases along the DNA chain 'represents', or determines the specific activity of, a gene, and eventually, the specific protein that will enter into some reaction in the cytoplasm. The 'genetic instructions'* are imparted to the cytoplasm by means of ribonucleic acid molecules. These are essentially replicas of the DNA 'code' and exercise their effects in producing particular proteins by acting as 'messengers' and by attaching themselves to cell particles known as ribosomes. The proteins are also long-chain molecules of very considerable complexity, i.e. there may be several hundred aminoacid units, arranged in a particular sequence, in a single molecule. The aminoacid sequence is determined by the coded genetical information carried by the RNA. The details of the 'genetic code' proposed by Crick *et al.*, i.e. that each of the 20 or more aminoacids is determined by the mutual arrangement of three of the bases, need not be discussed here. They have been mentioned here merely to indicate the intricacy of detail and elaboration of theory that are emerging from contemporary work on the chemical nature and action of genes.

Since a typical molecule of DNA may be as much as 10,000 units long, and a gene, consisting of a particular sequence of side groups, may be 1,000 units long, a number of genes may be disposed along the length of a single DNA molecule. The contemporary picture is that if a single atom or group is modified in one of these very long and complex gene macromolecules, a more or less considerable genetical change may follow. A point that Crick (1960) and others have made is that the basic molecules of DNA, as also of proteins, are very similar in plants, animals, micro-organisms and viruses. The view that genes control the synthesis of proteins is becoming increasingly validated as evidence accumulates.

The recent advances in molecular biology are impressive, indeed almost overpowering, particularly in the refinement of detail that has

---

* A philosopher of biology might perhaps detect a suggestion of anthropomorphism or teleology in this terminology, though that is almost certainly not intended by the authors of it.

been obtained. Some important general points have also emerged. One of these is that no major cell component or factor can function in isolation – a point recently re-emphasized by Sonneborn (1963). On the evidence, it always functions, and can only function, as a component of an intact, integrated reaction system. DNA, RNA, ribosomes, enzymes, substrates, and the factors which control the overall state of the cell, are all interrelated and interdependent; they are all involved in the particular functional activity in which the cell is engaged, or in the sequence of activities which it undergoes during growth and differentiation (*see* Chapter 9). Moreover, although specific details may differ, this general observation appears to be true of cells in all classes of plants.

ALLELOMORPHIC GENES

As a complex entity like a gene must have been built up before it can be degraded by mutation, the inception and evolution of individual genes must be postulated. It has been suggested that, in early primitive cells, the gene was the simplest molecule (or structure) capable of self-reproduction, the larger genes being built up from smaller ones (Darlington and Mather, 1949). It is only when a gene has mutated and is present as two (or more) alleles that its existence can be detected in Mendelian segregation. It follows that the total number of genes present in a higher plant or animal is difficult to ascertain, but the number is stated to be very large, e.g. 10,000 to 100,000 in a human sex cell (Dobzhansky, 1955). Nevertheless, as Haldane (1954) noted, the genes only account for a small fraction of the cell protein.

The properties of heredity and mutation extend from viruses and bacteria to the higher plants and higher animals. This may indicate that all life had a common origin, perhaps based on the same underlying genic mechanism. If the gene is a large nucleoprotein molecule, then equally it could be said that, as a matter of physical chemistry, such molecules must possess 'living' properties. Darlington (1939, 1958) suggested that the naked gene may be the prototype of living matter and of the several types of gene in the cell, the plasmagene being a relic (but *see* Chapter 6). In his view, three levels of organization may be recognized, namely, that based on undifferentiated genes, that based on differentiated genes but without sexual reproduction, and that in which sexual reproduction occurs together with alternation of generations.

Each detectable gene exists in an alternative form, or allele (or allelomorph). A gamete contains only one set of alleles but the diploid plant which results from sexual reproduction has the two alternative sets. Alleles occupy the same locus on the chromosome. The existence of multiple as well as paired alleles is recognized by geneticists. Allelism, which connotes that a gene may exist in alternative states which produce different phenotypic effects, is thus, in the geneticists' concept of organism, of primary importance in morphogenesis and organization. Alleles can only be detected by their effects, in particular by the fact that one allele of a pair manifests itself by its 'dominance' and the other by its 'recessiveness'. Dominance, however, is not an invariable property of a dominant allele: it is subject to modification in different conditions, e.g. by environment, age, or the presence of certain other genes. There may also be different degrees of dominance.

Although, as already noted, the number of genes in the genotype of an angiosperm is very large, striking morphogenetic effects may be associated with the action of individual genes, e.g. the determination of tallness or dwarfness, zygomorphic or peloric flowers in some species, and so on. A dominant gene may thus produce one effect and its recessive allele another. From the physico-chemical and physiological standpoint, this is a very intriguing problem and we may ask what constitutes the ultimate difference between the two genes of an allelic pair. Here we may recall that, according to classical genetics, allelic genes which, in conjunction with other factors, determine contrasting characters, do not blend, modify, or absorb each other when they are present together in a diploid nucleus: they usually segregate unchanged. Yet they are very closely related, constituting a pair in the same locus in the chromosome. On the evidence, the difference between the dominant and recessive genes of a pair cannot be resolved by the presence-absence theory. Also, recessive mutant genes may sometimes revert to the dominant normal state, and many, if not most, recessive alleles 'produce' physiological and/or morphological effects which suggest that they resemble the dominant allele but are of lower activity, i.e. a recessive gene is a dominant gene which has lost some of its activity. The alleles may be envisaged as nucleoprotein molecules which are closely comparable in their main configuration, as, indeed, we now know them to be, but the recessive allele molecule has been structurally modified in some way that restricts its biochemical activity. Some support for this view is seen in the fact that the multiplication of a recessive gene (i.e. several doses of it) may yield a character effect not unlike that produced by the dominant allele. A relevant observation is that plants with experimentally-induced chromosome deficiencies often

resemble the homozygous recessives (*see* Sinnott, Dunn and Dobzhansky, 1950). It will be a matter of very considerable interest to see
if, and how, this and related problems will be resolved by molecular
biologists.

Stern (1955) described alleles as being 'qualitatively different representatives of the genic material at each locus' – and, as such, produce

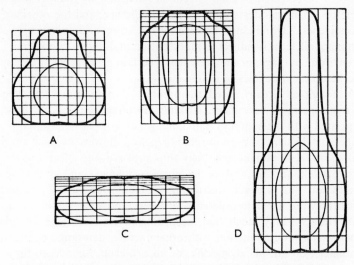

Fig.4.2 Genes and organization. The illustrations show some characteristic shapes of fruits of hybrid gourds which have been studied
genetically. These are projected on variously modified Cartesian co-
ordinates, *A* having equal co-ordinates. The inference is that particular
genes, by changing the rate of growth in a particular direction, or directions, or in different regions of the developing ovary, change the overall
pattern of differential growth and hence determine the ultimate shape
of the fruit. (After E. W. Sinnott, *Plant Morphogenesis*, 1960.)

different effects by which their existence is recognized. He held that the
primary products of different alleles may differ quantitatively as well
as qualitatively, the multiple alleles of a particular gene usually affecting
the same phenotypic character in a graded manner. He cited a case in
Drosophila where 'different alleles of the vestigial locus control the
appearance of a fully formed wing, of a slightly nicked wing, a deeper
notched one, a short vestigial wing stump, and a wingless condition'.
Goldschmidt (1938) regarded these gene-controlled reactions as being
qualitatively alike but proceeding at different rates according to which

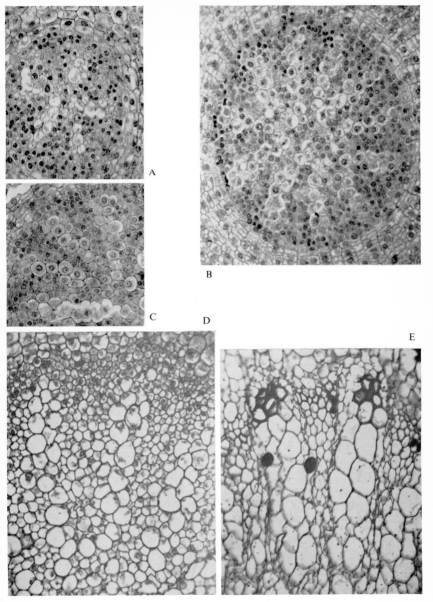

5. *Marattia attenuata.* Transverse sections of roots of different diameters, taken close to the apex, showing the early differentiation of the protoxylem and protophloem and also the inception of metaxylem elements. In each instance the distribution of xylem and phloem constitutes a symmetrical, radiate pattern. These patterns appear to illustrate Turing's Theory of Morphogenesis. A, A small root with 5 protoxylem groups and developing metaxylem rays; smaller roots may have 2, 3 and 4 xylem groups. B, A larger root with 11 xylem rays. C, Sector of a still larger root with 15-16 xylem rays. D, E, Sections, at different levels, of a very large root with about 18 xylem rays. (All × 230; from an unpublished investigation.)

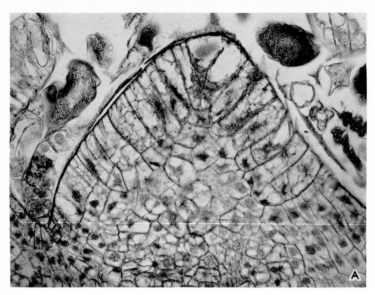

6A. Shoot apex of the fern *Matteuccia struthiopteris* in longitudinal section showing the organization of the apical meristem: the apical cell gives rise to characteristic, superficial, prism-shaped cells which, in turn, give rise to all the organs and tissues of the axis. Incipient vascular tissue originates below the apical meristem.

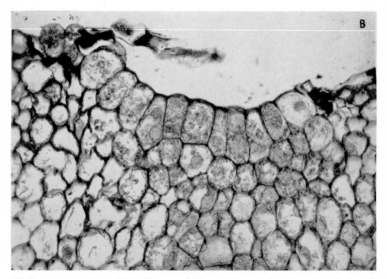

6B. Transverse section of the rhizome of *M. struthiopteris* showing a detached meristem. This consists of a group of prism-shaped cells, which once constituted part of the apical meristem (*see* A), but which have become separated from it during growth. Such detached meristems may remain inactive but, if the apical dominance is removed, they give rise to lateral buds. Meristematic tissues, originating in the distal meristem and broadly the equivalent of the detached meristems of ferns, have been recognized in plants as taxonomically remote as brown algae and dicotyledons (both × 225). (*Annals of Botany.*)

allele is present. The finding that a major effect of a gene and of a gene mutation in development is that it determines the rate, or relative rate, of development of some particular organ or tissue is of special interest in the analysis of some aspects of organization (*see* Chapter 10). The shapes of different hybrid gourds, for example, have been referred to gene-determined differential growth (Fig.4.2).

Since allelomorphy is a general phenomenon, there may be some general cause (or perhaps a small number of general causes) of dominance and recessiveness in alleles. If the wild type of a species was characterized by homozygosity, with the two genes of a pair alike, then allelomorphy could have been brought about by a modification, i.e. a mutation, of one of the pair; and this kind of change may have become general in gene-pairs in the course of evolution. There is evidence that a gene may be replaced by another gene and yet continue to produce the original characteristic effect. This raises the question of the specificity of the molecule that is recognized as a particular gene. In other words: how different are the molecules of different genes?

Most recessive alleles show some decrease as compared with the normal gene activity. Ordinary allele differences probably originated by sudden steps, i.e. by mutations, these providing the main bases for evolutionary change. All degrees of mutational change may be produced, but smaller rather than larger changes are usual. As the specific effects of the mutant genes may be slight, they have been described as being 'physiological' rather than 'morphological' (Muller, 1951). In a large organism, the smaller the gene changes are, the less likely are they to be detrimental. Most gene changes make for disorder but some neomorphic genes, i.e. producing new effects, are also known. As a gene may mutate in different ways, its mutant forms may affect different processes and eventually characters; usually, however, it is the same character that is affected.

CHROMOSOME MODIFICATIONS

Differently constituted chromosomes may result from breakage and reunion but these are of exceptional and sporadic occurrence. The chromosome changes observed by cytologists or inferred from genetical investigations include loss, deficiency, inversion and interchange or translocation, of chromosome material. The majority of these structural changes are harmful and the chromosomes in which they take place are unlikely to survive, though some do (Darlington, 1939, 1958). Chromosome changes affect genic action in that genes, which normally produce

D

their effects in conjunction with other genes, find themselves, as it were, in a new reaction association or environment. In most, though not in all organisms, an exchange of groups of genes between homologous chromosomes takes place during meiosis, this being the well-known phenomenon of crossing-over (*see* Swanson, 1958, for an account of these phenomena).

THE ACTION OF GENES

In different instances, Mendelian differences may be effected by various intergenic changes, e.g. mechanical defects in the segregation of genes, by changes in their proportions, and by changes in their positions. The action of genes may be very varied and has been specified as being direct, successive, co-operative and competitive (Darlington and Mather, 1949). A single gene may affect a single process, or it may modify many developments and thus be important in the overall development of the organism. Where a gene is active in the development of different parts of an organism, its effects are said to be multiple or pleiotropic. It may be that all genes have such effects, but usually one effect is more evident than the others. Different genes may apparently have comparable effects, e.g. various genes are known which 'convert' stamens into petals or carpels (Darlington and Mather, 1949), or they may cause a loss of parts (Fig.4.1*c*).

As to the effects of quantitative variability of the genic content, as in the members of a polyploid series, Stern (1955) noted that conspicuously different phenotypic effects do not usually result from the simultaneous multiplication of all the genes, though various relationships, e.g. between nuclear and cytoplasmic volume and surface, are likely to be modified. Changes in the numbers of cells per organ and differences in absolute and relative growth have been recorded. Partial quantitative changes in genic content, on the other hand, may have much more striking developmental effects. The effects of allopolyploidy on leaf and fruit organization in *Aesculus carnea*, a hybrid between *A. pavia* and *A. hippocastanum* were investigated by Upcott (1936). (*See also* Darlington and Mather (1949).)

Genes differ in their time of action. The action of a particular gene may be evoked by the general developmental situation and by the competence of cells to react to gene-determined metabolic stimuli. The cytoplasm may be envisaged as a complex reaction system which changes throughout development, its state at any time having been determined by the antecedent physiological-genetical activity.

Although genes are the units of heredity, separable by nuclear division, they do not behave as independent units in physiological processes or in development. It is held that they react within the nucleus, and their products react together in the cytoplasm to produce the visible structural developments. Or, as Darlington (1939) has aphoristically stated: genes are independent in heredity but integrated in development.

Many gene effects are sharply localized in one organ or tissue, e.g. as in the distinctive developments of the several organs of a flower.

GENES IN DIFFERENTIATION

It is generally held that there is no somatic segregation of genes and that each embryonic cell has initially the same potentiality as its neighbours. There may be some exceptions (*see* Stern, 1955), but in the words of Sturtevant (1951): 'There can be no escape from the conclusion that particular types of differentiation occur in cells that carry the genes on which depend a whole series of wholly different kinds of differentiation.'

The cytoplasm is the medium and site of differentiation and histogenesis. In it the several developmental factors, genic, organismal and environmental, react and interact and produce their effects. Differentiation takes place under the direct or indirect influence of the nucleus and is normally a co-ordinated effect. Relationships of a reciprocal nature between the nucleus and the cytoplasm must also be taken into account: the cytoplasm, for example, may control the synchronization of mitosis in a group of cells, as in the early embryogenesis in some gymnosperms. When a suitable substratum has been provided in the cytoplasm, a hitherto inactive nuclear gene will be stimulated to activity. The substance (or substances) produced by it will react on the cytoplasm and may effect some kind of differentiation in it; and as the cytoplasmic changes produced by one gene may create a situation in which other genes can become active, a progressive or sequential differentiation becomes possible. It is difficult to specify the relative importance of nuclear and cytoplasmic components in development but, in the long-term hereditary relations, the nucleus appears to be the major determiner (Darlington and Mather, 1949). The way in which a cell differentiates has also been explained in other ways, e.g. by reference to the position which it occupies in the tissue mass.

In discussing his concept of genic action in differentiation, Stern (1955) showed that the seeming contradiction between the assumed genic equality of all the embryonic cells in a developing organism, and the differentiation of these cells into very different tissues, can be reconciled.

His hypothesis is that *regional cytoplasmic differences in the egg cell, and in the cells to which it gives rise during embryogenesis, i.e. different cytoplasmic environments, evoke a differential response in the genes.* As the embryo develops, the physiological diversity of its several regions or parts increases, and the opportunity for more varied genic action, i.e. of gene-substrate interaction, also increases. The result is seen in the progressive ontogenetic differentiation of organs and tissues. This concept can also have a wide application to the phenomena of development in plants, e.g. to floral ontogenesis as discussed by Wardlaw (1957e). As Stern noted, the concept may relate either to the behaviour of different genes in the same cytoplasmic environment, some of the genes becoming active, others remaining inert, or to the quantitatively or qualitatively different activities on the part of the same genes in differently constituted cytoplasms. He also pointed out that an interpretation of genic action along these lines could apply to the concept of embryonic fields, i.e. a specific allele may alter the extent or activity of a field in some characteristic manner.

Somewhat similar ideas have been expressed by other geneticists. Thus Catcheside (1956) maintained that all the characters of a plant are due to genic action in the particular environment. The cytoplasm, which he regarded as being of minor importance in heritable variation, has a major part in 'expressing the characters determined by the genes, and its history and the effect of the environment upon it are not without influence upon the characters expressed, just as the genes influence one another'. Hence genic action may become apparent in some cells but not in others. Catcheside's thesis is that each 'physiological gene' liberates a product of characteristic configuration, designated as a *plasmid*, into the cytoplasm. According to the state of the cytoplasm, so may the configuration of the plasmid be affected and, moreover, the configurations of the plasmids of different allelic genes would be differently altered by different conditions in the cytoplasm. In a cell at a particular state of differentiation, then, a plasmid may 'be accepted into the existing (cytoplasmic) structure at some convenient place where it will fit and act with the rest of the structure to bring about its characteristic effect'; at a different state of cellular differentiation, the plasmid may fit into a different place and have a different effect. But the altered plasmid of a mutant gene might not find a place in the cytoplasmic-plasmid-complex, or it might be deformed, or cause deformation, before it could be fitted in and begin to function. Hence the results produced would be different from those associated with the normal gene.

However acceptable, or otherwise, the reader may find this interesting attempt to explain the effects produced by genes and their mutants – and it is unavoidably a great simplification of the actual physical situation – the hypothesis rests on the assumption that the cytoplasm, in which the gene products act, *is a spatially organized structure*; and, as Catcheside explicitly stated, his suggestion 'places the main weight of mutual adjustment upon organized systems of enzymes and structural proteins rather than upon the reactants controlled by these systems'. The physico-chemical mechanism of genic action in morphogenetic processes is an exceedingly complex problem. For even if we accept that a gene determines the metabolism of auxin, or gibberellic acid, etc., as recent investigations indicate (*see* p. 199), there is still the problem of showing precisely how the auxin, etc., together with other substances, eventually yields not only a characteristic morphological development, but one which is appropriate to the overall economy of the plant at the particular stage reached in its ontogenesis. (The topic of genes and differentiation is considered further in Chapter 9.)

GENES AND INHERITANCE

The commonest cause of heritable variability in sexually reproducing organisms is the combination of the slightly different genes from the two parents, typical results of which can be seen in the phenotypic differences between homozygous and heterozygous offspring. As already noted, the hereditary materials may be modified by gene mutation, loss of genes, excess of genes, and positional and other changes in genes due to chromosomal changes.

According to Darlington (1939), selection may act on the organismal system at any level – gene, chromosome, cell, organ and individual. He also pointed out that the unit of variation is not the unit of selection; that chromosome changes take place at random, but that the end product must possess stability; and that genetic systems can change while external forms may remain unchanged. Larger mutations which yield sports, i.e. new stable strains, are now recognized as being occasional special cases. Most of the constructive and adaptive changes in evolution are now considered to be due to polygenic changes: the steady evolutionary advance does not take place by large jumps, no matter how potentially constructive these may be, since there must be steady adjustment of the whole genetical system. The capacities of a genetical system for evolutionary change are determined and limited by its properties at every level, the stability of the genotype being important. Within these limits, natural selection determines what will happen in the further elaboration of the system.

Dobzhansky (1955) distinguished two fundamental evolutionary processes, namely, 'that of the origin of the raw materials from which evolutionary changes can be constructed, and that of building and perfecting the organic form and function'. Gene mutation and recombination provide the former, while natural selection, as related to the environment, determines the latter, i.e. selection also has a 'creative aspect'. The essential Darwinian view – that evolution is the result of the natural selection of spontaneous but initially unadapted small variations – is thus upheld by contemporary geneticists. The concept of selective action has, however, been considerably broadened, its nature, in the contemporary view, being determined by the level of organization. Relaxation of selection would lead to disorganization, degeneration and anarchy. The *direction* of evolution, in the view of Muller (1951), is determined by selection and not by the tendency of an organism to vary preferentially, the new developments being usually due to a combination of small mutational steps. But he also noted, having reviewed what is known of gene mutation and chromosome change in producing variation in species, that 'the real core of gene theory still appears to lie in the deep unknown'.

PHENOTYPIC DIFFERENCES IN POPULATIONS

Some of the relationships between variations in genetical constitution, environment, ontogenesis and the eventual phenotypic organization of representative individual plants from different populations of the same or closely related species, are being elucidated by investigations in the general field of experimental taxonomy. Only a few examples can be considered here.

In a study of genetical variation as affecting leaf shape in *Geranium sanguineum*, collected from widely separated areas, Bocher and Lewis (1962) showed that leaf shape varied (i) during the ontogenesis of the individual plant, i.e. the leaves showed heteroblastic development; (ii) as between plants obtained from different localities when grown under the same conditions, i.e. affording evidence of differences in genotype; and (iii) as between clonal materials when grown under contrasted environmental conditions (*see* Figs. 4.3, 4.4).

Valentine (1961) demonstrated that of nine taxa of *Primula*, in the section Vernales, with $2n = 22$ chromosomes, all are capable of intercrossing to some extent (Fig.4.5, Plate 4 and Table 2). The different crosses not only yielded evident differences in foliar and floral characters but also in the type and viability of the seed. In studies of introgressive hybridization, Anderson (1949) analysed the results of intercrossing

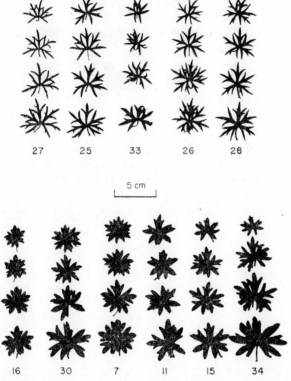

Fig.4.3 Genetical variation as affecting leaf shape in *Geranium sanguineum*, in plants grown under uniform conditions: the illustrations show (diagrammatically) four representative leaves, in acropetal sequence, from different strains, these being the extremes of a collection of some thirty-six different strains from various European localities. In some strains the chromosome number was definitely ascertained to be $2n = 84$; in the collection of strains the number was $2n = c.\ 84 \pm 4$. (After T. W. Böcher and M. C. Lewis, *Biol. Skr. Kongel. Danske Vidensk, Selsk.*, 1962.)

Nicotiana Langsdorffii and *N. alata*. As shown in Fig.4.6, the F_1 hybrids were uniform and intermediate in floral characters between the parents whereas the F_2 hybrids were highly variable; the progenies obtained by

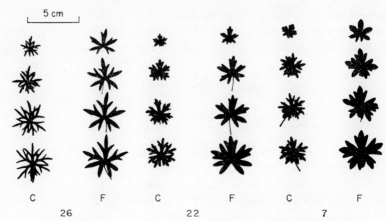

Fig.4.4 *Geranium sanguineum*. Representative clones grown in C, the cactus house and F, the fern house: the numbers refer to the strains; the leaves are in acropetal sequence. (After T. W. Böcher and M. C. Lewis, 1962.)

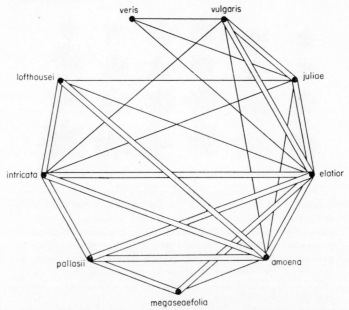

Fig.4.5 *Primula* spp. The crossing behaviour of phylogenetically closely related species. The crossing polygon for nine taxa of *Primula*, all with $2n = 22$ chromosomes in the section Vernales, indicates the crosses obtained in experimental studies. Gaps in the polygon denote that repeated efforts have failed to yield hybrids; single lines indicate that crossing has only been effective in one direction (*see* Table 2). (After D. H. Valentine, *A Darwin Centenary*, 1961.)

backcrossing F_1 individuals with the parents generally resembled the recurrent parent.

TABLE 2. The crossability series

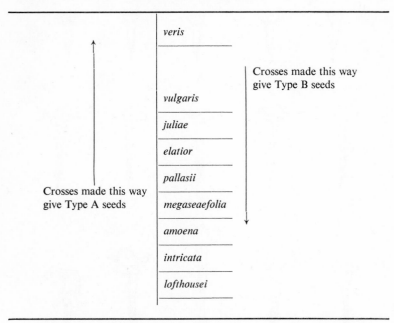

NOTE.—The "goodness" of the seeds produced is roughly proportional to the distance between the species.

GENETICAL CONSTITUTION, ORGANIZATION AND EVOLUTION

Goldschmidt (1927) considered biological organization in terms of genetical constitution, development and evolution. The development of an organism, he said, results from many correlated reactions which take place at definite relative velocities, the action of genes consisting essentially in modifying the rates of one or more of these reactions. Waddington (1939, 1940, 1942, 1948, 1957) has elaborated this general conception: the course of a developmental reaction, or the process of development, is the resultant of a number of interacting factors and is characterized by dynamic equilibrium. In a normal organism, only certain resultant states are possible. Since fully differentiated tissues do not merge gradually one into another but are usually distinctive and

D*

more or less sharply defined, e.g. the phloem and xylem in a vascular strand, it may be inferred that development is characterized by a succession of critical situations ('branching points'), at each of which one or other of a few alternative paths may be followed. At these critical

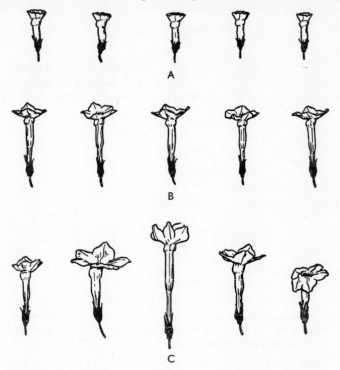

Figs. 4.6, 4.7 *Nicotiana Langsdorffii* and *N. alata* species crosses (graphically summarized).

Fig. 4.6 A, Representative flowers of *Nicotiana Langsdorffii*.
B, The F_1 hybrids with *N. alata*.
C, The F_2 hybrids with *N. alata*.

points, the indeterminate tissue is competent to react in different ways to certain different stimuli. Waddington considered that the definiteness of the alternative modes of development is due to natural selection and is characteristic of organisms in a state of Nature. An explanation along these lines may be valid but, eventually, investigations of the physics and chemistry of the situation may afford other and perhaps rather different interpretations.

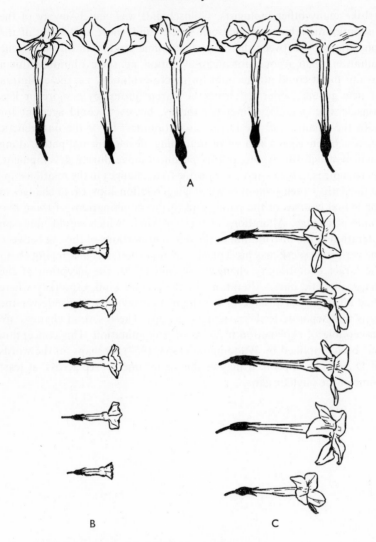

Fig.4.7 A, Representative flowers of *Nicotiana alata*.

B, Backcrosses of the F_1 to *N. Langsdorffii*.

C, Backcrosses of the F_1 to *N. alata*.

(All shown to scale). The uniform and intermediate F_1, the highly variable F_2, and the generally close resemblance of each back-cross to its recurrent parent may be noted.

(After E. Anderson, *Introgressive Hybridization*, 1949.)

Like many other biologists, Goldschmidt was acutely aware of the discontinuities that exist between species and, more strikingly, of the 'phyletic gaps' between the larger taxonomic groups. In his view, gene mutation might account for micro-evolution, i.e. the evolution within a group; but it could not account for macro-evolution, i.e. the evolution of new groups, separated from the parent group by a more or less considerable gap. Waddington's theory, however, could account for both the smaller and the larger discontinuities; for if the ontogenetic process be envisaged as a set of branching, developmental paths, along each of which the zygote and its products move during development, then changes in the system may be due (i) to changes in the relationships of the paths – their pattern or topological relationships, (ii) to changes in the actual courses of the paths, and (iii) to combinations of these two kinds of change. Alterations of the first kind, 'which would imply an alteration in the distribution of the different portions of the egg between the various tissues', may have played an important part in bringing about the larger evolutionary changes associated with the inception of the major phyletic lines. Alterations of the second kind, especially where they affect an early stage of development, may be responsible for the gaps that separate lesser systematic groups. These several changes are susceptible of explanation in terms of gene mutation. This conception has been amplified by Waddington (1953, 1957): perhaps, in the words of D'Arcy Thompson, it may enable us in time to 'see across' at least some of the phyletic gaps.

CHAPTER 5

Genetical Investigations of Homology and Evolutionary Parallelisms

In this chapter the genetical approach to the problems of homology, homology of organization, and parallel evolution, is considered (*see* p. 56).

GENIC HOMOLOGY

In the 1878 edition of *The Origin of Species*, Darwin noted that 'distinct species present analogous variations' and referred to the 'law of equable variations' propounded by Walsh (*see* Haldane, 1952). Some considerable time later, Vavilov (1922) reformulated this concept as the Law of Homologous Variation.

Comparative genetical investigations have shown that, in different species, similar abnormal characters are inherited in the same way. Haldane (1927) thought that homologous variations occurring in related species were due to similar mutations in corresponding genes; and he suggested that 'genic homology, probably with a biochemical basis, would prove to be more fundamental than structural homology'. However, as he subsequently pointed out (Haldane, 1952), this simple view has since been shown to be inadequate, especially in the light of Harland's (1933) observations. Haldane has cited work undertaken by Spurway (1949) in which it was found that some variations within a species, due to gene mutation, and yielding a specific character, may be virtually neutral from the selective point of view. Comparable mutations might be expected to occur in related species although homologous genes may not necessarily be involved. Spurway's interpretation of such phenomena is that, in some groups of animals, a particular developmental process may be altered without major effects on other developmental processes; but in other species, where the whole developmental process is closely integrated, such partially independent developments would be impossible. These observations are of special interest in reaction system theory (*see* Chapter 7, p. 155); for, as Haldane pointed out, the possible range of variation in a group is determined not only by the genes which can mutate but by all that is involved in the physiology of development.

The variation of which a species is capable is one of its most important characters, the mutational changes undergone being determined by their selective advantage: 'there is nothing surprising in finding parallel evolution in related species, genera, or families' (Haldane, 1952). What is surprising, in Haldane's view, is that in some groups a particular kind of variation is possible and apparently takes place readily, whereas in others such variation just does not occur. He also noted that the constancy of variation within a group is still unexplained and that variation, though a complex phenomenon, is not merely a matter of chance; it obeys a number of laws which appear to be chiefly of a statistical character.

In a discussion of the genetical conception of the species and of homology, Harland (1933, 1936) noted that many of the resemblances between species of the same genus appear to be 'due to some genic homology'. Closely related species probably have many genes in common, as well as many different genes, the latter often producing only slight effects. A survey of the relevant literature indicates that interspecific and intergeneric crosses always afford evidence either of identical or homologous genes, occupying homologous loci; and that taxonomic divergences may be correlated 'with an increasing tendency to change the genes from an identical to an allelomorphic state'. However, genetical analyses of various characters in species of *Gossypium* (Harland, 1936), and other relevant data, have shown that homologous morphological characters in a genus, or in related genera, are not necessarily to be referred to identical genetical bases. In these *Gossypium* species there is evidence of three different genetical bases of homologous characters: (i) a gene complex in which the only common resemblance is that the main gene occupied the same locus in the two species compared; (ii) the action of different members of a pair of duplicate genes, in association with a specific modifier complex: (iii) the accumulation of *plus* modifiers in the absence of the main gene.

Haldane (1932) pointed out that, in allopolyploids which possess several pairs or sets of genes, one gene of a pair may be altered without disadvantage provided the functioning of the other continues; and hence, as Harland (1936) noted, many genes may become available for mutation 'with concomitant augmentation of genetic variance and potentiality for evolution'. Harland concluded that, genetically, a character or organ is not in a static but in a dynamic condition and that the genes determining or controlling it are continually changing.

On the dynamic view of organs and functions we are able to see how organs such as the eye, which are common to all vertebrate animals, preserve their essential similarity in structure or function, though the genes responsible for the organ must have become wholly altered during the evolutionary process, since there is now no reason to suppose that homologous organs have anything genetically in common.

It would appear, however, that the underlying physico-chemical reaction systems must have something in common, however that 'something' may be defined. The view that a gene can become 'wholly altered' and yet contribute to a relatively unchanged morphological feature requires validation. Does the gene-molecule really undergo major changes in its chemical constitution and properties, or does it merely undergo changes of a relatively insignificant kind, i.e. that do not affect its main biochemical activities?

Because of their accessibility, the characters studied by plant geneticists have typically included pigmentation, pollen, flower and fruit colour, the size and shape of floral and other members, the presence or absence of seed fuzz, the habit of the plant, e.g. tallness or dwarfness, etc. Major morphological developments, for example, the inception, characteristic disposition, symmetry and structure of foliar organs, usually remain untouched by these studies. Abnormal floral developments of various kinds, however, have been recorded in certain interspecific crosses, these being ascribed to lack of harmony between the relevant parental gene complexes. Since most combinations yield perfect flowers, it is inferred that the species possess either a common stock of identical genes or an assemblage of mutually replaceable ones (Harland, 1936).

Genetical views on homology raise subtle and difficult problems. Thus, it has been stated (i) that characters controlled by identical genes need not be homologous; (ii) that homologous characters may be, but are not necessarily, or invariably, determined by identical genes, and (iii) that structures may owe their similarity to different organizers without forfeiting their homology. It is evident that the relationships between genetical constitution, homogeny and homology of organization are still very incompletely understood. However, it appears that closely comparable genes, but also quite different genes, as components of organismal reaction systems, may bring about closely comparable developments. If, as Harland suggested, the genes determining a character are constantly changing, what gives that character its morphological stability or constancy? One inference which may be drawn is that, although the development of particular characters requires the presence of particular genes (or their substitutes), it is the working of the organismal reaction system as a whole that is of paramount importance. De Beer (1951) made the point that individual genes cannot provide the genetical basis of homologous structures; and in that genes may be modified and replaced, the homology of phenotypes does not necessarily imply the homology of genotypes. In the present writer's view, however, it does imply some important similarity in the reaction systems; and, as Turing (1952) explained in his diffusion-reaction theory of morphogenesis, differently constituted organismal reaction systems may yield closely comparable patterns (*see* Chapter 7).

HOMOLOGY IN ANIMALS

De Beer (1951) noted that, in animals,* the analysis of homology on the basis of cellular or pre-cellular correspondence of position during the individual development is untenable. In considering the homology of a

---

　　* *Homology in the Animal Kingdom.* De Beer (1951) considered the problem of homology in the Animal Kingdom in the light of his general thesis that ontogeny is the result of the impact of external factors evoking the internal factors transmitted in heredity; that phylogeny deals with a series of disconnected and causally unrelated adult forms, each adult form being the end point of an ontogeny which differs from the ontogeny of the previous member of the series; that the successive ontogenies of a series are related to one another by the transmission of hereditary factors from fertilized egg to fertilized egg; and that ontogenetic modifications are due to genetical changes. In short, phylogeny is due to modified ontogeny. Recent embryological studies support the view that homologous structures in different animal species, however modified these structures may be, had a common underlying genetical similarity, based on descent from a common ancestor. The post-Darwinian phylogenetic schemes were essentially based on the existence of homologous structures and their modifications, the essential idea of homology being not so much the resemblance between homologous structures but rather their continuity in phylogeny. This becomes clear when we bear in mind that structures which are undoubtedly homologous may be unlike anatomically and histologically. In the strictest sense, homologous organs and structures in a phylogenetic series must be traceable back, as visible evidence, to the point of divergence from the common ancestor. Such evidence thus relates to homology of phenotype. On this view De Beer comments that 'in requiring the visible presence of structures as far back as the point of divergence from the common ancestor, the theory of homology was over-exacting'. Where closely comparable structural features appear to have originated independently in two related but divergent phyletic lines, the contemporary zoological view is that the phenomenon can be explained by the concept of *latent homology*. This means that a common genetical basis is present in the two phyletic lines, but the manifestation of the character in the common ancestor was obscured or delayed by processes in the mechanism of genic action. Where the homology is not a close one, very diverse genes may be involved. On the other hand, cases are known where quite different genes – the so-called 'mimic' genes – may produce identical effects.

particular organ or structure in animal embryology, both the originating tissue and the inducing substances must be considered. De Beer is in agreement with Wilson (1894) – cited by De Beer – that 'embryological development does not in itself afford at present any absolute criterion whatever for the determination of homology'. Comparative anatomy (he maintained) is the primary criterion for this study, for it is the constancy of morphological relations that is important. Morphological correspondences afford indications of community of descent, and the more numerous and exact the correspondences, the greater is the probability of their exemplifying homology. 'But the interesting paradox remains that, while continuity of homologous structures implies affinity between organisms in phylogeny, it does not necessarily imply similarity of genetic factors or of ontogenetic processes in the production of homologous structures' (De Beer, 1951, p. 126).

In the view of Dobzhansky (1955) the phenomenon of homology 'extends right down to the gene level of organization'. Genes which behave as alleles are descendants of the same ancestral gene and are homologous. Homologous genes may still be present in different species of mammals, these having been derived from the common ancestors. But he also pointed out that phenotypically similar forms may be pro-duced by non-homologous genes, i.e. the similarity of the eventual development does not necessarily mean that identical genes are in-volved. Muller (1939), cited by Dobzhansky (1955), also discussed the possibilities of changes in gene function during the evolutionary process: morphological homologies (he said) may persist long after the causally related initially homologous genes have been modified or replaced. But, one may ask, modified to what extent and in what respects? That is, having in mind the size and stability of the gene-molecule.

BIOCHEMICAL HOMOLOGY

Although the theory of evolution was initially elaborated on the evidence of comparative morphology, it is now apparent that studies of evolu-tion should also include comparative physiology, and that considera-tion should be given to biochemical homology just as it has been to structural homology. Indeed, in its final form, the theory of evolution may perhaps be stated in terms of biochemical processes (Haldane, 1954). As already noted, many of the fundamental cellular processes found in very different plants and animals seem to, and probably do, afford remarkable examples of biochemical homology. At the present time, organic chemists, biochemists and physiologists are not only concerned with tracing the pathways of biosyntheses, but also in considering to what extent the evidence they obtain can be applied to the many unsolved problems of taxonomy and phylogeny (*see* Birch, 1963; Alston and Turner, 1963; and various relevant symposia, e.g. Swain, 1963).

In studies of the fatty acid, unsaponifiable lipoid, total nitrogen, and polysaccharide contents of representative algae from different classes, Collyer and Fogg (1955) found that species from the same class resemble each other in their relative contents of crude protein, fats and hydrolysable polysaccharide. Although marked differences in composition have been found in species from different classes, these investigators consider that there are no fundamental differences in the physiological relations of fat accumulation in algae belonging to Chlorophyceae, Euglenineae, Xanthophyceae, and Bacillariophyceae – each a separate and distinctive class according to contemporary algologists. Investigations by Allsopp (1948), by Steward *et al.* (1954, 1955) and others, have shown that a large number of the common aminoacids are present in all classes of green plants; and hexose sugars, starch and cellulose, and their associated enzymes, have long been known to be of very general occurrence. In fact, a general biochemical homology may be recognized in all classes of green plants. That the details of individual biochemical processes may differ, and that particular processes may be inhibited, accelerated or modified by changes in the genetical constitution, has now been shown in a number of instances; but that the fundamental biochemical organization of species is directly and mainly gene-determined has not yet been demonstrated, though in time it seems likely that it will be. Indeed, some biologists, e.g. H. Graham Cannon (1956, 1958, 1959; and *see* Chapter 15), maintained that the fundamental protoplasmic organization and activities are not primarily gene-determined; but many biologists would probably regard this as going too far in the opposite direction. Moreover, the importance of DNA, the key substance in inheritance, is becoming increasingly evident in other critical cellular activities.

From this brief survey of genic relationships in homology, it appears that notwithstanding the mutable nature of genes, and the changes undergone by genotypes during descent, the morphological developments to which they contribute may nevertheless retain a very considerable measure of stability and constancy. This organizational stability in the midst of genetical change is evidently a phenomenon of the greatest interest and importance and should be more fully investigated. As Picken (1960) pointed out, integration, which may perhaps be recognized as the *sine qua non* of organization, is *the* essential condition for the endurance or persistence of the system as such. But has it been shown that integration can be referred solely, or mainly, to genic action? (For a fuller discussion, *see* Chapters 6, 7, 15.)

EVOLUTIONARY PARALLELISMS IN ANGIOSPERMS

Reference may now be made to some major problems in taxonomic botany, namely, the genetical interpretation of the evolutionary divergences, parallelisms and convergences in the large group of the flowering plants.

With regard to the differentiation of the families of angiosperms, Stebbins (1950) stated that phenotypic modifications can be explained in terms of gene mutation, time of action of genes, growth substances, allometric growth and environmental factors; the forces that induce mutations and make for their establishment in natural populations being of primary importance. In this view, evolutionary change proceeds from the variety to the species, the species to the genus and so on. This is the opposite of the view originally advanced by St. Hilaire (1837) and supported by more recent workers such as Willis (1940). The genetical evidence points to the probable random nature of individual mutations and the accumulation of those which have a relatively slight effect on the phenotype, while selective advantage is conferred on individuals and populations by combinations of different gene-dependant properties. As many biologists have recognized, most long-continued evolutionary trends appear to be governed by some guiding force. Among the possible effective forces, natural selection is generally accepted as being of primary importance. However, this conclusion rests on reasoned argument and the general weight of evidence, rather than on experimental validation. Some biologists, e.g. Stebbins (1950) and Dobzhansky (1955), have ascribed a 'creative function' to selection. Nevertheless, as Stebbins has been at pains to point out, the evidence also indicates the action of 'some unexplained force which, presumably by causing the more frequent or predominant occurrence of mutations which are genetically unconnected, but have a similar morphological and physiological effect on the phenotype, directs or canalizes the course of evolution'. Some understanding of the nature of this force – if that is how the phenomenon should be described – is clearly of great importance in evolutionary theory, especially as it applies to the flowering plants. So we may ask: Is the force essentially extrinsic to organisms but capable of inducing gene mutation? Or is it an intrinsic property, e.g. an energy relationship or an instability of some of the molecular materials of the cell nucleus or cytoplasm (Stebbins)? Or is it related to some other *general* feature of cell organization to which insufficient attention has been paid?

To account for the differentiation of the major systematic groups in the angiosperms is not necessarily an impossible task; but as Stebbins (1950) has pointed out, it will unavoidably contain much that is speculative. As interpreted by Stebbins, the trends which led to the differentiation of families probably took place simultaneously at a relatively early stage in angiosperm evolution, possibly in Jurassic times, when new angiosperm populations, with the basic characters of the Ranales, were in a minority, the major competitors being the gymnosperms with their less efficient methods of reproduction. As climatic conditions were comparatively uniform throughout the world during that period, selective pressures affecting vegetative adaptation would be low. During the Jurassic period, moreover, insects and birds, important in effecting cross-pollination and seed dispersal respectively, seem to have evolved rapidly; and hence genic changes and combinations, making for adaptive biotic features in flowers and fruits, would have high selective value. (These arguments would not apply to certain major groups, e.g. the Glumiflorae, in which the flowers are mostly anemophilous.) Since the flower is a harmoniously developed and functionally effective organ, any viable change in one of its parts would 'immediately change the selective value of modifications in all the others, as well as the value of such general characteristics as the size, number, and arrangement of the flowers produced'; and other variables would be introduced into the situation by the economy of the plant as a whole, its habitat and mode of life. Much of this may be true but it is still, unavoidably, very general.

The eight characters used in taxonomy and held to be primitive in floral morphology, namely, presence of a corolla, polypetaly, actinomorphy, numerous stamens, apocarpous carpels, many ovules, axial placentation and ovary superior, may each show characteristic evolutionary advances, e.g. actinomorphy to zygomorphy. As, theoretically, several or all of these morphological advances might be combined, many different combinations (actually 256) are possible. However, as Stebbins has shown, only some 34 per cent of the possible combinations are realized. About half of these are found in only one or two families (or groups), but certain combinations are present in a large number of groups. Of some 438 groups studied, 200 showed only 12 combinations, i.e. less than 5 per cent. of the total number possible. Stebbins therefore concluded that the eight characters are not simply combined at random in the different families and genera, but the combinations may perhaps be related to constructional feasibility, functional efficiency, and adaptation. Some combinations do not occur because they are virtually impossible as structural developments. Others which are found in a relatively large number of unrelated groups may result from relatively slight modifications in a number of floral types with more primitive features. These typically have few genera and species. Certain combinations occur in only a few groups, e.g. the Leguminosae (*sens. lat.*), but in them the number of genera is very large. The same is true of the Orchidaceae, Gramineae, Cruciferae, Malvaceae, Scrophulariaceae, Rubiaceae (in part) and Compositae. In these families, the combinations of characters are less easily brought about,* but, once achieved, they apparently 'permit a wide range of variation in the adaptive types of floral structure'. Some combinations of two or three characters are especially prevalent, e.g. apetaly combined with a reduction in ovule number, floral symmetry and inflorescence type, e.g. zygomorphy and racemose inflorescence; etc. Correlative development is a conspicuous feature of floral evolution and it may extend to related vegetative and habitat features. Lastly, evolutionary innovations which affect a single fundamental character in a flower at the primitive, unspecialized level of organization, are likely to have the greatest chance of being successful.

ADAPTIVE RADIATION

The evolution of the genera and families of flowering plants affords evidence of *adaptive radiation*, the number of combinations functionally adequate for cross-pollination and seed dispersal being quite large; and although the relative simplicity of plant structure, as compared with animals, restricts the extent of any evolutionary progression, it admits of 'an exceptionally large amount of parallel variation, so that morphological similarity is much less indicative of phylogenetic relationship in plants than it is in animals' (Stebbins, 1950).

---

* It would be interesting to test this idea by morphogenetic investigations.

A POSSIBLE CAUSE OF PARALLEL EVOLUTION

Among Stebbins's many interesting arguments, one is of particular importance here because of its bearing on parallel evolution. He noted that a brief growing season may act as a selective agent and hence the value to a species of mutational changes which would (i) shorten the time required for its cycle of flowering and fruiting and (ii) effect economies in the materials required by its reproductive structures. As correlative effects, such mutations might make for a reduction in the number and size of the floral parts.

If a generalized selective agent of this kind were at work, 'we should expect to find a great amount of parallel evolution in the fundamental organization of the flower and this appears to have taken place'. But, simultaneously, divergences might also be produced by special environmental agents.

EVOLUTIONARY DIFFERENTIATION IN RANALEAN STOCK

The members of this ancestral stock (said Stebbins) were probably scattered in small numbers over the earth, spatial and ecological isolation being important. Mutations leading to one or more of the several kinds of floral specialization may have occurred independently in different areas and been perpetuated in the population because of their adaptive value. The establishment of one such morphological change would increase the selective value of other mutations making for adaptive floral specialization. Thus the new population would eventually possess a combination of features not present in the original one. In any one line of descent, the elimination of intermediate types by competition would leave a gap between the original and the more evolved forms. Furthermore, the adaptive characters possessed by the new forms would enable them to spread to new habitats, and an ever-increasing divergence would be brought about by isolation, hybridization and selection. The reader is referred to Stebbins (1950, p. 509) for his detailed argument as to the origin of species, genera and higher taxa, but the essential feature of it is that the process envisaged could yield a *series of populations*, or *species*, all of which would have 'the same selectively advantageous and diagnostic modifications of the flower which arose monophyletically'. The species, however, would differ from each other in the various characteristics that they had acquired as a result of independent variation under isolation and hybridization; and such a group of species would constitute a new *genus*. Further evolutionary expansions, elaborations and extinctions would lead to the creation of a *family*. Stebbins concluded that 'the earliest appearance, on the species level, of individual characteristics now considered to be characteristic of families and orders was largely associated with chance, but the moulding of the higher categories themselves through the assembling of successful combinations of characteristics was guided mainly by natural selection'. Moreover, the greater the degree of specialization, the less likely is it that chance variations in fundamental characteristics will occur, and the more will natural selection tend to direct development in a particular direction. The result will be an *orthogenetic drift* or *trend*. Thus, the processes of mutation, recombination, selection, isolation and extinction, which yielded subspecies and species, could in time, and with further genetic and environmental changes, have given rise to the higher taxonomic categories.

It will be noted that the parallelisms in angiosperm evolution are of different kinds and cannot be attributed to a single cause. Under some environmental conditions certain mutations, either similar in kind or with similar functional value, would tend to be selected; and the morphological similarities in the different organisms would exemplify homology of organization and not homogeny. Also, some unspecified force which caused more frequent mutation in particular directions, together with natural selection, might have resulted in comparable phenotypic developments. In the primitive flowers of the initial radiating lines, it is conceivable that advances may have been possible only in certain directions; e.g. an apocarpous gynoecium could remain unchanged or evolve towards some kind of syncarpy; a symmetrical flower could so remain or develop some kind of asymmetry; and similarly, only certain combinations of new floral developments would be possible. In short, on grounds of possibility and probability, only certain evolutionary developments were likely to take place.

THE COMPARISON OF RELATED GROUPS

When one compares related groups, e.g. genera, or families, it is theoretically possible to distinguish (i) characters which are alike because they are determined by homologous or common ancestral genes, or other heritable attributes, from (ii) other characters which are also alike but which may have arisen independently during the further evolution of the individual groups, and which may therefore not be strictly genetically homologous. Also, as phenotypic characters result from the action of the organismal reaction system in a particular environment, this separation of characters may, in any particular instance, require extensive investigations (*see* Figs. 4.3–4.6).

Some morphological parallelisms may indeed be new developments determined by gene mutation, recombination and selection, but others may be attributable to *latent homology* or to the fact that mutant genes still share some, or even many, of the physico-chemical properties of the parental genes.

In each of the radiation lines in early angiosperm evolution, only some of the mutant genes are considered to have survived the selective process; and some of these, working as components of their respective genetical systems, contributed to comparable phenotypic effects, i.e. in what became different phyletic lines. Stebbins referred to these mutations as being 'genetically unconnected'. But is this view acceptable? On the evidence, genes, being large organic molecules, are mostly of a high order of stability; and if the new mutant genes are capable of functioning harmoniously in the gene complex and therefore of being selected, it seems improbable that they differ fundamentally in their main configuration and action from the original or wild-type genes. As we are told, a mutant gene may revert to the parental gene. How is this possible if the gene-molecule has been extensively modified? Again, if a mutant gene is duplicated or replicated, it may produce the same kind of reaction as the parental gene. As it is a relatively stable physico-chemical entity, it seems probable that a gene can only have its basic structure changed in a limited number of ways and be carried on into the genotype of the progeny. This view is in accord with contemporary discoveries on gene structure and activity, and no doubt many of the points under discussion will be resolved as molecular biology progresses.

When a gene is replaced by another gene, or gene complex, and the new genotype still produces the same character as the parental genotype, it is reasonable to infer that the chemical action of the substituted gene is, at least in some respects, akin to that of the original gene. It may therefore be inferred that when several phyletic lines stem from a common ancestral group, some genetical, i.e. biochemical, homology persists and may partly determine the seemingly independent but parallel morphological innovations. We do not know the extent of this residual genetical homology but, in many instances it may be quite considerable. The increasing divergence of such phyletic lines is a measure of the increasing differences in their initially homologous genetical systems; and the greater the divergence the more difficult it is likely to be to demonstrate the reality of this assumed homology. Whether studies in biochemical systematics will resolve some of these problems, or merely create new ones, as may well happen, remains to be seen. Adherents of this branch of science for the most part adopt a rather cautious attitude to the results of their investigations. (*see* p. 430).

DIVERGENCE AND PARALLELISM IN OTHER GROUPS

Evidence comparable with that set out above is also to be found in other major systematic groups; e.g. in the Algae (*see* Chapter 8); while, in the ferns, Bower's (1923–28) phylogenetic scheme is essentially a portrayal of both radiate and parallel evolution from a Palaeozoic ancestral group. Whether the several classes formerly recognized as constituting the pteridophytes are the result of radiate evolution from a group of prototypic vascular cryptograms, e.g. the Psilophytales, as some botanists think, or whether they evolved independently from algal progenitors, is still unresolved.

In each of the major taxonomic groups of plants the same *general* kinds of evolutionary change appear to have taken place. Thus, the brown algae, the mosses, the ferns, the gymnosperms and the flowering plants are all characterized by progressive refinements and seeming economies in the production and dispersal of their reproductive structures, and by trends towards increased differentiation of organs and tissues; i.e. towards a higher level of organization. These observations prompt the reflection that, in the evolution of plants, a comparatively small number of common causal factors may have been involved. Whether or not contemporary genetical interpretations alone can adequately account for the close similarities in evolutionary trends in unrelated groups remains an open question, at least for the uncommitted observer.

CHAPTER 6

The Origin of Primitive Living Systems and Simple Organisms

LIVING AND NON-LIVING ENTITIES

There was a stage in the development of the natural sciences when complex organic substances were regarded as being outside the laws of chemistry: they were only found in living organisms and they were accordingly attributed to the working of some unspecified vital force. This notion died hard: it even persisted after Wohler had synthesized urea from inorganic ammonium cyanate in 1828. From the middle of the nineteenth century, however, rapid progress was made in the study of the simpler organic compounds and also of important ingredients of living cells, including sugars, proteins, polypeptides, purines, and so on. These discoveries led naturally to the view that the chemistry of organisms was simply classical chemistry, though it was recognized that the substances involved were complex and were usually formed under rather special conditions. Today, those who interest themselves in problems of the origin of life are usually reluctant to draw any sharp line between non-living and living systems or entities. Indeed, a generally acceptable definition of life in its simplest conceivable form or manifestation has yet to be formulated.

A richly inventive, highly speculative and controversial, but fascinating literature now exists regarding the nature of life and its origin and development. Needless to say, the whole topic is obscure and enigmatic to a degree. Calvin (1961: this contains useful up-to-date references) has called attention to *Sketches of Creation* (1870) by A. Winchell, a professor of geology in the University of Michigan. Winchell may be regarded as one of the first of the 'modern' exponents of what today is commonly referred to as *chemical evolution*. Moore (1912) was also early in the field; and Moore and Webster (1914) contributed a paper on the synthesis of formaldehyde. Pirie (1952, 1953, 1954, 1960) has recapitulated some of the ideas of the ancient natural philosophers on the origin of life. In 1868, T. H. Huxley set out many percipient ideas on the subject. Indeed, some contemporary writers consider that, in essentials, little new advance has since been made. However, this over-cautious attitude does rather less than justice to the constructive thinking and critical investigations of Haldane (1929), Oparin (1961) and others. In fact, recent decades have witnessed a lively interest in this theme on the part of biochemists, geochemists, physicists, geneticists, biologists and philosophers, viz. Haldane (1929, 1954), Oparin (1938, 1953, 1957, 1961), Horowitz, (1945, 1960), Bertalanffy (1952), Madison (1953), Bernal (1951, 1954, 1962), V. M. Goldschmidt (1952), Pirie (1952, 1953, 1954), Miller (1953), Pringle (1953, 1954), Perret (1952), Fox (1956), Calvin (1956, 1961), Lemberg (1951), Bray and White (1954), Schrödinger (1944). (Various aspects of chemical evolution have also been dealt with in more or less comprehensive symposia.)

CONJECTURES ON THE ORIGIN OF LIFE

Speculations on the origin of life – what Pirie (1952, 1954) described as *biopoiesis* – are numerous. Some of the ideas have much in common though the details may differ. The relevant ideas may be classified in various ways (Haldane, 1954) but here our principal concern is with such light as they may shed on the *inception of organization*, i.e. in ancient and primitive living entities. Accordingly, it will suffice to indicate briefly some of the leading hypotheses, inferences and investigations. (For a closely argued and coherent individual thesis, the reader is referred to Oparin, 1961.)

1. Contemporary living organisms are exceedingly varied and morphologically diverse, but the same kind of life appears to be present in them all, whether they are bacteria, algae, higher plants, reptiles or mammals.

2. As life is essentially chemical activity in a biological context, the evidence of evolution in organisms points to an antecedent phase of chemical evolution. Bernal (1954) suggested that the commonest processes in the cells of living organisms are likely to be the oldest; and following L. J. Henderson's (1913) principle of the fitness of the environment, he held that nascent organisms probably made use of the substances and reactions of the commonest elements then available at the earth's surface (Figs. 6.1, 6.2).

3. Lyell's evolutionary *principle of continuity*, namely, that those geochemical processes which were important in the origin of life are likely to have persisted in some recognizable measure in contemporary living organisms, still appears to be of the highest relevance. Since vast spans of time are involved, it could, perhaps, be argued that initial organizations of living matter have been changed out of all recognition; but studies of the very ancient plant fossils, and other surveys, do not support this

view. These observations suggest that in all living entities there is a persistent, or residual, chemical homology. Oparin (1961) has emphasized this point: in his view a major part of cellular organization is of very great antiquity and is, accordingly, common to all organisms.

4. Evolution from the non-living to the living state was an exceedingly slow and gradual process. The intervention of special events of an

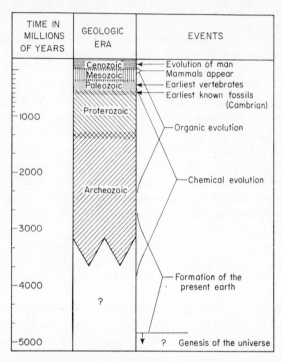

Fig.6.1 An estimate of the time scale for total evolution on the earth, comprising the period of planet formation, the long period of chemical evolution, and the subsequent periods as revealed by palaeontology. (After M. Calvin, *A.I.B.S. Bull.*, 1962.)

exceptional or cataclysmic nature was probably not essential though Haldane (1954) did not exclude this possibility. Estimates of the time scale of the earth's history indicate that the period of chemical evolution, i.e. the pre-organismal or abiotic period, was of very long duration. As it were, chemical evolution had time on its side. It may reasonably be surmised that the *general* biochemical and biophysical features of protoplasmic organization were established before individual organisms began to acquire the distinctive and specific properties which are now known to be due to the action of genes (Fig.6.1).

5. Reaction systems can change in various ways, yielding the possibility of biochemical evolution (Horowitz, 1945). In this process it is held that rapid reactions will tend to replace slow ones. In the evolution of metabolic processes essential to the living state, the acceleration of reactions by specific autocatalysts was probably important from an early stage. With the synthesis of autocatalysts, chemical evolution

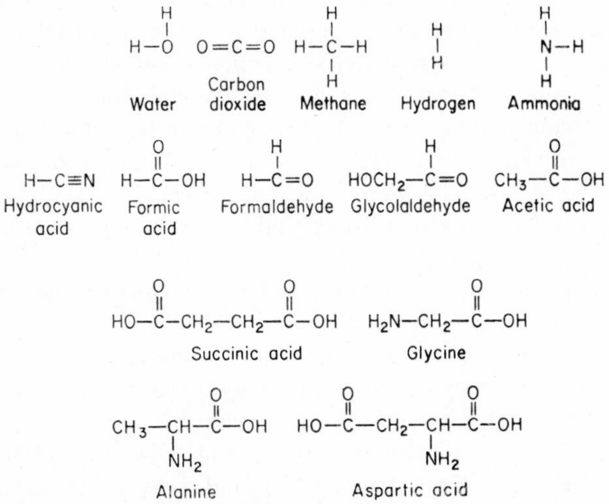

Fig.6.2 The simpler and more elaborate organic molecules which may have participated actively in the earlier phase of chemical evolution. These 'primeval and primitive' molecules afford evidence of increasing, orderly complexity. (After M. Calvin, *A.I.B.S. Bull.*, 1962.)

would pass from the phase of *random syntheses* to that of *selective syntheses* (Calvin, 1961).

6. The reactions involved in the inception of 'living substance' proceeded by small steps. They were probably isothermal and collectively constituted an 'open system', capable of existing in the steady-state equilibrium recognized by physical chemists (Bertalanffy, 1952; Perret, 1952; Oparin, 1961).

7. The nature and course of the initial syntheses of simple organic compounds into more complex ones, in pre-organismal or abiotic times, or in subvital systems, are very controversial topics. The various accounts which have been given differ according to the assumptions

that were made regarding the nature of the earth's primordial atmosphere, the temperature of the lithosphere and the access of ultraviolet or other radiation from the sun. (Some writers have side-stepped the ultimate problem by assuming an extra-global origin of life.)

8. According to Calvin (1961), the 'completely reduced' concept of the earth's primeval atmosphere has met with increasing acceptance. At an early stage, the earth's atmosphere probably contained little free oxygen, but it probably included gaseous ammonia, hydrocarbons such as methane, gas from volcanoes, etc. (Haldane, 1929, 1954). With ultraviolet solar radiation as an energy source, metastable organic molecules were synthesized, with a concomitant storing of energy. An energy source thus began to become available for the activities of incipient living matter. The complex photosynthetic mechanism was probably evolved very much later. In other words, anaerobiosis was the primitive condition. This view, which was rejected by Madison (1953) and Pringle (1953), has been strongly advocated by Oparin (1961) (Fig. 6.2).

9. During the abiotic period, before destructive agencies and organisms, or living systems, were at work, it is probable that many relatively complex organic substances were synthesized. Haldane (1954) suggested that complex phosphates may have provided the basic mechanisms for the initial subvital systems, i.e. systems capable of using energy and of undergoing growth and self-reproduction. These general ideas have been used and expanded by other writers, e.g. Oparin (1938, 1957, 1961), Bernal (1951, 1954), Pringle (1953, 1954) etc., but the details, which are necessarily highly conjectural, need not be closely specified. The important point is that complex organic molecules could probably have been synthesized and that, under the prevailing conditions, some of them might have persisted and accumulated. In a wide range of experiments, Calvin (1961) and his colleagues have shown that substances which we know to be essential in the synthesis of basic cell components can be obtained by subjecting mixtures of simple gases to ionizing radiations, ultraviolet light, and electrical discharges (simulating lightning). These substances include formic acid, acetic acid, succinic acid, glycine, etc. (Fig.6.2).

10. The localized accumulation of such organic molecules as may have been synthesized may have been effected by their being absorbed in waterlogged 'soil'. Bernal (1951), who envisaged the formation of proteins as an essential early stage in the evolution of life, thought that the necessary accumulation, condensation or polymerization of smaller

molecules into more complex ones might have been effected by their being adsorbed on to the surface of clay particles. Pringle (1953, 1954), who considered that the oxidation of hydrocarbons was of primary importance in the inception of subvital systems, postulated a mechanism for the concentration of patterns of substances in the undisturbed depths of the ocean. The idea that synthesized substances became localized in an aqueous medium by coacervation, i.e. the separation of droplets which may contain several organic substances, has been advocated by Oparin (1957, 1961). Oparin has laid great stress on the probable importance of coacervation in the bringing into close proximity important ingredients of the 'primordial nutrient broth'. Some such process could have prepared the way for the organization of primordial cells. Millich and Calvin (1961) have demonstrated the aggregation into droplets of a polymer such as polyvinyl-sulphonic acid, in a dilute solution, by the addition of traces of iron. (Bernal (1954) may be consulted for details of the physical properties of some of the possible kinds of aggregates.)

11. The synthesis of simple proteins was an essential step in the evolution of life. Here, unavoidably, the topic becomes both complex and controversial. Some interesting experimental evidence is now beginning to accumulate. For example, Fox *et al.* (1959) have shown that if some of the simpler aminoacids are treated under what may have been pre-biological conditions, they can be converted into protein-like materials. The general idea is that, during the phase of chemical evolution, large protein macromolecules could have come into existence as a result of random processes, autocatalytic selection, and the forces associated with atoms when they are assembled in particular configurations or arrangements. When some still larger organic molecules crystallize out of solution, they do not do so at random but form a characteristic orderly pattern, e.g. certain plant viruses. Palm and Calvin (1961) have shown that electric bombardments of simple gases and water will yield HCN, adenine and other bases. When radioactive methane (with labelled C^{14}) was irradiated, several compounds, including adenine, HCN, urea, glycine, alanine, various aminoacids, sugars, some fatty acids and hydroxyacids, were subsequently identified. These are substances which enter into the composition of living matter (Calvin, 1961). Pirie (1952, 1953, 1954) has opposed the view that proteins were essential in the earlier phases of evolution: 'The statement that all living organisms contain protein is unproven. . . . Present day conditions tell us nothing about the qualities necessary or desirable

at the beginning' (i.e. perhaps 2,000 million years ago). The initial steps towards 'the living state' may have been taken repeatedly and, indeed, some such process may still be in operation (Pirie, 1952) (Fig.6.3).

12. In a geochemical view, as expressed by V. M. Goldschmidt (1952), it is assumed that carbon monoxide was present in the primeval

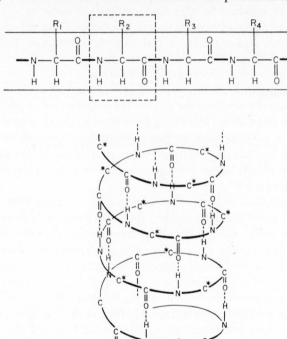

Fig.6.3 Organization in complex molecules: the highly ordered arrangement of the atoms in a long-chain, helical protein results spontaneously under certain conditions. R_1, R_2, R_3, etc., carboxyl groups at the ends of side-chains. (After M. Calvin, *A.I.B.S. Bull.*, 1962.)

atmosphere. Under the prevailing conditions of higher temperatures, and in the presence of water, the CO would soon be transformed into CO_2, the H_2 being dissipated into space. Goldschmidt also inferred that nitrogen compounds (e.g. ammonia and its salts, oxides of nitrogen, and nitrous and nitric acid) as well as sulphur compounds, would be available and enter into further combinations as a result of photo-chemical activation, electric discharges, etc. Prior to active photo-

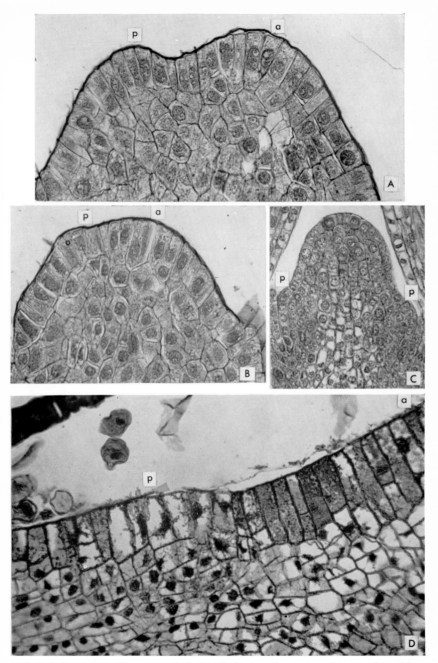

7. A, B, *Psilotum nudum* (*P. triquetrum*). A, Longitudinal median section of the apex (*a*) and last-formed leaf primordium (*p*): some of the superficial cells of the primordium have divided by periclinal walls and there is evidence of active division in the underlying cells. B, A very young leaf primordium (*p*); *a*, apical cell. C, *Ephedra* sp. As in A, the young leaf primordium is essentially a multicellular organ (all × c.200). D, As above, apex of *Dryopteris dilatata*, showing young leaf primordium: both superficial and underlying cells contribute to the formation of the young leaf primordium. *a*, direction of shoot apical cell; *p*, young primordium. (*Annals of Botany*.)

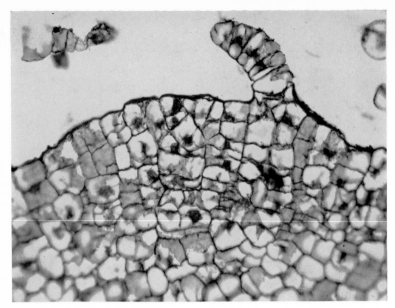

8A. *Dryopteris dilatata*. Longitudinal median section of a shoot apex after direct application of thiamine hydrochloride to the apex. The normal distinctive organization of the apical meristem has been lost: the apical cell and the prism-shaped cells of the apical meristem have become much divided and precociously parenchymatous; leaf primordia are very inconspicuous; and scales have been formed all over the meristem, including the modified apical cell region (× 255).

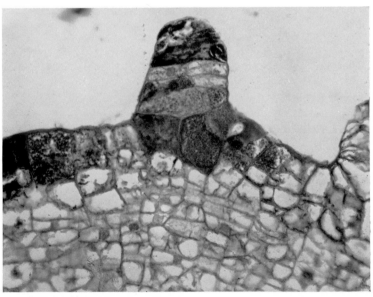

8B. *Dryopteris dilatata*. Longitudinal median section of a shoot apex which has become disorganized as a result of direct application of yeast extract to the apex. A parenchymatous development has been induced in the region of the apical cell and has given rise to a large, deeply staining, spine-like scale (× 225). (*Annals of Botany*.)

synthetic activity by plants, oxygen was probably present in traces only; and, in the absence of organisms and of oxygen, many compounds would persist which, under contemporary conditions, would be consumed or destroyed by bacteria, plants and animals, or by oxidation. In this view, there was a pre-organismal phase which was characterized by the survival of organic molecules, some of which might have been quite large and complex. How these initially dispersed molecules were brought together and organized into complex aggregates is not known. Adsorbing surfaces, e.g. the surface of phase boundaries between the atmosphere and hydrosphere or at the surface of inorganic mineral crystals, may have been specially important in this connection. Thus the surfaces of mineral crystals may have contributed to the building up of complicated organic molecules, including asymmetric ones. 'The hypothesis of asymmetric synthesis in adsorbates on asymmetric crystal faces or on crystals which, like quartz, are asymmetric in tridimensional space, is the most reasonable conception of abiotic asymmetric synthesis in nature' (Goldschmidt). The assimilation of CO_2 in abiotic autotrophic molecules, as in the accumulation of organic matter by plants, is a fundamental point of Goldschmidt's scheme – 'the assimilation of CO_2 still is the common denominator of all living matter on the earth'. Goldschmidt indicated a number of common minerals which could have been active collectors of dispersed organic molecules in the pre-organism phase.

13. Haldane (1954) directed attention to adenosine-triphosphoric acid (ATP) as being 'the most lifelike molecule known to us at present'. He suggested that metastable molecules, e.g. phosphate ions, were probably present in pre-Cambrian waters in sufficient amounts to admit of the growth, splitting and increase in the numbers of catalytically active molecules. In this connection, Haldane also noted that of the three principal kinds of long-chain molecules in living organisms, the nucleic acids have a 'backbone' of phosphoric acid residues; proteins a 'backbone' of glycerine residues; and polysaccharides and related substances one consisting of pentose residues. At some early stage, primitive catalysts, each adapted to a different 'food' of smaller metastable molecules, may have united to form catalysts with a wider range, till eventually a relatively large molecule, still able to grow and divide, was formed: 'The result might be something like a simple molecular virus or a very small chromosome with different catalytically active groups corresponding to different genes' (Haldane, 1954, p. 21).

14. The origin and activities of catalysts and the functional, or

E

integrated, association of different catalysts occupy a prominent place in the literature relating to the prebiotic phase. It is somewhere about this historic stage that we touch the borderlines between the non-living and the living, or between purely chemical and nascent biological phenomena. Haldane (1954) suggested that self-reproducing chain molecules may have existed together 'in a sort of symbiosis', using each others' 'metabolic' products. He conjectured that the decisive step in the inception of a primordial living entity was the formation of the first cell, 'in which chain molecules of at least two of the three types now represented by nucleic acids, proteins and polysaccharides were enclosed in a semi-permeable membrane which kept them together but let their food in'. (If the hypothesis that life originated as the result of a very (mathematically) improbable event has any validity, Haldane considered that it would apply to the formation of the first functioning cell rather than to events in some earlier phase of biochemical evolution.) Calvin (1961) has pointed out that once autocatalysts had been formed, i.e. by the same processes as smaller molecules of simpler construction, the selection and conservation of such larger molecules from among the random transformation products would follow as a natural conse- quence. Thus, during the phase of chemical evolution, molecules with simple rudimentary functions would become transformed into larger molecules with the refined and extended properties of catalysts.

15. During the phase of chemical evolution, and by gradual steps involving ordinary chemical systems and reactions, different subvital systems may have appeared. But, still at the purely chemical level, selective forces would already be at work, especially where autocatalysts were active; and only a few of the tentative subvital systems would 'survive', i.e. persist (Pirie, 1954). It was from some, perhaps only one, of these, that living organisms eventually evolved. There is agreement among investigators of these phenomena that (a) where complex 'viable' systems had come into existence by coacervation or other means, (b) where such systems necessarily had the power, or capacity, of taking up substances from the aqueous environment, and (c) where autocata- lysts were included among the components of the system, selective processes were already at work. Haldane (1954) suggested that such nascent systems of the abiotic period may not have been completely self-contained in their variability. Interchanges between systems may have taken place, constituting, as it were, a possible forerunner of sexuality. Thus whereas Boyden (1953) thought that the reproduction of primitive cells was probably asexual over a long period of time, Haldane

envisaged the possibility of fusion between primitive cells, sometimes with useful exchanges of parts or materials, giving new possibilities for development, as a relatively early event in organic evolution.

16. The enclosing of a subvital system, capable of self-maintenance, growth and reproduction, within a membrane, was an event of profoundly critical importance in organic evolution. When this had been achieved, the nascent 'organism' had the beginnings of an integrated unity and at least some distinctive and 'specific' properties. Various ideas as to how a wall or external membrane originated have been proposed or suggested, e.g. that it could have consisted of a lipoid protein layer with air and water contacts respectively (Goldacre, 1958; Calvin, 1961). If such an external layer surrounded a complex coacervulate droplet, with its network of ingredients, and if it admitted of a selective interchange of materials with the environment, an entity of very primitive organismal character, standing at the junction of the chemical (abiotic) and biotic periods, may perhaps be envisaged. Haldane suggested that the inception of the first living cell should perhaps be attributed to some 'highly improbable event'. According to Bernal (1954), all the major types of biochemically active molecules – the lipoids excepted – might have evolved in the pre-organismal phase, the great gap to be filled lying between this phase and the first recognizable organism (*see also* Lemberg, 1951).

17. A considerable body of research, as distinct from conjecture, has shown that many syntheses of more complex organic molecules from simpler ones can be achieved by the use of ultraviolet light, by electrical discharges in gases, by higher reaction temperatures, and by providing other reaction conditions, such as may have obtained in the abiotic period (Oparin, 1938, 1961; Miller, 1953; Calvin, 1956, 1961; Fox, 1956). Miller, for example, demonstrated the formation of glycine, α- and β-alanine, and other compounds, in a mixture of methane, ammonia and carbon dioxide which had been subjected to an electrical discharge. In the phase of biochemical evolution, the synthesis of aminoacids as protein precursors, and of coloured compounds capable of absorbing solar radiations of longer wave-lengths, i.e. preparing the way for photosynthetic activities, were essential steps in the evolution of primitive organisms.

Because of the vast period of time that was required for the chemical evolution of primitive living matter and subsequently of the organized living cell, Astbury (1957) and Oparin (1961) consider that it is very unlikely that any independent syntheses of *major* biological significance can ever be achieved in the laboratory.

SOME POINTS FROM OPARIN

'Life', said Oparin (1961, p. 201), 'is a special and very complicated form of the motion of matter'. It originated as a new property of matter and is the result of its orderly development. To understand the essential nature of life it is not enough to study the properties of living organisms: a knowledge of its origin and development is essential.

Oparin's analysis of the problem led him to recognize the existence of successive evolutionary phases or stages; and from his survey of these phases he has drawn important conclusions. Some of these are indicated below. The mechanistic details are omitted, but many of them are the same as, or cognate with, those already outlined.

In the earliest phase of the earth's development, the phenomena were purely physical and chemical in nature, this initial 'chemical phase' being characterized by a gradual increase in the complexity of the organic compounds formed, or evolved. As a result the waters on the earth's surface became enriched with many organic compounds, including protein-like substances. But even during the chemical phase, natural selection was operative, and only those systems of synthesis were perpetuated which had such an organization as to make for increasing self-maintenance and self-reproduction under the prevailing conditions. The selective forces contributed both to the perfecting of single substances such as enzymes and to the progressive, functional organization of the whole metabolic system. In this interaction between nascent or primitive organizations and environment, Oparin perceived the beginning of living matter, with its adaptation or structural 'purposiveness'. The steps in the evolution of life were typically associated with 'a progressive improvement in the organization of metabolism'.

The further evolution of life followed strictly selected pathways. These were determined by various sustaining conditions, e.g. of the prevailing environment, the state of the evolving system, and the close and obligatory interrelationship between them. From this point onwards, said Oparin, 'The paths followed by life in its further evolutions are also incomprehensible on the basis of physical and chemical laws alone. . . . ' The establishment of all that is implied by the orderly metabolism of cells must have occupied a vast period of time. At each stage the mechanism had to possess survival value. Such considerations may help to explain why many basic cell properties are common to all organisms. There is support for the view that the first organisms were anaerobic heterotrophs, the inception and perfecting of autotrophic photochemical metabolism belonging to a much later evolutionary phase. Because of the complexity of the photosynthetic mechanism, and all that is involved in its co-ordinated functioning, Oparin considered that it could only have been evolved in organisms which possessed the necessary basis in their existing systems. The origin of the process of respiration, involving as it did the presence of atmospheric oxygen, is a comparatively recent evolutionary innovation. The origin of the living cell, with its many highly organized components, nucleus, organelles, etc., and the coordination of its manifold activities, is exceedingly obscure. In Oparin's view, preconceived ideas that the cell became organized round some highly complex substance are naïve and scientifically unsound: 'the belief that deoxyribonucleic acid, which is one of the most important components of the nucleus, appeared at the very moment of the origin of life and was, in fact, the "first living molecule", is one such preconceived idea' (p. 150). DNA probably only became necessary when cell organization had already reached a comparatively high level. However, it may be noted that DNA is becoming recognized as a component of an increasing number of cell organelles.

As evolution continued, the basic properties of organisms became progressively more complicated; they also became transformed into 'qualitatively new forms of manifestations of life' (p. 203), branching out along different lines. A feature of the evolutionary process is that it proceeds with increasing acceleration as each new higher level of organization is attained.

BIOCHEMICAL EVOLUTION

In recent years biochemists have recognized that a process of chemical evolution probably took place early in the history of the earth and that biological concepts of random variation in systems and selection can be applied with some propriety to non-living systems. Calvin (1956, 1961) has discussed these possibilities in some detail and has concluded that systems approximating to nascent or primitive living cells could have resulted from non-living systems 'in the normal course of events'; for a vast span of time, in the period between 2,500 and 1,000 million years ago, was available for the phase of chemical evolution. Calvin has indicated four different ways in which the synthesis of more complex organic molecules from simpler ones might have taken place. These have now been tested in the laboratory and several positive results have been claimed. Once some of the evolving substances had developed autocatalytic properties, selection within the system would become a possibility. The elaboration of catalysts would also enlarge the scope for new syntheses, and we may suppose that chemical evolution gradually moved towards the syntheses of substances of the kind which we find in living organisms. As non-living systems evolved, some of the energy available would be utilized in the creation of order, as in living systems – the 'negative entropy' of Schrödinger (*see* Chapter 2). In general, the reactions that yield order in open systems require energy. The elaborate molecules of deoxyribonucleic acid may be regarded as an example of order achieved, as Calvin says, by 'an incipient crystallization while still in solution'. The energy used in bringing molecules together to form one of greater size and complexity has its basis, or resides, in their structural features, i.e. energy is used in producing the higher organization of the larger molecule. Oxidative phosphorylation affords a mechanism whereby a reaction which liberates energy can be linked with one in which energy is utilized. This mechanism is present in the cells of living organisms, the important mediating substance being adenosine triphosphate.

THE EVOLUTION OF PROTEIN MOLECULES

As early as 1898 Herbert Spencer had discussed the idea of evolution at the molecular level. Today, many biologists find no difficulty in accepting the view that families of molecules afford evidence of Darwinian evolution (Fox, 1953, 1956). The heterogeneity of proteins in living species is held to be the inevitable outcome of molecular variation and diversification, selection, and the persistence of those molecules which are more adapted to the environment afforded by the living cell. This has been fully and cogently argued by Oparin (1961). If this idea is extended, it becomes evident that molecular and biological evolution must be closely related in a reciprocal manner.

Although a large number of protein isomers is theoretically possible (Asimov, 1954), the actual number of protein molecular types is only a small fraction of the theoretical number. Fox (1956) inferred that the rate of evolution of these molecules must be very low. By using improved techniques, he found that the critical aminoacids are present in two blue-green algae – usually rated as very primitive organisms – and that their proportions are as in the proteins of more advanced organisms. This result confirms and extends earlier findings of Lugg (1943, 1949), namely, that the most primitive known proteinaceous matter is closely comparable with that in higher plants.

Primordial Protein. As an outcome of practical investigations Fox

(1956) indicated the possibility that, 'in a pre-enzymic world, aminoacids reacting at elevated temperatures might determine their own order in a primordial peptide chain'. There is also evidence that proteinoids can be formed by heating one or two aminoacids. Also, after thermal polymerization of one or two aminoacids, with subsequent hydrolysis and paper chromatography, many ninhydrin spots from aminoacids and other amines were obtained. Such observations led to the conclusion that the known aminoacids may originally have been formed as a result of the thermal rearrangement of one, or a few, initial aminoacids. Fox also discussed other aspects of thermal synthesis, especially the work of Copeland (1936) on the thermal algae at Yellowstone. This is to the effect that low temperature algae evolved from high temperature forms, and suggested 'the probability of the origin of living organisms in the thermal waters'. Fox also remarked that 'in the growing sequence of thermal reactions simulating prebiological chemistry ... internally directing principles appear to be at work'. The sequence of reactions is not haphazard but appears to be in conformity with physico-chemical laws. Hence, with appropriate qualifications, Fox has stated aphoristically that 'biochemistry recapitulates pyrochemistry'.

On Protein Synthesis. At this point it may be useful to recall some major features of proteins in the economy of plants. In general terms, it may be said: (i) that water apart, proteins constitute about half of the material of a cell; (ii) the number of different proteins in a higher plant is large and their functions are very diverse; (iii) most of the proteins are enzymes, with catalytic activities, at least 500 enzymes having now been specified (but this figure may well be doubled or trebled as research progresses); (iv) proteins, which consist of linear chains of aminoacids (of which some 20 are of common occurrence), differ from one another (a) in the length of the chain, (b) in the way the chain is folded upon itself, and (c) in the sequence of aminoacids in the chain – the last (c) determining the specific character and properties of the protein; (v) the aminoacids are apparently not obligatorily associated one with another in any specific or distinctive sequence, i.e. they can become linked together at random in any sequence; but most proteins usually contain at least one of each of the 20 different aminoacids; (vi) the sequence of aminoacids in any particular protein is always the same, i.e. each protein has a specific structure which is determined by the sequence of aminoacids; and proteins are evidently formed in the organism in an orderly manner; (vii) the rate of protein formation in different tissues is directly correlated with the amount of ribonucleic acid (RNA) present in the cells; (viii) deoxyribonucleic acid (DNA) has the ability to modify the nature of proteins and through them other cell substances (E. F. Gale, 1957); (ix) the ability to make proteins depends on the presence of nucleic acids, both RNA and DNA being necessary (Fig.6.4).

DNA in Transformation Experiments. In transformation experiments, using phage and bacteria, it has been shown that by altering the DNA inside a cell a change can be effected in the nature of the proteins which

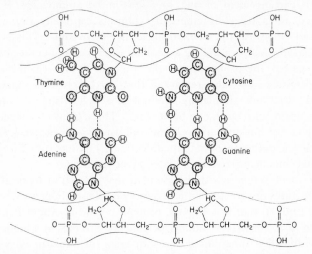

Fig.6.4 Diagrammatic indication of the molecular components of deoxyribonucleic acid (DNA). (After M. Calvin, *A.I.B.S. Bull.*, 1961.)

are synthesized; i.e. DNA has controlling effects on enzyme and related syntheses in cells. However, it may be duly emphasized that although DNA and RNA are of paramount importance in protein synthesis, they can only function when the reaction system in which they participate is intact; i.e. their activity depends on the organization of the cell.

In the contemporary view, DNA determines the specificity of the proteins that can be synthesized; RNA is directly involved in the actual synthesis; and the intact, organized cytoplasm is an essential sustaining medium if the reactions are to proceed. The sequence, or disposition, of the nucleotide units in the DNA determines the specific constitution of the RNA molecules, and the sequence of nucleotide units in the RNA determines the sequence of aminoacid units, and therefore the specificity of the proteins which in due course are synthesized. On the evidence to date, RNA includes an important component, other than the nucleotides, which is essential in protein synthesis but which has not yet been detected or isolated (Gale, 1957; Allfrey and Mirsky, 1961).

Nucleic Acids and Proteins. Calvin (1961) has considered which of these two essential components was formed first during the phase of chemical evolution. Garrison *et al.* (1961) have shown that sugar and aminoacids can be synthesized by subjecting aqueous solutions of simple substances to ionizing radiations. When mixtures of methane, water, hydrogen and ammonia – considered to be components of the earth's primordial atmosphere – were subjected to high energy processes, the random substances formed included aminoacids but not the bases required in the formation of nucleic acid. This led Fox (1960) and Calvin (1961) to the view that, during chemical evolution, the formation of proteins preceded that of the nucleic acids – a conclusion with which, for other reasons, Oparin is in agreement. On the other hand, Horowitz (1960) stated that the nucleic acids preceded the aminoacids in the evolutionary sequence. These controversial issues seem to be assured a lengthy future! However, Calvin (1961) has now reported that when mixtures of simple gases were bombarded with high energy electrons (resembling the radiation from K^{40}) both hydrocyanic acid (HCN) and the bases for nucleic acids were obtained. It may therefore be conjectured that the basic ingredients of the nucleus and the cytoplasm were formed in the abiotic phase and, although almost certainly modified, are common to all living cells. However, as Oparin has emphasized, it is one thing to show how some cell component might have been synthesized, but it is a very different matter to show how it became a component of an organized system. In recent years, the synthesis of DNA in a cell-free system has been achieved, using the four nucleotides, the enzyme polymerase, and a small amount of DNA to 'prime' the reaction (*see* review by Allfrey and Mirskey, 1961). An interesting result was that the proportion of the bases in the product was comparable with the base composition of the primer which had been used.

Most of the molecules in the basic structural features of the cell are chain-molecules, the chain being capable of being stretched out or coiled or folded in a number of ways; also, the units of the chain, and the sequence in which they are disposed, may be altered. These structural features of chain-molecules, whether they consist of glucose residues or aminoacids, allow of great potential diversity in their physical and chemical properties, especially when we consider the

E*

further possible diversification afforded by the attachment of additional side chains. The physico-chemical constitution and activities of chain-molecules, then, constitute a basic part of the living cell.

PROTOTYPIC CELLS

The nature of the chemical events which resulted in the origin of life cannot be known with certainty, though some of the ideas that have been advanced may be close to the truth. What we find in the literature is a varied and abundant fund of reasoned conjecture, usually coloured by the special knowledge, interests and prejudices of the exponents and, of course, affected by the historic period in which the work is being done. Some measure of agreement between the several views may, however, be noted.

That there was an abiotic, or prebiotic, phase of chemical evolution has been cogently argued. During this phase progressively larger organic molecules and molecular aggregates, able to persist and repro-duce themselves, came into being. With the formation of autocatalytic agents, macromolecular aggregates began to acquire properties that were of a biological rather than of a purely chemical nature. When these autocatalytic aggregates became enclosed with semipermeable membranes, prototypic cells may be said to have been evolved. These hypothetical cells, no doubt, bore little resemblance to the complex system that we recognize in the cell of a contemporary living plant, but the basis of the cell type of organization had been established. If some such process of chemical evolution did indeed take place, it is under-standable why certain quite fundamental features of cell structure and reaction are apparently common to all organisms. This is a point on which there appears to be an increasing measure of agreement. Thus Perret (1952) described life as 'a potentially self-perpetuating open system of linked reactions, catalysed stepwise and almost isothermally by complex and specific catalysts which are themselves produced by the system'. This definition could comprise both the general and specific properties of the cells of different species.

ORGANISMS AS PHYSICO-CHEMICAL SYSTEMS

In attempts to trace nascent organisms back to an antecedent chemical phase, it is usually assumed that the proto-organism was a more or less complex 'physico-chemical machine'. This assumption also underlies many of the working hypotheses in contemporary plant physiology, although cautious exponents usually avoid pressing the 'machine' analogy too far. As Oparin (1961, p. 14) pertinently observed, 'the ideas of each age tend to be expressed in terms of its technology'.

Students of evolution also recognize the machine-like attributes of organisms, and have often had occasion to ponder the seeming or actual purposefulness of many developmental features, especially those which exemplify a high degree of adaptation. It is a commonplace of observation that certain characters, which may be morphological, structural or physiological, appear to satisfy, sometimes in a very adequate manner, the special needs imposed on the organism by particular factors in the environment. The Lamarckian concept of the inheritance of acquired characters, in which the new development is seen to be in close accord with the biological need or requirement, belongs to this kind of thinking. But to explain the evolutionary mechanism underlying such developments is not a simple task (*see* Chapter 15). Bray and White (1954) have argued that, when the growth and development of an organism proceed as if to achieve some definite goal – a teleological and vitalistic conception (*see* pp. 9, 10) – the processes involved are, nevertheless, to a large extent predictable, i.e. indicating the working of some kind of law, or laws. They also made the percipient observation that the concept of organization in living organisms – 'the mode of arrangement of the unit processes involved' – affords an alternative to that of vital force (*see also* Thomas, 1961).

Open System Theory. When simple reactions become integrated into a more complex system, new features, seemingly endowed with 'vital' attributes, tend to 'emerge'. These properties are the result of, and pertain naturally to, the new organization. A knowledge of open system theory in physical chemistry enables us to gain at least a partial understanding of some of the 'vital' developments that appeared so enigmatic to earlier biologists. If an open system in a steady state is subjected to a stimulus of some kind, e.g. an increase in one of its components, it can react in such a way that it returns to its previous steady state. If the stimulus is prolonged, perhaps as a result of a permanent change in a metabolic pathway, the open system can react in such a way that another, new steady state results. Now, organisms are largely self-regulatory and tend to remain relatively unchanged in spite of changes in the environment, etc.; i.e. they exhibit the phenomenon of homeostasis. In this respect they behave like open systems. But like an open system which has been subjected to a prolonged stimulus, involving an element of permanent change, organisms tend to react in conformity with Le

Chatelier's principle. This states that a system in a state of equilibrium, or in a steady state, responds to changes in external conditions in such a way as to counteract the effect of such changes. In this there may perhaps be a basis for explaining the development of adaptive features and a possible physico-chemical mechanism for the inheritance of acquired characters (*see* Chapter 15). As Bray and White (1954) have commented: 'The ability of an open system to achieve the same steady state whatever the starting conditions, and to return to a steady state after deviation, can obviously give the appearance of purposefulness, since the activity of the system seems to be directed towards the attainment of a given state in the future.' Open system theory, in which the growing organism is envisaged as an open system tending towards, but never actually achieving, a steady state can be applied with propriety to all the levels of organization – cell, tissue, organ or individual – with which we are here concerned.

THE TREND TOWARDS BIOLOGICAL COMPLEXITY

A major phenomenon in evolution is the trend towards biochemical complexity (Haldane, 1954). This trend has probably had various further effects. One of these was 'the apparently useless development of morphological complexity in many organisms'* (Haldane, 1954, p. 122). If we assume, as many geneticists do, that natural selection is at work at every developmental stage and in every biological situation, it is difficult to see how, during the trend towards biochemical complexity, the concomitant morphological elaborations, or 'byproducts', failed to be eliminated.

Haldane suggested that a history of biochemical evolution might be treated in four parts. As early as 1929 he had outlined the idea, subsequently elaborated by Oparin and others, that primordial organisms obtained their free energy from metastable organic molecules, synthesized by ultraviolet radiation from the sun in the absence of atmospheric oxygen. If this notion is on the right lines, it may be inferred that these most primitive organisms required various preformed substances such as sugars. Their first syntheses would include those of complex catalysts, and as Horowitz (1945) suggested, 'they would develop chains of syntheses in the opposite order to that in which the

---

* This statement, coming from an eminent worker in genetics and other branches of biology, is of special interest in relation to the view widely held by geneticists and evolutionists that *all* features are adaptive.

synthesis occurs', though this principle might not hold after the first stage.

In Haldane's view,

Photosynthesis would be of little advantage to an organism which could not build all, or almost all, the required molecules from phosphoglyceric acid, or whatever may be the primary product of photosynthesis. The second stage of evolution would, perhaps, have been rather rapid and catastrophic, namely, the perfection of photosynthesis, and the adaptation of some types to life in an atmosphere containing oxygen, while others died out.

The third stage, as envisaged by Haldane, was that in which energy, derived from oxidations by molecular oxygen, was utilized. The ability to obtain and utilize energy from food by oxidative processes would confer a great advantage.

The multicellular plants have probably always needed molecular oxygen at some stage in their life cycles, if only the flagellate stage, and there may be no more perfect mechanisms for its use in the root of an oak tree than in the zoospore of an alga, but the oxidative mechanisms have probably evolved to some extent in the last few hundred million years.

Haldane's fourth stage was one of adaptive radiation, 'accompanied by some loss of function in all organisms but the photosynthesizing plants, but also by considerable increases in synthetic capacities in all or almost all groups'. Whether new mutations will give rise to new and useful (i.e. upgrade and constructive in the evolutionary sense) 'adventures in metabolism' remains to be seen and will be a matter of acute interest.

Haldane has also made the important suggestion that

progressive biochemical evolution has *not been by making enzymes or genes of a radically new character*, but by broadening and narrowing their ranges of specificity, so that *one enzyme in an ancestral form would be represented by a battery of enzymes in a descendant*, which could be regarded as descendants of the original enzyme. (My italics: C. W. W.)

DESCENT FROM A MOLECULE!

If concepts of the origin and evolution of primitive living systems appear to be remote from what we know of cells in living plants and animals, they are very remote indeed from the ideas and information that have been accumulating in recent years round the branch of science now known as molecular biology, or molecular genetics (*see also* Chapter 4). However, some of the findings of molecular genetics are also being applied to the problem of the origin of life. Thus Darlington (1957), admittedly in a journalistic context, stated that each gene has a precise chemical structure; and he has enquired: 'How can a structure, made of DNA and protein, account not only for the whole character of one living organism but also for all the differences of character of all living organisms?' In the writer's view, the answer appears to be quite simple: it can not. For however specific and effective genes may be in their organizing activities, they must have something upon which to exercise their effects. That 'something' is not simply a mass of heterogeneous material; it is the cytoplasm, an organized matrix, or system, of at least the antiquity, ubiquity, stability and permanence of the genes. Darlington (1957) pointed out that when chromosomes are broken, as by the application of maleic hydrazide, new arrangements become possible. The essential change is considered to consist of a rearrangement of the nucleotides. 'These are the simplest form of change in heredity: and they are universal.' Darlington has envisaged evolution as being essentially descent from chromosomal DNA, i.e. 'descent from a molecule'. Some measure of over-simplification may perhaps be detected in this statement. But the idea may afford a basis for interpreting some of the prevailing homologies of organization in plants.

CELL ORGANIZATION, GENES AND DEVELOPMENT

With the information of this chapter before us, we may briefly return to the topic of the action of genes in development (*see also* Chapter 4, p. 84). In the contemporary neo-Mendelian, genetical view, gene-controlled chemical activities underlie or determine all the visible morphological and functional characteristics of a species. Since genes are complex molecules, they admit of wide variations and fluctuations in their structural configuration and thus afford the possibility of substances of different specific catalytic properties being formed. So the view emerges that the genes collectively, through the specificity of the enzymes which they control, eventually determine the pattern of reactions in cells. In this way, genes are considered to be the ultimate determiners of all the characters, shape, size, colour, etc., by which a species is recognized. When a gene is modified, so also is its enzymic activity within the cells, with consequential further changes, some of which may reach the visual level.

While the foregoing argument may be provisionally accepted – it has been very fully and forcibly urged by geneticists and, in part at least, validated by experiments – a major problem still remains, namely: how much of the overall, basic activity of a cell is due to specific genic action and how much to those more general physico-chemical properties which were established in it during an earlier phase of less specialized cell organization? Or, to put the question in another way, we may ask: has it been demonstrated that major cell activities, such as photosynthesis, respiration, the inception of the cytoskeleton and organelles, and the co-ordination of cellular activity, are primarily due, directly or indirectly, to the action of genes? Or were the structural bases for these several activities established in an earlier, pre-genic phase of cellular evolution? Or did they evolve side by side with the genetical system? It is generally agreed that cytoplasmic reactions are modulated by genic action.* We also know that numerous families of gene-protein-enzymes are available for the manifold activities of organisms during every phase and aspect of their development, and that mutant genes affect both physiological processes and morphological developments. But do we know that genes determine the basic processes or structures in plants and that they are therefore to be regarded as the sole hereditary agents? This, as it seems to the writer, is still not proven. In a recent discussion of molecular biology, or the 'new genetics', Sonneborn (1963) has arrived at a similar conclusion.

All the foregoing may be summarized by saying that there are cell structures, or components, other than chromosomes and genes, which are also transmitted at reproduction, and which are not known to be specifically gene-determined but which are also pervasive in development. Hence the conclusion that *all* the features that are part of the permanent organization of a cell must be given due consideration in the investigation of organizational phenomena.

The point of view indicated above may be briefly illustrated by some simple examples. When a unicellular green alga divides, giving rise to two daughter unicells, each not only receives the full complement of genes but also the basic features of protoplasmic organization. Genes do not have to induce these protoplasmic features: they are already there having been transmitted at reproduction. But a mutant gene might modify a cytoplasmic feature in some way. Similarly, in the reproduction of a vascular plant, however much the male gamete may be diminished, so that it is little more than the chromosomes of a haploid

---

* There is evidence (Waddington, 1962, p. 138) that various cell organelles are under the control of nuclear genes. Genes may affect some cytoplasmic components without necessarily affecting all of them simultaneously. Waddington has cited the case of the gene for *white eye* in the retinula cell of *Drosophila* which removes the pigment from rhabdomeres but apparently leaves the organelles themselves unaltered.

nucleus, the ovum is not simply a nucleus: it is a cell, with all the organizational features of the species. Accordingly, the zygote proceeds on its ontogenetic trend, not only with its complement of genes, but also with all the other, non-genic, but nevertheless hereditary, properties and organizational features of the cytoplasm. There is thus the outstandingly difficult problem of distinguishing between those general effects which are due to the basic metabolism of living matter and those other more specific effects which are now associated with DNA-protein specificity.

GENERAL CONCLUSIONS

The basic components of cells, both nuclear and cytoplasmic, have remarkable stability and the ability to persist relatively unchanged over vast periods of time. In contemporary biology, deoxyribonucleic acid (DNA) and the processes in which it is involved occupy the centre of the picture. It is, of course, understandable that investigators are liable to over-emphasize new discoveries and not infrequently to abstract the phenomenon with which they are preoccupied from its biological context. But a critical view requires that all aspects, and especially those that are interrelated, be given due attention. Accordingly, while we recognize the fundamental importance of DNA as the focal point in contemporary molecular genetics, we should equally recognize that it can only exist and function in the system afforded by the intact and fully integrated cytoplasm (Gale, 1957). We may further recognize that the cytoplasm, or, more generally, the cellular organization, is not less stable than DNA, though it is probably of much greater evolutionary antiquity. It follows that the constitution of the cytoplasm, which enables the various gene-determined proteins to be formed in an orderly manner and co-ordinated sequence in relation to functional needs, is in no sense less important than the nucleus. Indeed, there may be developmental situations in which it is considerably more important (though, in fact, we know that nucleus and cytoplasm function in a reciprocal relationship). A considerable body of evidence, based on studies of embryogenesis and morphogenesis, indicates that it is to the general organizational properties of cells that some of the major developmental features in plants are due. Some such conception would contribute towards an explanation of the numerous instances of homology of organization. As we have seen, much of the evidence and conjecture regarding the origin and evolution of life tends to support this point of view.

The fact that many important cell substances, including DNA are generally, and often closely, comparable in animals, plants, micro-organisms and viruses suggests that these substances, or their pre-cursors, were formed and established as essential cell components at a very early stage in the evolution of organisms. It is thus possible that a general chemical homology underlies the cellular organization in all green plants.

Oparin (1961) has emphasized that the various nucleic acids, en-zymes, etc., are only important when their functional activities are harmonized with the vital activities of the organism as a whole. Indeed, relationships of this kind must have governed their evolution: ' . . . it would be wrong to suppose that, in the organically rich waters of the primaeval ocean, there arose proteins and nucleic acids with a "pur-posive" structure extremely accurately and well adapted to the carrying out of particular biological functions and that, later, by their combina-tion, the living body itself was created' (Oparin, 1961, p. 31). The proteins and nucleic acids, as we know them in living cells, could only have evolved in conjunction with the elaboration of an organized matrix suitable for their formation, i.e. the biosynthesis of a protein 'requires the co-ordinated participation of a series of protoplasmic systems'. There is thus no question of the origin of life being ascribed to the very occasional chance formation and conservation of an elaborate mole-cule such as a virus or a nucleoprotein, since such substances can only exist and be replicated in an organized living cell. Similarly, Oparin regards the discussion of topics such as the assumed evolution of nucleic acid before protein, or *vice-versa*, as being unlikely to be fruitful: both must have first existed as very simple precursor compounds and have subsequently evolved during the progressive organization of the cell.

Oparin has made the further point that during the evolution of co-ordinated metabolism, new and more effective components would be introduced into the system, eventually yielding those particular phenomena which we associate with living organisms. But, says Oparin, 'the new sets of biochemical reactions which were always arising did not, by any means, always completely replace the older metabolic processes but usually made use of them, simply supplementing them with newly developed reactions' (p. 99). If this conjecture is valid, it is of considerable importance. For it could be inferred that even although quite different genetical systems may have evolved in the several major phyletic lines, their cells would still retain many basic organizational features and reactions in common. It is a fact that many genetical investigations have been concerned with relatively minor modifications of well established structures rather than with more profound changes.

Some relatively simple and poorly developed sets of metabolic reactions are actually the same in all contemporary living things. However, the more complicated combinations of these sets of reactions may vary, differing in some degree from one of the main biological groups to another but always keeping the same universal foundations (Oparin, 1961, p. 99).

With regard to the evolutionary history and status of DNA, Oparin's view is that the organization of 'living bodies' was already well advanced before the need for a more precise and consistent mechanism for self-reproduction, i.e. 'which would guarantee the essential conservation of the living system', was experienced. DNA, 'with its great metabolic inertia' afforded such a mechanism. In other words, DNA only became necessary when cell organization had already reached a high level. If this is a valid conclusion, it affords further support for the idea of the probable commonality of basic cell characters.

Summary. In attempting to ascertain what constitutes organization in plants, and to understand why parallelisms of development are so general in different and seemingly unrelated phyletic lines, we have to evaluate the relative importance in morphogenesis of what for convenience may be regarded as two different components of living cells. On the one hand, we have to bear in mind that the cells of all green plants have many of their basic structural and functional properties in common, these having been established before the branching-off of the great phyletic lines had begun. There is no reason to assume that these properties or activities are not still important in the process of development. On the other hand, we have to assign due functional value to the numerous, varied and potent enzymes, many of them demonstrably gene-determined, which have been evolved during the course of descent. In fact, the two components under consideration are inseparable. They both contribute to the organization and functional harmony within cells that have been established during the very long evolutionary process. The solution to our problem, then, lies in a judicious evaluation and synthesis of the effects produced by the two major components; for it would be just as injudicious to assert that 'basic structure' is the master factor in organization as to claim that 'genes do everything'. Rather let us say that both participate and contribute.

CHAPTER 7

Non-genetical Factors in Organization

INTRODUCTION

In discussing the contribution which non-genetical factors make to organization, some qualifying observations should be made at the outset. Some factors which are strictly non-genetical and which may contribute significantly to organization can be indicated. These include such factors as gravity, temperature, light, the supply of mineral nutrients and water supply. They are all extrinsic to the organism, it is true; but their ultimate differentiating, morphogenetic, and organizing activities are always mediated through the living protoplasm. Then there are various other phenomena such as surface tension, the order inherent in the association of certain large molecules, changes associated with increasing size, the differential development of cells in relation to their position in the plant, etc., which have impressed some biologists as being more physical and mathematical than they are genetical. Nevertheless, in each instance, there is a genetical basis or interrelationship. Surface tension, for example, is a purely physical phenomenon. But, in organisms, the materials in which the relevant forces are generated, and on which they act, have been synthesized by the specific living substance. Thus, in action, genetical and non-genetical factors work together. However, it should not be inferred that the phenomena should not be analysed further. Non-genetical factors, just like genetical ones, can never be solely and directly responsible for morphogenetic or organizational developments; but they may be important proximate causes of the assumption of form, the inception of histological pattern, and the overall organization of the individual plant. The aim in this chapter is to consider what emphasis should be placed on such factors, especially as they may relate to homologies of organization.

As biologists have long appreciated, the hereditary constitution of a species determines its potentialities for development and the nature of the materials on which various physical forces may act; but a number of extrinsic factors, and various forces determined by organismal relationships which come into being during ontogenesis, are directly involved in the actual organizing process. Many of these extrinsic, or 'non-genetical', factors are common to plants at large.

A GENERAL ANALYSIS OF PATTERN IN PLANTS

Although plant species are exceedingly diverse and varied in their size, form and structure, a closer analysis shows that the number of basic kinds of pattern, or types of configuration, is, after all, relatively small. There are, as it were, many variations on a few main themes: underlying the diversity there is much essential similarity. Thus, viewed as three-dimensional dynamic geometrical systems, the configurations of nearly all plants can be considered in terms of the following categories:

Axial construction, which normally follows the early establishment of polarity, is common in all classes, from filamentous algae to massive flowering plants, the evident exceptions being certain unicellular, thalloid and colonial organisms.

Concentric construction is a normal concomitant of the ontogenetic increase in size and is exemplified by the dermal layer, cortex and stele in shoots and roots, by secondary thickening in shoots, by the wall and archesporium in bryophyte capsules, by the tissue systems in the larger red and brown algae, and so on.

Radiate construction is typically seen in the tissue pattern in root steles, in the shoot stele in *Lycopodium*, in the arrangement of medullary rays and vascular strands in dicotyledons, etc. The branch filaments in *Chara* and other algae, and lateral members (leaves, buds, etc.) in vascular plants also belong to this category.

Mosaic construction is suggested as a term to denote such patterns as the distribution of stomata on the surfaces of leaves, the arrangement of tracheids and parenchyma in certain steles, etc. Within this category, the term *specific locations* may prove convenient to indicate such specifically localized features as the conceptacles in brown algae, the sori of ferns, etc., in which a patternized distribution can be discerned.

Symmetry, which may be radial, bilateral, dorsiventral or irregular, is usually such as to make for balance or equilibrium in the organismal pattern as a whole.

The separation of the several aspects of pattern is, of course, artificial. During the growth and differentiation of a root, for example, axial, concentric and radiate developments are proceeding more or less simultaneously. The essential point of the foregoing is quite simply, as D'Arcy Thompson pointed out, that the assumption of form by organisms during their growth and development must take place in obedience to the laws of physics and mathematics. And this will be true whatever the constitution of the specific hereditary substance may be deemed to be, and however much the processes of growth and development are considered to be specifically gene controlled.

THE INCEPTION OF PATTERN

Some assumptions relating to organization have already been considered. The zygote, spore, generative cell, or meristem – the embryonic unit – may be envisaged as a complex reaction system which obeys the laws of physical chemistry, various physical properties and physiological relationships of the growing, gene-determined system being important in the elaboration of form and structure and the functional activities associated with them. It is accepted that a patternized distribution of metabolites, which is characteristic of each 'stage' of the essentially continuous ontogenetic process, precedes and determines the visible histological, structural and morphological developments. But by what forces these patterns are brought about is one of the most enigmatic problems in biology. However it may be envisaged or understood, the reaction system of an embryo or shoot apex is not constant and uniform in its components and activity. Under the impact of genetical and environmental factors, and of organismal relationships already established, e.g. polarity, the inception of gradients, correlative developments, etc., the reaction system becomes modified in characteristic ways as development proceeds; and so, too, does the pattern to which it gives rise. Changing nutritional relationships during ontogenesis, e.g. variations in the quantity and quality of the metabolic materials supplied to the apical reaction system, may have profound morphogenetic effects, such as those seen in the heteroblastic development of leaves, the changing vascular differentiation in many species, and so on (*see* Chapter 10).

The problem of discovering how the characteristic patterns of organs and tissues are brought about has both a general and a specific aspect: for although there is great variety in the details, many of which are now known to be due to specific gene action, the number of fundamental developmental patterns in plants is quite small (*see* preceding section).

THE ACTION OF PHYSICAL FACTORS

Plants and animals (said D'Arcy Thompson, 1917, 1942), are essentially physical systems and, like all such systems, they constantly tend towards

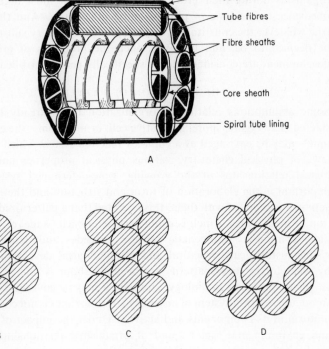

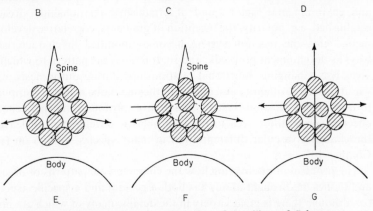

Fig.7.1 A, Diagrammatic reconstruction of the cilium of *Sphagnum*: the cilium consists of nine tube fibres surrounding two central ones, each fibre being divided.

B, C and D illustrate the possible geometrical arrangements that can be obtained by combining various numbers of strands of uniform diameter. In B, one central strand can accommodate six peripheral

(*Continued at foot of facing page*)

a state of equilibrium – actually a dynamic equilibrium or steady state. By reference to a wide range of biological materials, he showed that physical factors of various kinds are probably involved in the inception of form and structure and contribute to the harmonious development of the organism. Thus the shapes of individual cells and the position of the partition walls in multicellular organisms may be referable to the balance of internal and surface forces in the growing cell, though, in fact, this has not been conclusively demonstrated. Within wide limits, explanations of this kind, based on physical chemistry, could apply to quite differently constituted cells or systems. For example, closely comparable patterns of growth and segmentation are found in the early embryogeny of virtually all classes of plants (Wardlaw, 1955; *and see* Chapter 3). Thus while, in each species, genetical factors determine the specific cytoplasmic substance on which extrinsic factors must act – these substances presumably differing to a greater or less extent in the several major systematic groups – the visible homologies of organization seem to be due directly to the physical forces generated; i.e. in the major organizational phenomena, energy relations appear to be of greater importance than the specific cell components.

The mechanical elements in plants (collenchyma, fibres, etc.) are typically differentiated in patterns which are closely related to functional requirements. Now, it is a fact that, in organisms of quite different taxonomic affinity, closely comparable distributions of mechanical tissue are found. This is perhaps to be expected, for, as D'Arcy Thompson has shown, mechanical tissues are characteristically induced along the lines of force; and these will be comparable in equivalent organs,

---

contact strands; in C, two central strands can accommodate eight peripheral contact strands; but in D, with nine peripheral strands, contact with the central strands is lost. The arrangement of strands or fibrils shown in D has been observed in ferns, mosses, green algae, yellow-green algae, brown algae and in various fungi. (After I. Manton and B. Clarke, *Jour. Exper. Bot.* 1952). E,F,G, Some possible arrangements of the eleven strands of a plant cilium in relation to external appendages; the pairs of lateral lines in each case indicate alternative positions for the lateral rows of hairs, the positions most probable at the date of publication distinguished by arrow heads.

E, Reconstruction of *Dictyota* from morphological evidence only.

F, A more correct version of (E) allowing for two alternative positions of the central strands.

G, Arrangement of the front flagellum of *Fucus* as seen in section; the long arrow marks the plane of bilateral symmetry. (After I. Manton, in *Cellular Mechanisms in Differentiation and Growth*, 1956.)

irrespective of the taxonomic affinity, provided, of course, the species is so constituted as to be able to respond. Furthermore, it has been shown experimentally that mechanical stresses have a direct effect on the quantitative development and distribution of mechanical tissues; e.g. tree trunks subjected to a prevailing wind have the greatest formation of fibre in regions of greatest stress (Haberlandt, 1914).

D'Arcy Thompson has given a reasoned account of the action of physical factors in the causation of form and structure and new examples daily come to light. Manton (1961) has shown by means of electron microscopy that the flagella in organisms of quite different systematic affinity are closely comparable in the minutiae of their construction. In the contemporary genetical view, the substance of the flagellum, in each of the organisms showing this remarkable homology of organization, is determined by genes specific to the organism. Nevertheless, a closely comparable structure is present in all. It would appear that the forces at work in the system, which determine the disposition of the terminal metabolic products, are of greater importance in the organization of the flagellum than the specificity of the gene-determined substances which are utilized. The same general argument may also apply to many other morphological and structural features (Fig.7.1).

Environmental factors, such as temperature, light, humidity, mineral nutrients, gravity, etc., i.e. physical and chemical factors, may have more or less conspicuous effects on the form and structure of organisms. These factors act on the cytoplasm in conjunction with genetical factors. Many of the effects which they induce are more or less closely comparable in unrelated as well as in related organisms: witness the close similarities in the conformation and structure of hydrophytes, of xerophytes, of shade plants, etc., of quite different systematic affinities.

SELF-ORGANIZATION

The structure and physical properties of rod-like or long-chain organic molecules are such that they tend to become combined or associated in some characteristic order. Many differently constituted long-chain molecules behave, in some respects, in a closely comparable manner. Such phenomena are 'non-genetical' in the sense of this chapter.

Weiss (*see* Waddington, 1959, p. 5) has referred to organization in the cell as 'ordered heterogeneity' and has pointed out that organizational phenomena may be due both to the orderly aggregation of units and to the sequence in which formative processes take place. In such instances, organization emerges 'by virtue of the properties which reside in the basic elements of the system' (*ibid.*, p. 9). Although subject to variation, usually in minor details, these basic elements seem to be common to all cells and are, presumably, of great evolutionary antiquity. Many mutant genes and gene combinations are known which modify the photosynthetic mechanism in various ways, but the basic and essential features of that mechanism have, as far as we know, persisted over vast periods of time. Similar observations could be made regarding other basic cell processes.

Since the days of Vöchting and Driesch, botanists and zoologists have recognized that the way in which a cell becomes differentiated is related to the position which it occupies in a developing organism or tissue system. Thus cells on the outside become different in form and function from those inside. Organisms of very varied taxonomic affinity afford evidence of this self-organizing process. It is seen in the differential development of epidermis and cortical parenchyma in any vascular plant; in the dermal and inner tissues of the larger brown algae, etc. Also, where differences between outer and inner tissues have appeared, a third type of cell or tissue is often formed, presumably as a result of interaction between the two regions. In vascular plants, for example, the shoot apical region shows an early histological differentiation of incipient cortical parenchyma and incipient vascular tissue; and, on further development, distinctive tissues such as endodermis and pericycle are typically formed at the junction of the two major tissue systems. These developmental patterns are common to all vascular plants. They also occur in mosses and may even be found in some of the larger brown algae. In different species, however, the details of development, e.g. the relative radius of stele and cortex, and the histological constitution of the different regions, may be very different, reflecting differences in the genetical constitutions. Part of our task, then, is to assess the extent to which self-ordering basic patterns are modified by the impact of genetical factors.

To summarize: different aspects of organization may be related (i) to the innate physical properties of structures or substances of general occurrence in organisms, (ii) to the spatial relationships of parts or tissues during development, (iii) to the impact of external factors, and (iv) to more or less specific genic factors.

THE INCEPTION OF PRIMARY PATTERN

Zoologists have recently discussed this topic in some detail in a symposium on *Biological Organization* (edited by C. H. Waddington, 1959;

and see also Waddington, 1962). It was noted (i) that at present there are no methods, e.g. histochemical techniques, for detecting the first evidences of pattern (p. 251); (ii) that we do not know what kind of chemical differences, e.g. in protein or other metabolism, we should be trying to detect; and (iii) that we do not know what kind of interactions may give rise to the initial pattern (p. 252). Pollock suggested that the differences involved in embryonic induction may be largely quantitative, that 'there is a sort of spontaneous element leading to differentiation which is either complemented or hastened under certain particular conditions' (p. 252). Thus, in various biochemical processes, including enzyme induction, changes which are mainly quantitative in the first instance may nevertheless lead to very marked end differences in the chain of reactions. This may be particularly so when, for example, a mutant gene, by blocking some stage in a chain of reactions, results in an alternative metabolic pathway being followed. Micro-organisms, such as *Neurospora*, afford examples of this eventuality.

According to Goldschmidt (1927, 1938), development is essentially a process involving chemical actions of a catalytic nature. These are initiated by the genes and result in a differentiation within the cytoplasm of the ovum or zygote and subsequently of the cell regions of the embryo. Goldschmidt envisaged the differentiated regions of protoplasm as becoming localized to form a definite pattern as a result of the trend towards physico-chemical equilibria; this involving the harmonizing of the velocities of the many reactions that are proceeding simultaneously. In brief, he held that the inception of pattern in animal embryos is a result of 'chemo-differentiation', involving reaction rates, equilibria, etc., as in physico-chemical systems. Turing's (1952) theory also rests on a recognition of the self-ordering principles inherent in organismal reaction systems (*see* p. 156).

GENERAL CELL PHYSIOLOGY

As we have seen, certain basic structural features and functional activities of the cells of green plants appear to be of very long standing. They are certainly of very general occurrence. We do not know that these common cell properties originated in direct relation to the evolution of genes. What we do know is that they are heritable. Many biochemical activities in cells are associated with particles, with small organized cell bodies, and with membranes, all of these being of protein-aceous composition. The point to be made here – and it is one that appears to be tacitly recognized by plant physiologists – is that while some metabolic activities are of a quite specific nature, suggesting close specific genic control, others are of such general occurrence as to be accepted as *basic cell features*; or as Thomas *et al.* (1956, p. 11) have said: 'All living forms possess a certain community of structure as well as of faculty, but each form is in some respect *sui generis* in point of structure, and, consequently, of functional power.'

Physiologists have long recognized that no matter how homogeneous protoplasm may appear under low magnifications, it is nevertheless a very complex and heterogeneous system, comprising many components and phases. Some, perhaps many, aspects of order in cells are directly attributable to the innate, i.e. physico-chemical, properties of the metabolic substances in the cell. The components of the living cell are often present in the colloidal state and, in the words of Thomas *et al.* (1956, p. 16), 'Mechanical and electrical absorption and the forces determining the orientation of molecules at phase boundaries, may cause order to develop in what might otherwise be a chaotic mixture of solutes'. Frey-Wyssling (1953) envisaged the protoplasm as a colloidal system with a solid, or coherent, micellar membranous framework of elongated protein molecules, with interspaces containing aqueous solutions of various substances. Such a framework, or cytoskeleton, and the many important functional activities based on it, depend primarily on the inherent properties of long-chain organic molecules. 'In a single cell there are many millions of molecules of organic and inorganic solutes in solution, and their fate will be largely determined by the physical and chemical forces resident in these extensive and highly differential internal surfaces' (Thomas *et al.*, 1956, p. 16). This is as much as to say that important and fundamental aspects of order are unavoidable concomitants of the presence in the cell of substances common to green plants.

Most of the metabolic activities of cells are accelerated by the presence of common or of more specific enzymes. It is worth recalling that many of these processes can take place spontaneously in the absence of enzymes but, of course, they do so much more slowly; i.e. an enzyme, be it specific or less specific, promotes an activity that is already actually or potentially there. Since enzymes are readily inactivated by unfavourable conditions, the possible effects on them of environmental as well as of genic factors must be considered.

In contemporary genetics, the specific activities of particular genes are investigated and duly emphasized. In its most extreme expression, the concept of genic action takes the form of 'one gene, one enzyme';

and the validity of this view has been demonstrated in some instances. However, the biological situation is by no means simple and direct and physiologists now recognize (i) that there is no universal enzyme that can catalyse all metabolic reactions; (ii) that there is not necessarily a specific gene-enzyme-protein for every stage in a complex metabolic process; (iii) that some enzymes can catalyse many processes; and (iv) that some enzymes are very highly specific for the substrate with which they can react. Item (ii) above is of special interest here in that some metabolic processes, once started, may continue because of the innate properties of the reactions involved, i.e. a process once activated will follow a particular trend because of inherent physico-chemical forces or relationships. Item (iii) may be important in our search for factors common to the cells of many species. Thus, as Thomas *et al.* (1956, p. 33) have noted, a single protease may hydrolyse peptide linkages in a great many animal and plant proteins; all starches can be hydrolysed by amylases and phosphorylases; and all fats can be split by esterases.

As to the orderly metabolism of cells, physiologists maintain that the numerous enzymes cannot simply be distributed through the protoplasm at random. A developing cell behaves in an orderly manner according to its position in the plant, its age, distance from the apex, and so on. The potentiality of such a cell for this or that characteristic differentiation must, fundamentally, be determined by its hereditary properties. The views of Thomas *et al.* (1956, p. 35) on cellular organization include the following points that are relevant to the present discussion. (i) The metabolizing protoplasm may be regarded as an organized system, based on colloids, in which enzymic activities are linked; and linked processes must be based on the chemical feasibility of the linkage. (ii) The hereditary constitution of the cell will direct metabolism along particular lines, this process being mediated through specific enzymes and the way in which they are linked. (Hence the value of detailed study of particular reactions.) (iii) Individual reactions typically constitute parts of aggregate or block reactions, some of which can be studied as an entity, e.g. alcoholic fermentation. 'The fact that there are block processes which can be abstracted from total metabolism for special study is in itself evidence of the organization of biochemical events in visible or invisible fragments of the whole metabolizing protoplasm' (Thomas *et al.*, 1956, p. 35).

Thomas *et al.* have further argued that ATP (adenosine triphosphate) is one of the key substances in bringing about the integration of enzymic partial reactions and therefore in imparting order to the metabolism of the cell as a whole. In this connection they have emphasized the importance of the physical structure of protoplasm in regulating the movement of substrate molecules and therefore the order and rate of enzymic changes. They have also noted that comparisons of normal metabolism with that in injured cells, showing autolytic metabolism, 'compels belief *in the controlling influence that the physical organization of protoplasm exerts on the total chemical behaviour of living cells*' (Thomas *et al.*, 1956, p. 37; *my italics*, C. W. W.).

SINNOTT'S TREATMENT OF NON-GENETICAL FACTORS

In his discussion of factors in morphogenesis, Sinnott (1960) pointed out that the study of the effects of changes in the outer and inner environment of the plant on its morphogenetic development is essentially part of plant physiology. He distinguished two main kinds of factors, namely, environmental and genetic, but, like others, he recognized the difficulties of separating their effects. In a sense, every phenotypic trait is inherited since it is typically produced by a specific genotype in a particular environment; but the developmental response of a plant may vary widely under the impact of different environmental factors such as light, temperature, gravity, water supply, concentration of nutrients, mechanical stresses, etc. For convenience, and realizing that they can only be separated on an arbitrary basis, Sinnott has recognized that different aspects of morphogenetic development can be ascribed to physical factors, including those indicated above; to chemical factors, including soil nutrients and substances synthesized in the plant, especially growth-regulating substances; and to genetical factors, these including the genes, the chromosomes which may have effects apart from the genes, and cytoplasmic factors. (For a survey of the morphogenetic effects of the several physical and chemical factors, the reader is referred to Sinnott, 1960.)

ORGANISMAL RELATIONSHIPS

During ontogenesis in *all* vascular plants certain characteristic relationships become established between the different parts, members or regions. The result in each instance is the development of an organism of characteristic size and form. The several aspects of this regulated and integrated development, or developmental relatedness, are often described as correlations. These have been variously classified, e.g. environmental, physical, morphological, physiological, genetic, compensatory, and meristic (Sinnott, 1960). Sinnott grouped them together as *physiological correlations*, i.e. where some physiological mechanism, e.g. metabolic, hormonal, etc., can be specified; and as *genetic correlations*, where factors in the genetic constitution seem to be more directly and specifically involved. Here the writer proposes to use

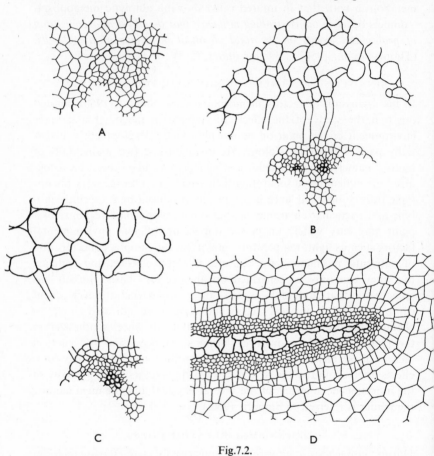

Fig.7.2.

the term *organismal relationships** to indicate certain developmental phenomena which are of very general occurrence but which are apparently not closely and specifically genetical. Among such general organizational phenomena are polarity, the early organization of an apical growing point, often but not invariably showing sustained apical dominance, the concomitant establishment of acropetal and basipetal gradients, the inception of regularly-spaced growth centres and primordia in the apical meristem, correlation and mutual regulation of parts, heteroblastic development, size and form correlations, unity

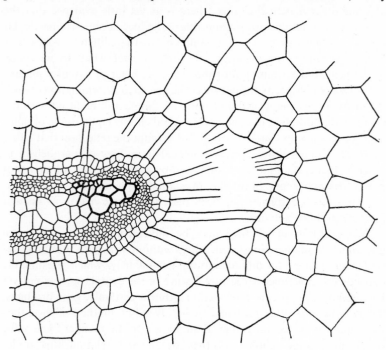

Fig.7.2 E

Fig.7.2 A, B, C, *Selaginella selaginoides (spinosa)*: (× 140). D, E, *S. Wallichii* (× 100). Cross-sections of the stem from the apex downwards, showing how localized differential growth can affect the histological pattern. As development proceeds in the subapical region of the shoot, cells of the inner cortex grow more rapidly than do those of the stele: hence the stele becomes suspended in a cavity (or lacuna) by drawn-out cells, or trabeculae; the latter, in fact, being modified endodermal cells. In sections A and D, which were taken close to the apex, the cells of the inner cortex, endodermis and pericycle are still of approximately the same size. (*Trans. Roy. Soc. Edin.*)

in the overall development, etc. Some of these developmental relationships are also found in algae and bryophytes (*see* Figs. 7.3–7.7).

These several relationships* – and others could be added – contribute

---

* Relationships: as Beckner (1959) has pointed out, *relationships* are not agents: they do not *do* anything. But, as used here, the term serves as a convenient shorthand expression of the result of the action of specified and unspecified factors.

to major aspects of organization in the individual plant. And while some of them may be modified by the action of mutant genes, or as a result of some other genetical change, there is as yet little evidence that the fundamental relationship is mainly due to the specific action of particular genes or groups of genes. It is well known that different genes may determine tallness or dwarfness in a shoot; but what do we know of the genetic determination of the axial character of vascular plants? Even if we could specify the nature of the genetical determination of such major organs as shoot, leaf and root, we should still be faced with the problem that different gene complexes yield closely comparable organogenic developments. Such observations prompt the reflection that either (i) there is much more *general* genetical homology or parallelism in vascular plants than has been supposed by geneticists and adherents of polyphyletic concepts; or (ii) that, in relation to phenomena of organization, too much emphasis has been placed on genic action as distinct from general cell activity.

The inception of polarity may be indicated as a developmental phenomenon of the widest generality, without which, as Bünning has said, there can be no differentiation. Yet polarity, which presumably depends on some microstructural feature of the cytoplasm, has not yet been referred to specific genic action. Almost certainly, gene products, e.g. enzymes and other proteins, are involved but, on the evidence, they participate in a general rather than in a specific manner. The same conclusion would apply to other organismal relationships under consideration.

For reasons that are still but little understood, contiguous tissues may sometimes grow at very different rates. As an inevitable consequence, tensions are set up between the more rapidly and the more slowly growing cell layers. A particular example of this is seen in the genus *Selaginella*, where the inner cells of the cortex expand to large size whereas those of the pericycle and peripheral region of the stele remain small. As a result a considerable cavity or lacuna develops round the stele and the endodermal cells not only become separated tangentially but become extended radially as trabeculae (Fig.7.2).

Experimental Investigations. Organismal relationships lend themselves to experimental investigation (*see also* Chapter 14). Although the shoot apices of pteridophytes, gymnosperms and angiosperms differ genetically and histologically, they all have major organizational features and morphogenetic activities in common. For example, they all give rise to regularly-spaced growth centres which usually develop into leaves. If

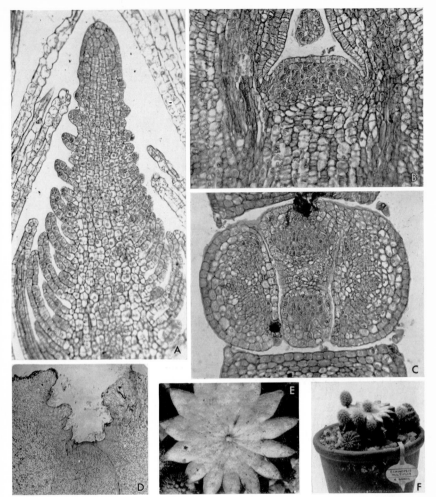

9. Various apices in longitudinal median section, showing differences in histological organization, and the effects of differences in the distribution of growth. A, *Elodea canadensis* (× 112). B, C. *Loranthus globulifera* in l.s. and t.s., showing the large size of leaf primordia relative to the apical meristem (× 112). D, E, F, *Echinopsis multiplex*. D, the deeply sunken shoot apex as seen in longitudinal section (× 7·5). E, F, when the apex was laid bare and isolated by vertical incision, a new plant duly developed. E (× ½) shows an early and F a later stage (reduced in size). (Figs. B, C by courtesy of Dr. E. G. Cutter.)

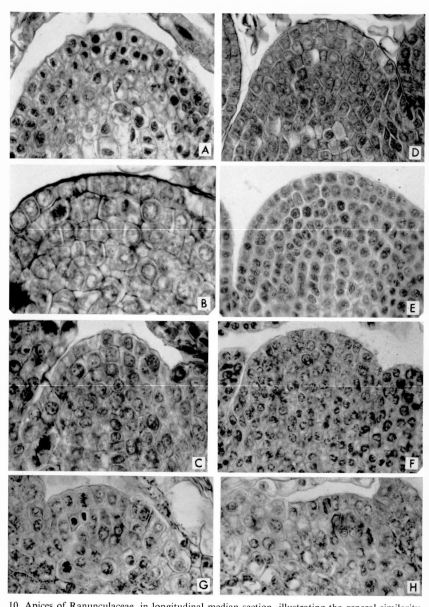

10. Apices of Ranunculaceae, in longitudinal median section, illustrating the general similarity in histological organization in related genera and species.

A, *Caltha palustris*. B, *Trollius europaeus*. C, *Anemone nemorosa*. D, *Ranunculus acris*. E, *Ranunculus repens*. F, *Ranunculus ficaria*. G, H, *Ranunculus ficaria*, two apices both showing active cell division at or near the centre of the apical meristem. Similar evidence was encountered in other species of Ranunculaceae during this investigation (unpublished). (All × 280, except B × 560.)

the same surgical treatments are applied to the apices of ferns and flowering plants, comparable organographic developments may ensue. When the shoot apices of a eusporangiate fern, *Angiopteris evecta*, a leptosporangiate fern, *Dryopteris dilatata* (*D. aristata*),* and a flowering plant, *Primula* sp., were isolated from the adjacent organs and tissues by vertical incisions, with concomitant severing of the incipient vascular

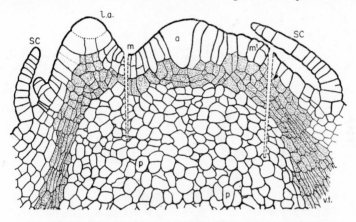

Fig.7.3 *Dryopteris dilatata.* An experimental treatment of the shoot apical meristem, here seen in median longitudinal section (traced from a photomicrograph). The apical meristem (*m-m'*) has been isolated from the adjacent lateral organs and tissues by four vertical incisions (vertical broken lines), so that the meristem is seated on a plug of developing pith parenchyma (*p*). The incipient vascular tissue (*vt*) is severed by the operation. *a*, apical cell; *la*, apical cell of a leaf primordium; *sc*, scales, which typically develop at the junction of the apical and subapical regions (× 130). (*Phil. Trans. Roy. Soc.*)

tissues (or prestelar tissue, or early procambium), the apex continued to grow and gave rise to a short, vascularized leafy shoot in which the normal anatomical pattern was soon reconstituted (Wardlaw, 1952). In the experimental region, the cross-sectional outline of the vascular tissue was in conformity with the outline of the plug of tissue on which the apex had been isolated; i.e. a triangular or a rectangular stele could be induced at will. Moreover, in *Primula* as in *Dryopteris*, the leaves formed on the new axis were in approximately normal phyllotactic sequence with those already present at the beginning of the experiment; and in both species the inception of the new vascular tissue was due to the activity of the terminal meristem. Comparable results have been

* *D. dilatata* = *D. austriaca*; *D. aristata*

F

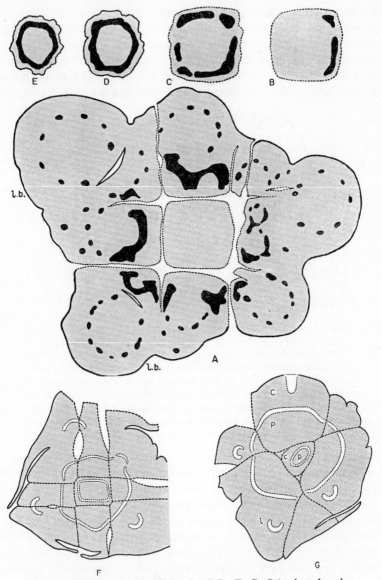

Fig.7.4 A–E, *Dryopteris dilatata* (× 7·5); F, G, *Primula polyantha* (× 14). In both species – a fern and a flowering plant – generally comparable developments were observed when an apical meristem was subjected to the same experimental treatment, i.e. when it was isolated

(Continued at foot of facing page)

demonstrated by Ball (1948) in similarly isolated apical meristem of *Lupinus albus* L. (Figs. 7.3, 7.4).

In ferns and flowering plants, the formation or further development of lateral buds is typically inhibited by the actively growing shoot apical meristem; but if the latter is destroyed, or if its activity is arrested, lateral buds develop. In the ferns, buds originate from detached meristems, or bud rudiments, these having formed part of the apical meristem at an earlier stage. They become isolated from the apical meristem during growth. In some flowering plants in which bud inception has been closely studied the buds also originate from comparable meristematic areas, though there are, as might be expected, considerable differences of histological detail. (Plate 6).

In experimental investigations of phyllotaxis in flowering plants, M. and R. Snow (1931–35, 1948) showed (a) that the next leaf primordium to be formed at the apical meristem arises in the first space of a certain minimal size between and above the last formed primordia; (b) that the position of the new primordium within this space is determined by the two adjacent older primordia only, and not by all the primordia of the top cycle; (c) that the position of a new primordium can be modified at will by incising the apex in a particular position; and (d) that the direction of the phyllotactic spiral may be reversed by appropriate experimental treatment. In comparable experiments with *Dryopteris dilatata* all of the above findings have been borne out. Closely comparable phyllotactic systems occur in taxonomically unrelated species. And although the phyllotaxis would undoubtedly rank as a character of a species, nevertheless one system may readily merge into another, as Richards (1951) has shown to be possible on mathematical grounds and Cutter and Voeller (1959) have demonstrated in a single apex of *Dryopteris dilatata*.

The evidence from many experiments supports the conclusions that, given a supply of nutrients from below, the apical meristem in vascular plants is a self-determining region, capable of forming a new axis, new

from the adjacent organs and tissues by four vertical incisions (in A–F) (*see* Fig.7.3), or by three incisions (in G). In each species the apical meristem grew on, gave rise to new leaf primordia in characteristic sequence and induced a basipetal differentiation of a new, inner vascular system; the outline of the new stele is in conformity with that of the isolated plug as seen in transverse section. A–E are representative transverse sections of a treated fern apex in acropetal sequence: *lb*, leaf-base; *l*, leaf-trace; *P*, *p*, pith: *C*, *c*, cortex. (*Phil. Trans. Roy. Soc.*)

lateral members, and a vascular system, without the help of the older preformed organs, i.e. the organizing activity resides in the embryonic

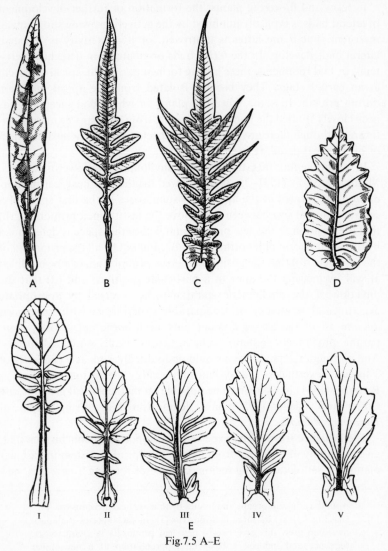

Fig.7.5 A–E

apex and not in the older differentiated parts of the plant. And it is evident that, however much the apices and lateral members of flowering plants and ferns may differ from each other genetically, anatomically and histologically, they show close similarities in their general construction, symmetry and function.

Leaves in different classes of vascular plants show heteroblastic development, i.e. a progressive ontogenetic elaboration of leaf size and shape (Fig.7.5). This process may be reversed when well-developed plants are subjected to unfavourable, e.g. 'starvation', conditions. In a

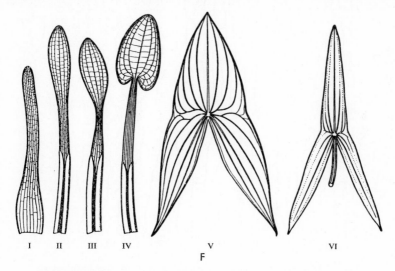

Fig.7.5 Heteroblastic development in a fern, a dicotyledon and a monocotyledon.

A–D, *Drynaria quercifolia* (an epiphytic fern). A–C, Assimilating leaves of varied configuration. D, A 'nest-leaf'.

E, *I–V, Barbarea vulgaris. I,* Basal foliage leaf; *II–V,* Various stem leaves.

F. *Sagittaria sagittaefolia. I–IV,* Sequence of leaves on a rhizome. *V,* Lamina of an adult foliage leaf. (After Goebel). *VI, S. hirundinacea.* Foliage leaf lamina. (After W. Troll, *Vergleichende Morphologie der höheren Pflanzen,* 1938.)

review of the relevant theories, Allsopp (1954) indicated that heteroblastic manifestations in different and unrelated species can usually be attributed to the size and nutritional status of the apex. He also showed that both morphological and anatomical features are closely determined by common nutritional relationships in developing primordia (Fig.7.6).

The Sequence of Metabolic Phases. If the photosynthetic systems in different classes of green plants are basically alike, then, under comparable external conditions, closely comparable sequences of metabolic phases might be expected to occur during the ontogenetic development; i.e. some products of metabolism will appear at an early stage and others at a later stage; and under particular conditions of age, duration

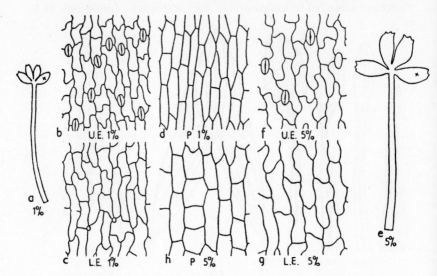

Fig.7.6 *Marsilea drummondii.* Various aspects of the histological organization of a leaf are determined by nutritional and other physiological factors during growth and development. The effect of transfer of sporeling plants from a medium containing 1 per cent. glucose to a medium with 5 per cent. is here illustrated.

(a), (b), (c), (d) third leaf before transfer, with upper and lower epidermis of lamina, from part marked X, and epidermis of petiole. (e), (f), (g), (h) corresponding figures for the second leaf formed after transfer. (Leaves × 2·5. Epidermis × 157). (After A. Allsopp, *Annals of Botany*.)

of exposure to light and dark, and so on, substances of special physiological importance may be formed. It is a very general fact that a vegetative phase usually precedes the reproductive phase, this affording one of the outstanding parallelisms of development in algae, bryophytes, pteridophytes and spermatophytes. Needham (1942) and de Beer (1951) pointed out that the comparative study of animals has brought to light many examples of what has been described as *recapitulatory parallelism*. Thus the nitrogen excreted by adult invertebrates, fishes and birds consists of ammonia, urea and uric acid respectively; while the chick embryo begins by excreting ammonia followed at successively later stages by urea and uric acid; i.e. there appears to be a parallelism of processes, involving the recapitulary repetition of adult ancestral characters. But as de Beer noted, the production of urea in adult fishes and in chick embryos takes place by quite different metabolic paths, the sequence of metabolic stages being attributed to the fact that 'there is apparently a natural order in which things can be done, a necessitation which affects all ontogenies alike'. The repetition may be regarded as the inevitable result of the working of a metabolic system in obedience to the laws of chemistry.

SIZE AND FORM CORRELATIONS

During the growth of any plant from the embryo to the adult state, the progressive accumulation of material is attended by a series of changes in the external form and internal tissue pattern; and the overall organization usually passes from a state of relative simplicity to one of relative complexity. Throughout this process, the genic complement in individual cells remains unchanged, though different genes, or groups of genes, may become specially active at particular times and in particular situations. (Some evidence of genic changes in individual cells has occasionally been noted.) An increasing structural complexity with increasing size, and the reverse with decreasing size, are typically found in the vascular tissues of species in which secondary thickening is absent; i.e. there is a size-structure correlation. For example, the roots in various ferns, dicotyledons and monocotyledons may range from small thread-like organs to thick fleshy ones and these afford excellent examples of the size-structure correlation in their vascular patterns (Wardlaw, 1928, 1952b; Bower, 1930). In very small root steles, the xylem and phloem may be arranged in a diarch pattern (i.e. two alternating groups of xylem and phloem); but in steles of successively greater diameters in the same plant, the vascular pattern becomes elaborated and increasingly complex, so that there may be sixteen to twenty alternating rays of xylem and phloem surrounding a central pith. In each root apex, the vascular pattern is determined as a whole, the pattern in the larger roots being essentially an amplification of that seen in the smaller ones. Thus, in their endogenous origin, apical growth, inception of tissue pattern, order of maturation of vascular tissues, manifestation of the size-structure correlation and functional activities, all roots, whether of pteridophytes or seed plants, exemplify a remarkable homology of organization. How can we account genetically for these close organizational similarities in the roots of unrelated species? In any one species particular groups of genes with specific properties undoubtedly participate in the histogenic processes. But are closely comparable genes present in different classes of vascular plants? Or are the genes which are involved in root morphogenesis of different molecular construction in different species, yet capable of contributing to closely comparable organizational developments? (*see* Figs. 3.3–3.6, Fig.7.9 and Plate 5).

Let us assume, for the moment, that particular gene-products are factors in the differentiation of the more central root embryonic tissues into protoxylem and protophloem, and that other gene-products determine the potential diameter of the root and its stele. The actual inception of the stelar pattern, however, which involves growth and therefore the movement of particular metabolic substances to particular positions, i.e. the characteristic positioning of protophloem and protoxylem precursors round the periphery of the nascent stele, according to its size, is essentially a physico-chemical process. And whether, in different species, the participating gene-molecules are considered to be like or unlike, the working of the reaction systems in the different root apices results in closely comparable histogenic patterns. In short, both gene-products and physico-chemical equilibria are involved in the inception of pattern. Only if the potentiality for a particular morphogenetic development is present in the hereditary constitution can that development take place. But in its visible manifestation and physical characteristics, i.e. its pattern or tissue organization, the physical aspect with its concomitant mathematical relationships appears to be just as fundamental as the genetical aspect.

A consideration of the differentiation of the several lignified elements, e.g. in a fern with its annular, spiral and scalariform tracheids, leads to the same general conclusion. As physical entities, these cells are conspicuously different in position, in size and in wall structure (or pattern of thickening). Since the same genetical components are involved in each, it is to physico-chemical factors, as the proximate causes, that the different tracheidal wall patterns must be attributed. Closely comparable tracheidal patterns occur in quite unrelated species, though certain distinctive tracheidal features are characteristic of particular groups.

The argument outlined above could also be applied to other homologies of organization. Waddington (1953) remarked that in recent investigations of development considerably more attention has been focused on the formation and action of chemical substances than on the physical aspects of the assumption of form, probably because the chemical processes are more basic, i.e. antecedent to the physical proceses. In the phenomena of organization, however, the two aspects are inseparable.

The general idea of *organismal reaction systems* has already been introduced in Chapters 1 and 2. The concept may apply to the activities in a single cell, e.g. a zygote or spore, or in an embryonic region, e.g. a shoot or root apex. Any of the physical or chemical properties of a cell may affect its action when it functions as a component of the reaction system in an embryo or shoot apical meristem. There appears to be agreement among biologists that general and more specific metabolic processes affecting growth, differentiation and morphogenesis take place in the cytoplasm.

When an embryonic unit, i.e. a zygote, young embryo, shoot apical meristem, etc., is supplied with suitable nutrients for its further development, it synthesizes a wide range of organic substances in an orderly manner. This aspect of order must be in conformity with the laws of physical chemistry. Moreover, in the embryonic cells of a shoot apical meristem, all of which may initially (as a convenient over-simplification) be regarded as being physiologically equivalent, with metabolic substances homogeneously distributed in them, a patternized distribution of metabolites takes place. One characteristic result is the inception of evenly-spaced growth centres round the base of the apical meristem. These growth centres are of characteristic size and shape for the species; they occur at some characteristic distance below the summit or centre of the apex, and they typically develop into leaf primordia. These observations apply to virtually all vascular plants, the very occasional exceptions being such ancient fossil species as those found in the Rhynie Chert. In all classes of plants, then, there is evidence of the inception of *primary patterns* in individual embryonic cells or in multicellular embryonic regions.

That a primary organogenic pattern can originate spontaneously at the shoot apical meristem is well illustrated by the embryos of *Pinus* spp. In the young, club-shaped embryo, in which leaf primordia have not yet appeared, the apical meristem consists of a conical or rounded mass of seemingly homogeneous embryonic cells. But later, on further growth, a number of evenly-spaced mounds – the cotyledon primordia – appear simultaneously in a ring round the apex. Now, in *Pinus ponderosa*,

F*

the embryos may vary over a considerable size range and 6 to 16 evenly spaced primordia may be present in different instances, the number being in direct proportion to the size of the apical meristem (Buchholz, 1946). It thus appears that, at a slightly earlier stage in the embryogeny, the reaction system in the meristem, in relation to its size, gave rise to a characteristic pattern of growth centres, i.e. to discrete or localized regions in which certain metabolic substances had become aggregated. Plant morphology affords many other examples of regular patterns of organs and tissues in which an antecedent patternized distribution of metabolic substances must be deemed to have taken place (Wardlaw, 1955c, d). Some of the explanations which have been proposed may now be considered.

TURING'S DIFFUSION-REACTION THEORY OF MORPHOGENESIS

In the inception of new organs and in the differentiation of tissues, usually in characteristic well-defined positions, a localized accumulation of 'morphogenetic' and other substances is regarded as an essential prior condition. The problem is to explain how the characteristic and regular distribution of these substances is brought about. This, indeed, is probably the most important and enigmatic phenomenon in morphogenesis; for biochemical and genetical concepts alone cannot account for the inception of pattern and the progressive ontogenetic organization. Such knowledge as we have of metabolism in the embryonic regions of plants is quite inadequate and so far has contributed little to the interpretation of the assumption of form or of tissue differentiation: Collectively, the evidence suggests that the mechanism of morphogenesis is to be sought in the laws of physical chemistry as they may apply to active metabolic systems in organized embryonic regions. As already noted (p. 140), Goldschmidt thought of the inception of biological pattern in terms of the harmonizing of reaction rates and trends towards physico-chemical equilibria. It is to Turing (1952), however, that we are indebted for a theory of morphogenesis which incorporates genetical, physiological, physical and mathematical aspects. This theory may, or may not, stand the test of further examination, but it appears to be the *kind* of theory that may eventually be shown to be valid (*see* Figs. 7.7–7.10; also Figs. 3.4–3.6).

Turing's theory (1952) is based on a consideration of the diffusibilities and reaction rates of substances which may be involved in growth and morphogenesis in embryonic regions or tissues. It makes use of well-known laws of physical chemistry, and, as Turing has shown, these

seem likely to be sufficient to account for many of the facts of morphogenesis. The underlying point of view, in fact, is closely akin to that
expressed by D'Arcy Thompson in *Growth and Form*: and, if it can be
validated, it could account for the general occurrence of many organizational features in plants and for some homologies of organization. An
essential feature of the theory is that it deals with the inception of a
morphogenetic *pattern as a whole*; but it is not inconsistent with epigenetic development when other organs or parts have already been
formed (Wardlaw, 1953). The essence of Turing's theory is that, in an
embryonic tissue of equivalent cells, in which the metabolic substances
may initially be distributed in a homogeneous manner, a regular,
patternized distribution of specific metabolites may eventually result,
thus affording the basis for the inception of a morphological or histological pattern.

An embryonic region may be envisaged as a reaction system, or as
the seat or locus of such a system. Some, perhaps many, of the principal
reacting substances may be gene-determined, but their distribution in
the embryonic tissue will necessarily take place in accordance with the
laws of physical chemistry. Turing has envisaged an idealized and
simplified 'model of the embryo'.

The model takes two slightly different forms. In one of them the cell theory is
recognized, but the cells are idealized into geometrical points. In the other the matter
of the organisms is imagined as continuously distributed. The cells are not, however,
completely ignored, for various physical and physico-chemical characteristics for the
matter as a whole are assumed to have values appropriate to the cellular matter. *

Thus both the classical view of Hofmeister and de Bary – that the tissue
mass as a whole determines differentiation and not the individual cells –
and of physiological genetics – that gene-controlled substances, proceeding from individual cells, are the real determiners – are represented.
The following passage further indicates Turing's approach:

With either of the models one proceeds as with a physical theory and defines an
entity called 'the state of the system'. One then describes how that state is to be
determined from the state at a moment very shortly before. With either model the
description of the state consists of two parts, the mechanical and the chemical. The
mechanical part of the state describes the positions, masses, velocities and elastic
properties of the cells, and the forces between them. In the continuous form of the
theory essentially the same information is given in the form of the stress, velocity,
density and elasticity of the matter. The chemical part of the state is given (in the cell
form of theory) as the chemical composition of each separate cell: the diffusibility of
each substance between each two adjacent cells must also be given. In the continuous
form of the theory the concentrations and diffusibilities of each substance have to be

given to each point. In determining the changes of state one should take into account: (i) the changes of position and velocity as given by Newton's laws of motion; (ii) the stresses as given by the elasticities and motion, also taking into account the osmotic pressures as given from the chemical data; (iii) the chemical reactions; (iv) the diffusion of the chemical substances; the region in which this diffusion is possible is given from the mechanical data.

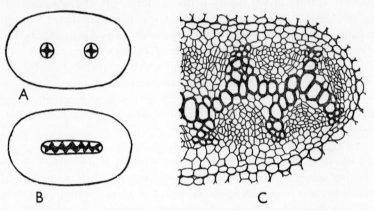

Fig.7.7 Illustrating Turing's Theory. *Caltha palustris*: fasciated roots.

A, A fasciated root in transverse section, with two normal tetrarch steles.

B, A fasciated root in which the stele has become laterally enlarged, but the general relationship of the xylem to the other vascular tissues is maintained.

C, Detailed drawing of a fasciated stele. (After E. H. Moss, *Annals of Botany*.)

The mathematical treatment of changes in the state of even an arbitrary and greatly simplified diffusion reaction system is unavoidably complex. For many contemporary investigators of morphogenesis, however, it is the possibility of the general result indicated by the theory, rather than the intricate details of the process, that is probably important.

Applications of the Theory. That diffusion-reaction systems are present in all growing regions, indeed in all living matter, is basic to the phenomena of metabolism. What is novel in Turing's theory is his indication that, under suitable conditions, many different diffusion-reaction systems will eventually give rise to stationary waves; in fact, to a regular patternized distribution of metabolites. The theory could thus account for the inception of the symmetrical, radiate pattern of vascular tissues in the apices of roots (Wardlaw, 1955). The inception of polarity, i.e. of axial development in an embryo, may perhaps be attributed to a redistribution of metabolites in a cell in which, at an earlier stage, the reacting substances were homogeneously distributed. Turing regarded this as a very simple case of a stationary wave.

The following may be tentatively indicated as examples of pattern in

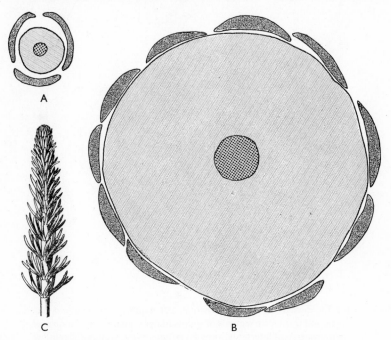

Fig.7.8 *Hippuris vulgaris.* A species with whorled phyllotaxis, illustrating Turing's Theory.

A, B, Thin and thick stems, as seen in transverse sections of nodes, showing a smaller and a larger number of leaves respectively (× 12). (By courtesy of Dr. E. G. Cutter.)

C, Appearance of axis with verticillate leaves. (After W. Troll.)

plants which may perhaps be explained, in whole or in part, as the theory is more fully developed and explored: the number and arrangement of the cotyledons in seedlings; phyllotactic systems; whorled branching in algae; the pattern in root steles and in lycopod shoot steles; etc. (*see* Wardlaw, 1953, 1955, 1957). An important feature of Turing's theory is that *differently constituted reaction systems may give rise to closely comparable patterns.* This again raises the question as to

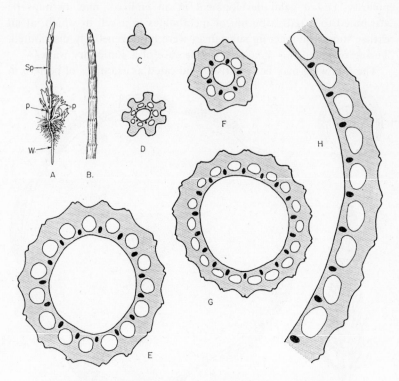

Fig.7.9 Illustrating Turing's Theory: leaf numbers in *Equisetum* spp. Stems and transverse sections of shoots (diagrammatic): the number of stem ridges, or of internodal vascular strands, is the same as the number of scale-leaves (or microphylls) formed at the node.

A, *E. telmateia.* Young sporophyte, still attached to its prothallus (*p*), showing nodal whorls of three or four leaves (or microphylls).

B, *E. fluviatile (heleocharis).* An adult shoot with many leaf-teeth at the nodes (A and B, after W. Troll).

C, *E. arvense.* A young sporophyte with three leaves at the node.

D, E, *E. trachyodon.* Stems of different thickness, with seven to fifteen ridges, i.e. leaves at nodes.

F, G, H, *E. robustum.* A very large species in which an adult shoot has many leaves at the nodes; smaller shoots and branches have proportionately smaller numbers.

(Sections, all × 12). (By courtesy of Dr. E. G. Cutter.)

whether the principal features of a nascent organismal pattern are mainly due to the general metabolic ingredients of the reaction system, i.e. common to all cells, rather than to more specific gene-determined substances.

Characteristic modifications in an initially homogeneous system

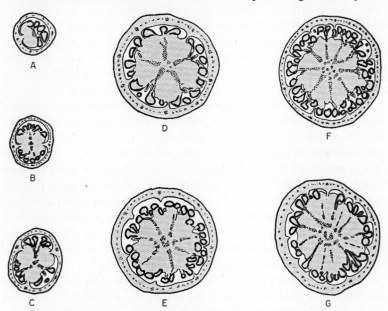

Fig.7.10 *Lychnis alba*. Variations in the size and complexity of the gynoecium, illustrating Turing's Theory. The number of styles, and of carpellary loculi, is usually five, the carpels being formed simultaneously. The number of styles and carpels may vary from none to thirteen. There is an evident progressive increase in the cross-sectional areas of ovaries and in the number of carpels – also of the associated vascular strands (dark stippling) – up to nine carpels; thereafter, further increases in carpel number are not attended by conspicuously increased ovary diameter. (After H. L. Dean, *Phytomorphology*, 1963.)

were regarded by Turing as initiating the process of differentiation; for the system may reach a state of instability in which the irregularities, or certain components of them, tend to increase. If this happens, a new and stable equilibrium is usually reached, and this may show a considerable departure from the original distribution pattern of the metabolites. Thus, in contiguous cells which are initially metabolically identical, a drift from equilibrium may take place in opposite directions as a result of statistical fluctuations in the components of the reaction system, or of small changes induced by neighbouring cells. Changes of this kind may account for the very different developments in two adjacent, equivalent embryonic cells. Also, such differences may be important in evoking the action of different sets of genes in adjacent cells, this eventually resulting in specific histological developments. These differential developments have long been recognized by anatomists as constituting one of the central problems in the higher plants. Today, they are again attracting attention and new discoveries and theories, relating to the processes which may be involved, may be expected from contemporary studies of molecular biology.

Turing's theory relates to relatively simple and symmetrical patterns. Its application to more complex patterns will undoubtedly be difficult; and its mathematical presentation is likely to be beyond the non-mathematical biological investigator. Nevertheless, once the central idea of the theory has been grasped, one can understand that a reaction system, which initially gives rise to relatively simple patterns, is likely to become more complex and to give rise to more complex patterns as development proceeds. Moreover, asymmetries in the environment of the reaction system, e.g. actively growing adjacent organs and differentiating tissues, may induce characteristic asymmetries in the system and in the patterns to which it gives rise.

Bünning's Concept. Bünning (1948, 1952) has ascribed the patternized distribution of growth centres to the mutual incompatibility of regions of vigorous protoplasmic growth. In his view, competition for nutrients cannot be the decisive factor underlying or determining the distribution of growth centres; rather it is that 'a certain type of embryonic growth will not allow the same type of growth to take place nearby', but a different type of embryonic growth may proceed unimpeded. The processes are probably enzymatical in nature, i.e. in the inception and development of a growth centre, a particular enzyme may become quantitatively predominant and this will lead to a diminution of the corresponding substrate in the surrounding field. While these ideas may be applicable to an organic situation in which some organs are already present, they do not explain how a patternized distribution of metabolites can be brought about in a new embryonic region in which no organs or tissue systems have yet been formed or differentiated, as in the formation of *Pinus* cotyledons already mentioned.

The Reaction System. The concept of physico-chemical organismal reaction systems in zygotes, embryonic regions, etc., has an evident general application to the phenomena of organization. It would be idle to pretend that we can specify in detail the nature of such systems at the present time. But some relevant general points may be tentatively indicated:

(i) The components of the system will include the basic features of cell organization and metabolites, e.g. carbohydrates, aminoacids, enzymes, growth substances, etc., which are common to all cells. The components will also include other substances that are specifically gene-controlled.

(ii) The state and activity of the system at any time may be affected by external factors such as temperature, light, water and soil nutrient supplies, by the position of the reaction system in the plant, and by the stage reached in ontogenesis. Thus, when a new substance enters the shoot apical reaction system of a flowering plant as a result of some particular photoperiodic exposure, the system remains essentially unchanged in some respects but is greatly modified in others; gene-determined sequential syntheses are evoked and flower formation begins. Reaction system theory, in short, affords a meeting place for the interaction of environmental and hereditary factors.

(iii) The products of mutant genes must be such that they are either compatible with the other components of the reaction system, or they are neutral. If they are incompatible they may block some important process, with consequential disorganizing or lethal effects. Selection, in fact, begins in the reaction system.

(iv) Whatever transitory or permanent effects an environment may have on a species, especially in its development or 'acquisition' of adaptive features, such effects must be mediated through the reaction system.

(v) Reaction system theory could afford a basis for developmental and functional harmony, a concept which now tends to replace the older idea of division of labour (*see also* Chapter 13).

REACTION SYSTEM THEORY AND TISSUE AND ORGAN CULTURES

Indirect and sometimes direct evidence that organizational features are the result of the working of reaction systems in embryonic regions has been obtained from organ and tissue culture investigations. When a complex reaction system is supplied with different nutrients in different circumstances, it seems evident that within the system there must be balanced reactions, antagonisms and competition. For example, many authors, when considering the effects of aminoacids, have indicated the significance of antagonism and balance in nutrient media (e.g. Audus and Quastel, 1947; Sanders and Burkholder, 1948; Fries, 1951; Harris, 1953; Skoog and Miller, 1957; Street, 1957; Steward and Pollard, 1958; Miettinen and Waris, 1958; Street, Hughes and Lewis, 1960; Sutton, Scott and Street, 1961; Reinert, 1962; Waris, 1962). With many cultures, complex media have been found suitable for normal development, but the addition of single aminoacids may promote or inhibit the development of particular organs or of a certain phase in differentiation. Indeed, Steinberg (1947, 1949) compared the effects of aminoacids with those of the hormones. Roots are particularly sensitive to aminoacid inhibitive effects, e.g. as shown by Fries (1951) for the pea plant and Waris (1959, 1962) for *Oenanthe* spp. In leucine-induced neomorphosis in *Oenanthe lachenalii* (*see* p. 346), the capacity for forming roots was lost for an indefinite period of time. Other instances of a close relationship between the nature of the embryonic development and nutritional factors, including aminoacids, have been reported by Sanders and Burkholder (1948), Steward and Pollard (1958), Steward, Mapes and Smith (1958), and Reinert (1962). Tissue cultures often yield forms comparable to 'neomorphs' (*see* p. 199). In carrot tissue cultures, Reinert (1962) observed filamentous organs resembling those of the leucine-induced neomorphs of *O. lachenalii* (*see* Waris, 1962, and p. 346). Aminoacids may thus have important organizing effects, probably because they are involved in the synthesis of nucleic acids and proteins. Moreover, in the contemporary view, proteins of abnormal composition can be produced and enzymes may be affected by aminoacid replacement (Chantrenne, 1961).

Criticisms of Turing's Theory. In discussing primary pattern-forming mechanisms in organisms, Waddington (1953) criticized Turing's theory on the grounds that, in animals, patterns typically appear as complete units and that they are not closely limited by the quantities of material available. In plants, however, primary patterns are modified by nutritional factors which affect the size of embryonic regions. Waddington has referred to observations by Henke on the patterns in butterflies' wings. The pattern has its inception as random coloured spots of varying size scattered throughout the wing; and from these spots rhythmic patterns develop. In extreme instances, the wing area may only be large enough for a single element of this rhythmic development; but in others, as a result of physico-chemical processes, the basic pattern may grow in complexity. D'Arcy Thompson regarded some biological patterns as being the expression of dynamic equilibrium. Waddington (1953) has suggested that it is improbable that simple physico-chemical concepts, such as those of diffusion, reaction rates, etc., afford an adequate basis for the inception of primary pattern in organisms. More subtle concepts seem likely to be necessary, but the kind of assistance biologists need from physical chemistry is not yet in sight.

In a further discussion of the theory, Waddington (1962) noted that Turing, through unfamiliarity, thought that the problems of embryology were even more difficult than they actually are.

Just as some geneticists seem to feel called upon to explain differentiation into alternative end-states by purely genetical processes which do not involve the region-ally differentiated cytoplasm of the egg, Turing felt that we have to be able to explain the appearance of regularly formed structures from a completely homogeneous initial situation. He envisaged the typical blastula, for instance, as a radially symmetrical spherical figure, and seems to have been unaware that it possesses both an animal vegetative axis and a dorsal meridian axis. However, he proceeded to show how, starting from this very unpromising beginning, much more definite structures could appear than seems likely at first sight.

While this criticism is no doubt valid for zoological materials, it is not necessarily so for some of those with which the botanist has to deal. The inception of the cotyledons in *Pinus*, for example, affords a clear case of the development of pattern in an embryonic region which initially consisted of equivalent embryonic cells (*see* p. 155).

With regard to the working of Turing's reaction system, the follow-ing quotation from Waddington is of interest.

First, the patterns produced are rather irregular. The computer, which was cal-culating for him the situation at successive times, produced a number of patterns which were either irregular dapplings, or at best, roughly periodic stripings. How much would such patterns be tidied up if one could introduce into the system some element of whole control, some feedback from the already existing area? Presumably any system which involves diffusion contains already a certain degree of feedback; but could one not postulate some other physical system in which a greater intensity of feedback was in operation, and would one not in this way generate something a good deal more regular and orderly than Turing produced?

A further criticism by Waddington is that, according to Turing's theory, in a cylindrical organ, the number of lateral organs formed, e.g. tentacles, should be related to the dimensions of the circumference. But, in living coelenterates, the number of tentacles is approximately the same in large and small specimens. However, as the writer has shown (Wardlaw, 1953, 1955), this does not hold for plants; and many examples can be cited, both of organ formation and tissue pattern, where the morphogenetic complexity is more or less directly correlated with actual size (*see* p. 158).

General Biological Aspects. However critically we may view the results to date of the application of physico-chemical and mathematical concepts to the problems of organization, two points emerge clearly: (i) this approach has helped to eliminate many of the more metaphysical ideas with which earlier generations of morphologists diverted and, not infrequently, tormented themselves; and (ii) the physico-chemical approach is not only unavoidable: it also opens up virtually unlimited prospects for new experimental investigations of organization as new ideas and techniques are devised and refined.

A point that emerges from reaction system theory, and which merits special emphasis, is that almost everything that happens during development is likely to have some functional aspect, since the essential feature of a reaction system is its functioning. What may impress us as a purposeful development could also be interpreted as a harmonious developmental relationship between an organism and its environment; i.e. in physico-chemical terms, as the result of the sustained tendency in an organismal reaction system, in which both inherent and environmental factors operate, to reach a state of dynamic equilibrium. Reaction system concepts also afford a basis for interpreting genotype/phenotype relationships of the same and different varieties when grown in various environments.

In support of the writer's emphasis on the value of reaction system concepts, reference may be made to Dobzhansky (1955). This author stated that the processes of heredity, development and evolution are essentially epigenetic in nature and that it is 'the developmental system as a whole which is preserved or modified by natural selection in the process of evolution' (p. 242). In Haeckel's biogenetic law Dobzhansky simply sees an expression of 'the unity and of a relative stability of the developmental system in evolution'.

Reference should also be made here to a study by Melville (1957) of some taxonomic implications of Turing's theory, in particular to the following statement (p. 299). 'Hitherto it has been assumed that each change of shape from one leaf to the next in the leaf spectrum of a plant and from one part of a leaf to another must, necessarily, require some considerable number of genes for its control. Similarly many genes are assumed to be responsible for the development of corolla forms and pigment patterns. It now seems more probable that such morphological details are the result of the interaction of comparatively small numbers of morphogens subjected to physical forces and under the ultimate control of a small number of genes only. The enormous complexity of evolutionary processes appears much simplified and more comprehensible in the light of this theory. It is evident that there is a wide field for research into the taxonomic implications of the theory by experimental and biometrical techniques.'

GENERAL CONCLUSIONS

In the organization of plants, both general and specific features may be distinguished; e.g. the axis with leaves is a general or common feature of all vascular plants, but the length of the adult axis and the outline of the leaves are usually distinctive and specific. Even in a very general principle like Gallileo's principle of similitude, although increases and decreases in the sizes of organisms are usually attended by certain common main effects, each species also shows individualistic, or specific, effects.

Although various non-genetical factors are among the proximate causes of the assumption of form and of organization, hereditary factors are the basic determiners. The hereditary constitution, however, should be envisaged in its most comprehensive aspect; i.e. it includes not only the genes but also heritable basic cell features. The latter are of at least the same antiquity as the genes and are not known to be gene-determined. These cell features and gene-determined substances react in a harmonious and reciprocal manner.

During the growth of an embryonic region, characteristic and orderly patterns of organs and tissues are formed. These are ascribed to the activities of the organismal reaction system. The system, e.g. in the shoot apex, undergoes gradual changes during early ontogenesis and more abrupt changes at the induction of the reproductive phase.

Since the reaction systems of genetically unrelated species, presumably with very different genotypes, may give rise to similar patterns of organs and tissues, it is to the physico-chemical activities of the systems that major morphogenetic and organizational developments should be ascribed. Alternatively, one may assume either (a) that some genetical homology is much more common in plants at large than is usually thought; or (b) that different genes may induce closely comparable effects; or (c) that basic cell features, which are apparently homologous throughout the Plant Kingdom, are of major importance in morphogenetic developments. In different instances these several possibilities may all be contributory in varying degrees.

Factors in the genetical constitution, together with environmental factors, determine the nature and amount of the metabolic materials available for development. It is conceivable that certain genes, which tend to be evolved in different genetical systems, behave as common cytoplasmic factors and so contribute to the inception of common patterns and therefore to homologies of organization. Such patterns may be variously and distinctively modified by the action of more specific genes.

CHAPTER 8

Organization in Algae and in Early Land Plants

No comprehensive survey of organization in the Plant Kingdom can be attempted here. The treatment adopted will necessarily be selective, the aim being to consider aspects of organization at different evolutionary levels and, as far as possible, to assess the particular effects of the different kinds of contributory factors. The writer will be mainly concerned with autotrophic plants, as constituting a broadly coherent group comprising the major phyletic lines; but similar observations could also be made on other groups. (For an account of morphological progression and evolution in plants, especially in the algae, readers are referred to Böcher, 1951.)

An examination of organization in the Plant Kingdom might well begin with viruses, bacteria and some of the simpler Protophyta. One might also begin by setting out some facts about the organization of cells in general. It is the latter course that will be followed here.

GENERAL FEATURES OF THE LIVING CELL

As the past decade of electron microscopy has shown, *any* living cell is a very complex and highly organized structure, not only at the molecular level, but in respect of its numerous cytoplasmic components and its nucleus. It may be accepted that a cell from any contemporary systematic group is vastly more complex and more highly co-ordinated than any early, or prototypic, cell could have been. Although quite understandably we regard the larger and morphologically more complex vascular plants as being much more highly organized than the green algae, yet at the cellular level, they are not so very different, at least in some important respects. Manton (1961), for example, has shown that in the very small flagellate *Micromonas squamata* which personifies, as it were, the minimum needs of an autotrophic unicellular organism, there are the following components: a multilayer external wall (plasmalemma, or outer cytoplasmic surface); a nucleus (of normal type); a chloroplast with a pyrenoid; a mitochondrion; a Golgi body; granules; vesicles; and a flagellum. Here we have most of the apparatus found in cells in higher plants; i.e. as Manton has noted, these minute algal cells cannot be regarded as primitive in any absolute sense (Fig.8.1).

In more advanced plants, from Bryophyta to Angiospermae, there appear to be no fundamental differences in cell structure. What the electron microscope and biochemical studies have revealed, and are increasingly revealing, is the quite extraordinary complexity of the

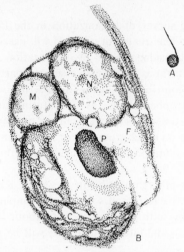

Fig.8.1 *Micromonas squamata.* A, Dried cell (redrawn from a photograph taken with the light microscope), to show the body and single flagellum of a very small green flagellate (× 1000) (After I. Manton and M. Parke.)
B, Diagrammatic indication of the organizational features (redrawn from an electron micrograph): *N*, nucleus; *M*, mitochondrion; *C*, the large chloroplast, with its pyrenoid *P*. A fibrous connection, *F*, joins the base of the flagellum with the nucleus (× 15,000). (After I. Manton.) (Both A and B after I. Manton, in *Contemporary Botanical Thought*, 1961.)

individual cell. It is not only that the cell of a green plant has a surprisingly large number of different kinds of components (*see* Chapter 2, p. 40), and that some of these, e.g. the nucleus, the chloroplasts and mitochondria, are structurally exceedingly complex, but that the whole of this very complex system functions with such a high measure of order, each component, whether it be a dividing chromosome or a specific enzyme, 'doing the right thing at the right time'. In terms of contemporary theory and observation, we have to recognize (a) that each organelle, e.g. mitochondrion or chloroplast, may carry on its

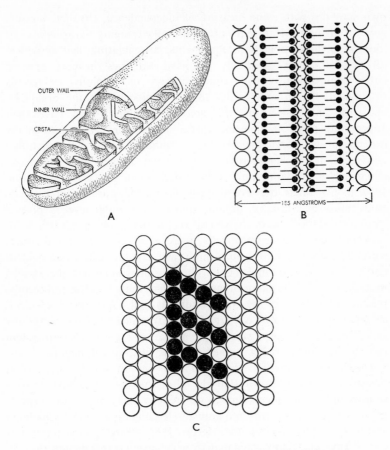

OUTER WALL
INNER WALL
CRISTA

125 ANGSTROMS

A

B

C

Fig.8.2 The highly complex organization of very small cellular inclusions, as illustrated by the structure and chemical constitution of a mitochondrion.

A, diagrammatic reconstruction of a mitochondrion* (greatly magnified): this organelle consists of a minute vessel, containing fluid; it has an involuted, double-membrane wall; the infoldings of the inner membrane are known as cristae.

B, each membrane consists of a layer of protein molecules (large clear circles) lined by a double layer of lipid molecules (small black circles).

C, the respiratory chain electron carriers and enzymes are thought to be regularly spaced units (black circles) in the protein monolayers. (After J. Brachet, *Scientific American*, 1961.)

* Since going to press, more elaborate illustrations have become available.

own activities with some measure of independence; (b) that 'messengers' from the nuclear genes are constantly bringing 'information' or 'orders' to the cytoplasmic components, so regulating their activities; (c) that all these essentially chemical activities have to proceed either simultaneously with some measure of harmony, or serially or sequentially, in some order that is significant for the organism; and (d) that collectively the activities within a cell have their appropriate place in time and space, so that they contribute to the orderly growth, organogenesis, tissue differentiation and functional activities that are characteristic of the normal ontogenesis of the species and make for its adaptation and survival. As Lehmann (*see* Waddington, 1959, p. 17) stated, the several types of organelles are essential to the constitution of a cell, i.e. organization at the cellular level involves a close interrelationship of the several very varied components (Fig.8.2).

When a cell divides mitotically, there is not only nuclear division, with all that that entails in furnishing each daughter cell with a nucleus and a full and equal complement of chromosomes and genes; there is also multiplication of the major organelles such as mitochondria and chloroplasts, and possibly of the minor bodies as well.* *In short, much if not all that we understand by cell organization is involved in, and transmitted at, cell division.* These organelles are all part of the cell reaction system in which specific gene-determined proteins, etc., must function.

The Organization of the Blue-green Algal Cell. In recent years, several investigators have shown that the ultrastructure, or cellular organization, in the blue-green algae is different in many important respects from that of higher plants and animals (Ris and Singh, 1961; Chapman and Salton, 1962; Wildon and Mercer, 1963, where earlier literature is cited). Thus, the cytoplasmic matrix, which extends throughout the cell, is without membranous organelles such as the nucleus, mitochondria, chloroplasts, Golgi bodies, or endoplasmic reticulum. However, two regions, which merge with one another, can be distinguished in the cell. These are (i) a peripheral region containing paired membranes, or 'photosynthetic' lamellae, and various granular bodies; and (ii) a central region with crystalline granules and areas of low electron density, comparable in structure and staining reactions with the 'nucleoid regions' in bacterial cells. Granules of ribosome character are present throughout the cytoplasmic matrix. Wildon and Mercer (1963) have

---

* It is appreciated that, with the research that is now in progress, this statement may require some qualification.

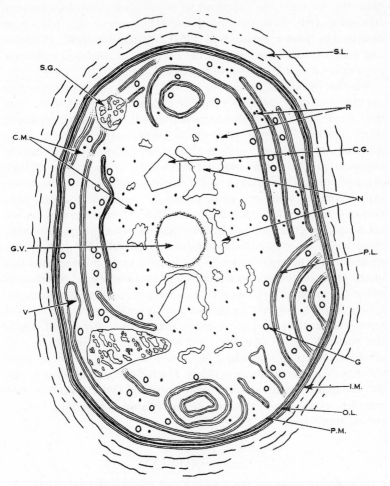

Fig.8.3 Diagram illustrating a section of a 'typical' blue-green algal cell: slime layer (*S.L.*); investment membrane (*I.M.*); osmiophilic layer of inner investment (*O.L.*); plasma membrane (*P.M.*); peripheral photosynthetic lamellae (*P.L.*); vacuole (*V*); granules 3000Å in diameter (*G*); gas vacuole (*G.V.*); ribosome-like granules (*R*); structured granules (*S.G.*); cytoplasmic matrix (*C.M.*); crytalline granules (*C.G.*); areas of low electron density (*N*). (The structural components are not drawn strictly to scale.) (After D. C. Wildon and F. V. Mercer, *Australian Jour. Biol. Sci.*, 1963.)

been able to detect the continuity of the plasma-membranes between contiguous cells. Cells showing this level of organization have been described by Stanier and van Neil (1962) as 'precaryotic cells'. Chapman and Salton (1962) have reported the presence, in *Anabaena cylindrica*, of an internal membrane system as well as lamellae.

Whether or not the precaryotic cells of bacteria and blue-green algae are 'fundamentally' different – they are undeniably very different – from the cells of higher plants, should perhaps, for the time being, remain an open question. The new evidence, however, enables some tentative inferences to be drawn, such as (i) that, in the evolution of cellular organization, the nucleus was not necessarily, or invariably, the first organelle to be elaborated; and (ii) that the evolution of cytoplasmic organization in some groups of organisms preceded, and may have prepared the way for, nuclear organization. These inferences do not necessarily preclude the possibilities that, in other groups, especially those which have undergone more or less considerable evolutionary development, the organization of the nucleus may have preceded that of the other cytoplasmic components, or that the several components of the cell, as physico-chemical entities, were necessarily elaborated contemporaneously. Support for the last point is perhaps forthcoming from recent and contemporary observations that DNA is present not only in the 'nucleoid' regions of bacteria and blue-green algae but also in some of the cytoplasmic organelles. No doubt we shall hear much more about these matters in the near future. For the moment, an enquiry into the sustaining conditions for the synthesis of DNA – which is now regarded as the key substance in protoplasmic organization – is of critical importance.

CELL COMPONENTS

Contemporary views on the range of cell components as revealed by electron microscopy have been surveyed by Hodge *et al.* (1956), Buvat (1958), Whaley *et al.* (1960), Manton (1961), Brachet (1961) and others. The physical configuration and properties of the various organelles, e.g. of a mitochondrion or a chloroplast, are assuming increasing importance in the literature – a new micro-morphology is in the making. It is not yet clear if the several organelles are closely gene-determined, though there is evidence that, in some instances, they are subject to genic modulation. This is to be expected. A chloroplast, for example, is now known to be a very complex and highly organized structure, endowed with very considerable stability. And although the chloroplasts in different taxonomic groups may show considerable differences in shape, size, complexity, etc., they have the same essential structural components, suggesting that the same common factors are involved in their construction. The complex chloroplasts of many algae can multiply by direct fission and thus keep pace with cell division. In other algae, e.g. those with apical growing points, and in the higher plants, the multiplication of chloroplasts involves the division of small colourless proplastids. These pass through a series of quite complex developmental stages before becoming fully developed chloroplasts (Mühlethaler and Frey-Wyssling, 1959).

Of mitochondria, with their important respiratory enzymic activities, it need only be noted here that they are very similar both in structure and function not only throughout the Plant Kingdom but also in plants and animals (Manton, 1961; Brachet, 1961). They are present in all intact plant cells above the level of the blue-green algae; and their reproduction is typically by the division of pre-existing mitochondria. (However, the latter statement may require modification in the light of new discoveries.)

The details of the numerous cell components need not be laboured here. One point may, however, be duly emphasized, namely, that the two most important organelles involved in energy relationships, i.e. the chloroplasts and mitochondria, are typically cytoplasmic components: they divide and keep pace with cell division, and they are perpetuated in hereditary processes as components of the ovum. Like other structural features of cells, it has not been demonstrated that these organelles are formed under close genic control, though they may be. It is known, however, that many mutant genes affect their functional activities (*see* Lamprecht, 1960, and Blixt, 1961).

Zoologists and botanists now recognize that nuclei show differential activity, such as the uptake of aminoacids, according to the tissue in which they are present, i.e. in relation to the state of the cytoplasm. But the state of the cytoplasm is itself partly determined by the nucleus. The question is sometimes asked as to what the cytoplasm can do in the absence of the nucleus. The answer, based on the small number of cases so far examined, is different in different instances, e.g. in *Acetabularia* as compared with *Amoeba proteus* (*see* Waddington, 1959). Of course, one could equally enquire what the nucleus can do without the cytoplasm. These queries again remind us of the essential functional integration of the major cell components: over-emphasis of any one of them, or abstracting it from its context, can only obscure the reality of the situation.

Electron microscopy has now shown that even in parts of the cell which appear to consist of more or less homogeneous, 'granular' cytoplasm, where the activities might be regarded as being essentially biochemical and molecular, there is often evidence of quite elaborate structural organization. Waddington (1959, p. xiv) noted that genetical analyses indicate that there are 'cytoplasmic particles or elements which have a considerable degree of autonomy in duplication', genes and cytoplasm standing in a reciprocal relationship; and that 'influences impinging on the cell from outside may cause profound changes in cytoplasmic organization'.

Cellular organization, as it now seems, is not simply to be equated with the collective action of the genes. The importance of other permanent cell components is becoming increasingly evident both from electron microscopy and from other sources (*see* Chapter 6); and it is to a synthesis of the activities of genes and of other cell components that we must look for a better understanding of cell organization. In a cell, envisaged as a very complex, heritable, physico-chemical open system, the several component parts must co-exist, function and evolve in harmony, i.e. in dynamic equilibrium. In short, it is the cell as a whole which constitutes an orderly reaction system, or organization, and which is transmitted at cell division and in heredity.

ORGANIZATION IN THE ALGAE

Only a few of the many aspects of organization in the algae, of which Fritsch (1935, 1945) enumerated eleven classes, can be touched upon here. Some of these have been discussed by Bonner (1952). If, as an arbitrary starting point, we begin with early, primitive unicellular algae, which had acquired the basic structural features and physiological mechanisms essential for survival as autotrophic organisms, then it is apparent that their further evolution has been marked by numerous organizational innovations, i.e. the various components which we find in the cells of living species. Although some classes of algae, e.g. the flagellates, have remained at the unicellular level, there can be little doubt that, in the matter of cellular organization, the living species are vastly different from their early prototypic ancestors.

Even small and simple flagellates, as Manton (1961) has demonstrated, have all the essential cell components that we find in higher plants (*see* p. 169). The unicellular algae show a considerable range of diversity in respect of their size, shape, chloroplast structure, pigments, reserve materials, mode of asexual and sexual reproduction, and tendency to become associated into more or less highly organized assemblages. In the inception of their structural features, observers like D'Arcy Thompson have emphasized the importance of physical factors such as the balance of internal and surface forces, or of the innate physico-chemical properties of the substances of which the organisms are composed. On the other hand, the numerous investigations of their highly varied metabolism and sexual reproduction bear witness to the many genetical changes that must have taken place in the development of the several phyletic lines. In particular, these developments afford much interesting evidence of evolutionary parallelism.

EVOLUTIONARY PARALLELISM IN THE ALGAE

The eleven classes of algae (Fritsch, 1935, 1945) afford remarkable evidence of evolutionary parallelism. Fritsch (1935, pp. 26, 27) assembled this information in two comprehensive tables. In one of these he showed that, in five different classes of the simpler Protophyta, essentially the same types of basic construction and elaborations of them are known. In the second table, reproduced here, he showed that the many aspects

Table 3. *Showing Parallelism in Evolution of Advanced Types of Algal Construction*
(after Fritsch, 1935)

	TYPE OF CONSTRUCTION	CHLOROPHYCEAE	PHAEOPHYCEAE	RHODOPHYCEAE
(a)	Heterotrichous filament	*Stigeoclonium*, etc.	*Ectocarpus*, etc.	*Chantransia*, etc.
(b)	Discoid (prostrate) type[1]	*Protoderma*, etc.	*Ascocyclus*, etc.	*Erythrocladia*
(c)	Crusts or cushions[1]	*Pseudoprings-heimia*	*Ralfsia*	*Hildenbrandia*, etc.
(d)	Elaborated erect type	*Draparnaldia Draparnaldiopsis*	*Desmarestia*	*Batracho-spermum*
(e)	Compact (pseudo-parenchymatous) type (uniaxial)	Dasycladaceae (siphoneous)	—	*Lemanea*, etc.
(f)	The same (multiaxial)	Codiaceae (siphoneous)	*Castagnea*, etc.	*Nemalion*, etc.
(g)	Foliose, parenchymatous type	Ulvaceae	*Punctaria*	*Porphyra*
(h)	Tubular parenchymatous type	*Enteromorpha*	*Asperococcus*	—

[1]Also in *Pleurocapsa*, *Oncobyrsa*, etc. (Myxophyceae).

of vegetative construction known in the Chlorophyceae also occur in the Phaeophyceae and Rhodophyceae (Figs. 8.4, 8.5).

In some instances the external similarities are so close that, as Fritsch stated, a close study of cell structure and reproduction is required before forms that are really quite unrelated can be distinguished. Because outward form is so unreliable as a guide to systematic affinity in the algae, 'it is quite impossible to establish with any measure of certainty the systematic position of the simpler types of algae found in the fossil condition' (Fritsch, 1935, p. 28).

Zoologists accept the concept that higher levels of organization may emerge as a result of the collective and integrative action of constituent elements (Weiss, *see* Waddington, 1959, p. 16). This has an evident application of colonial algae such as members of the Volvocales, *Hydrodictyon*, etc.

The algae thus yield convincing evidence that the course of evolution has been closely comparable in several different groups: the same kinds of events appear to have occurred, seemingly quite independently, in different phyletic lines. In this we may perhaps perceive a resultant effect of (a) the existence, in a common ancestral type, of well established and persistent basic cell features, (b) the action of physical, environmental and various self-organizing or self-ordering factors, (c) viable genetical changes, many of which must have been at least functionally comparable, and (d) the action of selective forces which canalized the evolutionary changes.

EVOLUTIONARY TRENDS

In the unicellular algae the same basic cell features are very generally present. Under the impact of genetical change and selection, however, individual organelles, e.g. the chloroplasts, have become modified in a considerable variety of ways; but the functional activities of the several components, and the contribution which they make to the overall economy of the organism, appear to have remained relatively unchanged over a vast period of time. Genetical studies have revealed gene-controlled changes in the chloroplasts and in the sexual mechanism (Lewin, 1954; Levine and Ebersold, 1960).

The elaboration of organization in the algae, from the unicellular to the multicellular state, has taken place along a number of different lines. In some green algae, for example, the dividing unicell, instead of giving rise to two separate non-motile or motile individuals, retained a varying measure of coherence, yielding (a) indefinite assemblages of

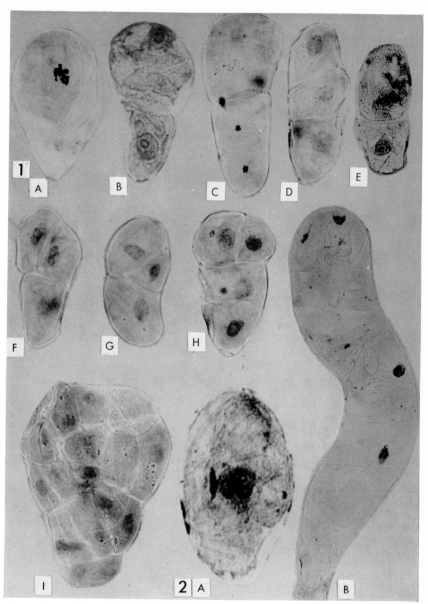

11. *Haplopappus gracilis.* 1 A-I. Division stages and cell lineages as seen in fixed preparations of suspended cells and cell aggregates (× 375). A, Single cell with a dividing nucleus (metaphase). B, Form of two-celled structure, seemingly by division of one cell, as shown in (A). C, Similar situation as in (B), with lower cell showing division (late anaphase). D, Three-celled group which may have originated from a structure like (C). E, Two cells, forming threes by division of the upper cell, the plane of this division being nearly at right angles to the first-formed wall. F, G, Groups of three cells, evidently derived from a form like (E). H, Four-celled aggregate by division of the lower cell in a structure like (F) or (G). i, "Embryo-like" structure developed by further division of a form like (H). 2. The bi- and multi-nucleate condition of cells. A, Bi-nucleate cell, showing metabolic nuclei adpressed (× 375). B, Very large free cell with at least five nuclei, one of which (indicated by the arrow) appears to be hapoid (× 300). (After F. C. Steward *et al., Amer. Jour. Bot.*)

12A. *Syringa vulgaris:* bud apices which have been successfully grafted into an undifferentiated callus of the same species, grown in aseptic culture. (After R. H. Wetmore, S. Sorokin and J. Arnold Arboretum.)

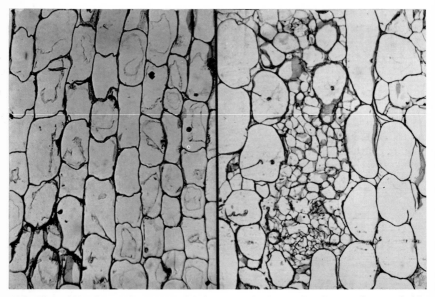

12B. Effect of kinetin on tobacco stem pith tissue, growing in aseptic culture. Left, normal pith parenchyma on basic medium. Right, evidence of cell growth and division in tissue growing on the basic medium, to which had been added indoleacetic acid (2.0 mg/l) and kinetin (0.2 mg/l). (Original photograph, by courtesy of Drs. F. Skoog and C. O. Miller.)

unicells, such as the *Palmella*-stage found in different groups; (b) well-defined integrated colonial organisms, or coenobia, such as *Volvox* or *Scenedesmus*; (c) various characteristic dendroid assemblages of uni-

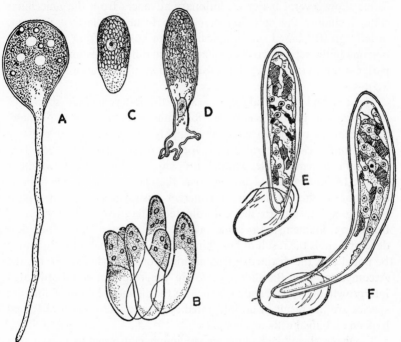

Fig.8.4 Organizational features in young plants of various green algae: the cell elongates, manifests polarity, shows a movement of the more dense protoplasmic materials towards the distal, or apical, pole, and vacuolation at the proximal, or basal, pole.

A, B, *Protosiphon botryoides*. A, Normal plant developed from a zoospore. B, Group of plants, grown from zoospores in a nutrient solution, showing the distal aggregation of dense protoplasmic contents (after Klebs).

C, D, *Oedogonium concatenatum*. Germinating zoospores (after Hirn).

E, F, *Spirogyra neglecta*. Germinating zygospores (after Tröndle). (From C. W. Wardlaw, *Embryogenesis in Plants*, 1955.)

cells; (d) coherent, integrated filaments, either simple or branched; and (e) coenocytic, simple or branched, multinucleate filaments, e.g. the Siphonales.

The filamentous green, brown and red algae include (a) species in which the filament is typically simple, unbranched and with diffuse, or

G

intercalary growth; (b) species with a more or less well-defined pattern of branching; and (c) species with a dominant and well-defined apical cell and a regular pattern of branches. Collectively, these filamentous forms show several major evolutionary advances from the unicellular state, including the cohesion of cells to form a polarized filament, orderly growth based on an apical cell, an advance from isogamy to oogamy in the reproductive elements and, in different instances, various patterns, more or less regular, of alternation of generations (Figs. 8.4, 8.5).

The red and brown algae, especially the latter, include species of large size and relatively complex form and structure. Some of these, e.g. members of the Fucales, have highly organized apical growing points and various lateral organs formed from them (Figs. 3.1, 3.2). They afford remarkable parallelisms with developments in vascular plants. In other red and brown algae the elaboration of the soma is due, not to the formation of coherent tissue masses by an apical growing point, but to the co-ordinated intergrowth of systems of branching filaments. In some algae, the eventual morphological development is the result of both kinds of process. In parenthesis, it may be noted that the distinctive fructifications of the higher fungi, i.e. the Ascomycetes and Basidiomycetes, are the result of a co-ordinated intergrowth of hyphae; and in the lichens the distinctive thalli of different species are the result of an integrated symbiotic intergrowth of fungal hyphae and algal cells or filaments.

The green algae (with which we are mainly concerned in a discussion of organization and evolution in the higher plants) are remarkable in that they have remained at the filamentous, branched-filament or thalloid stage. Apart from *Chara* and *Nitella*, the most somatically elaborate green alga so far described, *Fritschiella tuberosa* (Chaetophorales), consists of a basal filament which gives rise to a tuft of filaments, each with an apical cell and a tendency to divide by both longitudinal and transverse walls, so forming an incipient tissue mass. There is also a downwardly-growing rhizoid.

Fritsch (1939, 1945) enquired why it is that the green algae do not show advances in somatic organization comparable with those in the brown and red algae. His answer was that the advanced green algae became the plants of the land and, in the course of time, they evolved into the several phyla of higher plants. In the several major algal groups Fritsch (1939) recognized a basic type of organization – the *heterotrichous habit*. Filamentous organisms (he said) tended to form some of their filaments in the plane of the substratum and others in an upright direction. He argued, with supporting detail based on comparative morphological studies of the living green algae and the evolutionary tendencies which they show, that various elaborations of the heterotrichous habit could have led to the kind of organization that we observe in Bryophyta and Pteridophyta (Fritsch, 1945; Wardlaw, 1952). Put very briefly, Fritsch's theory would be substantially supported if fossil plants intermediate in structure between the green algae and the Psilophytales were to be discovered. If we begin with a heterotrichous green alga, then, in Fritsch's view, essential evolutionary steps would have included the parenchymatous development of the upright filamentous component of the system, the acquisition of an apical growing point, dichotomous branching, the differentiation of a vascular system, and so on (*see also* Fritsch, 1952).

THE ELABORATION OF ORGANIZATION IN THE POST-ALGAL PHASE

It seems probable that the kind of morphological progression broadly outlined by Fritsch may have taken place. However, somewhat different conceptions of the processes which may have been involved emerge if one has in mind the point of view and the results of recent work on morphogenesis. In the writers' view, the essential evolutionary developments can be referred to genetical and environmental changes which made for progressively enhanced and varied metabolism in the green algal progenitors. Necessary conditions and steps in the progressive organization of higher plants may be indicated as follows.

1. Green unicells or simple filaments, with polar organization developed as a self-ordering principle based on metabolism and the impact of external factors, e.g. light, gravity, communal secretions, etc., are taken as a starting point.

2. In the developing reproductive cells of green algae, e.g. the zygospore of *Spirogyra*, or the zoospore of *Oedogonium*, as in the zygotes of higher plants, the polarized cell shows an accumulation of the denser protoplasmic materials towards the distal pole, while the basal pole tends to accumulate osmotically active substances and becomes vacuolated. (Closely comparable developments are found in the developing zygotes of animals, an early accumulation of proteins taking place at the animal, i.e. the apical or distal pole.) This very general phenomenon is probably a manifestation of a self-ordering physico-chemical principle inherent

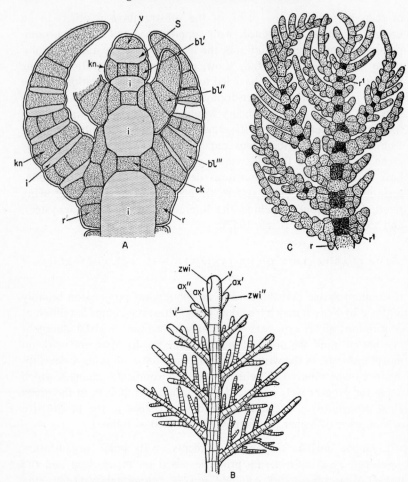

Fig.8.5 Regulated development resulting from the activity of an apical cell in green, brown and red algae.

A, *Chara fragilis*. In this beautifully regulated green alga, the whole vegetative structure, consisting of nodes and internodes, is demonstrably the result of apical activity and regulated development.

B, *Halopteris filicina*. In this brown alga (Sphacelariales), a distinctive organization results from the regular but unequal divisions of the apical cells of main and branch filaments. V, V^1, apical cells; zwi, branch initial cell; ax^1, ax'', sites of pseudoaxillary filaments or 'shoots'.

C, *Ptilota plumosa*. A red alga (Ceramiales) showing organizational features which are generally comparable with those found in green and brown algae. (After F. Oltmanns, *Morphologie und Biologie der Algen*.)

in the cell substances. It probably occurred also in early prototypic filamentous algae (Fig.8.4).

3. In ancestral green algae, successive hereditary changes and selection, making for more efficient photosynthesis, protein and nucleoprotein synthesis, would have admitted of the development of organisms of larger size with larger and physiologically more active multicellular apical growing points.

4. In relation to its large size and active metabolism, such a massive apex would constitute a metabolic sink, drawing to itself substances from more proximal regions of the plant. If we suppose that in these older regions the maturing tissues became rigid, then we would have a primitive or nascent apex giving rise to a cylindrical axis by an accretionary or epigenetic process. (Such an apex might have evolved from an algal progenitor already equipped with an apical cell, or from a filament with a less definite apical cell. The writer would not exclude the possibility that a massive apex might have originated from a growth centre, or region of concentration of proteins, etc., in a flat thallus, in much the same way that an apogamous fern sporophyte originates from a localized region of active growth in the prothallus.)

5. The more progressive and rapidly evolving early green algae, which were beginning to colonize exposed muddy areas and which were capable of growing to some considerable size, probably manifested structural diversity and also homologies of organization. In time, some of the various innovations yielded divergent evolutionary lines, some of which have persisted; but it may be conjectured that many intermediate and less successful forms were eliminated.

6. In the course of this upgrade evolution, it would appear that certain populations, though able to survive, were limited by some major restriction in their metabolic capacity or in the scope or flexibility of their reaction systems; i.e. the embryonic regions were incapable of giving rise to a large plant body. The bryophytes may perhaps be accounted for along these lines.

7. With the progressive improvements in the mechanisms of energy utilization, synthesis, and uptake of nutrients from the substratum, etc., especially when associated with favourable environmental changes, the nascent land plants formed more massive and efficient apical growing points. As active metabolic sinks, these apices would set up gradients leading from the older photosynthetic regions of the axis. In the pathway set up by this tension, some differential development of tissues was induced and, in time, a nascent conducting tissue came into being, to be

followed by the evolution of more efficient conducting tracts. As a result, the supply of nutrients to the apex was increased.

8. The earlier nascent land plants – no doubt a rather varied assemblage – may have been ribbon-like or cylindrical structures, perhaps showing dichotomy, but lacking foliar development. However, with the increase in apical size, organization, and metabolic diversity, the apical reaction system would become capable of new differential developments. A characteristic activity was the inception on the flanks of the apex of centres of specially active metabolism. These centres grew out as lateral members, thereby increasing the photosynthetic potentiality of the organism. Initially, the growth centres were probably relatively small and feeble and gave rise to small protophylls or other microphyllous foliar organs. But in plants with larger and more active growth centres, a megaphyllous development would become possible. The evolution of the genetical mechanisms relating to enhanced and diversified metabolism would be of primary importance in these developments.

9. Side by side with these foliar innovations, the inception of roots was evidently of great importance. So far, however, apart from such observations as that root initials in ferns are associated with young leaf primordia and that roots are formed more or less simultaneously with the shoot apex in the embryogenesis of vascular plants, there is little that can be said about their evolutionary origin(s).

10. The organizational advances in the vegetative phase were attended by innovations in the reproductive phase; but conjectures about the evolutionary elaboration of reproductive meristems will not be entered upon here (*but see* Chapter 11).

We have virtually no information on 'the progressive green algae' or early land plants. By analogy with the massive brown algae, however, we can see that whereas some of them, such as *Ascophyllum*, have well-defined apical meristems, they do not give rise to lateral foliar members (though they do give rise to lateral buds), others, such as *Sargassum*, have apical meristems which give rise to lateral pseudo-foliar members.

The evolution of effective foliar members in primitive land plants probably took place over a very considerable period of time. It is relevant to emphasize that leaf formation by apices is one of the most general phenomena in green plants. We see it in the gametophytes of mosses and leafy liverworts and in all vascular plants, apparently with only some very occasional exceptions; i.e. among the leafless Psilophytales such as *Rhynia*, *Horneophyton*, etc. But, in fact, some of the Psilophytales did form microphylls, e.g. *Asteroxylon*; and the still more ancient Silurian *Baragwanathia* had a foliar development like a small lycopod. As the writer has pointed out (Wardlaw, 1957c, d), a very general feature or function of shoot apical reaction systems is that they give rise to growth centres in a regular and orderly manner. This activity of apices, in quite different classes of plants, is probably the most important common homology of organization with which the botanist is concerned. That genetical changes are, and have been, closely involved in this aspect of apical organization is evident from the arguments set out above. But basic cell features of long standing, and the self-ordering properties of substances common to green plants in general, must also be included in any attempt to account for apical organization. As Waddington (1957) stated, orderly development in organisms involves the co-ordinated activities of genes, on the one hand, and of epigenetic factors, on the other. A somewhat similar view of the factors involved in organization has been expressed by Steward and Mohan Ram (1961).

CHAPTER 9

Tissue Differentiation and Organogenesis

DIFFERENTIATION IN THE ZYGOTE

The investigation of tissue differentiation and organization in higher plants properly begins with a study of the ovum. For some considerable time, botanists have surmised that gradients may be present not only in the encapsulated zygote in archegoniate and flowering plants, but possibly also in the still unfertilized ovum. Gradients and polarity are known to be established in the free-floating zygotes of Fucales at a very early stage after fertilization (for review, *see* Wardlaw, 1955). Evidence of gradients in the ova of higher plants is still scanty, being chiefly based on observations of the distribution of cytoplasm in fixed materials as seen under the light microscope. Zoologists have made considerably more progress. Thus Brachet (*see* Waddington, 1959, p. 227) reported that in amphibian and vertebrate eggs there are demonstrable gradients of a number of substances, including RNA and possibly specific attached enzymes, the highest RNA concentration being at the animal pole. These are essentially metabolic gradients, the oxygen consumption and reducing activity being different in different regions of the egg. Also, the incorporation of $^{14}CO_2$ into proteins and RNA follows the same kinds of gradients. In time it may be shown that comparable situations obtain in the ova and zygotes of plants (*see* Fig.2.8).

In organizational phenomena, such as polarity, which involve the movement of specific substances to the distal and proximal poles of the developing zygote, the cause is still unknown. In Waddington's (1953) view, 'we may have to take account of more subtle concepts than the simple ones of diffusion, reaction-rates and so on with which theory is trying to get along now'. This may or may not prove to be the case. It is, of course, conceivable that the solution will eventually be found in still unknown properties of large protein and other molecules, yet to be explored by the methods of physical chemistry.

During the cleavages of the zygote, Brachet (*ibid.*) reported that the synthesis of nuclear DNA and its associated proteins appears to be the major activity of early ontogenesis: little cytoplasmic RNA or protein synthesis takes place at this stage. As gastrulation proceeds, a secondary dorsiventral gradient becomes superimposed on the initial animal-vegetable gradient, and the reaction system in the developing organism becomes still more complex. To those who are familiar with plant embryology, it may well appear that some of these interesting zoological findings could also have an application to plants, e.g. to ferns (*see* Wardlaw, 1955). For example, most plant embryos begin by developing as radially-symmetrical, spindle-like or club-shaped bodies, in which polar gradients have almost certainly been established. But later, as in many dicotyledons, the embryo becomes flattened so that its symmetry is bilateral. In many monocotyledons, the embryo is dorsiventral or asymmetrical. In some ferns, which are characterized by dorsiventral rhizomes in the adult state, this asymmetry may already be apparent in quite young sporophytes, e.g. species of *Pteridium*, *Polypodium*, etc. (Fig.9.1).

Embryonic Induction. According to Nieuwkoop (*see* Waddington, 1959), certain comparable induction effects may be due to quite different processes, and very different inducing agents may evoke more or less closely comparable effects, though they may not necessarily have exercised comparable actions. Nieuwkoop suggested that the reacting system has only limited possibilities of responding, i.e. the number of alternative developmental pathways is small. 'A large number of agents might only be able to push the reaction system into one of these pathways, but these actions may also not be identical with the factors which are responsible for doing this in normal development' (p. 203).

The term *induction* has been applied to a considerable number of processes. Very often the agent inducing, or stimulating, some physiological or developmental change is an enzyme; but Nieuwkoop pointed out that many aspects of embryonic induction in animals do not belong to this category: processes other than enzymological ones may be involved.

As Waddington (1953) noted, the investigator of higher organisms is seldom confronted with the inception of a pattern *de novo* in a previously homogeneous matrix. Many examples could, however, be cited from the Plant Kingdom (Fig.9.2); but, most commonly, we are concerned with the elaboration of an originally simple system. An animal ovum or zygote, for example, typically has 'a certain inherent structure which it owes largely to the geometry of the processes by which it was formed in the ovary'. As Waddington and others have pointed out, a biological pattern tends to be progressive, self-maintaining, and capable of restoring itself after injury or disturbance.

G*

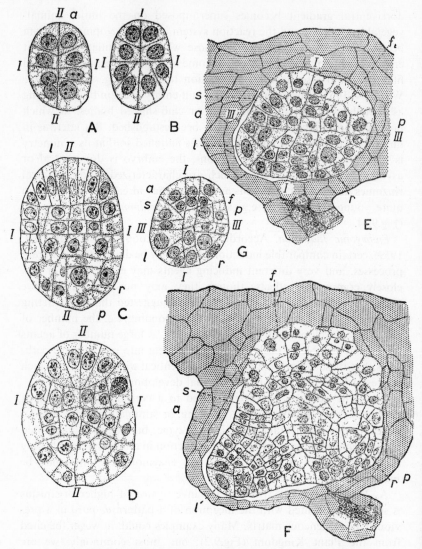

Fig.9.1 *Gymnogramme sulphurea*, a leptosporangiate fern, the early embryogenesis of which exemplifies the inception of chemical pattern. A, B, Sections of 16-celled embryo, cut at right-angles to the archegonial axis; the sections traverse the inferior octants in A and the superior octants in B; the anterior octants are uppermost (× 380). C,D,E, Older embryos; in C and D the inferior and superior octants respec-

(*Continued at foot of facing page*)

THE SHOOT APEX

The shoot apex in vascular plants is an embryonic and formative region which shows some 'plasticity' in its morphogenetic and histogenic activities but nevertheless has a relatively stable organization. In other words, following Nieuwkoop (*see* Waddington, 1959, p. 203), it has a limited number of possible alternative developments. Wardlaw (1957) has shown, by the direct application of a considerable range of quite different substances to the apex of *Dryopteris dilatata*, that comparable responses were often obtained, indicating that the apical reaction system can only be modified in a small number of ways and remain viable, though it may become *disorganized* in various ways. Moreover, after most surgical treatments of the fern apex, there is usually a return to the original organization, provided the apical cell region has not been damaged (Figs. 9.3, 9.4, 9.5; Plate 8).

That vegetative apices remain constant in some respects yet change in others during ontogenesis and, more especially, at the onset of flowering in angiosperms, may be recognized; i.e. a reacting embryonic tissue behaves in a way that is characteristic of its age (connoting its size and the stage reached in ontogenesis). This aspect of cellular organization has also been recognized by zoologists though in a rather different context (Toivonen, *see* Waddington, 1959) (Fig.9.6).

In vascular plants, the primary tissue systems originate at the apical meristems of vegetative main shoots, branches, leaves, flower buds and roots. A brief account of the histological constitution and organization of the shoot apical growing point is relevant at this point (for fuller refs., Wardlaw, 1952, 1957, 1963; Esau, 1953 and Sinnott, 1960).

What has long proved so puzzling to botanists may be stated quite simply: it is that, whereas certain major functional, i.e. morphogenetic

---

tively have been cut parallel to the transverse wall; in E, the section is a longitudinal median one; i.e. it is cut parallel to the axes of the archegonium and the prothallus; C, shows that the first leaf is derived from both octants; the root initial can be seen in one of the posterior octants; in E the first leaf, the shoot apex, the first root and the foot are distinguishable (× 380). F, A still older embryo in longitudinal median section. G. *Scolopendrium vulgare.* Longitudinal median section of embryo, showing the obliquity of the first partition walls in the anterior octants, no 'epibasal disc' being formed; I–I, first or basal wall; II–II, second or median wall; III–III, third or transverse wall; *l*, leaf; *s*, shoot apex; *r*, root; *f*, foot. (A–E, G, × 380; F, × 190.) (After Vladesco, from C. W. Wardlaw, *Embryogenesis in Plants.*)

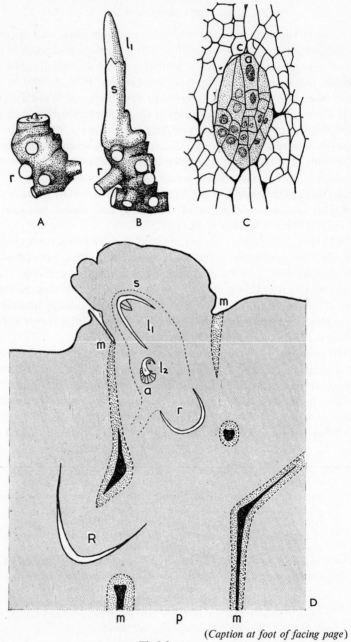

(*Caption at foot of facing page*)

Fig.9.2

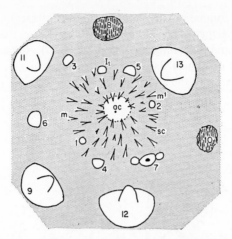

Fig.9.3 *Dryopteris dilatata.* A shoot apex as seen from above, after treatment with yeast extract. The original conical apex, indicated approximately by *m-m'*, has become rather flattened and scaly (*sc*) close to the apical cell (*ac*). The younger leaf primordia (P_1-P_7) which were present at the beginning of the experiment have remained rather small, as also has the next primordium to appear, I_1. The apex of P_7 was slightly damaged and two lateral primordia have been formed. P_8 and P_{10} were damaged at the outset. (× 13). (*Annals of Botany.*)

Fig.9.2 *Ophioglossum vulgatum.* Endogenous regenerative growth from the pith of a decapitated shoot.

A, An early stage, after a few weeks;

B, An older stage, after 4–5 months. l_1, the first leaf of the endogenous bud; *s*, sheath, formed from pith parenchyma; *r*, roots of parent shoot (× 3).

C, Inception of the apex, *a*, of an endogenous bud. A group of cells within the ellipsoidal mass of meristematic cells has elongated and divided by longitudinal walls. The adjacent cells are dividing by anticlinal walls, and a lysis of the overlying cell walls, which will result in the development of a cavity, *c*, above the apex, is beginning to take place. (× 200).

D, A well developed endogenous bud differentiated in the pith at the distal end of a decapitated shoot. An ellipsoidal mass of meristematic cells was first formed; within this a shoot meristem and first leaf became differentiated, followed by the inception of the first root. *m*, meristeles of parent shoot; *p*, pith; *a*, bud apex; l_1, l_2, leaves of newly organized bud; *r*, bud root; *R*, root of parent shoot; *s*, sheath of first leaf, consisting of modified cells of pith parenchyma (semi-diagrammatic, × 45). (*Annals of Botany.*)

activities are common to the shoot apices in all classes of vascular plants, they may nevertheless be very different in their size, shape, histological constitution and differentiation pattern (Fig.9.7). Apices may be conical paraboloidal or almost flat; their leaf primordia may be of small or large size relative to the apical meristem; and they may arise close to the

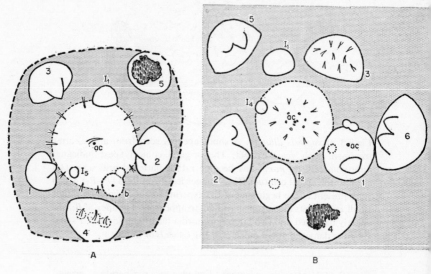

Fig.9.4 A. *Dryopteris dilatata*. As in Fig.9.3, showing an apex which had been treated directly with dinitrophenol. A large scale has developed close to the apical cell (*ac*) and a bud (*b*), with one leaf primordium, has been formed in the I_2 site. B. Another apex treated with dinitrophenol. The apical meristem has become scaly to the summit and P_1 has been induced to develop into a bud of considerable size ($\times$ 20). (*Annals of Botany*.)

summit or centre of the meristem, or in positions well down its flanks. For many recent and contemporary anatomists, the great diversity in the histological constitution of apices, e.g. in the number and relationships of their histogenic layers, has provided much scope for observation and conjecture. In fact, some seven or more 'apical types' have now been described (for reviews and literature *see* Gifford, 1954; Buvat, 1952, 1955; Bersillon, 1955). Yet, notwithstanding the differences of detail, an inference that may justly be drawn is that, in their overall organization and morphogenetic activities, all shoot apices are essentially alike. It should, therefore, be possible – it should certainly be the aim – to formulate some general ideas which would explain, in part at least, why axis apices show this remarkable homology of organization. So we may ask what conclusions may be drawn from an objective survey of the constitution and activity of shoot apices when due account is taken of the facts known from anatomical, experimental, genetical and other investigations.

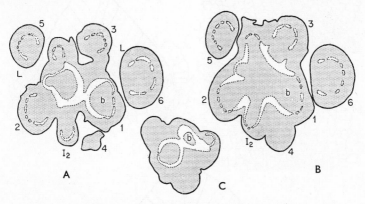

Fig.9.5 *Dryopteris dilatata*. Transverse sections of the apices illustrated in Fig.9.4 A, B. A, B, show the large solenostelic bud (*b*), with its leaf primordium, as illustrated in Fig.9.4 B. C, shows the position of the bud (*b*) in Fig.9.4 A. (× 8). (*Annals of Botany*.)

APICAL ORGANIZATION AND REACTIVITY AS DETERMINED BY GENETICAL FACTORS

The aspects of apical organization and reactivity which appear to be closely and primarily determined by the genetical constitution may be indicated as follows, due allowance being made for the effects of environmental factors and for the stage reached in ontogenesis.

1. *The Size and Constitution of the Cells of the Meristem*. The view that the size of meristem cells is determined by genetical factors is supported by a growing body of evidence (summarized by Wardlaw, 1952b, 1953b). Since, in the ontogenetic development of any species, there is no absolute size for meristem or embryonic cells, this statement must be qualified in various ways; but it serves to convey a general truth, namely, that when the individual plant has reached a certain size, under the usual conditions of growth, the cells of its apical meristem are of a characteristic size (Fig.9.6).

2. *The Relative Rates of Growth in the Vertical and Transverse Planes.*

This relationship is a very important one, because it determines the shape of the apical and subapical regions (*see also* Chapter 10). In conjunction with the factors of cell size and constitution, the specific

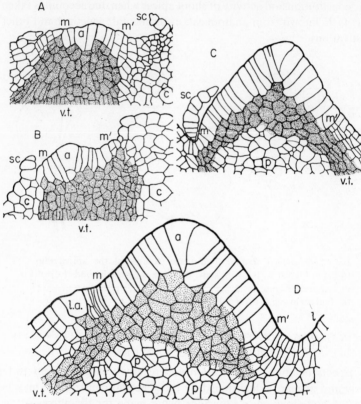

Fig.9.6 *Matteuccia struthiopteris.* Longitudinal median sections (semi-diagrammatic) of shoot apices of different sizes: the essential features of the organization of the apical meristem, with its conspicuous apical cell, as established in the young sporophyte or a bud, (A), are retained as the meristem increases in size; but there are evident changes in cell size and in the distribution of growth and of tissues, e.g. the transverse component is conspicuous in the subapical region of large shoots in which a pith is present. *a*, apical cell; m–m′, apical meristem; *la*, leaf apex; *c*, cortex; *p*, pith parenchyma; *vt*, incipient vascular tissue; *sc*, scale (× 135). (*Annals of Botany.*)

distribution of growth may largely determine the characteristic cellular constitution of the apex, i.e. the disposition of embryonic cells in a characteristic number of histogenic layers, or whatever the cellular pattern may be. Qualifications of the kind indicated in (1) will also apply here (Fig.9.7).

3. *The Absolute Size of the Apex.* In all embryos the apex is initially of very small size; but whereas in some species it undergoes a relatively small ontogenetic increase in size, in other species, e.g. in ferns and cycads, it undergoes a progressive ontogenetic enlargement and is eventually of large relative size. Genetical factors as in (1) and (2)

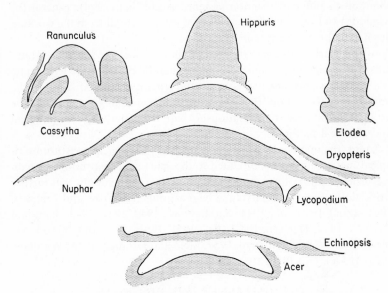

Fig.9.7 Outlines of various shoot apices, as seen in longitudinal median section, to illustrate the very varied distribution of growth in different species. (All × 150.)

above participate closely in these developments, but environmental and other factors, which may affect the supply of nutrients to the apex, must be given due weight.

4. *The Positions of Growth Centres.* The concept of growth centres is considered later (*see* Chapter 10). A leaf primordium typically develops on the meristem at a locus of special metabolism, i.e. at a growth centre. The positions of such loci are specific. In different species, growth centres may be high up or low down on the meristem, and may comprise cells pertaining to relatively superficial or relatively deep-seated histogenic layers. These positional relationships affect the size and shape of primordia and their phyllotaxis.

5. *The Nature of the Apical Reaction System.* The apex is the seat of many complex but interrelated chemical reactions, all the necessary metabolic substances being contained in the embryonic cells or supplied from below. As the components of the apical reaction system are directly or indirectly determined by hereditary factors, each system is specific in character; but since many of the major metabolic processes are common to all green plants, certain components are likely to be common to different reaction systems. Accordingly, both general (or common) and specific effects may be expected to result from the working of an apical reaction system.

At this stage in the investigation of shoot apices the foregoing statements are unavoidably no more than general indications of what may, at a later stage, become the basis of valid criteria of comparison. For the time being, they show that the diverse apical configurations can be brought into at least some relationship with the underlying physiological and genetical factors.

So far, the number of papers in which the histological constitution of apical meristems has been related to the genetical constitution is small. Nevertheless the points enumerated above leave little doubt that further work along these lines is likely to be rewarding (*see* Cross and Johnson, 1941; Randolph *et al.*, 1944; Satina *et al.*, 1940, 1941, 1943; Bain and Dermen, 1944; Dermen, 1945, 1947, 1951, 1953; Abbe and Stein, 1954; Stein, 1955; Weber and Stein, 1954; Stein and Kroman, 1954; Wardlaw, 1952, 1957c). (*see* Plate 10).

THE DIFFERENTIATION OF TISSUES

In an actively growing meristematic region, such as the apex of a shoot or root, some of the cells retain their densely protoplasmic embryonic character and persist as initiating cells, but others undergo characteristic physiological and morphological changes and at maturity have special functional activities. These modified or derivative cells are described as having become differentiated. Among the flowering plants, primary and secondary meristems, e.g. cambium, give rise to a considerable number of different kinds of specialized cells. Gymnosperms and pteridophytes have vascular tissues which are less highly differentiated (Bailey, 1954); and in bryophytes tissue differentiation is considerably less varied still. Green algae exemplify a very small measure of differentiation but in some brown algae there is quite a high degree of differentiation which, indeed, affords parallelisms with developments in higher plants (Fritsch, 1945).

Although all the embryonic cells of a shoot, leaf or root apical meristem are initially identical in respect of their genetical constitution, they may give rise to very different kinds of cells. Quite unlike cells may be differentiated side by side, although both originated from the same mother cell. Students of botany have long been familiar with this curious and still enigmatic phenomenon. They have also been aware of a second and not less important phenomenon, namely, that the process of differentiation is one in which order normally prevails: differentiating embryonic cells *typically give rise to a characteristic tissue pattern*, e.g. the rays of xylem and phloem as seen in a cross-section of a root stele. These two features of differentiation, which afford good visual evidence of organization, are among the great unsolved problems of botany. In the development of a plant the process of differentiation, involving the formation of tissues specialized for different functions, photosynthesis, conduction, storage, mechanical support, etc., has often been described as exemplifying the principle of division of labour. That this is an end result, and that it is very important in the economy of the plant, cannot fail to be recognized. To the contemporary student of morphogenesis, however, the differential development of contiguous or adjacent cells suggests that the factors which are operative during the earliest stages are those which must be specially investigated, i.e. those relating to developmental harmony. The advent of the electron microscope has given renewed impetus to these enquiries (*see* Esau, 1963).

If all embryonic cells are genetically identical, as has long been maintained, what explanation can we offer of their development into such different elements as epidermis, fibres, endodermis, tracheids, storage parenchyma, etc.? And what can be said of the causation of the characteristic tissue patterns in stem, leaf, and root? In fact, two rather different kinds of explanation, or interpretation, have been advanced.

All explanations of differentiation must evidently include some reference, explicit or implied, to the genetical constitution; for this must be such as to admit of the observed developments. However, it is quite clear from the literature that many workers simply accept the genetical constitution as 'given' and thereafter proceed to account for cell differentiation in one or other of several ways, but usually without reference to the specific action of genes. For convenience, these may be grouped together as 'non-genetical explanations'. With the advance of physiological genetics, however, attempts are now being made to explain differentiation more closely in terms of genic action. These will here be referred to as 'genetical explanations'.

'NON-GENETICAL' FACTORS IN TISSUE DIFFERENTIATION

Although all differentiation must be based on the specific hereditary substance of the cell, many important differential developments do not appear to be closely and specifically gene-controlled, or gene-determined. Polarity, for example, which is a primary feature of all filamentous and axial development, is not demonstrably gene-controlled.

Again, in *all* organisms which form any considerable tissue mass, there are evident differences in the outer and inner cells. The position in the plant in which a cell undergoes its development, as Vöchting and Driesch long ago observed, seems to determine how it will become differentiated and specialized. And this is just as true of *Fucus serratus* as it is of *Bellis perennis*. Even among the lowly Protococcales (Chlorophyceae), e.g. *Scenedesmus* or *Pediastrum*, the peripheral cells are different from those within. Further light is shed on this interesting relationship by recent investigations. When cells are removed from their normal tissue environment, as in the aseptic culture of single cells in an aqueous medium, they show quite different conformations and activities from those in a coherent tissue matrix (Steward and Ram, 1961; Steward, 1961) (Fig.9.8 and Plate 11).

In the shoot of a vascular plant, the outline of the stele, as seen in a cross-section, is usually in close conformity with that of the stem, suggesting that pressures within the developing system are responsible for moulding the column of incipient vascular tissue (Priestley, 1928). That the contour of the stele is indeed directly related to that of the stem has been demonstrated in experiments in which the apical meristem in flowering plants and ferns was isolated from the adjacent tissues by three or by four vertical incisions. On further growth a short shoot was formed. In it the stele was of triangular or quadrangular outline, in accordance with the incision pattern. When the apex of *Dryopteris dilatata* was radially incised at several points, a stellate stele was obtained (Wardlaw, 1952). The literature also contains many interesting examples of the dedifferentiation of adult parenchyma, with subsequent redifferentiation, the development of new patterns being in accord with the new situation (Esau, 1953, and Wardlaw, 1964; *and see* Fig.9.9, p. 214).

As already noted in Chapter 8, the early segmentation pattern in developing embryos is closely comparable throughout the Plant Kingdom. These patterns are in general agreement with Errera's Law and suggest that physical and other self-ordering principles are of primary importance in this aspect of development. In other words, *closely comparable physical or physico-chemical events take place in cytoplasm governed by quite different genotypes.*

A number of growth-regulating (or growth) substances, variously described as auxins, phytohormones, etc., are of wide occurrence in the Plant Kingdom. These are important, sometimes essential, factors in particular morphogenic and histogenic developments. The effects with which some of them are associated are very variable indeed, e.g. the action of different concentrations of indoleacetic acid on buds, leaves

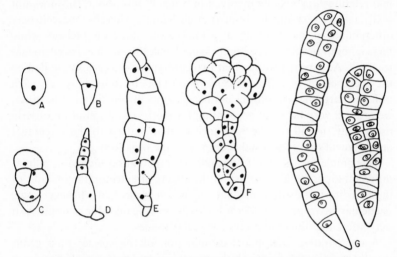

Fig.9.8 *Daucus carota* (carrot): A–F, Embryo-like bodies and other cellular groups obtained by the culture of individual cells (from phloem tissue) in media of known composition. (After F. C. Steward *et al. Amer. Jour. Botany.*) G, Normal embryos. (After H. A. Borthwick, *Bot. Gaz.*)

and roots and on various tissues (reviews in Wardlaw, 1952; Audus, 1959; Steward and Ram, 1961). Comparable morphogenetic effects have also been produced by applications of a considerable range of quite different synthetic organic substances. In short, during their development, embryonic cells, e.g. a zygote or a cell in the shoot apex, are subjected to nutritional and other stimuli and respond by developing in characteristic ways. Although these stimuli are related to the genetical constitution of the species, physiologists such as Steward and Ram (1961) have emphasized they are of common occurrence in the cells of many different species. These authors regard them as factors in the category of 'nurture' rather than of 'nature' (implying close genetical control). In other words, chemical growth regulation, in the sense used by Steward and Ram, is due to 'non-genetical' factors; but these factors work in close conjunction with more specifically genetical controlling agents. However, it would perhaps be more correct to recognize that hormonal and other substances are typically formed under genic control in other parts of the plant.

Now, while one may recognize that a cell differentiates according to its position in the plant, and that various extrinsic factors and organismal relationships may be involved in bringing this about, this does not really tell us very much about the mechanism whereby one cell may differentiate in one way, e.g. as a thick-walled fibre or tracheid, while its neighbour develops as a highly vacuolated, thin-walled, parenchymatous cell. And even if we say that two contiguous cells are stimulated by the metabolism of adjacent cells to develop in different ways, each utilizing particular substances not being competitively used by the other, we are still very far from accounting for (i) the inception of an orderly tissue pattern and (ii) the relevance of that pattern to the integrated development and functional economy of the organism.

The simple fact is that, in virtually every situation involving cellular differentiation, we have to assess the effects of extrinsic factors and of the hereditary constitution. That this is so can be seen whenever some particular environmental factor is closely investigated; for example, as it may affect the differentiation of vascular tissues.

A comparative anatomical examination of the species of a genus usually reveals that, although the cross-sectional patterns of their adult stems, or steles, are generally comparable, there are many differences of detail. For example, in the shoots of *Lycopodium*, *Selaginella* spp., or in the roots of various related genera, there may be evident differences in the diameter of the stele, the disposition of xylem and phloem, and the size and wall thickness of the tracheids (Wardlaw, 1924, 1925, 1928). Anatomists cannot but be familiar with observations of this kind. In a recent investigation, Larson (1962) has shown that in *Pinus resinosa*, the diameter of tracheids is indirectly affected by photoperiod. When buds and needles were exposed to long-days, needle elongation and tracheid diameter were increased, whereas short-days resulted in a cessation of needle elongation and in tracheids of narrower diameter. These responses to different photoperiodic exposures varied according to the stage of development. During the phase of active elongation of the shoot, the terminal bud exerted a decisive regulatory effect on tracheid diameter; but the leaves (needles) were the main source of this tracheid-enlargement stimulus once shoot extension growth had ceased. Larson concluded that the effects of photoperiod on tracheid diameter are probably indirect and that they may be referred to auxin production and distribution in terminal meristems.

GENES AND DIFFERENTIATION

During recent years evidence has been accumulating that the kind of differentiation that an animal or plant embryonic cell undergoes is subject to much closer genic control than had hitherto been thought. The view has also been gaining ground that, in some materials at least, all the daughter nuclei in a meristematic region are not necessarily of identical potentiality (*see also* Chapters 2 and 4).

Comparative morphological studies of genetical materials, differing in single genes, or as a result of genic mutation, polyploidy, aneuploidy, etc., have shown that definite organizational changes can be associated with known changes in the genetic constitution (*see* Wardlaw, 1952). When one considers the multiplicity of organelles and particles of different sizes, colloids, etc., in the cytoplasm of an embryonic cell, the mechanisms of the genic control of differentiation, so that, as it were, 'the right things' happen in the right place at the right time and in the appropriate sequence, raise problems of the most profound nature. A recognition of the contribution of non-genetical factors does not get us very far. The genetical theories that have been advanced and the investigations undertaken show awareness of some aspects of the problem; but the work is still at a very early stage.

In the process of differentiation, many substances, including proteins, are simultaneously involved; there are also reactions which probably take place in a stepwise sequence; i.e. there is not the gradual working out of a single process (Waddington, 1948). At any particular phase, differentiation tends to be autocatalytic. The evidence indicates that trends tend to be canalized, with the result that definite and distinct organs and tissues are formed; and the processes involved are largely irreversible. The concepts of alternative chains of syntheses, based on the protein-forming action of specific genes, and of competition by the different proteins for the same substrate materials, are important in Waddington's theory of differentiation.

Some recent investigators have emphasized that the genetical constitution and related potentialities of cells change as differentiation proceeds. Other cytogeneticists, however, maintain that, during mitosis, each daughter cell receives a complete complement of genetical materials (*see* Mazia, 1961). Contemporary views on how genes may determine cell specialization in animals have been discussed by Fishberg and Blackler (1961) and may be summarized as also having relevance to plants.

(i) The nucleus, the cytoplasm and the cell environment all participate in differentiation, the environmental factors being secondary or non-dominant.

(ii) The development of the egg is attended by active synthesis of glycogen, lipids, proteins and nucleoproteins. The substances synthesized are numerous, varied and complex. It is held that they originate at the sites of 10,000–20,000 genes, each of which may give rise to a different substance.

(iii) With the establishment of polarity in the zygote, the nucleus, mitochondria, clear cytoplasm and RNA particles concentrate near the distal or animal pole, whereas the yolk granules become larger and more densely packed towards the basal or vegetable pole. There is thus evidence of a differential, or heterogeneous, distribution of metabolites; and gradient effects may be expected to follow.

(iv) The initial radial symmetry of many animal eggs is eventually changed to bilateral symmetry. (According to the species this may take place before or after fertilization.) These and other observations suggest or indicate that the main configuration of the future embryo is predetermined in the undivided egg, i.e. by the distribution of metabolic substances and organelles.

(v) Accordingly, as cell division progresses, with deposition of cell membranes, *each daughter nucleus is in a different cytoplasmic and biochemical environment.* While all the nuclei at this stage are held to be still genetically identical and totipotent, they may show differences in activity, particular activities being evoked or induced by factors in the cytoplasmic environment of the individual nucleus. In other words, *different cytoplasmic states influence identical nuclei to react in different ways.* Or, one might also say that the cytoplasm in a particular condition provides a suitable substrate for some of the gene-controlled enzymes and, accordingly, their respective genes are those which become active.

(vi) It is now known from cytological studies that particular gene loci on giant chromosomes typically become active at certain times. In fact, they swell, or puff-up, into what are known as Balbiani rings. These occur in a specific pattern, e.g. quite different 'puffs' appear in mature as compared with young larvae. Such observations support the view that certain genes become specially active at particular stages of development.

(vii) Experiments in which the nucleus was removed from the egg and replaced by a nucleus from another egg (zygote), or from the tissue of a later embryonic stage, of the same species of frog, have yielded information on the relation between nucleus and cytoplasm. In such 'transplant' embryos it was found: (a) that an implanted nucleus from the blastula stage usually yielded a normal transplant embryo; (b) that implanted nuclei from advanced embryonic stages yielded fewer normal embryos, most of the transplant embryos failing to cleave normally, dying, or becoming arrested after a phase of abnormal growth; i.e. some of these nuclei appear to have lost their totipotency, or to have become limited in their ability to contribute to normal development; (c) implanted nuclei taken from a particular nascent organ, e.g. the gut, yielded a considerable variety of embryos, suggesting that nuclei may not only vary from one organ to another but that considerable nuclear diversity may exist within a single organ; (d) it is apparently during the period when the young embryo is changing rapidly that nuclei become most diverse; implant nuclei taken from later embryonic stages, e.g. newly hatched tadpoles, tend to yield embryos showing considerable uniformity; (e) in experiments in which the nuclei from 'nuclear clones' were used, the embryos formed from a clone of early embryonic origin were closely comparable; but there was considerable variability in the embryos provided from clones of later embryonic origin, indicating or suggesting that nuclear changes due to natural differentiation are relatively stable, irreversible, and heritable.

Some years ago it would have been almost unthinkable to consider that nuclei might, during differentiation, change in their genetical qualities. Recently more and more cases of irreversible nuclear changes induced by cytoplasmic factors have been brought to our attention. ... Differentiation is most likely to result from nuclear-cytoplasmic interactions which cause progressive individuation of the cytoplasm and increasing specialization of the nuclei of particular cells (Fishberg and Blackler, 1961).

These are interesting and important findings. Whether they are generally applicable to the normal embryonic development in plants and animals will require a great deal of further research. Some of the results could perhaps be explained by loss of gene function as development proceeds (Mather, 1961). The possibility that nuclei may undergo changes during ontogenesis and tissue specialization has now been discussed over a considerable period of time, e.g. by Sinnott (1946). He pointed out that a hitherto unsuspected aspect of differentiation may be due to the fact that many mature cells do not possess the basic chromosome number of the embryo or meristem but a multiple of it, such somatic polyploidy being characteristic of certain tissues. Plant cells in general do not provide clear evidence of nuclear changes during cell division and development. It is true that not all maturing cells remain totipotent, but many of them which have not become too specialized, e.g. with thick lignified walls, can become dedifferentiated and redifferentiated to yield, for example, active cambia or bud meristems. There are also many instances where a specialized organ, such as a root, can give rise to a bud, the bud to a plant with roots, and so on (*see* Wardlaw, 1952, p. 189 *et seq*.).

Occasional cells in different parts of the plant may change genetically by mutation or other mechanisms but, in general, these have no significant effects on the organization of viable species. However, against that finding may be placed the fact that, in intact plants and in tissue cultures, like tends to beget like, i.e. a phloem mass in a tissue culture tends to proliferate into phloem, and so on; and in the normal differentiation of tissues below a meristem the newly differentiated xylem and phloem tend to be in normal acropetal continuity with the strands of xylem and phloem respectively which are already present in the older regions. These relationships, however, need not necessarily denote permanent changes in the complement of genes in the nucleus.

To widen the discussion, it may be noted that the zoological findings briefly outlined above could be given a rather different emphasis. In item (v), it may be conceded that each nucleus finds itself in a different cytoplasmic or biochemical environment as the embryonic development proceeds and that it may show different activities from other nuclei in other cytoplasmic environments. The nucleus must, admittedly, have this repertory of potential activities or it could not display them. Moreover, it is held by geneticists that nuclei have many potential activities that are never, or only rarely, displayed. It is no less cogent to emphasize that the actual or proximate cause of a particular nuclear activity is the reactive state of the cytoplasm. And if we enquire how the state of a particular mass or region of cytoplasm is determined, the answer appears to be that it is mainly due to an earlier patternizing of the protoplasm, e.g. during the establishment of polarity by self-ordering, spatial or largely 'non-genetical' factors. Moreover, the cytoplasmic reactivity is due, to an extent that is difficult to specify, to physiological properties which are universal in green plants.

With regard to item (viic) above, the variable behaviour of implant nuclei taken from different nascent organs, or even from the same organ, suggests that the nucleus is very stable in some respects but somewhat plastic or labile in others. The importance of this plasticity may be recognized but, in plants at least, much more evidence is required before its significance can be properly assessed. Indeed, in species of higher plants, in the development of which very large numbers of genes are involved, it appears that many genes must exercise very much the same kind of effects on the cytoplasm and yield closely comparable metabolic end-products.

'*Messenger RNA.*' The 'information', or 'specifications', required for the development of an organism, is held to be 'coded' in the nuclear genes and from them it is transmitted to ribosomes in the cytoplasm (*see* Chapter 4, p. 79).* As a result, a very large number of enzymes (proteins) is formed – reference is made to numbers such as 1,000–2,000 in the cells of animals – and these determine the characteristic and varied metabolism of the cell. Recent investigations, chiefly based on bacteria, indicate that the 'messengers' between nuclear genes and cytoplasmic ribosomes are RNA molecules (for review, *see* Hurwitz and Furth, 1962). The biochemical details of the process, whereby genetic DNA determines the formation of different protein molecules on the surface of ribosomes, are of great complexity (*see* Crick *et al.*, 1961). They need not be considered at length here, though one cannot fail to pay tribute to the ingenuity that has made this information available. These investigations help us to understand how different specific enzymes may be formed; and, given the enzymes, many different metabolic developments will be able to take place in the cell; or particular reactions may be accelerated, and so on. We can also see that various sequential reactions may be set in motion and that these may contribute to the orderly differentiation of the cell. But, profoundly important as these new advances in biochemical genetics are, they must be greatly supplemented by other kinds of information if we are really to understand why particular cells differentiate as they do; and how the various kinds of differentiation in contiguous cells, constituting a

---

* This development of contemporary botany impresses the author as having two very contrasted aspects: on the one hand, it constitutes an almost incredible advance, albeit with some highly speculative elements; on the other, it is a great over-simplification of a complex physico-chemical system.

tissue pattern, take place in such a way as to fulfil the functional needs of the developing and adult organism. The physical aspects of the movements of large numbers of 'messenger' molecules, on different 'errands' to specific locations in the cytoplasm, seen in relation to the enormous complexity of the cytoplasm, raise problems of formidable magnitude.

PARAMUTATION AND DIFFERENTIATION

Mutations may be of different kinds (Mather, 1961): (i) undirected sporadic mutation of the usual kind recognized by geneticists; and (ii) *paramutation* in which the change in the allele, under certain conditions, is of a directed, determinate character; i.e. it occurs regularly and is attended by the same effects under particular conditions; it can give rise to a graded series of products; and changed alleles are metastable rather than stable. It is not essential to go into the details of paramutation here but, briefly, the gene locus is held to be dual, containing both orthochromatin and parachromatin. Of the latter, Mather has stated that although it is 'not of the essence of gene structure', it nevertheless 'affects the expression of the gene's action'; and also that parachromatin, or 'ancillary materials', behave as regularly as genes and are 'transmitted as precisely as the genes themselves'.

Genetical views on the relation of nuclear paramutation to cytoplasmic change are of some considerable interest in the context of this book. Some kinds of paramutation may be important in that the activity of certain genes, as in *Drosophila*, changes differentially during development: the changes are characteristically associated with different tissues, 'so that they are determined by the state of the cells in the tissues and indeed are inevitable under the condition of the tissue . . . '. Mather has suggested that the incidence of paramutational changes during development may, or could, have important constructive effects on differentiation, the cytoplasm being the seat of the relevant activities. 'The divergences of differentiation must spring basically from differences in the cytoplasmic materials even though secondarily it may involve nuclear differences, including paramutational changes, arising as responses to the initial cytoplasmic differences.' In short, changes in the cytoplasm are responsible for changes in the nucleus. But since the cytoplasm is itself conditioned by the genotype, we are really dealing with reciprocal relationships. Mather has stated:

Thus paramutation, like any other nuclear change in development, must be due directly to an action of the cytoplasm (or at least extra-chromosomal plasm) on the nuclear materials and only indirectly on the genes which acted to change and mould that cytoplasm in the first instance. The significance of paramutation in development would thus be that it fixed, so to speak, the initially cytoplasmic changes, and gave to them a precision in cell heredity that purely cytoplasmic transmission could not guarantee.

Paramutational changes, based on the presence of ancillary materials in the chromosomes, could, in this view, be

of great significance in development. But in differentiation they could have only a derived significance springing from and dependent on the reflexion – one might almost say crystallization – by paramutation of primary changes in the cytoplasm to which indeed differentiation must still ultimately be referred.

Mather's interesting speculations have taken him still further. For, he has argued, if cytoplasmic changes effect paramutational changes in the chromosomes, external factors, working through the cytoplasm, may also 'bring about directed changes in the hereditary materials' (*see* Chapter 15). Evidence of this sequence in transmitted change is beginning to be obtained, e.g. Durrant (1958) and Roper (1958).

CELLULAR DIVERSITY

Although the tissue patterns in the organs of plants are exceedingly varied, the number of different kinds of cell involved is not very great; but, as every student of anatomy knows, there is great variety and specificity in the histological details. The flowering plants afford the widest range in histological diversity. From comparative studies of fossil and living flowering plants, gymnosperms and pteridophytes, it has been conclusively demonstrated that the course of evolution has been attended by increasing specialization and diversification of cells. In physiological investigations it has been shown that, during the differentiation of embryonic cells, e.g. into parenchyma, a segment of a wood vessel, etc., growth-regulating substances, general metabolites, and sequential or serial enzymatic activities are involved. But we know little as yet about specific genic action in these histogenic processes.

The number of enzymes involved in the growth and differentiation of an embryonic cell is usually described as being very large: geneticists speak in terms of thousands of genes, so by implication there is an equivalent repertoire of enzymes. But one may enquire if, after all, the number of enzymes obligatorily involved in the formation of a parenchymatous cell, or a fibrous tracheid, is so very large. It is a fact that, in plants and animals collectively, as many as 1,000 different proteins are known and, indeed, the number may well be considerably greater. But do we know how many proteins are necessarily involved in the major kinds of cellular development, or how many of these are common to plant cells in general? That several enzymes are required in the synthesis of relatively simple substances is well known. It certainly would be interesting to know how many enzymes – and therefore presumably genes – participate in the expansion of an embryonic cell into a vacuolated parenchyma cell, or in the formation of a sieve-tube.

The points indicated above, and many others of the same general kind, concerning which one can find very little specific information in standard texts, are clearly worthy of much fuller exploration. The many close similarities in the cells and tissues of unrelated species, e.g. ferns and flowering plants, suggest that, however complex the enzyme systems are deemed to be, and however closely they are controlled by the nuclear genes, the evolution of certain major, common biochemical processes and trends as well as of many specific ones, has attended the process of descent. Although the great biochemical complexity of plants, especially those of more advanced organization, is being increasingly demonstrated, it does appear that some valid simplification of present views on differentiation may eventually become possible. It is an interesting and possibly significant fact that conspicuous organizational changes are sometimes determined by quite small genetical differences, e.g. zygomorphy and peloria in snapdragon.

ULTRASTRUCTURE OF DIFFERENTIATED CELLS

As Esau (1963) has noted, many of the initial investigations of the ultrastructure of protoplasm have been made on meristematic and relatively undifferentiated cells; and, with personal contributions, she has reviewed what is known to date regarding the appearance of some of the principal organelles and other components during cellular differentiation. (Readers are referred to this paper for recent literature.) It is typical of differentiating cells that they develop more or less conspicuous vacuoles. How vacuoles originate and develop is still controversial; but tannins appear to have some important association at their inception and, as electron microscopy has revealed, their peripheral tonoplast, though a single-layered membrane, and apparently thinner than the endoplasmic reticulum, is a conspicuous feature. Tonoplasts can be recognized in parenchyma cells and in young tracheary and sieve elements; but as sieve-tubes mature, the tonoplast disappears, though the ectoplast persists; and, in vessel segments, tonoplast disappearance is a concomitant of the general protoplasmic breakdown. As to the nucleus, Esau has shown that although changes in its shape and activity may attend differential developments, e.g. the formation of 'extensions' of the membrane, the assumption of various amoeboid, lobed or invaginated conformations, etc., we do not yet know what are the essential or significant changes in it that attend the several kinds of cellular differentiation. In the mitochondria, the abundant development of cristae or tubules is typically associated with a high rate of enzymic activity. Buvat (1958) observed that mitochondrial cristae became more numerous in differentiating photosynthetic leaf cells of *Elodea*; but in cells in which starch storage is evident, the mitochondria remain relatively undifferentiated. In *Cucurbita* Esau observed that well differentiated mitochondrial cristae are present in phloem companion-cells and parenchyma, whereas in mature sieve-tubes the mitochondria are devoid of cristae. The endoplasmic reticulum is relatively poorly developed in the embryonic cells of shoot and root apical meristems and consists of relatively small and short, individual tubules or cisternae, though a somewhat similar development has been observed in highly vacuolated procambial cells of *Datura*. In fact, the endoplasmic reticulum appears to vary in amount and conformation at different stages in differentiating cells. Whaley *et al.* (1960) concluded that there is a progressive breaking-down of these organelles during differentiation in the root cells of maize; but Buvat (1961) reported no change in the appearance of the reticulum during vacuolation in root parenchyma cells in *Triticum*. Other records, e.g. of abundant endoplasmic reticulum in particular cells, do not yet provide us with a clear general conception of the behaviour of this ultrastructural feature during differentiation (*see* Esau, 1963, for a detailed review of the relevant literature). The effect of differentiation on the dictyosomes (approximately synonymous with the *Golgi complex* or *apparatus*) is still obscure. On the whole, they appear to be less abundant in highly vacuolated cells and in sieve-tubes and tracheary elements which are approaching final maturation, with their well-known concomitant protoplasmic changes. Electron microscopy has provided convincing evidence of the continuity of plasmodesmata through cell walls and of their close connection or relationship with the endoplasmic reticulum. During cell differentiation, the plastids which will become chloroplasts develop the now well-known elaborate grana-pattern. But, as Esau has reported, the plastids in many cells may remain in their poorly organized juvenile state. The degree of elaboration of plastids appears to be closely related to the kind of maturing cell in which they occur. Esau's survey indicates that, broadly speaking, the main concepts of cellular differentiation based on the use of the light microscope have been confirmed and extended by electron microscopy; and she concluded that while the position in which a cell occurs in a developing organ affects its differentiation, this postulate affords only a partial solution to a major problem: 'Positional relations are reflections of an organization of high order, that of the plant as a whole. The ultimate basis of this organization has yet to be discovered.'

Weier (1963), in a critical review of the changes that take place in the fine structure of chloroplasts and mitochondria during phylogenetic and ontogenetic development, has indicated that the numerous contemporary hypotheses relating to the origin and development of cell organelles, e.g. by the transformation of one organelle into another, need to be treated with considerable caution, particularly if their genetical and biochemical implications are borne in mind. Weier has emphasized that mitochondrial structure has great stability as compared with the variability seen in plastids and has suggested that variations in the pathways in photosynthesis may have been a factor in evolution. He has advocated an approach to plant cellular biology in which observations on comparative ultrastructure would be combined with others on comparative biochemistry.

Marinos (1963) reported that the elongation of the shoot apex in barley is retarded by deficiencies in N, P and Mg, but not by K or S. When the related ultrastructural developments were examined, it was found that these either preceded or occurred simultaneously with the aforementioned external changes. These included (i) the appearance of many intramitochondrial granules and a reduction in the length of the mitochondrial tubules; (ii) the accumulation in the cytoplasm of dense manganophile inclusions, which appeared to be formed by the Golgi bodies (dictyosomes); (iii) the accumulation of starch in P-deficient plants only – in a normally starch-free region of the apex. Marinos concluded that altered mitochondrial function is an early response of cells to a deficiency in essential mineral nutrients. This study is significant in that it demonstrates that an important feature of cellular organization is apparently highly sensitive to the action of external factors.

INTERACTION OF ENVIRONMENTAL AND GENETICAL FACTORS

The interaction of environmental and genetical factors in stomatal differentiation in three genotypes of barley has been examined by Ariyanayagam and Stebbins (1962) with interesting results. This is part

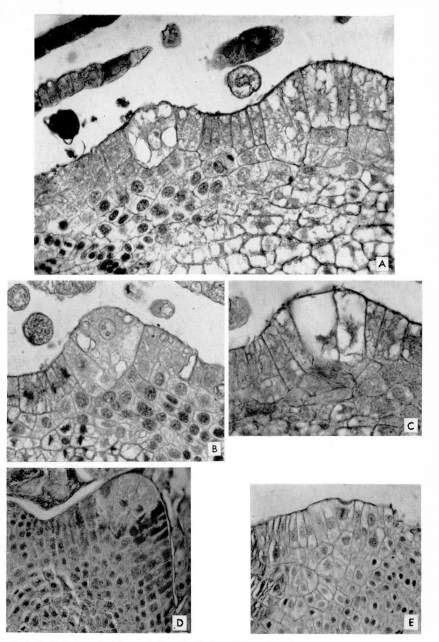

13. A, B, C, *Dryopteris dilatata*. A, Longitudinal median section of shoot apex (apical cell group on right) showing a young leaf primordium and the differentiation of its large apical cell (left). Note the differences in nuclear staining below the primordium and below the more acropetally situated prism-shaped cells of the apical meristem; pith parenchyma developing below (× 270). B, The conspicuous apical cell of the leaf has divided recently: the shoot apex is to be left (× 270). C, A recently divided leaf apical cell (× 270). D, *Matteuccia struthiopteris*. Longitudinal median section of the shoot apex in the winter, resting condition. Starch is present in cells close to the apical cell; the latter affords evidence of fairly recent division (× 150). E, *Cyathea manniana*. The apical meristem of a small lateral bud, the apical cell being in the course of division (× 150).

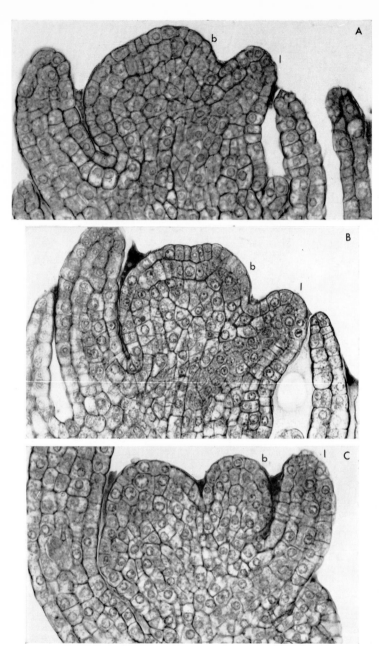

14. *Hydrocharis morsus-ranae*. Longitudinal sections of shoot apices, showing the inception of leaves (1) and buds (b) (× 360). (After Dr. E. G. Cutter, *Amer. Jour. Bot.*)

of a wider investigation in which these workers have tried to discover (1) whether, in a group of related genotypes, such differences as may be observed in the amount of developmental irregularity are chiefly due to genetical or environmental factors; (2) if there is any correlation between the amount of meristem present at any one time (i.e. at the leaf-base) and the size either of the leaf or of the plant as a whole; and (3) whether the extent to which the amount of leaf meristem can be altered by changing environmental conditions is related to the 'modifiability' or stability of the genotype as a whole; in other words, to its developmental homeostasis.

In an earlier investigation Stebbins and Shah (1960) suggested that the stomatal sequence in a grass leaf is largely determined by the autonomous action of the cells in the row in which the stomata become differentiated. They argued that if the rate of stomatal development was chiefly due to gene-determined hormonal or other substances produced in other parts of the plant at an earlier stage, 'then the very different over-all reaction of the genotypes of the different varieties to environmental change should be expressed in variations of stomatal development. But under the hypothesis of autonomous differentiation we can regard the different cells in a particular stomatal row as a population of cells with identical genotype whose behaviour depends upon their reaction to their immediate environment'.

In the barley investigations mentioned above, seedlings of three genotypes, known as *Atlas* 46, *Atlas* 57 and *Vaughn* were grown in the dark under constant temperature conditions. The intercalary meristem at the base of the first seedling leaf was fixed and stained for comparative studies of stomatal development. It was found that irregularity in stomatal succession was significantly greater at 35° C than at 20° or 10° C, but the overall irregularity did not differ significantly between the three genotypes. Of the histological irregularities in stoma formation, one type was equally frequent in the three varieties at the three temperatures used; the second type was less frequent at 35° C, especially in the two *Atlas* varieties, while a third type was more frequent at 35° C in these two varieties. These investigators also noted that the amount of intercalary meristem in the first leaf was significantly different between the three genotypes at the optimal temperature of 20° C and showed significantly more variation in *Vaughn* and *Atlas* 57 than in *Atlas* 46. They concluded that estimates of variation in the amount of meristematic activity 'may provide a useful index to variability in growth and yield, or the degree of homeostatic buffering of a variety'; but estimates of

H

irregularities in stoma formation within a row are chiefly of interest as contributing to our understanding of stomatal development.

These investigations indicate that, in some materials at least, the effects of genetical, environmental and self-ordering factors in organization can be distinguished.

AUXIN IN TISSUE DIFFERENTIATION

The action of indoleacetic acid (IAA) in contributing to the elongation of the coleoptile in *Avena*, and therefore of its constituent cells, and its effects on the growth of other plant organs, have now been known for some considerable time. More recently Jacobs (1952, 1959 and 1960, in which earlier work is summarized), and Jacobs *et al.* (1957, 1959) have shown that IAA is causally involved in the differentiation of xylem (wood vessels) and that, in regeneration experiments with *Coleus*, there is a close quantitative relationship between the amount of auxin moving downwards or upwards in the stem from actively growing leaves and the amount of xylem regenerated. A similar xylem-forming effect was obtained when a synthetic source of auxin was used. From his interesting and important investigations Jacobs concluded that the amount of auxin from the leaves is the limiting factor in xylem regeneration or differentiation, the amount which the stem can transport being also a factor in the situation. Other observations showed that auxin controls normal xylem differentiation. A further observation was that auxin production reaches its maximum during the night and that new sites of xylem formation – in fact, where the first xylem of a leaf-trace differentiated – could be observed in plants collected at night. Jacobs and his colleagues found that about 14 times as much auxin was required for the formation of regeneration xylem as for xylem formation during the normal development. Evidence from other sources supports Jacob's findings regarding the action of auxin in xylem differentiation.

It should be noted, however, that while Jacobs and others have shown that auxin is an essential factor in xylem differentiation, other factors must also be involved in what is evidently an orderly system of processes (*see* below). At this point, also, we may note the relative simplicity of the physiologist's and biochemist's approach, as compared with that of the geneticist, to these phenomena. Rules for the validation of the hypothesis that a particular substance normally controls, or limits the rate of, a particular biological process have been discussed and illustrated by Jacobs *et al.* (1959).

INTEGRATED ACTION OF FACTORS IN DIFFERENTIATION

The first thing that strikes one about tissue differentiation in plants is that we know singularly little about it. To put the matter quite simply and plainly, we cannot turn to any standard text for an adequate account of the differentiation of a sieve-tube or a tracheal segment. Descriptive accounts have, of course, long been available. It is also apparent that any 'explanation' that is more or less exclusively genetical, biochemical or physical is unlikely to be satisfactory. And even where the action of some particular factor has been shown to be essential in the differentiation of a particular kind of cell, e.g. auxin in xylem formation, many other aspects still remain to be explored and interpreted, e.g. the lignification of tracheids and tracheae, their characteristic pattern of pits, the relevance of the differential development to the function to be performed, and the hereditary perpetuation of the character. And similarly for sieve-tubes and other specialized cells.

If, then, we ask what causes differentiation, the only acceptable answer, here offered tentatively, seems to be that it is the whole comprehensive system of the developing entity, be it the whole organism or one of its parts. To attempt to give an adequate account of the differentiation of any particular kind of cell requires both analysis and synthesis. Such an account will involve a consideration of:

(i) factors in the genetical system, not only as defining in general terms the scope and limitations of the genotype for development, but the evocation and action of particular genes in particular circumstances;

(ii) biochemical factors, including the formation of both general metabolites such as sugars, aminoacids, etc., and special metabolites such as growth-substances, enzymes, etc.;

(iii) physiological factors of various kinds, e.g. relating to sites of active growth, development and differentiation, and the translocation to them, and utilization in them, of different metabolites; and

(iv) physical factors, such as the tensions set up by regions of active metabolism, the physical properties of the substances synthesized, etc.

The differentiation of lignified xylem elements may be taken as the basis for a general discussion; for it will soon be apparent to the reader that their differentiation cannot be studied as an isolated event. As we

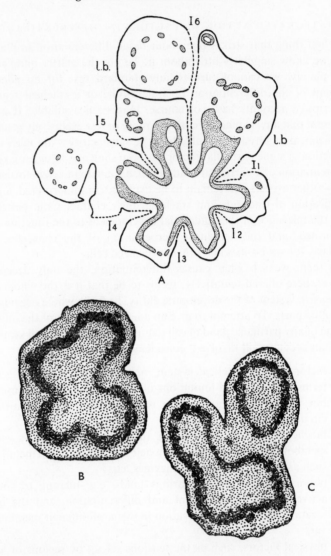

Fig.9.9 A, *Dryopteris dilatata*. Stellate stele, as seen in a transverse section of the shoot, on the further growth of an apex which had been incised radially: the outline of the stele is in close conformity with that of the shoot. (× 10). (*Phil. Trans. Roy. Soc.*)

B, C, *Lupinus albus*. Vascular arrangements at two levels in an apex which had been subdivided by two vertical incisions at right-angles: the ring-like regeneration of vascular tissue, which can only be attributed to the apical meristem, follows the outline of the shoot periphery. (× 60). (Redrawn from a photomicrograph, by E. Ball, *Amer. Jour. Botany.*)

have seen, Jacobs has shown that, in the normal stem development, auxin is the limiting factor in the differentiation of tracheae and that there is a direct relationship between the amount of auxin moving downwards from the shoot apex, with its rapidly growing leaves, and the amount of xylem differentiated. But, as Jacobs (1952) also pointed out, the action of auxin in this process is closely dependent on the presence of adequate supplies of sugar. Indeed, the latter is liable to be limiting in the apical meristem, i.e. above the level of the differentiated sieve-tubes. Now, the shoot with its associated leaf primordia and young growing leaves is a region of active metabolism. The apex and primordia constitute physiological sinks into which water and nutrients from below are drawn and directed. It seems probable that basipetal tensions are set up by these distal regions of active growth, and that the lines of greatest tension 'block out' the future vascular tract or tracts. These lines of tension – the result of physiological and physical factors – will be situated in the stem in relation to its overall size and geometrical construction; in fact, in relation to its characteristic morphology. If these views are valid, it is not surprising that protophloem and/or phloem-like elements are among the first to be differentiated. If we suppose that the lines of tension in a cylindrical stem occupy the periphery of a cylinder within, the inception of protophloem would mark the first stage in the inception of a tissue pattern. Tensions associated with the active utilization of water by the shoot apex and leaf primordia would lead to the inception of xylem elements in regions of the inner cylinder not occupied by the protophloem. And so on: only the general idea need be indicated here. In general terms, differential developments of the tissues of the initial pathways may be expected in relation to the passage in them of metabolites and aqueous solutions. Such incipient pathways may afford a route for the basipetal movement of auxin. The results of various experiments relating to the inception and pattern of vascular tissues are illustrated in Figs. 9.9–9.14.

Although the movements of sap and of organic substances are still controversial subjects, there is evidence which indicates that active metabolism in meristematic regions may, by setting up tensions, or by some other mechanism, have a direct effect in determining pathways of translocation. Thus Camus (1949) showed that if a bud of chicory was grafted on to the phloem region of a piece of root tissue, growing in culture, vascular tissue was induced in the tissue below the bud (Fig. 9.12). Wetmore (1954) noted that when apices of *Syringa vulgaris* were grafted into callus of that species, they grew into apparently normal

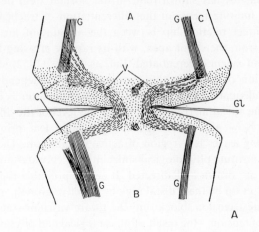

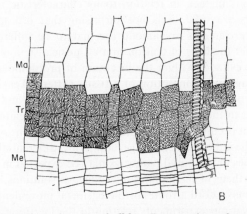

Fig.9.10 A, *Achyranthes Verschaffeltii*. Regeneration of vascular tissue. When the original vascular strands (*G*) were cut through transversely, in some instances so that only part of the central column of pith remained, new vascular strands (*V*), linking up the severed strands above (*A*) and below (*B*), were induced basipetally. *C*, callus tissue in region of incision.

B, *Coleus hybridus*. Part of a regenerated vascular strand, consisting of lignified elements (*Tr*), with actively-dividing cambiform tissue (*Me*) in proximity. (After S. Simon, *Ber. Deutsch. Bot. Ges.* 1908.)

plants some 2 cm in height though lacking roots. The active apex was able to withdraw from the callus the materials needed for new growth, this activity being attended by the formation in that tissue of numerous vascular strands. In the latter development, the downward movement of auxin, and/or other 'histogenic' substances, from the bud seems likely to have been involved. The elucidation of these developments in scion and callus thus calls for consideration of both acropetal and basipetal factors. Wetmore also found that small central pieces of the

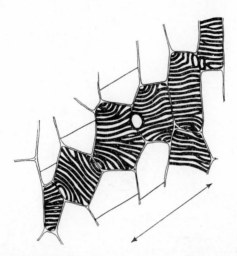

Fig.9.11 *Coleus hybridus.* A regenerated vascular strand, linking up the two parts of a severed strand, has been induced in parenchymatous tissue. The lignified tracheidal elements have a pore-to-pore connection; characteristic divisions in the adjacent parenchymatous tissue have been induced. (After E. W. Sinnott and R. Bloch, *Proc. Nat. Acad. Sci., Wash.* 1944.)

Syringa apex showed little growth as explants on seemingly suitable culture media, whereas larger apical explants grew well. Physical as well as metabolic factors seem likely to be involved in these developments (Fig.9.12 and Plate 12A).

The more rapid the uptake and utilization of water and nutrient substances by an actively growing region, the greater will be the effect on the tissues lying in the path of conduction. As Thomas *et al.* (1956, p. 196) have stated, 'the migration of solutes is governed by metabolic events at source and sink'. They also noted that active absorption of

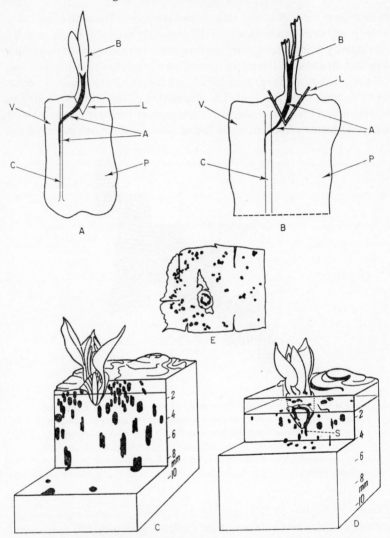

Fig.9.12 A, B, Chicory (*Cichorium* sp.):

A, Effect of a bud (*B*) grafted on to the phloem region (*P*) of a piece of root tissue grown in culture: the bud has stimulated the development of vascular tissue below it, i.e. probably in relation to the basipetal movement of a growth substance and the upward movement of metabolic substances.

B, A similar experiment, but here a sheet of cellophane, *L*, was placed

(Caption continued at foot of facing page)

materials, as well as physical diffusion, may be responsible for the conduction of solutes in parenchymatous tissue.

The formation of a wood vessel involves a sequence of processes including, as more evident visual features, the active enlargement of an embryonic cell and the loss of its living contents, a characteristic peripheral distribution of cytoplasm, and lignification of the walls in a characteristic pattern. Since the purely physical diffusion of solutes, even of a highly soluble substance such as sodium chloride, is a very slow process, Thomas *et al.* (1956, p. 196) consider that, in living tissue, 'there must be some protoplasmic mechanism for promoting along the directing concentration gradients the conduction of solutes that diffuse in water even more slowly than does sodium chloride'. This mechanism, the present writer submits, may precede the more evident features in the differentiation of the conducting tracts. Where several active growth centres are in competition, those with the highest rate of utilization will tend to induce the most conspicuous vascular tracts.

Cells adjacent to incipient pathways of translocation may be drawn upon by active meristematic regions, or they may be affected by substances moving outwards from the pathways. If so, they may be expected to show characteristic reactions. Sinnott and Bloch (1944, 1945), in experiments in which a main internodal vascular strand was severed, showed that the isodiametric parenchymatous cells in the path of the new strand soon become more densely cytoplasmic and divide by walls at right-angles to the path (Fig.9.11). The major wall pores in the line of cells which become transformed into tracheids are aligned; and the cytoplasmic bands, which precede the deposition of lignin, form

---

between the bud and the tissue below. The same effect was produced, i.e. organic continuity was not essential. *V*, vascular parenchyma; *C*, cambium; *A*, histologically altered tissue; *L*, line of contact between bud and stock, in B with cellophane (double line). (A and B after G. Camus, from E. W. Sinnott, *Plant Morphogenesis*, 1960.)

C, D, E, *Syringa vulgaris*. When a bud was grafted into a quite undifferentiated mass of callus tissue, growing in aseptic culture (*see* Plate 12A), a basipetal differentiation of vascular tissue was induced. C and D show (diagrammatically) the relation of the bud to the induced vascular strands as seen in longitudinal section; and E the relationship in transverse section; tracheidal tissue, black. (C, D, E, after R. H. Wetmore and S. Sorokin, *Jour. Arnold Arboretum*, 1955.)

H*

a continuous system from tracheid to tracheid and are generally disposed at right-angles to the direction of the strand. These early changes in the cells which constitute the incipient pathway point to the importance of both physical and chemical factors in the inception of the new bridging strand. The importance of auxin in the subsequent differentiation of xylem appears to have been established (*see also* Fig.9.10).

In some respects the inception of vascular and of mechanical tissues is not unlike. As Haberlandt (1914) and D'Arcy Thompson (1917, 1942) pointed out, the strengthening materials are typically deposited where the tensions are greatest; mechanical tissues in the nascent state tend to become coincident with the lines of force, their further development along these lines making for equilibrium and stability during the growth of the organism (*see* Wardlaw, 1952). The foregoing discussion shows how necessary it is to consider any process of cellular differentiation both factorially and in its comprehensive organismal relationships.

The numerous comparative anatomical studies, undertaken during the past hundred years, have yielded abundant evidence of the cumulative effects of changes in the genetical constitution on differentiation. These can be seen in comparisons of the species of a genus, the genera of a family, and so on (*see* Metcalfe and Chalk, 1950; I. W. Bailey, 1954), close or more general similarities, and also more or less considerable differences, all being evident. It is curious that the further study of materials which afford such a vast and fascinating accumulation of evidence of the effects of genetical change and selection in particular environments, sometimes with features persisting from an earlier phylogenetic phase, is so much neglected by many contemporary exponents of physiology, genetics and evolution.

Changes in the normal course of differentiation which can be associated with the action of particular mutant genes are of special interest. As an example, reference may be made to some maize strains, studied by Postlethwait and Nelson (1957), in which a single recessive factor, referred to as *wilted*, delays the differentiation of the two large metaxylem vessels in the vascular strands. As a result, wilting takes place during periods of high transpiration. These metaxylem elements eventually become differentiated; in some strands they are normal, in others they may be compressed because of the earlier differentiation of the associated tissues. Related to these developments is the fact that the lower leaves in wilted plants become normal in upward succession. These investigators suggested that if indoleacetic acid is a limiting factor in xylem differentiation, it would be interesting to observe the effects of applications of IAA to the upper leaves of wilted plants, and also to ascertain the amount of that substance in them.

DIRECT CHEMICAL INDUCTION OF XYLEM AND PHLOEM

Although thorough anatomical studies of phloem differentiation have now been made (cf. Esau, 1953; Cheadle, 1956, for reviews), the investigation of related biochemical factors has been limited until quite recently. This is indeed strange when the functional activities of phloem in relation to the nutritional needs of morphogenetic regions are borne in mind. Recent reviews, e.g. by Esau, Currier and Cheadle (1957), are chiefly concerned with the functional aspect of mature phloem. The probable importance of relatively undifferentiated vascular tissue, especially phloem, in the translocation of nutrients to distal formative regions, is suggested by an anatomical study of almost any apex. Thus, in a shoot of *Linum* with 3/8 phyllotaxis, Esau (1954) recorded that the first mature phloem element could be observed in the fifteenth, and the first xylem element in the twenty-second leaf from the apex; and, in a shoot with 5/13 phyllotaxis, the corresponding observations were made in the twenty-fifth and thirty-ninth leaves respectively. In other words, a very considerable amount of primary morphogenetic development, possibly the major part of it, takes place before mature vascular tissue is differentiated.

As already noted, Wetmore and Sorokin (1955) showed that if buds of *Syringa* are grafted into undifferentiated callus tissue, growing in aseptic culture, vascular tissue, mostly tracheidal, can be induced in characteristic patterns in the callus (Fig.9.12). Wetmore (1956, 1959) has also reported that both xylem and phloem elements may become differentiated in the callus tissue of *Syringa* if auxin and sugar are applied in an incision on the upper surface. An interesting and still unexplained feature of this observation is that, for phloem differentiation, a higher sugar concentration is required than for xylem differentiation. (For more extended treatments of cellular differentiation, readers are referred to the *Handbuch der Pflanzenphysiologie*, vol. 16, 1964.) In further studies of the induction of vascular tissue in unpolarized and undifferentiated callus of various angiosperms, grown in pure culture, Wetmore and Rier (1963) have reported findings of great interest and importance (Figs. 9.13, 9.14). Using the techniques already described, they successfully induced the formation of vascular strands in homogeneous tissue of *Fraxinus americana, Syringa vulgaris, Ligustrum*

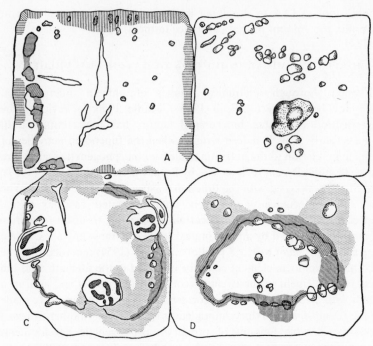

Fig.9.13 *Syringa vulgaris.* Further evidence of the induction of vascular tissues, as seen in cross-sections of variously treated callus tissue. Buds were grafted into undifferentiated callus tissue, growing in culture, or a central incision in the upper surface of the callus was filled with agar containing NAA and sucrose. The induced vascular nodules are represented by irregular small circles. The cambium, when recognizable, is indicated by a black line; it is more or less continuous in Figs. C and D; cellular regions resulting from cambial activity are indicated by radial shading, e.g. in Figs. C and D. Areas of active mitotic activity, in which mitotic spindles are variously orientated, are indicated by stippling, e.g. around nodules not in 'the ring' (Fig. D), or near a single-grafted scion in Fig. C, etc. Wound-meristem surface activity is indicated in Fig. A (right and below). Irregularly arranged flanking nodules, of early formation, can be observed in sections which traverse the scion but not well below it (Fig. B).

A, Transverse section of a callus mass near the bottom of a deep central incision, 31 days after the latter had been filled with agar containing 5 mg./l naphthaleneacetic acid and 5 per cent sucrose, the mixture being replaced once. There is a general absence of nodules near the central incision but vascular nodules have been induced near the periphery, in a rectangular conformation, especially at the left and above;

(Caption continued at foot of facing page)

vulgare, Salix purpurea var. *lambertiana, Parthenocissus tricuspidata* and *Helianthus tuberosus.* The principal results obtained may be briefly indicated as follows. In each of these species, an auxin (IAA or NAA) and a sugar (sucrose or glucose) are necessary for the induction and complete differentiation of xylem and phloem in callus tissues. The concentration of sugar determines the proportions of xylem to phloem; low concentrations, 1·5–2·5 per cent, favour xylem formation; high, 3–4 per cent, favour phloem. Middle concentrations, 2·5–3·5 per cent, induce both xylem and phloem, usually with a cambium between. The almost universal association of xylem and phloem may have its explanation in this middle concentration of sugar. Grafting of apices into callus, or direct application of appropriate concentrations of an auxin and a sugar in agar to the surface of callus, causes nodules of vascular tissue to be formed, mostly in a circular pattern when seen in section transverse to the axis of orientation of the callus in the medium. The diameter of this circle varies directly with the auxin concentration

---

but no vascular nodules had developed in the peripheral wound meristem, at right and below. In older specimens of this series, i.e. after 50–60 days, the nodules showed well-defined differentiation into xylem (tracheids), phloem and cambium, a complete peripheral square of nodules (i.e. including some differentiated in the wound tissue) being present.

B, Transverse section, taken 500 μ below the surface, after 35 days, of a callus into which a bud had been deeply grafted. The lower-median part of the scion is shown near the centre. According to the authors, 'the nodules are seemingly more or less haphazardly distributed in the flanking diffusion zones of auxin and sugar in the callus'; i.e. metabolites are proceeding basipetally from the growing, grafted bud. A somewhat more regular circle of nodules was present in sections taken at the level of the base of the scion.

C, Transverse section of a callus (600 μ below the surface), after 54 days, into which four buds had been grafted: (only three of the induced nodules are shown in this illustration). The nodules are generally conjoined by an 'interfascicular', cambial-like layer in places (indicated by radial shading).

D, In this experiment *there was no bud graft*: 0·5 mg./l NAA and 4 per cent sucrose in agar were placed in an incision in the upper surface of the callus. Transverse sections, after 54 days, and at 450 μ below the callus surface, showed a ring-like, spatially intermediate, distribution of vascular nodules. Cambial activity associated with the nodules had been induced in the interfascicular regions. (After R. H. Wetmore and J. P. Rier, *Amer. Jour. Botany*, 1963.)

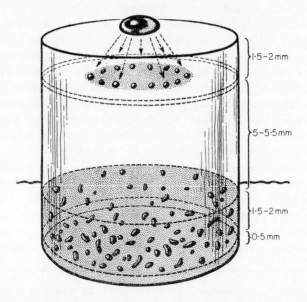

Fig.9.14 Differentiation of vascular tissues by direct chemical treatment. Stereogram of a piece of callus of *Syringa vulgaris*: on the top surface, a mixture of 0·1 mg/l NAA and 3·0 per cent sucrose in 1·0 per cent agar has been applied to a small area, the same concentrations being used in the synthetic culture medium. The position of the circle of induced nodules (each with tracheids towards the centre and sieve elements towards the periphery) is indicated. Some nodules (not shown) usually develop peripherally to and flanking the region delineated by the arrows. At the base of the callus plug, below the culture medium, nodules are also formed: these may be spherical or of irregular shape, or even resembling short strands, and are irregularly distributed; they are most abundant 1–2 mm. from the callus surfaces, with fewer nodules in the innermost tissue.

Between the upper circle and the level of the medium, nodules rarely occur, with or without vascular tissue. Occasionally a single tracheid or sieve element may be found in this region. The diameter of the upper circle of nodules increases with the concentration of auxin within the physiological range. The relative amount of xylem and phloem in nodules, whether in the circle or below the medium, depends upon the concentration of sugar; lower concentrations of sucrose favour xylem formation (1–2·5 per cent), higher concentrations favour phloem (3·5 per cent upward), and middle concentrations, both xylem and phloem (see text). (After R. H. Wetmore and J. P. Rier, *Amer. Jour. Botany*, 1963.)

at the place of application, 0·5 mg/l giving a narrow, and 1 mg/l a wide pith. In individual nodules, xylem is characteristically oriented towards the centre of the callus and the phloem towards the outside. Variable cross-sectional views of nodule distribution in calli under different treatments suggest the possibility of an experimental approach to the investigation of stelar patterns. Wetmore and Rier concluded that the induction and differentiation of xylem and phloem tissues in callus has no relation to conduction: any use of the vascular tissues can occur only after their induction (Figs. 9.13, 9.14).

From various supplementary studies, Wetmore and his co-workers have concluded that in the callus tissue, as prepared for these experiments, there is virtually no residual polarity in any direction. Accordingly, when auxin is applied to or at the surface of the callus, it moves only along diffusion gradients in the induction of vascular tissues in the callus. As Wetmore and Rier (1963, p. 421) have stated, 'one seems forced to a final conclusion that organization with its pattern of differentiated tissues is a part of the organization process in the growing plant'. As they have demonstrated, the induction of a pattern of vascular tissue in undifferentiated callus – an organizing process – can be obtained in quite different species using common metabolic substances. This is an important finding in that *the basic aspect* of a morphogenetic process as significant as the differentiation of phloem and xylem is apparently not closely and obligatorily determined by specific genic action. Some of the distribution patterns of induced vascular nodules obtained by Wetmore and Rier (Fig.9.13), suggest to the author that processes such as those envisaged by Turing (1952, *and see* p. 156) may have been at work.

The following observations from Wetmore and Rier may also be cited:

When an upright sterile pipette of narrow aperture, supplied with a sterile aqueous solution of IAA and sucrose of appropriate concentration – for example 0·5 mg/l of IAA and 3 per cent sucrose – was embedded to a depth of 0·5 cm or so below the upper surface of a piece of *Syringa* callus, an unexpected pattern of vascular tissues developed below the pipette by the end of 35 days. Instead of the characteristic nodules of vascular tissue, there was induced around the pipette a complete ring of xylem, or xylem with phloem, depending upon the concentration of sugar with the auxin supplied by the pipette (Fig.9.13).

After 56 days in culture, transverse sections were made of the tissue at a level 100–200 μ beyond the tip of the pipette. Vascular tissues, by this time, encircled the pipette in all experiments except those in which sucrose alone was used. In those cases, the tissue treated with NAA and sucrose were differentiated in a circular band of cells composed of six to seven rows of xylem elements lying towards the pipette.

Peripheral to but oriented away from the pipette were three to four rows of phloem cells. Between the two was a row of cambium (Figs. 9.13, 9.14).

These fascinating observations have led Wetmore and Rier into an interesting vein of discussion, some of which may be cited because of its high relevance to the theme of this book. Thus they ask:

Has differentiation of vascular tissue any relationship ontogenetically with function? Evidence produced here does not support an affirmative answer. Xylem and phloem cells, if continuous for a distance, may provide pathways for conduction preferred over existing diffusion gradients which prevail from living cell to living cell. Function cannot be a *sine qua non* for the induction of vascular tissues. That function follows the incidence and presence of vascular tissues in a growing co-ordinated system becomes important in phylogenetic considerations in which presence or absence of vascular tissues is recognized as having been of major importance in the classification of plants.

The authors consider of special significance the seeming comparison of their experimental findings concerning patterns of vascular tissue in callus to certain stelar patterns in stems and roots. Continuing studies in the directions suggested here may well cast new light on the time-honoured discussion of stelar patterns and their interpretation. To what degree are the modifications of vascular pattern during ontogeny the result of progressive ontogenetic increase in leaf size with the concomitant effect on photosynthetic output? Increase in available sugar and auxin would be important, as Jacobs and Morrow (1957, 1958) show. The progressive change from protostely to siphonostely in fern sporelings could be subjected to morphogenetic experimentation along lines of attack indicated here.

Further questions, generally interpreted as phylogenetic, will bear re-examination. Is the fact that the mosses (Musci) do not have vascular tissues of evolutionary significance? Can something, now lacking – perhaps genetically – be supplied to the moss plant, for example enzymes concerned with processes involved in the differentiation of xylem and phloem, which will stimulate the differentiation of vascular tissue in the column of elongate cells in the seta, which resembles very much a column of procambial initials? Or does the genetic background of the mosses make the use of such enzymes ineffective? Finally, is the existence of well-developed conducting sieve-tubes without accompanying xylem in the stipes of members of the brown algae (Phaeophyceae) of phylogenetic importance? Or do the auxin-sugar relations in the stipes favour only phloem formation rather than xylem formation in these aquatic plants?

CHAPTER 10

The Overall Organization of the Vegetative Shoot

INTRODUCTION

To comprehend the overall organization of a higher plant, indeed of any plant – i.e. whole-plant morphogenesis – is a difficult task. Still, as Waddington (1953) emphasized, if our aim is to develop a well-balanced science of biology, our understanding of form, which is the visible manifestation of the overall organization, should be as adequate as our knowledge of substance. Bonner (1952), too, pointed out that there 'is a general theory to cover every aspect of the control of growth save one, and this is the problem of configuration within the whole organism'. The inception of selected major morphological development ments and the configuration of the plant as a whole will accordingly be considered in this chapter.

Studies of embryological processes in different groups of plants not only reveal characteristic differences: they also impress upon the observer that all developing organisms typically afford evidence of order, unity, physiological differentiation, and integrated growth and morphogenesis at all stages. As a result, adult plants of different affinity are not only characterized by their distinctive specific features, but also by their many general similarities of development. The present discussion will be mainly concerned with vascular plants, but similar general ideas also emerge from the study of other systematic groups.

Although the vascular plants are a very numerous and morphologically varied assemblage, the number of basically different kinds of organs is really not great. Botanists of the nineteenth century, e.g. Sachs, following Goethe, recognized only four *fundamental categories* of parts, namely *caulome*, *phyllome*, *rhizome* and *trichome*. As flowers were held to consist essentially of metamorphosed leaves, they were not assigned to a special fundamental category. For the present purpose it will be convenient to recognize that a vascular plant typically comprises (i) an axis, stem or shoot; (ii) a root or root system; lateral members which include (iii) leaves, and (iv) buds, and various modifications of these organs; (v) reproductive organs and their associated modified foliar or axial members, or new structural features; (vi) occasional organs of indeterminate character; and (vii) various scales and hairs. The major lateral organs of the vegetative phase are, of course, leaves and buds. Directly or indirectly, these several organs all originate from apical growing points, the apical meristem of the shoot being responsible for the major part of the primary organogenic development.

It has long been recognized that a vascular plant typically consists of an axis, rooted in the substratum, which gives rise during growth and development to regularly disposed lateral members. This is the organization with which the botanist is primarily concerned. A tentative account of the evolution of the leafy-shoot, or axis with appendages (Bower, 1935), has already been given in Chapter 8. Earlier concepts have been discussed by Wardlaw (1952) and in Chapter 2.

While we shall be mainly concerned with the morphological and structural features which constitute the more evident and tangible expression of organization – in fact, the resultant effect of all the factors that have contributed to it – all development is, of course, based on metabolic and other physiological processes. While it cannot be doubted that chemical differences underlie and determine the visible morphological differences, the nature of the processes is still not sufficiently understood. To cite an evident example: we do not know what chemical substances or relationships determine the difference between a leaf and a bud primordium, both originating close together as lateral outgrowths of the axis. Sinnott (1960) has contributed a useful account of this aspect of organization under the heading of *physiological differentiation*, citing many interesting examples. Excised root tips, for example, require small amounts of vitamins, notably thiamin, for their continued growth in culture media containing mineral salts, sucrose, etc. It thus appears that root apices are unable to synthesize thiamin and, in the intact plant, must obtain it from the shoot where it is known to occur. This important physiological differentiation probably takes place at some stage, perhaps quite early, in embryogenesis. Roots and shoots also show important differences in their growth responses to different concentrations of auxin. Evidence is accumulating of important physiological and metabolic differences between vegetative and flowering shoots, though the cause of the organizational differences is still unknown.

That gene-controlled physiological differentiation is involved in sex determination, e.g. in dioecious flowering plants, has been shown by several workers (*see* Sinnott, 1960, for references). The ontogenetic changes in leaf size and shape have also been related to differences in physiological activity in various experimental investigations by Allsopp, Wetmore, Ashby, Steeves, Sussex and others (*see* Bibliography for collective references).

An analytical approach to the nexus of problems relating to the organism as a whole, its component parts, their similarities and differences of composition, and their mutual relationships during development, has been made by Lee (1950). In tomato seedlings, he showed that the relative growth values of the individual organs are different when the organs are isolated than when they are present as components of the intact plant. For example, isolated cotyledons have higher growth values than attached ones, whereas the reverse is true of stems and roots. The factors responsible for these differences in relative growth probably include the correlative effects of one organ or part on another, the relative availability of the substances required for growth, translocation effects, and the conversion of substances during translocation.

THE ORGANIZATION OF THE PLANT AS A WHOLE

The difficulty of accounting for the overall organization of a higher plant has usually been recognized by those who have reflected on this phenomenon. There appear to be few clear guiding ideas as to how it is determined. The collective effect of the multifarious factors involved is difficult to envisage; and, as it were, there is nothing tangible to grasp. Yet, we always return to the point that organization is *the* paramount phenomenon in organisms – the summation of events past and present. Notwithstanding the evident difficulties, the author considers that the organization of the individual plant is susceptible of analysis in terms of a few major interrelated concepts and that, accordingly, its fuller investigation is a possibility well within our grasp.

The thesis now proposed is that, in any vascular plant, *the primary organization* can be understood in terms of the integrated action of three main groups of factors (Wardlaw, 1963).

1. The factors which determine the inception of the primary organogenic patterns in shoot, and leaf and root apical meristems.

2. The factors which contribute to the elaboration of these primary patterns by effecting changes in the intensity and distribution of growth in the subapical and maturing regions.

3. Specific genetical and other factors which determine the sequential, or serial, syntheses of enzymes, growth-regulating substances, etc. These

factors are, of course, important in all development; but they are specially important in the formation of a complex structure such as the flower. They are, accordingly, given special treatment in the following chapter.

According to the species, what is here referred to as the primary organizational development may be modified in various ways, the most common being by the development of secondary thickening as a result of cambial activity.

APICAL ORGANIZATION AND THE INCEPTION OF PATTERN

The shoot apex, which consists of the apical meristem and the subapical and maturing regions, is a harmoniously developing whole, or *continuum*. In the *apical meristem* itself, one may recognize that there is substantial specific organization and physiological differentiation; it probably comprises several distinct though interrelated and integrated regions or zones, namely, (i) the distal, (ii) the sub-distal and (iii) the organogenic, zones (Schoute, 1936; Wardlaw, 1957). While it is in the third of these zones that leaf primordia can first be observed as localized outgrowths, their actual inception as growth centres must take place somewhat higher up in the apex, i.e. in zone (ii). The sub-distal zone is accordingly a region of great importance. It is envisaged as a complex physico-chemical reaction system (Wardlaw, 1957); and some evidence has been obtained that distinctive cytoplasmic changes take place in it (R. Brown, 1958). Although the mechanism involved in the accumulation of certain metabolites in particular positions, i.e. leading to the inception of regularly-spaced growth centres, is not understood, yet the reality of growth centres in the shoot apices in virtually all vascular plants may be accepted (Wardlaw, 1953, 1957) (*see* Chapter 7). Information on the physiology and cytochemistry of the embryonic cells in different regions of the apical meristem is also still very scanty (Fig. 10.1).

As apical growth continues, a growth centre occupies positions progressively lower down in the meristem, presumably with changing nutritional and possibly hormonal relationships at each level, until, in the organogenic zone, it begins to enlarge and becomes visible as a protuberant lateral primordium. In the *subapical regions*, the growth and differentiation of primordia continue with increasing acceleration. These and other observations support the view that the apical meristem is an organized unitary system, with physiological differentiation, to which the basic or primary pattern of the leafy shoot is due. This concept also emerges from a study of the distal and marginal meristems of fern leaf primordia (Wardlaw, 1958, 1963, Fig.10.2). With appropriate modifications, the same general idea can be applied to leaf formation in flowering plants.

The apical organization in shoots and in leaf primordia of ferns has very considerable inherent stability and, as the experimental evidence has shown, is not fundamentally modified even by quite drastic treatments, though such treatments may be attended by disorganization.

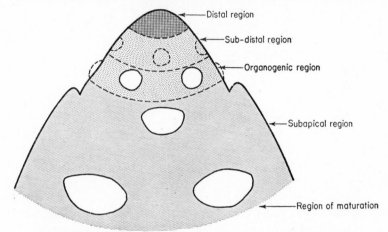

Fig.10.1 Diagrammatic representation of a shoot apex, with whorled phyllotaxis, envisaged as a system of contiguous, inter-related zones. (*Amer. Jour. Botany.*)

Quite small pieces of the shoot apex of pteridophytes and of some seed plants can be excised and grown in aseptic culture to yield normal plants (Ball, 1946, 1948; Wetmore, 1954). Also, as Sussex and Steeves (1953), Steeves and Sussex (1957), Sussex (1958) and Sussex and Clutter (1960) have shown by culturing excised fern leaf primordia in media of known composition, the basic and distinctive features of leaf morphogenesis, which are established in the young primordium in the apical meristem, are retained during the further development of the primordium into an organ of more or less considerable size and complexity (Plate 15).

These general aspects of organization and pattern at the shoot apex are well illustrated by the ferns (*see* Wardlaw, 1963); but species of flowering plants could equally be cited (Figs. 10.3, 10.4).

Phyllotaxis. In many procumbent, semi-erect and erect ferns, the leaves are formed on the radially symmetrical axis in a spiral sequence, e.g. *Osmunda, Dryopteris, Athyrium, Matteuccia, Cyathea, Dicksonia,* etc.

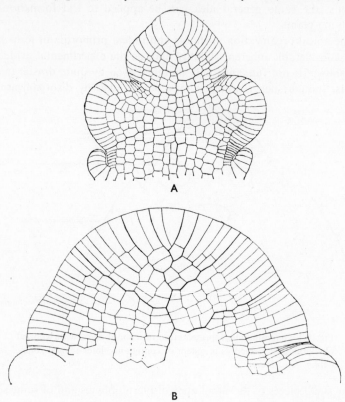

Fig.10.2 A, *Ceratopteris thalictroides.* Apex of young leaf as seen in surface view, showing the 'two-sided' apical cell and the marginal meristems formed from it. Young pinnae are being formed as a result of growth in localized discrete regions in the marginal meristems. (After Kny, from F. O. Bower, *The Ferns, vol.* 1, 1923.)

B, *Aneimia rotundifolia.* As in A, the organization of discrete pinna apical meristems from groups of the prism-shaped cells of the marginal meristem can be seen. (After Kupper from K. Goebel *Organographie der Pflanzen,* 1930.)

As Richards (1948, 1951) pointed out, the changes in spiral phyllotaxis which occur, for example, during ontogenesis, are continuous; and phyllotactic systems formerly considered discrete can be linked and also related to rates of growth. We may recognize that seemingly unlike morphological features may have their origin in identical or closely comparable primary patterns. In a young sporophyte, or in a lateral

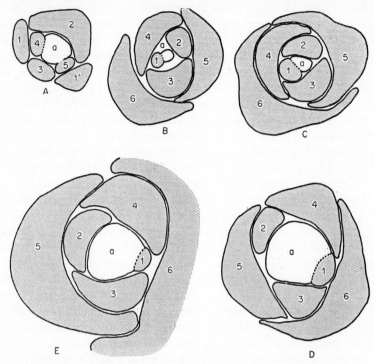

Fig.10.3 Various apices, cut in transverse section at or near the axil of the youngest primordium. Except in A, where the oldest leaves are indicated as 1, 1′, the leaves are numbered in the order of their increasing age, i.e. 1, 2, etc.

A, *Lycopodium selago*, young plant from a bulbil.

B, *Cassytha filiformis*, a parasite with 'reduced' scale leaves on the adult shoot.

C, *Rosa multiflora*.

D, *Cuscuta americana*, a parasite with greatly 'reduced' scale leaves on the adult shoot.

E, *Ranunculus acris*. (All × 67). (*Annals of Botany*.)

bud, e.g. of *Dryopteris dilatata*, the phyllotaxis index is low, the second leaf being almost opposite the first. But, with the ontogenetic enlargement of the apex, new primordia are formed in a close sequence and the spiral phyllotactic system becomes progressively more elaborate, with an increasing phyllotaxis index. Moreover, as Cutter (1955) and Cutter and Voeller (1959) have reported, several different phyllotactic arrangements, including spiral arrangements, a bijugate arrangement, and trimerous pseudowhorls, were observed at different times on the same apex of *Dryopteris dilatata*. Richards (1951) provided a method for quantitative comparisons of phyllotactic arrangements of diverse kinds, and for relating phyllotaxis to apical growth. In *Dryopteris*, the different leaf arrangements obtained must be due to growth changes in the apical meristem and are evidently not closely controlled by genetical factors. In the dicotyledons the seedling plant with its two cotyledons may, according to the species, develop into a more or less elaborate leafy shoot; but the formative processes involved appear to be closely comparable with those described for the ferns (*see* Wardlaw, 1964, for a brief survey of the several phyllotactic patterns) (Figs. 10.3, 10.7).

In some fern genera, e.g. *Pteridium*, *Polypodium*, *Drynaria*, *Platycerium*, etc., the primary organogenic pattern in the apical meristem is rather different. From a very early stage in ontogenesis, the axis is procumbent and dorsiventral, e.g. as seen in its cross-sectional tissue pattern, and it gives rise to leaves on the dorsal side only. The roots are mainly, though not necessarily entirely, on the ventral side. In *Polypodium vulgare* the genesis of these adult morphological features can readily be seen by laying bare the apex. As Hofmeister (1862) and Klein (1884) showed in their classical investigations of dorsiventral ferns, the apical meristem is lens-shaped and horizontally-disposed, the leaf primordia originating on the dorsal half, left and right alternately, with a divergence-angle of rather less than 90°. Collectively the leaves are thus formed in two rows on the upper side of the rhizome, while root primordia, as in *Polypodium vulgare*, can be seen emerging in subapical positions on the ventral side. Since, however, the young sporophyte in *Pteridium aquilinum*, *Polypodium vulgare*, etc., is initially of radial construction with spirally disposed leaves (Hofmeister, 1862; Bower, 1923; Gottlieb, 1958; and Dasanayake, 1960), it may be inferred that the subsequent dorsiventral leaf arrangement is derivable from the spiral arrangement without any essential discontinuity of development. In *Pteridium*, as described by Dasanayake, the inception of dorsiventrality is first seen in the two bud apices by which the original sporeling apex is replaced.

The flowering plants also afford many interesting examples of axes of bilateral and dorsiventral symmetry (*see* Goebel, 1900–30).

THE LEAF

The leaf is the primary expression of morphogenetic activity in the shoot apical meristem. Eames (1936) considered that leaves are probably of different phylogenetic origins, a view in which the present writer concurs. This adds emphasis to the remarkable homologies of organization which they display. In microphyllous species, e.g. Psilophytales, Psilotales and Lycopodiales, leaves are held to have developed as enations, or outgrowths of the apex (Bower, 1935); whereas the leaves of megaphyllous species, as in ferns and flowering plants, have been interpreted as modified branch systems, traceable back to original axial dichotomy (Bower, 1935). The writer (Wardlaw, 1956, 1957, 1961) has produced evidence supporting the view that all leaf primordia are essentially alike in their mode of origin in the apical meristem and that they differ organizationally from buds. Hence he does not regard megaphylls and microphylls as being fundamentally different kinds of organs, though they evidently differ in size, venation, etc. Nor does it seem probable to him that megaphylls are modified branch systems, although this view still seems to be held by a number of authors. Again, although leaves comprise several types of shoot appendage, differing more or less conspicuously in form and function, and variously described as prophylls, cotyledons, cataphylls, foliage leaves, hypsophylls, scale leaves, bracts, etc., they are all closely comparable histologically at the time of their inception in the apical meristem. Arber (1950) referred to these several foliar organs as phyllomes, this term including the floral foliar components. Esau (1953, p. 413) has commented that if phyllomes have a common phylogenetic origin, their difference 'appears to have arisen as modifications of their ontogenesis'. Bower (1919, 1947) stated that the constant features of leaves that define them morphologically are that they originate as 'lateral outgrowths from the apical cone, that they spring from the superficial and underlying tissues, and appear in acropetal succession; also that they do not repeat the characters of the shoot itself' (p. 69). He also noted that although the leaf usually differs from the stem in its symmetry, this is not invariable. Leaves are usually of dorsiventral symmetry, but they may be bifacial or of radial symmetry. Stems are usually of radial symmetry but may be flattened or of dorsiventral symmetry (Figs. 10.3, 10.4; Plates 1, 9, 14, 15, 16).

The Inception of Leaf Primordia. The orderly sequence of leaf primordia is a phenomenon of the widest generality in vascular plants. The relevant problems have a further interest in that some of the most

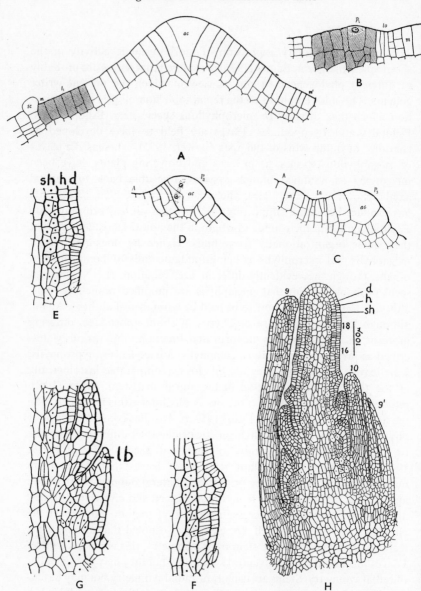

Fig.10.4 A–D, *Dryopteris dilatata*. Leaf inception at the apical meristem. Details of leaf formation, as seen in longitudinal median sections
of young primordia.

(*Caption continued at foot of facing page*)

ancient and primitive vascular plants were leafless. However, the capacity of apices to form growth centres and leaf primordia was apparently established at a very early stage in the evolution of vascular plants. As already noted, a leaf primordium, whether microphyllous or megaphyllous, is always a product of the apical meristem. The first leaves of embryos also originate in distal embryonic tissue, and these, too, in their symmetry and orientation, stand in a definite relationship to the nascent shoot apex.

The growth centres in the apical meristem typically develop as dorsiventral organs, though some interesting exceptions are known (Cutter, 1958). In all classes of vascular plants, the leaf primordium at its inception is a multicellular structure, comprising both surface and subsurface cells of the meristem (Wardlaw, 1956, 1957) (Fig.10.4; Plates 1, 7, 9, 13, 14).

When a leaf primordium first becomes visible, it occupies a characteristic and predictable position, i.e. some distance below the tip or centre of the meristem, and slightly above and between two of the older primordia. The very young primordium is a discrete outgrowth. Some are of relatively small size and occur in positions relatively remote from the apical cell group, e.g. as in ferns such as *Dryopteris*. Others are of larger relative size and lie close to the shoot tip, as in many flowering plants; and many intermediate conditions occur. As observed under the binocular microscope, a primordium of *Dryopteris* or *Solanum* first appears as an outgrowing mound of circular to elliptical outline, the adjacent surface of the apical meristem being flat. This development

---

A, A shoot apex, showing the group of meristematic cells (stippled and labelled I_1) which will give rise to a leaf primordium. *ac*, apical cell; *m-m'*, prism-shaped cells of apical meristem; *sc*, scale.

B, An older primordium, P_1, in which one of the prism-shaped cells has begun to enlarge. *A*, direction of apical cell of shoot; *la*, narrow cells of leaf axil.

C, An older primordium, P_3, with a large apical cell, *ac*.

D, The apical cell of a primordium dividing. (All × 85). (*Phil. Trans. Roy. Soc.*)

E, F, G, *Agropyron repens*. Development of a leaf primordium in a monocotyledon. *d*, dermatogen; *h*, hypodermis; *sh*, subhypodermis; *lb*, leaf-sheath of next leaf below.

H, *Agropyron repens*. Shoot apex with leaf primordia at different stages of development (indications as above).

(F–H, After B. C. Sharman, *Bot. Gaz.*)

is the result of growth and division in superficial and subsurface cells; in some flowering plants, cells of quite deeply seated histogenic layers may participate in leaf inception. As development proceeds, the primordium occupies positions progressively further away from the distal or apical cell group and, in conformity with the apical sector of which it is a part, its basal region widens radially and tangentially. Its *adaxial* face, which is in contiguity with the more slowly growing tissue of the shoot apical meristem, tends to remain flat or to become slightly curved only, whereas its *abaxial* face, which is in contiguity with the rapidly enlarging tissue of the subapical region, usually becomes more or less strongly curved. Differential growth as between the adaxial and abaxial sides, together with the more or less considerable tangential growth, are thus factors in the morphology of the primordium from the outset: they may, indeed, be the major determiners of the organization of its apex and therefore of its subsequent shape, dorsiventral symmetry and orientation; and this may still be valid even if we assume that a specific 'morphogenetic' substance is essential for leaf inception. It is a matter of considerable interest that, in the large apices of *Dryopteris* or *Osmunda*, the primordia P_1, P_2 and P_3, which are of small size relative to the apical meristem and occupy positions remote from the shoot apical cell, have usually not yet been finally determined as leaf as distinct from bud primorida (Cutter, 1954, 1956; Steeves, 1959); whereas in *Acer* the primordia are of large relative size, are formed close to the centre of the meristem, and are of dorsiventral symmetry virtually from the outset. (*see Loranthus*, Plate 9).

In many flowering plants, the youngest visible leaf primordium – sometimes described as the foliar buttress (*soubassement foliare*: leaf foundation) – may be tangentially elliptical or already dorsiventral as seen under the binocular microscope. As development proceeds, the basal region of the primordium merges and grows in harmony with the cortical tissue of the axis, while a more central group of superficial cells, which may soon become extended in the tangential plane, grows vigorously upwards and forms the leaf axis and later the petiole and lamina. In some species, characteristic tangential, basal enlargements of the young primordium lead to the inception of an encircling or clasping leaf-base, with or without the formation of stipules, e.g. in grasses, umbellifers, *Ophioglossum*, etc.

As already noted, both in ferns and flowering plants, the early establishment of the dorsiventral pattern or distribution of growth in the primordium appears to determine a dorsiventral pattern in its apical meristem which is concurrently becoming organized. Once established, this symmetry persists and is apparently not readily altered, e.g. to radial symmetry.

Leaf-forming Substances. Although there is little direct evidence of the action of specific morphogenetic factors in leaf inception, it is probable, at least possible, that specific 'leaf-forming' growth substances may be involved. Went (1938), on the basis of experimental observations, suggested that a specific 'leaf-forming substance' – *phyllocaline* – is present in the cotyledons and may also be formed in normal green leaves in the light. It is thought to be translocated acropetally to the shoot apex where it exercises a specific organogenic effect. In studies of leaf development in *Cucumis* under controlled conditions, Gregory (1928) concluded that a special substance, necessary for leaf growth, is formed in the older leaves in the light. However, it is not always clear if these investigators were concerned with the initial organogenic processes. Le Fanu (1936) and Snow (1936) concluded that specific substances other than, and in addition to, auxin, are involved in leaf formation. On the evidence of tissue culture experiments, however, White (1939) and Skoog (1944) rejected Went's hypothesis as unnecessary, in that tissue cultures, which had been maintained for long periods in the undifferentiated condition, can be induced to form leafy shoots and roots by appropriate treatments. Nor does the hypothesis apply to leaf inception in the ferns. In *Dryopteris*, for example, it is possible to induce bud formation in a leaf site and leaf formation in a bud site (Wardlaw, 1949, 1952). The present position may be summarized by saying that it is still not known whether a leaf primordium is formed in a particular position in the meristem because a specific 'leaf-forming substance' has reached a critical concentration in that position, or whether the effect is to be attributed to other, less specific factors; i.e. to the characteristic distribution of growth (*see* pp. 238, 242).

Evidence from Surgical Experiments. Direct observations of the inception and development of young leaf primordia indicate that their rates of growth and their development as organs of dorsiventral symmetry are related to and regulated by the physiological activities of the apical meristem and the adjacent, older leaf primordia. By using surgical techniques, the developmental potentialities of leaf growth centres and primordia have now been explored. Ferns such as *Dryopteris dilatata*, with large apical meristems and small, widely separated primordia, have proved particularly useful. The following observations relate to *D. dilatata* apices in which the apical cell remained intact (unless otherwise stated) (Wardlaw, 1949, 1952, 1956, 1964; Wetmore and Wardlaw, 1951; Cutter, 1954, 1956, 1957; Wardlaw and Cutter, 1955, 1956).

(1) When a deep and wide *tangential* incision is made on the *adaxial* side of an I_1 site, or an undetermined P_1 primordium (and sometimes P_2 or even P_3), a bud and *not* a leaf primordium develops. When a similar deep cut, or an undercut, is made on the *abaxial* side, leaves are formed.

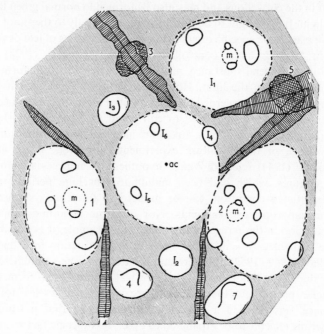

Fig.10.5 A

(2) When small, localized, deep incisions are made above undetermined leaf primordia, or their sites, thereby interrupting direct tissue continuity with the shoot apical cell group, leaf primordia are typically formed.

(3) If experiment (1) is carried out in such a way that a small bridge of intact tissue is left above the primordium or site, buds may sometimes be obtained in actively growing apices (Fig.10.5).

(4) When an I_1 site, or a young primordium, e.g. P_1, P_2 or P_3, is isolated from the adjacent older primordia by deep *radial* incisions, the

isolated site or primordium develops as a leaf: its rate of growth is greatly increased and it soon attains to abnormally large relative size.

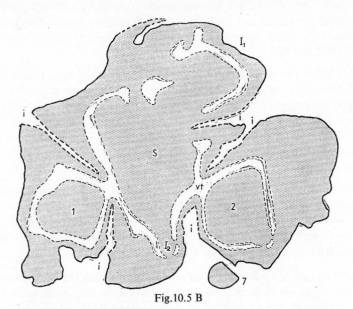

Fig.10.5 B

Fig.10.5 *Dryopteris dilatata*.

A, An apex, as seen from above (semi-diagrammatic), in which leaf primordia P_1, P_2 and the site of I_1 had been isolated from the upper region of the apical meristem by two deep tangential incisions but with a 'bridge' of uninjured tissue on the adaxial side of the primordium or site. *m*, apical meristem of induced buds. After some time the basal regions of primordia P_1 and P_2 became greatly enlarged, the original primordium being visible on the top of the tissue mound. Large buds were formed from each of these partially isolated primordia. New leaf primordia I_2–I_6 were formed during the course of the experiment. (× 20).

B, A transverse section of the specimen illustrated on p. 240. Cortex and pith, stippled; *s*, axis and stele of main shoot; *i, i*, incisions; *vt*, vascular tissue. The large solenostelic buds which developed in the several positions are in vascular continuity with the main axis, *s*; at this level the pith of bud I_1 is confluent with that of the main axis. (Semi-diagrammatic, × 25). (*Annals of Botany.*)

(5) If experiments (1) and (4) above are repeated but with shallow incisions which do not sever the incipient vascular tissue, normal leaf primordia are usually obtained.

(6) When undetermined primordia, e.g. P_1 or early P_2, on inactive or relatively inactive apices, are isolated on rectangular panels by shallow incisions, the primordium may disappear completely, its site becoming occupied by scales; and an I_1 site similarly isolated may fail to form a primordium. On more active apices, leaf primordia are typically obtained as in experiment (5).

(7) When the shoot apical cell group is destroyed by light puncturing, leaf primordia may continue to be formed in the normal phyllotactic sequence for some time and no buds or perhaps only one, may arise on the meristem. When, however, the distal region is more extensively damaged, two or three buds may soon be formed near the base of the cone; some leaf primordia may be formed higher up, usually in the normal phyllotactic positions.

(8) In apices in which the distal region has been fairly extensively damaged, some of the leaf primordia formed subsequently may show the normal acropetal orientation but others may (a) become orientated towards one of the rapidly-growing induced buds or (b) have their orientation reversed, i.e. point away from the apex.

The foregoing evidence is compatible with the view that the inception of a leaf primordium in a particular position on the apical meristem, its characteristic symmetry, its acropetal orientation, and its characteristic rate of growth and development, are determined and regulated by the organization and physiological activity of the apex as a whole (including the primordia on and near the meristem), the intact shoot apical cell being an essential element in the system. This conclusion, however, does not rule out the possibility that a growth substance, specific and essential for leaf formation, is normally present in a growth centre (Fig.10.6).

In surgical treatments of apices of dicotyledons neither leaf sites nor very young leaf primordia have been induced to develop as lateral buds. Some notable modifications in leaf development have, however, been reported, including the formation of centric and radial leaves (*see* p. 246). Genera such as *Nuphar* and *Nymphaea* are of special interest in that their flower buds originate in leaf sites and constitute part of the normal phyllotactic sequence (Wardlaw, 1956; Cutter, 1957, 1958; and *see* Fig.11.4). Also, there now appears to be general agreement in the view that the vegetative bulbils of *Lycopodium selago*, which are actually condensed leaf-bearing shoots or buds, are formed in leaf sites.

Active and sustained growth in the apical meristem must lead to the

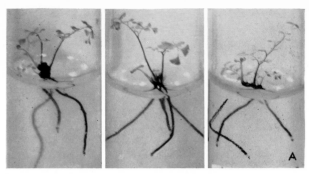

15. A, *Adiantum pedatum*. The apical meristems of some ferns can be excised and grown (eventually to the adult state as rooted plants) in organic media of known composition. Three young plants are here shown in tube culture. (After R. H. Wetmore.)

15. B, *Helianthus annuus*. The culture of leaves: young leaf primordia of flowering plants can also be excised from the shoot apical meristem and grown to organs of considerable size.

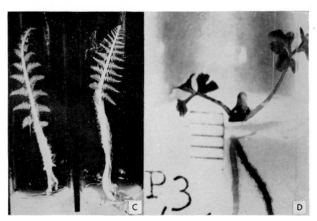

15. C, D, *Osmunda cinnamomea*. C, Primordial leaves grown *in vitro* to maturity. D, A small entire plant grown *in vitro* from an excised third leaf primordium (P_3). (B-D, After T. A. Steeves, *Jour. Nation. Cancer Inst.*, 1957.)

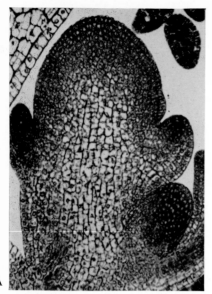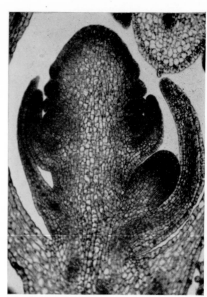

A

16. A, B, *Aquilegia formosa:* the inception of the floral organs.

A, Young floral apex of *Aquilegia formosa*, showing, in acropetal sequence, a bract with axillary bud and primordia of sepals and stamens. The tier containing the growth centres (which are not visible) lies closer to the tip of the apical meristem. B, An older apex than that shown in A, with several tiers of primordia (bracts, sepals, petals and stamens). (After S. S. Tepfer, *Univ. Calif. Publ. Bot.*)

16. C, *Tussilago farfara:* a capitulum, with bracts removed, showing young ray and disc florets (× 30). (*Jour. Linn. Soc. (Bot.)*)

setting up of acropetal and basipetal metabolic gradients; and, according to their position in the meristem, individual cells will tend to have a characteristic physiological constitution and therefore a competence to

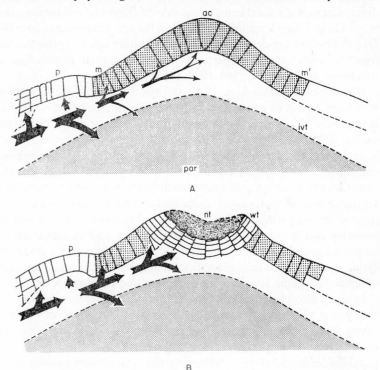

Fig.10.6 Bud induction in the apical meristem of *Dryopteris dilatata*. A, B, Diagrammatic representation of the movement of metabolic materials in a normal and a punctured fern apex. *ac*, apical cell; *m-m'*, apical meristem; *p*, very young leaf primordium; *ivt*, prestelar tissue; *par*, parenchyma of pith; *nt*, necrosed tissue; *wt*, wound tissue. When the apical cell group is damaged there is a considerable development of wound tissue. Larger amounts of metabolic materials are therefore being drawn upwards to the most distal region of the axis; a developing primordium (*p*) may thus find itself in a situation of equivalent nutrition on its adaxial and abaxial sides and develop as a bud. This, however, may be only a partial explanation. (*Amer. Jour. Botany.*)

react to some stimuli and not to others. Also, each leaf growth centre and young primordium may likewise determine characteristic centripetal and centrifugal movements of metabolites. A leaf growth centre or

I

young primordium is liable to be affected by the nexus of factors indicated above, including its proximity to the apical cell group. It thus becomes understandable why, in *Dryopteris*, there are marked growth differences on the adaxial and abaxial sides of the young primordium and why wide and deep tangential incisions of the apical meristem above the I_1 or P_1 positions, or deep radial incisions on either side of a primordium, result in such marked departures from the normal morphological development (Wardlaw, 1949, 1952, 1957) (Fig.10.6).

Histological Relationships. The histological details of leaf inception vary from species to species, but, in many of them, the initial outgrowth is the result of localized periclinal divisions in one or more of the sub-surface histogenic layers and of anticlinal divisions in the surface layer. The particular layer in which a growth centre has its inception, and the number of tunica layers present, will evidently determine the extent to which tunica and corpus contribute to the new primordium. As the relative proportions of tunica and corpus are fairly constant for the species and, basically, are genetically determined, the manner of inception of the primordium can be referred to, and affords some information on, the specific organization. In this connection, periclinal cytological chimaeras have proved useful in analysing the contribution of different histogenic layers to leaf inception and development.

In many dicotyledons it can be seen that the abaxial side, even of the very young primordium, is already abutting on that region of the apex where tissue differentiation and enlargement are taking place, i.e. the growth relationships and rate of differentiation of the adaxial and abaxial sides are different virtually from the outset. From an early stage, but varying according to the species, a strand of procambial tissue is differentiated in the primordium. Further research may show that this development has its inception in the growth centre. The leaf vascular tissue becomes conjoined with that of the axis.

In some monocotyledons, e.g. in *Elodea* and in grasses, in which the tunica may consist of one or two histogenic layers, leaf primordia originate at a considerable distance below the tip of the elongated apical meristem. The process involves periclinal divisions in the outer layers of cells, suggesting that the growth centres occupy superficial positions.

PRIMORDIA AND THE DYNAMIC GEOMETRY OF THE APEX

In different species, the meristem may occupy a relatively small or a relatively large part of the distal region of the shoot; it may be conical, rounded or flat; and it may be borne on a broadly extended subapical region or on a relatively thin cylindrical one; and, as already noted, leaf primordia may differ in various respects. The growing apex is essentially a dynamic geometrical system giving rise to lateral members, and therefore, according to the constitution and state of the system, there is scope

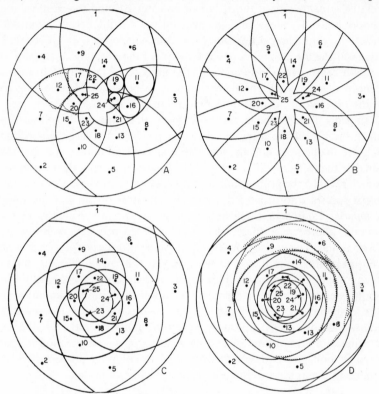

Fig.10.7 Fibonacci phyllotaxis. Ideal representations of four regular Fibonacci phyllotaxis arrangements in all of which the five-parastichies intersect the eight-parastichies orthogonally. In terms of contact parastichies these arrangements are as follows: A, (5+8); B, (8+13); C, (3+5); D, (2+3). Divergence = Fibonacci angle; the plastochrone ratio = 1·07296. (After F. J. Richards, *Phil. Trans. Roy. Soc.*)

for great diversity in the form of the leaf primordium at its inception and during its further development.

In a mathematical treatment of phyllotaxis, Richards (1951) showed that it is possible to have apices with the same divergence angle, the same plastochrone ratio, and the same proportion of new (or incipient) primordium area to apical area, but yet to have what appear to be very different phyllotaxis systems. The essential feature is the shape of the leaf primordium. For a given divergence angle, the contact parastichies depend on the plastochrone ratio (from which the radial relative growth rate of the apex can be assessed) and the primordium shape, both of which are dependent on the specific organization and reactivity of the apical meristem. Richards concluded that, to be valid, a causal theory of phyllotaxis must explain the absolute distancing of growth centres from one another, the absence of primordia from the central region of the apical meristem, and the factors determining its transverse size at the time of leaf inception (Fig.10.7).

In general terms, the larger the leaf growth centre and the closer it is to the centre of the meristem, the larger will be the leaf primordium relative to the apex and the lower the phyllotaxis; and conversely, the smaller the leaf growth centre and the further it is from the centre, the smaller will be the primordium and the higher the phyllotaxis. *Acer* and other species with decussate leaves are examples of the first instance; *Hippuris, Equisetum, Lycopodium* and *Dryopteris* are examples of the second; and between these extremes many intermediate conditions are to be found. The grasses, on the other hand, afford examples of growth centres remote from the tip of the axis, yet with low phyllotaxis; but in them, although the primordium begins as a localized growth centre, it soon extends laterally right round the shoot. In short, consideration of the dynamic geometrical aspects emphasizes the need for a fuller knowledge of specific apical organization and reactivity; for the inception of a primordium of characteristic form is an expression of that organization and is determined by the physiological processes which maintain the apical meristem in its active embryonic state.

DEVELOPMENT OF ISOLATED AND EXCISED LEAF PRIMORDIA

Experiments in which leaf sites and young primordia have been (i) partly isolated *in situ* from the adjacent organs and tissues by surgical treatments, and (ii) excised and grown in aseptic culture, have added to our knowledge of factors in leaf organization.

Radial and Centric Leaves. In ferns, lycopods and flowering plants, in which the apex has been incised in various ways, some of the young leaf primordia may develop as awl-like organs of feeble or restricted growth and of radial, or nearly radial, symmetry (M. and R. Snow, 1948, 1953, 1959; Wetmore and Wardlaw, 1951; Wardlaw, 1952, 1956,

1957; Sussex, 1955; Cutter, 1956). These *radial* and *centric** leaves, as seen in cross-section, have a cylinder or ring of vascular tissue whereas the stele in a normal petiole is crescentic. Young primordia of *Dryopteris dilatata*, i.e. P_1-P_4, which have been closely isolated by four deep vertical incisions, usually develop as radial leaves. Similar organs have also been obtained by direct chemical treatments of the apical meristem (Wardlaw, 1957).

Though of radial symmetry, radial leaves are quite distinct from buds, especially in their potentiality for development. As development proceeds, their marginal meristems disappear and the characteristic tangential widening of the primordium is thereby arrested or precluded and the apex sooner or later loses its embryonic character and becomes parenchymatous. Some of these anomalous organs are simply foliar structures in which the normal lateral growth has been suppressed, though some of them may show a brief renewal of lateral growth. As Cutter (1956) has noted, the three potential developments of a lateral organ on a shoot apex have been realized in *Dryopteris*, viz. buds, radial and dorsiventral leaves; and she has suggested that there may be three critical stages, or phases, in the normal development of a leaf primordium, namely, its inception as a growth centre, its determination as an organ of limited growth, and its development as an organ of dorsiventral symmetry. Under certain experimental treatments leaf apices become very slow-growing and fail to enter on the third phase: hence they come to maturity as small radial leaves. The nutritional relationships of these radial organs are not known, but it may be inferred that they are considerably different from those of buds, in which the nascent meristem soon develops to large relative size and becomes self-maintaining.

In various surgical treatments of apical meristems of flowering plants, M. and R. Snow (1931, 1935, 1953, 1955, 1959) and Sussex (1951, 1955) have obtained radial or centric leaves. Thus, in *Solanum tuberosum*, Sussex (1951 *et seq.*), frequently obtained radial leaves by isolating a presumptive leaf position (I_1) from the apical meristem by a wide and deep tangential incision close to the leaf site. (In *Dryopteris* a solenostelic bud almost invariably develops after this treatment.) By varying the size of the cut in *S. tuberosum*, it was possible to alter the shape of the primordium developing at I_1: with a very small tangential

---

* *Radial* leaves are organs of circular cross-sectional outline; *centric* leaves have a truly centric distribution of tissues.

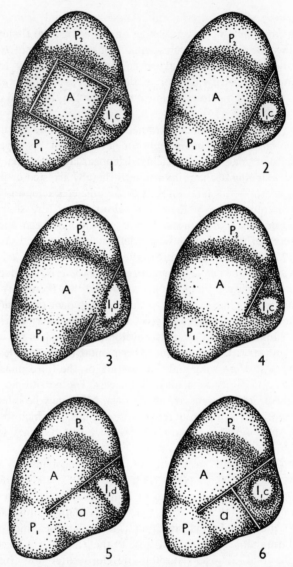

Fig.10.8 *Solanum tuberosum*. The apices of potato sprouts incised in various ways. These experimental treatments show that centric or awl-shaped leaves can be induced at will and that dorsiventrality in leaves is determined by the shoot apex. A, main shoot apex; a, a lateral apex; I_1c, centric leaf in the I_1 position; P_1, P_2, young leaf primordia. (After I. M. Sussex, *Nature*.)

incision, the primordium was dorsiventral; with a slightly larger cut, the primordium was at first radial but later became dorsiventral with a narrow lamina. When wide cuts were made close to the apex, dorsiventral leaf primordia were obtained (Fig.10.8). From this evidence Sussex inferred that the dorsiventrality of the young primordium is related to the organization and physiological activity of the apical meristem. As noted above, the formation of radial leaves has often been ascribed to limited nutrition, but Sussex suggested that a cessation of apical growth, or an elimination of its effects, may be a more important consideration. M. and R. Snow (1935) obtained radial leaves in apices of *Epilobium hirsutum* which had been incised in such a way that the leaf site occupied an almost terminal position. In a study of dorsiventrality in potato leaves, M. and R. Snow (1959) observed that when the presumptive area of I_1 or of I_2 was isolated from the apex by a vertical cut, the isolated regions typically formed dorsiventral leaf primordia. When apices of *E. hirsutum* were similarly incised, radial leaves were often obtained, but also some dorsiventral ones. Radial leaves were also formed when P_1 primordia, in early plastochrone, were isolated on small areas of meristem tissue. They concluded that, in normal *E. hirsutum*, leaf dorsiventrality is probably induced by the apex. They have also discussed the possibility that the small size of the tissue isolated may have been a factor in determining the configuration in radial leaves. In *Lupinus albus*, M. and R. Snow (1931) found that isolated I_1 and I_2 areas never yielded radial leaves, perhaps because in some specimens the primordia are already of dorsiventral symmetry when they first become visible on the apical meristem.

LATERAL BUDS

It is unusual though not unknown for buds to be formed on the intact shoot apical meristem; for example, in *Hydrocharis*, buds of conspicuous size are formed in the apical meristem (*see* Cutter, 1964). In many flowering plants, buds typically originate in, or just above, the axils of leaf primordia situated some distance below the apical meristem. They may remain dormant but, according to circumstances, they may, and often do, grow out as lateral branches. Axillary buds are common in seed plants, but they may be absent from some axils (Fig.10.9); on the other hand, in some species several buds may be formed in the same axil. Buds may also originate in more or less conspicuously supra-axillary positions; in interfoliar positions as in many ferns; in leaf sites as in

Nymphaea; on the leaf margin or leaf surface; and in roots (*see* Gutten-berg, 1960). Buds also develop adventitiously in various plant materials,

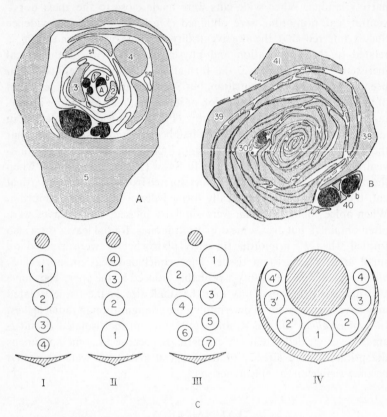

Fig.10.9 Distribution of buds in various Hydrocharitaceae, etc.

A, *Hydrocharis morsus-ranae*. A bud, and later two buds, are present in the axil of every other leaf.

B, *Stratiotes aloides*. Buds occur in leaf axils at wide intervals, e.g. leaves 30 and 40 (A, B, illustrations by courtesy of Dr. E. G. Cutter; A, from *Amer. Jour. Botany*, 1964).

C, Diagrams illustrating the various modes of origin and the patterns of multiple 'axillary' buds (Beiknospen). From W. Troll, *Vergleichende Morphologie der höheren Pflanzen*).

e.g. in the callus that develops on cut stems, and in tissue masses grown in culture. Most buds are exogenous organs but some originate endo-genously. The histological details of bud inception and development are now available for many species and adequate accounts are to be found in standard texts (Bower, 1923; Esau, 1953). As buds are the sources of lateral branches, the pattern of bud formation and the extent of their development relative to the main axis contribute significantly to 'whole-plant organization' (*see* Fig.10.9 Plate 14).

A growing lateral bud is an embryonic shoot, or a shoot in miniature; i.e. it consists of a short, polarized, vascularized axis, with a distal meristem which gives rise to lateral organs. Buds are potentially capable of unlimited growth and develop a tissue pattern similar to that of the main axis. The buds in many species are radially symmetrical; but even in species with a dorsiventral axis, the extreme dorsiventrality characteristic of leaves is relatively rare in buds.

A *bud rudiment* is a small, superficial region or mass of embryonic or meristematic cells which, on being stimulated to grow, will normally form a bud. At an early stage its distal tissue becomes organized as an apical meristem. The latter soon gives rise to one or more leaf primordia, while prevascular tissue, connoting the forerunner of mature vascular tissue, begins to be differentiated in the subjacent tissue. According to the proximity of the bud to the main shoot apex, its differentiating stele may become more or less completely conjoined with a meristele or vascular strand of the main axis; or it may fade out in the cortex, the latter condition being typical of bud formation in mature regions of the rhizome. These several developments are well exemplified by the ferns. In axillary buds, the bud vascular tissue typically becomes conjoined with that of the leaf base. In the ferns, buds are axillary in the Hymeno-phyllaceae but are typically interfoliar in most leptosporangiate ferns, e.g. *Dryopteris, Onoclea, Athyrium*, etc. (*see* Bower, 1923). They originate from *detached meristems* (Wardlaw, 1943, 1952), these being small, superficial areas of prism-shaped embryonic cells which originally formed part of the shoot apical meristem (Plate 6).

Detached meristems consist of *interfoliar* areas of the apical meristem which are (i) not used up in the formation and further development of leaf primordia, (ii) not differentiated into epidermis and cortical parenchyma, but (iii) which persist in an inhibited state and eventually occupy charac-teristic positions along the shoot or rhizome. In *Matteuccia* or *Onoclea*, a detached meristem in a mature region of the rhizome consists of a small area of distinctive embryonic cells overarched by scales, the underlying tissue consisting of the outermost parenchymatous cells of the cortex. When the main shoot apex is inert, or damaged, these detached meristems may become active and grow out as lateral shoots, runners or stolons.

I*

In seed plants, axillary buds *appear* to originate in the axils of leaf primordia (Esau, 1954), but, in fact, the position is variable. More often than not, a bud primordium originates on the stem just above the leaf axil, but later it comes into a closer relationship with the latter by displacement as growth proceeds (Esau, 1953). Such buds would be more correctly described as being of axial, internodal, or supra-axillary origin. In the grasses, a bud primordium typically originates closely below the base of a young leaf primordium. In different instances, the origin of the bud rudiment may be related directly to the shoot apical meristem or to a renewal of meristematic activity in partly differentiated internodal tissue (Esau).

In angiosperms bud inception includes the growth and division of cells of both tunica and corpus, the divisions in the former being usually anticlinal, and in the latter periclinal. The growth centre which gives rise to a lateral bud appears to be more deeply seated than that of a leaf primordium: thus bud inception is first indicated by periclinal divisions in the outer corpus. As Ball (1955) has shown, this is the region in which cells are most readily reactivated when the apex is vertically incised, with ensuing regenerative growth. As bud formation proceeds, there is a co-ordination of growth between its tunica and corpus regions.

Bud-Forming Substances. The difficulty of ascribing organ formation to specific biochemical factors is exemplified by buds. Reviews of this topic, e.g. Audus (1953), show that the inhibition of buds, and their further growth once they have been formed, have received much more attention than their inception, morphogenetic development and status as part of the primary organization of the plant. No naturally-occurring or synthetic 'bud-inducing substance' has yet been identified or isolated, though interesting and important results on bud induction in tissue culture have been obtained by Skoog (1944, 1950, 1954) and Skoog *et al.* (1948, 1951, 1957) using IAA, adenine and kinetin (*see* Literature and Wardlaw, 1964). In view of what is known of bud formation, it is probably unrealistic to think in terms of a specifically 'bud-forming substance'. However essential such a hypothetical substance may be shown to be, it will still be only one component of a complex system of factors.

Bud Inhibition. Among the most general observations on lateral buds are: (i) that their inception and/or development may be completely inhibited, or regulated, by the shoot apex – the phenomenon of apical dominance; (ii) that removal of the shoot apex admits of bud inception and/or development; and (iii) that if auxin is applied to the cut surface of a shoot from which the apex has been removed, lateral buds or bud rudiments behave as if the apex were still present; this, however, applies to some species but not to others (*see* Jacobs, 1959; Jacobs *et al.*, 1959). Causal explanations of bud inhibition include the concepts of (i) competition between the distal and lateral meristems for nutrients, the main apex, being usually the more active, directing the major flow to itself, (ii) direct inhibition resulting from the basipetal movement of specific growth-regulating substances formed in the main apex, and (iii) variations or combinations of (i) and (ii).

The extent of apical dominance varies according to the species: in some the main axis normally remains unbranched; in others it branches abundantly (Söding, 1952). It is evident that the general morphology of the plant, which is a taxonomic character, is closely related to the nature and extent of branch formation.

Bud Induction in the Fern Apex. As our main interest here is in the contribution which bud formation makes to the overall organization of the plant, the most relevant observations are those on bud inception in the apical region (*see also* p. 240). If the apex is removed from the rhizome of *Dryopteris dilatata*, *Matteuccia struthiopteris* or *Onoclea sensibilis*, lateral buds are formed from bud rudiments, or detached meristems, which occupy characteristic positions on the rhizome. These positions have been variously described, e.g. lateral on a leaf-base (Bower, 1923); but, in their origin at the apical meristem, they are inter-foliar (Wardlaw, 1952). If the tip of a large apex of *Dryopteris austriaca* is punctured, buds are typically formed on the meristem, at about the level of the youngest leaf primordia, in interfoliar positions; they may also originate in presumptive leaf sites or as a result of the transformation of very young leaf primordia. In the normal uninjured apical meristem, however, buds are never formed. As young leaf and young bud primordia are *histologically* very closely comparable, if not identical, both being formed from comparable groups of the prism-shaped cells of the apical meristem and contiguous underlying tissue, we have to account for the very curious fact that, in normal apical growth, leaf primordia are formed but bud primordia are not. In other words, we have to enquire why one group of cells of the apical meristem, those in a leaf site, grow out and form a leaf primordium, whereas an adjacent but closely comparable group, those in a presumptive bud position, remain inhibited in respect of organ formation. Any adequate account of organization at the shoot apex must therefore include both leaf formation and bud inhibition. There are, moreover, important questions relating to the size, symmetry, orientation and growth potential of the two kinds of organ.

The field concept as it may apply to the fern apex and its primordia and the results of surgical experiments relating to leaf and bud inception have already been given (*see* pp. 29, 240). Of special importance here is the observation in *Dryopteris dilatata* that if the I_1 position, or primordia P_1 and P_2 which have not yet been determined as foliar organs, are isolated from the upper part of the apical meristem by a wide and deep tangential cut, a bud and not a leaf is formed; i.e. an organ of radial symmetry can be induced to develop from a site or a primordium which typically gives rise to an organ of dorsiventral symmetry (Wardlaw, 1949, 1952; Cutter, 1954, 1956). Wardlaw and Cutter (1956) also showed that the prevascular tissue, which immediately underlies the prism-shaped cells of the apical meristem, and which is severed in these bud-inducing operations, is important in organogenesis (Fig.10.6).

It is relevant to note that when bud formation is induced in a leaf site, or by the transformation of a leaf primordium, the bud quickly develops a relatively large apical meristem and shows equally strong growth on its adaxial and abaxial sides. Also, whereas in a developing leaf primordium the vertical component of growth is greater than the transverse components, in buds this relationship is reversed. So it appears that the metabolic factors which control differential growth participate in determining whether the nascent organ will be a leaf or a bud. But we do not yet know how differential growth is controlled.

The destruction or isolation of the fern shoot tip will simultaneously eliminate both its regulative and competitive activities in metabolite utilization (Fig.10.6). As rapid wound-healing, with formation of parenchyma and an outgrowth of scales, takes place at the injured tip and in proximity to incisions, both the quantity and quality of the nutrients being directed upwards will be different from those normally utilized in the growth of the intact meristem. Scale and parenchyma formation, indeed, are characteristic of normal growth on the abaxial side of actively developing primordia, i.e. in the sub-apical region. Furthermore, in apices with a damaged tip, young primordia, already determined as leaf primordia, may be observed facing and curving outwards instead of inwards, indicating a higher rate of growth on the adaxial side. Such observations show how important the distribution of growth is in organizational phenomena, even though our knowledge of the underlying factors is still very scanty.

In the ferns, the apical cell group is the focal point in the meristem and is essential for the continuing growth of the axis. It may also be regarded as the ultimate determiner of the orientation and symmetry of leaf primordia. But such effects are apparently not produced by its direct action but are mediated through the organization and physiological activity of the apex as a whole. The same general conclusion is probably valid for flowering plants also.

The formation (i) of fern buds in positions that are away from the direct and immediate influence of the intact apical meristem, (ii) of axillary buds in subapical regions of flowering plants, and, not least, (iii) of adventitious buds in calluses, tissue cultures, or endogenously, all suggest that, provided the appropriate metabolites are present, some of the major aspects of bud inception and morphology may be due to some general self-ordering principle characteristic of a growing embryonic tissue mass. But such a statement merely reflects how little we really know of this important organizational phenomenon. That there are important genetical aspects of bud formation is indicated by the variation in the branching systems within particular groups.

DIFFERENTIAL GROWTH: GENERAL CONSIDERATIONS

In Chapter 9 (p. 193), it was pointed out that differential growth, variously determined, affects the conformation of the apical meristem. The importance of differential growth in embryonic regions has, over many years, been given considerable attention in both ontogenetic and phylogenetic investigations, especially by zoologists (*see* reviews and discussions in D'Arcy Thompson, 1917, 1942; J. S. Huxley, 1932; Hersh, 1941; Wardlaw, 1952, 1963; Rensch, 1959; Sinnott, 1960) (Figs. 10.10–10.14).

Partly in relation to their size and complexity, partly in relation to external forces, but largely in relation to internal factors which are still quite inadequately understood, few organisms grow with equal rapidity in all directions. As a direct and inevitable result, characteristic changes in shape attend the ontogenetic increase in size from the zygote to the adult state (*see* Hersh, 1941). The actual and relative proportions and shapes of the organs and the configuration of the organism as a whole continue to change throughout development. Where organs show a marked progressive change in relative size with increase in actual size, the process has been variously described as *heterogonic, dysharmonic, differential* or *allometric* growth. Reeve and Huxley (1945) regarded the first two terms as unsatisfactory and have suggested that the term *allometry* should be adopted. This term is now accepted to mean the changes of proportions, whether morphological or chemical, that attend increases in size, both within a single species (described as *ontogenic allometry* or *heterauxesis*), and between adults of related groups (described as *absolute-size allometry* or *allomorphosis*). (For further terminology, *see* Wardlaw, 1952.) Even a little study will show that differential or allometric growth must exercise profound and far-reaching effects on the organization and functioning of the plant.

The variations in size and shape during development sometimes take place in subtle and little understood ways; but, at any stage in onto-genesis, the shape is usually such as to indicate, or suggest, that balanced and integrated functional relationships underlie the development of the constituent organs. In other words, the wholeness or unity of the organization is present at all times. Throughout all the ontogenetic changes, one cannot but be aware, particularly when dealing with a familiar species, that a definite and characteristic pattern, i.e. a specific organization – the resultant of many orderly and mutually adjusted processes – is progressively becoming manifest.

DIFFERENTIAL GROWTH IN SHOOT DEVELOPMENT

With an outline of the inception of primary organization in the leafy shoot before us, the effects of differential growth in the subapical region may now be examined. Indeed, the importance of growth and the related pattern of cell division in this region was recognized by anatomists more than a century ago. Because of the absence of secondary thickening, the ferns afford admirable material for the relevant investigations. But comparable examples can readily be selected from the flowering plants.

In the ferns, the subapical region is characterized by active growth, both vertically and transversely, but usually more conspicuously in one direction than the other. Consequently, in different species, or during different phases of growth of the same species, the axis may show more or less marked differences in its morphological development. In the adult plant of many ferns, e.g. *Dryopteris filix-mas*, *D. dilatata*, etc., the vertical component of growth in the subapical region is small compared with the radial or transverse component. As a result, the leaf primordia and young leaves form a close spiral round the apex with a high phyllotaxis index, and the apical cone is seated on a conspicuously broad subapical region (Fig.10.10). This phenomenon is exemplified in a high degree in the cinnamon fern, *Osmunda cinnamomea*, as described by Steeves and Wetmore (1953); for although as many as

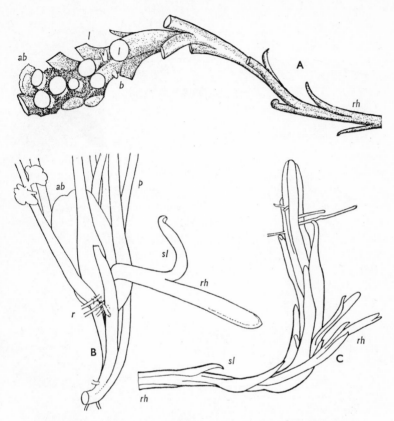

Fig.10.10 A, *Dryopteris dilatata*. Thin, horizontal underground rhizome, with widely separated scale-like leaves; at the distal end the apical bud (*ab*) has turned upwards and the distal region is becoming broader and bears a close assemblage of leaves (*l*), here dissected off; *b*, lateral buds; *rh*, rhizome. (× 1½).

B, C, *Matteuccia struthiopteris*. Two specimens of thin horizontal rhizomes which have turned upwards and are forming erect shoots with a close assemblage of foliage leaves and a stout apical bud (*ab*); new young rhizomes (*rh*) are growing out from the region of transition from the horizontal to the vertical habit; *r*, roots; *sl*, scale-like rhizome leaves; *p*, petiole. (B × ½; C × 2). (*Jour. Linn. Soc. (Bot.)*)

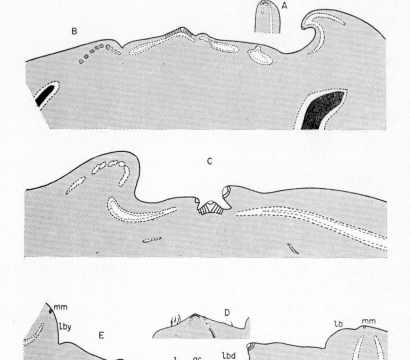

Fig.10.11 A–E, Longitudinal median sections of fern shoot apices (semi-diagrammatic, all × 6).

A, *Asplenium adiantum nigrum.* B, *Dryopteris dilatata.* C, *Cyathea manniana.*

D, E, *Asplenium nidus,* small and large apices; *ac,* apical cell; l_1, leaf primordium, recently formed in apical meristem; *lby, lbd* leaf-base; *mm,* marginal meristem of leaf; *ivt,* incipient vascular tissue. (*Jour. Linn. Soc.* (*Bot.*))

25 or more new primordia may be formed in the course of a year, the extent of internodal elongation is of the slightest. The rhizome develops as a short shoot. Among flowering plants, species with the rosette habit, e.g. many Compositae, exemplify the same general relationships.

In some epiphytic ferns, such as *Polypodium glaucum* (R. and C. Wetter, 1954) and *Asplenium nidus* (Wardlaw, 1956), the narrow axis of the young sporophyte tapers off into the apical cone. But, with the ontogenetic increase in size, radial growth is so relatively great that the apical cone is eventually seated in a saucer-shaped depression. The bases of the leaf primordia, which also participate in this characteristic distribution of growth, become almost circular in transverse section, and they too contribute to the sunken position of the apical cone. This is also seen in some tree-ferns, e.g. *Cyathea manniana* (Wardlaw, 1948). Similar configurations have been experimentally induced in *Dryopteris dilatata*, in which the apex is not normally sunken, by direct treatment of the shoot apex with aqueous solutions of indoleacetonitrile, and DNA (Wardlaw, 1957; Wardlaw and Mitra, 1958). Among the flowering plants, many Cactaceae show more or less deeply sunken apices. In them also the transverse component of growth greatly exceeds the vertical component. Among bulky monocotyledons such as bananas and palms, comparable relationships obtain, the characteristic developments being mainly due to the progressive augmentation of the cortical and medullary tissues (Figs. 10.11, 10.12).

Some ferns, which have a short, broad, erect axis, e.g. *Dryopteris dilatata*, *Matteuccia struthiopteris*, etc., give rise laterally to more or less extensive horizonal underground rhizomes, stolons or runners. In these branch shoots, the primary organization at the apex is basically the same as in the parent shoot. There is, however, one conspicuous difference: the vertical component of growth in the subapical region is large relative to the radial component. As a result the lateral bud develops into a thin, elongating rhizome, with widely-spaced leaves, each of the latter consisting of a closely adherent, elongated, narrow petiole with a small, underdeveloped lamina (Fig.10.10). Sooner or later, however, the rhizome becomes detached from the parent axis, or ceases to be regulated by it: its apex then grows upwards, becomes exposed to the light, and in due course it develops into a typical, compact, erect leafy shoot. In *D. dilatata* and *M. struthiopteris*, the transition region is characterized by (i) a marked shortening of the internodes so that the leaves form a tight spiral round the apex, (ii) an evident thickening of the stem, and (iii) the development of normal assimilating leaves. The elimination of the regulative effects of the parent stem and exposure to light thus have important effects on the distribution of growth in the subapical regions. In both species growth and correlative

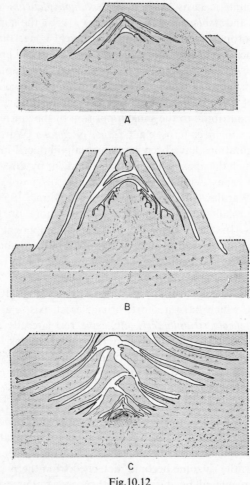

Fig.10.12

factors, rather than specific genetical ones, are evidently the proximate causes of the observed developments.

Comparable contrasted developments were obtained experimentally by growing pieces of *Matteuccia* rhizome on the soil surface and at

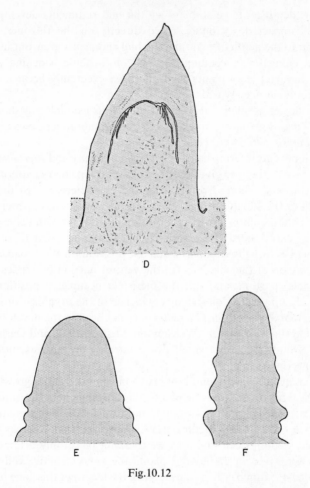

Fig.10.12

Fig.10.12 Various apices (diagrammatic, in l.s.), showing differences in the configuration of the leafy-shoot which result from characteristic distributions of growth in the apex.

A, B, *Musa* sp. (Gros Michel banana). A, Vegetative apex. B, The axis is elongating at an early stage in the development of the inflorescence.

C, D, *Elaeis guineensis* (Oil palm). C, Trunk apex. D, An inflorescence apex. (A–D, × 12)

E, *Hippuris vulgaris*. F, *Elodea canadensis*. (E, F, × 225).

(A–D, drawn by A. Walton).

various depths. At the soil surface the bud rudiments developed into stout, compact, leafy buds, seated directly on the rhizome; but, in relation to the depth of planting, the bud rudiments grew out into more or less elongated, ascending, thin rhizomes, these widening out into stout, compact leafy plants when the apex eventually became exposed at the soil surface (Wardlaw, 1963).

The flowering plants also afford numerous examples of short-shoot rosette plants giving rise to elongated horizontal runners, e.g. *Hieracium* spp., *Petasites hybridus*, etc.

In dorsiventral ferns such as *Polypodium vulgare* and *Pteridium aquilinum*, in which the apex gives rise to a dorsiventral primary pattern, further organizational changes result from the characteristic distribution of growth in the subapical region. As several workers have observed, the pattern of differential growth is also dorsiventral, growth being greatest on the ventral side. The organizational results are that (i) the apical meristem eventually occupies a sunken position on the broad, sloping, distal region of the rhizome, (ii) the ventral portion protrudes beyond the dorsal portion, and (iii) the meristem occupies a position facing obliquely upwards. Conspicuous evidence of the organizational effects of differential growth in *P. aquilinum* is also seen in the development of long and short shoots (*see* Webster and Steeves, 1958, and Dasanayake, 1960). Many aspects of shoot dorsiventrality are also exemplified by the flowering plants.

Reference to experimental observations on differential growth in the subapical region in flowering plants is appropriate here (*see* summary in Wardlaw, 1964). In a tall (normal) and dwarf variety of tomato (*Lycopersicum esculentum*), Bindloss (1942) observed that whereas in nine-day-old seedlings cell divisions were taking place only a few microns below the apex, in 38-day-old plants the zone of active cell division extended 4–5 mm below the apex. Also, the length of this zone in the tall variety was at least 1 mm greater than in the dwarf. Sachs and Lang (1961) made counts of cells showing mitosis in the growing region of shoots of several species and found that in vegetative rosette plants, e.g. species of *Hyoscyamus* and *Samolus*, the zone of such mitotic activity was very limited. On the other hand, in elongating rosette plants and in caulescent plants, i.e. those with more conspicuous stem development, the mitotic zone extended to 5–10 mm. Since these dividing cells in the subapical region eventually undergo more or less extensive elongation, important effects on the configuration of the leafy shoot follow as a natural consequence. Recent investigations of the effects of gibberellic

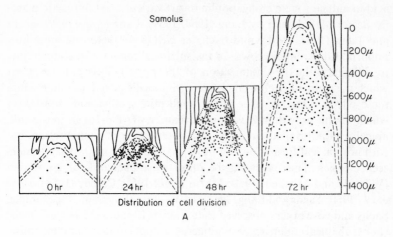

Distribution of cell division

A

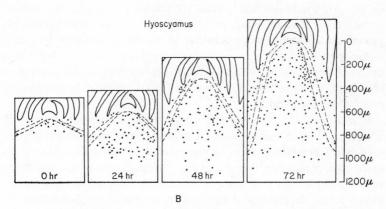

B

Fig.10.13 Distribution of cell divisions and shoot growth in A, *Samolus* and B, *Hyoscyamus* after applications of gibberellic acid (GA). Number and distribution of mitotic figures in the median 64 μ (8 median longisections, 8 μ per section) of the apices of *Samolus* and *Hyoscyamus* following application of GA (25 micrograms of GA were applied at O, 24 and 48 hr.). Each mitotic figure is indicated by a dot. The pith tissue is bounded by the apical meristem at the top and the vascular tissue on the sides. The boundaries for the vascular tissue and the lower limit of the apical meristem are indicated by broken lines.

Observations for cortical tissue were confined to the area bounded by the outer edge of the vascular tissue and the line connecting the leaf bases. (After R. M. Sachs, C. F. Bretz and A. Lang, *Amer. Jour. Botany*.)

acid in inducing stem elongation in dwarf varieties and in rosette plants
by Basford (1961) and by Lang (1957, 1959), Lang *et al.* (1959), Sachs
and Lang (1957, 1961), and Sachs *et al.* (1959, 1960), all show how
important differential growth in the subapical region is in contributing
to differences in the organization of the plant (Fig.10.13). In plants
which normally have elongated stems, gibberellic acid does not produce
these effects. On the other hand, applications of various substances
which inhibit growth, e.g. various carbamates (Amo-1618), to the subapical region, bring about a dwarf or rosette type of configuration, but
with normal leaf formation and phyllotaxis, in what are typically caulescent species. This effect can be offset by applications of gibberellin
(Wirwille and Mitchell, 1950; Marth *et al.*, 1953; Cathey, 1958; Sachs
et al., 1960; Sachs and Lang, 1961). In the chrysanthemum, for example,
Sachs and co-workers observed that Amo-1618 inhibited mitosis in the
shoot subapical region, whereas gibberellin, applied either simultaneously
or later, reversed this effect, so that the mitotic counts returned to their
normal level. It is important to note that, in all these experiments, the
growth and morphogenetic activities of the apical meristem remained
virtually unaffected. This affords further evidence of its stability and
other self-maintaining properties. The experimental results referred to
above are, of course, common phenomena in the normal development of
many flowering plants.

Evidence of the interest, importance and complexity of the subapical region in flowering plants, especially those showing the phenomenon of dwarfism, has been contributed by Gorter (1961). In an
investigation of three dwarf and one 'normal' tall variety of *Pisum
sativum*, Gorter showed that dwarfism is determined by light: when
grown in the dark the four varieties reached the same height; in the
light, growth was reduced but more so in the dwarfs than in the tall
variety. Moreover, in white and yellow light, of equal incident energy
level, different responses were obtained: the dwarfs showed much
higher sensitivity to white light by the reduction in their growth than did
the tall variety. But in yellow light the tall variety showed no reduction
in growth, no response at the higher intensities, and a 'yellow-etiola-
tion' at the lower intensities. The dwarfs, however, grew less at all
intensities. Gorter showed that gibberellic acid counteracts these light-
induced diminutions in stature; and GA-treated intact plants of all four
varieties grew to the same size. Isolated internode sections of the four
varieties responded very slightly to GA, but the responses were increased
by additions of sucrose and indoleacetic acid, the latter apparently

contributing more to this effect than the GA. Gorter also reported that no evidence of synergistic activities of GA, IAA and sucrose was obtained; in fact, provided other unknown factors were not limiting the reactions, these compounds showed antagonistic behaviour.

In a comparative morphogenetic study of wild type groundsel (*Senecio vulgaris*) and a radiation-induced dwarf, differing from the parental type by a single gene only, Basford (1961) showed that the dwarf could be induced by applications of GA to grow to approximately the same size as the normal wild type. But although its several morphological features were closely comparable with those of the wild type, significant differences of detail were noted. (For further refs. *see* Brian (1959); Lockhart (1956); Purves and Hillman (1958); and Stowe and Yamacki (1957).)

DIFFERENTIAL GROWTH IN FERN LEAVES

The elaboration and diversification of the primary pattern by differential growth is seen to advantage in fern leaves. As Bower (1916, 1923) and later investigators demonstrated, the increase in size of the successive leaves in the sporophyte is attended by a progressive elaboration of their outline and venation – described by Bower (1916) as 'leaf architecture' and by Goebel (1908) as heteroblastic development. The primary phase in the formation of a fern leaf is due to the activity of its distal and subsequently of its marginal meristems; and, without going into details, it may be noted that these regions have many of the organizational and morphogenetic properties of the shoot apical meristem. The leaf apical meristem, and the discrete marginal meristems, however, are of dorsiventral symmetry. Although all fern leaves have much in common, they are nevertheless exceedingly varied morphologically, ranging from simple, undivided organs to highly complex ones, including various interesting dimorphic developments (*see* below). This range in leaf shape is exemplified in the ontogeny of particular species, e.g. *Dryopteris*, *Osmunda*, etc. There may also be conspicuous differences in leaf morphology in land and water forms of the same species (Allsopp, 1955), these being referable to growth activities in the apical regions under consideration.

For convenience, the rate of subapical growth in the direction of elongation of a distal or marginal meristem, i.e. in the direction of the midrib or of a pinna vein, will be referred to as the vertical component (or V); and the rate of growth at right-angles to this in the plane of the lamina will be referred to as the transverse component (or T). Now in a leaf primordium in which a distal meristem and discrete, as distinct from continuous, marginal meristems are present, i.e. as part of the primary pattern, it is evident that if V is considerably greater than T, the lamina will become more or less deeply lobed or pinnate; conversely, if T > V, the lamina will tend to remain entire; and if V is only slightly greater than T, the leaf margin may be undulating or notched. In the young sporophyte of *Osmunda regalis*, for example, the earliest formed leaves are of oval outline, or they consist of oval bifurcated lobes, i.e. T equals or exceeds V. But as ontogenesis proceeds, V gradually becomes greater than T, and the leaf develops as an elongated rachis with lateral pinnae. Similar relationships also obtain in the development of pinnules and pinnulets in species with compound leaves. The ontogenetic elaborations of leaf form typically accompany a progressive increase in size in successive leaves, indicating the importance of nutritional factors. The validity of this view is supported by the observations that, in various 'starvation experiments', final leaf size and morphological complexity can both be diminished. Moreover, in organ culture investigations, it has been amply demonstrated that the size and shape of fern leaves can be controlled by varying the composition of the medium (*see* below), the effects being mainly, though not entirely, in subapical regions.

Species with dimorphic leaves, e.g. *Drynaria* and *Platycerium* spp., are of particular interest because, as Goebel (1905, 1928) pointed out, their primordia at the shoot apex are essentially alike in size, shape and position of origin. Yet how very different are the adult leaves. The species of *Drynaria* are epiphytes, the elongated rhizome growing upwards on tree-trunks and along the branches. The adult leaves, in two rows on the dorsal side of the rhizome, are of two distinct kinds: (i) there is a sequence of relatively small, somewhat pale, overlapping, entire but notched leaves, with the petiole short or absent; these so-called 'nest-leaves' are closely adpressed to the tree-trunk and constitute reservoirs for humus and water into which the roots penetrate; and (ii) there is a sequence of large pinnate leaves, full green in colour, bearing the sori, and pendent from the rhizome on long petioles. It is at once evident that both the total growth and the differential growth patterns in the two kinds of leaf are very different. In the small, sessile, entire but notched leaves, V does not exceed T; but in the large pinnate, assimilating leaves, V greatly exceeds T (*see* Fig.7.5).

THE DISTRIBUTION OF FERN SORI

The nature and distribution of the sori and sporangia in ferns have long been recognized as being among their most distinctive characters and therefore affording important criteria of comparison in phylogenetic studies (Bower, 1923). Here, again, a knowledge of the primary pattern in the leaf marginal meristems and of differential growth in the subjacent regions enables us to interpret the different manifestations of organization in the mature reproductive frond. Relevant concepts and facts have been considered by Wardlaw (1958, 1963), and Wardlaw and Sharma (1961); here it may be briefly noted (i) that the sorus develops from a special kind of meristem, (ii) that all soral meristems originate in the leaf marginal meristem, and (iii) that the ultimate position of the sorus, whether marginal, intra-marginal, or superficial, is determined by the distribution of growth in the marginal and submarginal regions. Thus, if marginal growth ceases with the onset of the reproductive phase, the adult sorus will remain marginal; but if growth is maintained in the marginal and submarginal regions of the leaf, the soral meristem will eventually occupy a position on the lower surface of the lamina, in some instances still close to the margin, in others more or less distant from it.

The adult organization is the result of the interaction of nutritional, hormonal and genetical factors. In this connection Sussex and Steeves (1958) have shown, by culturing excised primordia of *Leptopteris hymenophylloides*, *Todea barbara* and *Osmunda cinnamomea* in synthetic culture media, that high concentrations of sugar are among the factors which promote the inception and/or development of sori, though other metabolic factors must evidently be involved also. The correlative inhibition of growth in the lamina of the sporophyll is exemplified by many ferns.

DIFFERENTIAL GROWTH IN THE LEAVES OF FLOWERING PLANTS

Although the apical and marginal meristems of the leaves of flowering plants are histologically considerably less distinctive and evident than those of fern leaves, the inception of the primary pattern is not unlike that in the ferns. The general configuration of, for example, a compound or palmately-lobed leaf of a dicotyledon is established while the primordium is still in its primary phase of development. The numerous kinds of leaves in flowering plants are very varied in the manner of their development. However, the main difference between the leaves of ferns and flowering plants is that in the latter apical and marginal meristematic activity soon ceases, the further enlargement of the lamina being due to intercalary or diffuse growth distributed throughout its tissues (*see* Avery, 1935). As Sinnott (1960) pointed out, differences in cell shape have little to do with the overall expansion of the leaf; yet this process takes place in a regular and distinctive manner and is therefore under some kind of physiological-genetical control. In many leaves of seed plants, the several components of growth in the leaf are unequal and hence the lamina changes its shape during development. These are controlled changes and can often be analysed in terms of allometric growth. In fact, some dicotyledonous leaves of asymmetrical shape, such as those of *Begonia* spp., afford very remarkable examples of the effects of sustained intercalary differential growth (D'Arcy Thompson, 1917, 1942). This author also showed how the configuration of leaves such as those of the violet or horse-chestnut can be analysed in terms of simple allometric growth relationships.

In his famous chapter on 'The Theory of Transformations, or the Comparison of Related Forms', D'Arcy Thompson (1917, 1942) has shown how, by various deformations of Cartesian co-ordinates, seemingly very different shapes, or conformations, may be derived from initially simple forms. An important class of deformations, based on the use of radial co-ordinates, has an apt application to the way in which characteristic distributions of growth in leaves determine their eventual shape (Fig.10.14).

In biology these co-ordinates will be especially applicable in cases where the growing structure includes a 'node', or point where growth is absent or at a minimum; and about which node the rate of growth may be assumed to increase symmetrically. Precisely such a case is furnished us in a leaf of an ordinary dicotyledon. The leaf of a typical monocotyledon – such as a grass or a hyacinth, for instance – grows continuously from its base, and exhibits no node or 'point of arrest'. Its sides taper off gradually from its broad base to its slender tip, according to some law of decrement specific to the plant; and any alteration in the relative velocities of longitudinal and transverse growth will merely make the leaf a little broader or narrower, and will effect no other conspicuous alteration in its contour. But if there once come into existence a node, or 'locus of no growth', about which we may assume growth – which in the hyacinth leaf was longitudinal and transverse – to take place radially and transversely to the radii, then we shall soon see the sloping sides of the hyacinth leaf give place to more typical and 'leaf-like' shape. If we alter the ratio between the radial and tangential velocities of growth – in other words, if we increase the angles between corresponding radii – we pass successively through the various configurations which the botanist describes as the lanceolate, the ovate, and the cordiform leaf. These

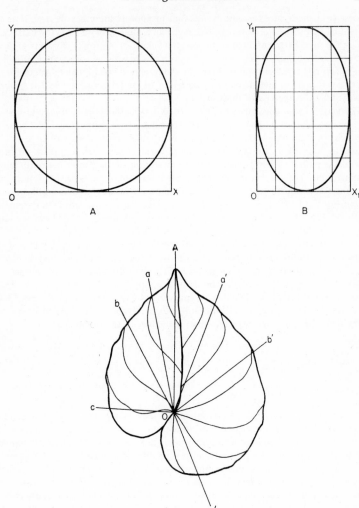

Fig.10.14 Configurations that may result from simple changes in Cartesian co-ordinates.

A, a circle projected on to a system of rectangular equidistant co-ordinates. B, shows the effect of changing the transverse component of the system. C, *Begonia daedalea*: *A*, apex of leaf; *O*, hilus; *a*, *b*, *c* are points taken at random on the smaller side of the leaf; a^1, b^1, c^1 are drawn so that $Oa = Oa^1$, etc. (see Text). (After D'Arcy Thompson, *On Growth and Form*.)

successive changes may to some extent, and in appropriate cases, be traced as the individual leaf grows to maturity; but as a much more general rule, the balance of forces, the ratio between radial and tangential velocities of growth, remains so nicely and constantly balanced that the leaf increases in size without conspicuous modification of form. It is rather what we may call a long-period variation, a tendency for the relative velocities to alter from one generation to another, whose result is brought into view by this method of illustration.

There are various corollaries to this method of describing the form of a leaf which may be here alluded to. For instance, the so-called unsymmetrical leaf of a begonia, in which one side of the leaf may be merely ovate while the other has a cordate outline, is seen to be really a case of unequal, and not truly asymmetrical, growth on either side of the midrib. There is nothing more mysterious in its conformation than, for instance, in that of a forked twig in which one limb of the fork has grown longer than the other. The case of the begonia leaf is of sufficient interest to deserve illustration, and in Fig.10.14 I have outlined a leaf of the large *Begonia daedalea*. On the smaller left-hand side of the leaf I have taken at random three points a, b, c and have measured the angles AOa, etc., which the radii from the hilus of the leaf to these points make with the median axis. On the other side of the leaf I have marked the points a', b', c', such that the radii drawn to this margin of the leaf are equal to the former. Oa' to Oa, etc. Now if the two sides of the leaf are mathematically similar to one another, it is obvious that the respective angles should be in continued proportion, i.e. as AOa is to AOa', so should AOb be to AOb'. This proves to be very nearly the case. For I have measured the three angles on one side, and one on the other, and have then compared, as follows, the calculated with the observed values of the other two:

	AOa	AOb	AOc	AOa'	AOb'	AOc'
Observed values	12°	28·5°	88°	—	—	157°
Calculated „	—	—	—	21·5°	51·1°	—
Observed „	—	—	—	20°	52°	—

The agreement is very close, and what discrepancy there is may be amply accounted for, firstly, by the slight irregularity of the sinuous margin of the leaf; and secondly, by the fact that the true axis or midrib of the leaf is not straight but slightly curved, and therefore that it is curvilinear and not rectilinear triangles which we ought to have measured. When we understand these few points regarding the peripheral curvature of the leaf, it is easy to see that its principal veins approximate closely to a beautiful system of isogonal co-ordinates. It is also obvious that we can easily pass, by a process of shearing, from those cases where the principal veins start from the base of the leaf to those where they arise successively from the midrib, as they do in most dicotyledons (D'Arcy Thompson).

If we combine the point of view expounded by D'Arcy Thompson with the genetical concept of Goldschmidt, i.e. that genes affect the rates at which different processes in development proceed, we have probably a rational basis for understanding some of the organizational features of leaves in general, and the distinctive features of the leaves of particular species.

The numerous examples of heteroblastic development in the leaves of flowering plants provide an unrivalled array of materials exemplifying the morphological diversity which results from the further elaboration of a primary pattern by differential growth (Goebel, 1928–30; Troll, 1928, 1937; Arber, 1919).

In different instances, the major factors which determine or control differential growth in leaves may be of different kinds. In a study of species with irregular nutrition, e.g. *Neottia*, including complete parasites such as *Cuscuta*, Cutter (1955) and Wardlaw (1957) showed that the leaf primordia at the apex were in all respects closely comparable with those of related and other autotrophic species, but that, during their further development in the subapical and maturing regions, they failed to undergo any considerable enlargement. As a result, they appear as insignificant scale-leaves on adult regions of the axis (Fig.10.3). Wardlaw (1957) showed that in the microphyllous pteridophyte *Psilotum triquetrum*, the very insignificant scale-leaves of the adult axis nevertheless have their inception as quite bulky primordia at the apical meristem (Plate 7).

In various leaves of complex morphology, in which there has been a departure from the usual dorsiventral symmetry, e.g. pitcher-plant leaves, as in *Nepenthes* or *Sarracenia*, the novel developments can usually be referred to the presence of a system of localized meristems (Roth, 1957). These exceptional types of leaf configuration, which are usually held to exemplify specialized and advanced adaptational mechanisms, will almost certainly repay further investigation from the morphogenetic and organizational points of view.

FACTORS IN DIFFERENTIAL GROWTH

The *subapical* region of the shoot is evidently one in which the interactions of genetical, nutritional, correlative and environmental factors contribute significantly to the organization of the leafy shoot. Cultural studies of excised leaf primordia and shoot apices have shown that the variable development of subapical regions is largely due to hormonal and nutritional factors (Wetmore and Morel, 1949; Wetmore, 1950, 1953, 1954, 1955, 1956, 1959; Allsopp, 1952, 1953a, b, 1954, 1955; Sussex and Steeves, 1953, 1958; Steeves and Sussex, 1957; Sussex, 1958; Steeves, 1959; Sussex and Clutter, 1960). These investigators have shown that, in media in which the other essential nutrients are presumably not limiting, lower sugar concentrations favour the development of the morphologically simple or 'juvenile' type of leaf, whereas higher concentrations tend to promote the development of the more complex 'adult' forms. However, it is pertinent to note that in some so-called 'starvation' experiments, abundant starch has been observed very close to apices of greatly diminished growth and morphogenetic activity (Wardlaw, 1945; Cutter, 1955). These variable developments are largely the result of changes in the amount and distribution of growth in the subapical and maturing regions, though changes in the size and primary pattern of the meristem are also involved. Important as sugar demonstrably is in the development of excised fern leaf primordia, the nutrients required for protein synthesis must also be present in adequate amounts to admit of meristematic activity in a primordium which becomes large and multipinnate (Wardlaw, 1945). Heteroblastic development in *Marsilea* is affected not only by sugar but also by variations in the inorganic salts supplied (Allsopp, 1953a).

Steeves and Sussex (1957) reported that whereas cell sizes in excised cultured fern leaves and in intact leaves on the plant are approximately the same, the final size of the cultured leaves is usually less, indicating that fewer cells are present. They accordingly suggested that there is a restriction in mitotic activity in cultured excised leaves, just as there appears to be in the leaves of young sporophytes or in those forced into precocious maturation by experimental treatments, e.g. defoliation. It appears that certain interactions which contribute to normal adult leaf development are absent or are precluded; and Sussex and Clutter (1960) have suggested that these probably do not involve carbohydrates but factors of a different kind, not yet closely specified, but with important regulatory effects (Foster, 1928, 1932; Wardlaw, 1945; Ashby, 1948; Ashby and Wangermann, 1950, 1951; Cutter, 1955).

That older leaves affect the morphology of younger ones is well known in flowering plants (Goodwin, 1937); and in the ferns also this aspect has been explored with interesting results. Thus Albaum (1938) showed in the young sporophyte of *Pteris longifolia* that an older leaf, or auxin applied to the stump of an older leaf, regulated, or delayed, the further growth and development of the next younger primordium; and Crotty (1955) ascribed heteroblastic development to a maturation-delaying effect of older leaves on younger ones in *Acrostichum danaea-folium*. He showed that in the first leaves of the young sporophyte the meristematic phase is of brief duration, there being no, or few, older leaves to provide an inhibitory effect on further development. Such leaves mature rapidly and are small and of simple shape. But, as onto-genesis proceeds, the successive new leaf primordia are increasingly subjected to the regulatory effects of the surrounding older leaves. The duration of the meristematic phase is thereby extended, the embryonic regions increase in size and complexity and, on maturation, the adult leaf is an organ of large size and complex morphology. These observa-tions indicate the probable value of fuller investigations of substances which may affect the extent and/or duration of leaf meristem activity (*see also* Sussex and Clutter, 1960).

Steeves and Wetmore (1953) demonstrated the regulatory effects of older leaves or primordia on the development of the next adjacent inner ones in *Osmunda cinnamomea*. This fern has dimorphic leaves, both fully expanded sterile and fertile fronds and also less developed foliar members known as cataphylls being present (Goebel, 1905; Bower, 1923–28). Special features of the cataphyll are (i) that, up to a point, its morphological development is identical with that of normal fertile and sterile leaves, (ii) that it shows an arrest of crozier develop-ment and concomitant broadening of the marginal regions of the petiole, and (iii) the prospective cataphylls can be induced to develop as normal leaves, e.g. by the timely, systematic removal of the surrounding older fertile and sterile leaves of the current year. The distinctive morphology of the cataphylls is thus in some way controlled by the adjacent older leaves. Steeves and Wetmore considered that this is probably due to a combination of factors rather than to a single factor, e.g. auxin, though possible auxin effects are not entirely precluded. Other instances of cataphyll formation in the ferns have been recorded (Goebel, 1905). The writer has suggested that whereas we tend to regard the nest-leaves in dimorphic ferns such as *Drynaria* spp. and the mantle-leaves of *Platycerium* spp. as specialized, adaptive structures, exemplifying division of labour, etc., it may well be that they belong to the same general category of organs as the cataphylls of *Osmunda* and result from the action of similar regulative factors (Wardlaw, 1963).

Although emphasis has here been laid on growth and development in the apical regions, other important phases of growth are also involved before a primordium becomes a fully expanded functional leaf. The reader is referred to studies by Steeves and Briggs (1958, 1960), Briggs and Steeves (1958, 1959) and Sussex and Clutter (1960), on auxin and other relationships in the expanding and maturing fern frond, including the eventual uncoiling of the crozier. Steeves and Briggs (1958) have shown, for example, that there are important and, indeed, striking differences in histological organization as between the basal region of the leaf and the more distal pinna-bearing rachis.

While it may be accepted that genetical, ontogenetic, correlative and environmental factors interact to yield the eventual organization of the leafy shoot, the effects of factors in one or other of these categories may vary widely in different instances. Pervasive as well as specific effects of genetical factors in development are well exemplified by the ferns. Andersson-Kottö (1929, 1938) showed that relatively small genetical differences, by changing the growth pattern, may determine morphological differences of a kind that would have been regarded as being of critical importance by comparative (phylogenetic) morphologists. In the foregoing sections it has been shown that, at different stages in ontogenesis, or in relation to particular conditions, very different adult organs may develop from closely comparable primordia. In these instances, the genotype must be such as to admit of the observed developments, but the actual morphological features cannot usually be directly or closely attributed to the action of specific genetical factors. Thus, although no absolute separation of the several kinds of morphogenetic factors is possible, a more precise evaluation of their specific effects may nevertheless be obtainable.

That the pattern of differential growth is under direct genetical control is often demonstrably true. This is well seen in the many examples of tall and dwarf mutant forms of flowering plants, in which it has been shown that only a single gene may be involved. But, as we have seen in ferns such as *Dryopteris dilatata*, *Matteuccia struthiopteris*, and in rosette flowering plants with runners, quite different allometric growth patterns are present in the apices of erect shoots and lateral rhizomes of the same plant. Species with dimorphic or heteroblastic leaves afford further examples of the same general kind. How the primary pattern is established in the apical meristem, and how differential growth, or modifications of it, are determined in the subapical regions, by genetical and other factors, are still very obscure phenomena. The more we study these formative regions as the sites of so many different but integrated reactions, culminating in morphological features with functional significance, the more remarkable and challenging the whole process of development is seen to be. In particular, the subapical region emerges as one which shows great plasticity under the impact of factors of different kinds. It is, of course, tempting to consider how some of the developments in the subapical region might be interpreted in terms of auxin, auxin-gibberellin, or auxin-kinetin activities, as recently discussed by

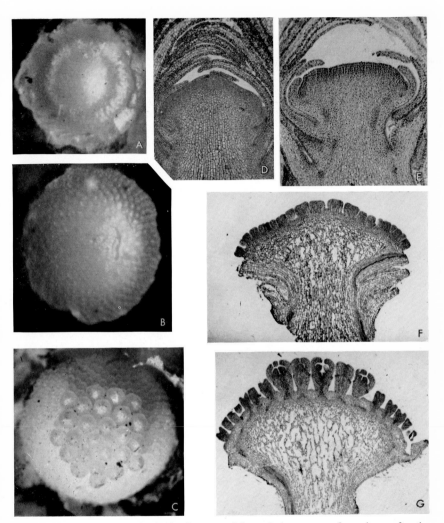

17. *Tussilago farfara*. Stages in the development of the capitulum, as seen from above, after the foliage leaves and bracts have been removed. A, The formation of florets is beginning around the base of the capitulum meristem. B, Florets have now been formed, in acropetal sequence, well up toward the summit, or centre, of the capitulum. C, The last-formed florets—male, disc florets—at the centre of the capitulum meristem have now outgrown the surrounding older florets (× 20). (*d-g*) Longitudinal median sections of capitula at various stages of development. D, A young capitulum; no florets have yet formed (× 75). E, Floret formation is beginning around the base of the capitulum, as in (*a*) (× 50). F, The terminal, disc, florets have enlarged. G, They are now conspicuously larger than the earlier-formed ray florets (× 33). (*Growth in Living Systems*, 1961.)

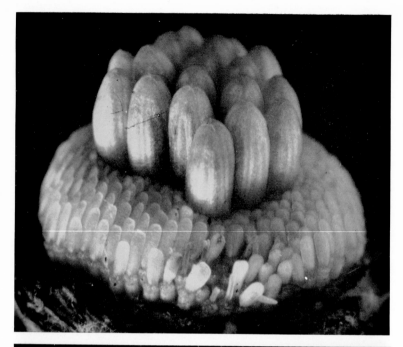

18. *Tussilago farfara*. Successively later stages in the development of the capitulum.
A, The disc florets have grown very strongly. B, A later stage: the ray florets are now catching up with the disc florets (× 20).

Kefford and Goldacre (1961, where the relevant literature is cited), but what is really needed is a new accession of fact. Recent experimental work indicates that this may well be possible.

CONCLUSION

It is sometimes thought that organization must necessarily remain a rather vague and ill-defined notion that does not lend itself to close analysis. This may be so at the present time. But, from the evidence advanced here, it does appear that at least some of the major organizational features in plants can be defined, analysed, and subjected to experimental investigation; and they can be considered in terms that are meaningful to morphologists, physiologists and geneticists. Accordingly, it may be expected that further investigations of the constitution and functional properties of meristems, as yielding the primary morphogenetic pattern, and of the control of differential growth in subapical regions, as yielding elaborations and variations of the primary pattern, will advance our knowledge of organization in all classes of higher plants.

K

CHAPTER 11

The Organization of the Inflorescence and Flower

INTRODUCTION

The serial, or sequential, evocation and action of genes has already been referred to as a feature of the organizational process in plants. Although this topic will now be examined with special reference to the inception and development of the inflorescence and the flower, it seems probable that serial genic action is probably involved in many, perhaps in all, formative processes.

Morphological developments in which particular characters can be ascribed to the action of individual genes, or to small groups of them, are of special interest. Inflorescences and flowers afford abundant materials for relating specific genic action to the inception of distinctive morphological developments, i.e. taxonomic or genetical characters. An outstanding feature of such phenomena is that the controlling or determining agents seem to be evoked or activated in a definite and characteristic sequence. It should perhaps be noted that the general idea of sequential activities is not strictly a genetical one: the sequential activities of enzymes have long been recognized by plant physiologists as a feature of all major metabolic processes. However, in recent decades, it has been realized that information on the physiology, genetics and morphogenesis of particular biological developments can and should be co-ordinated, and that in time a more adequate understanding of organization, even in complex structures such as inflorescences and flowers, may be achieved.

Floral morphology is, of course, a very large and many-sided topic, and its several aspects have by no means been co-ordinated. Thus Barnard (1961), in discussing the interpretation of the angiosperm flower, has commented on the fact that information on morphological and phylogenetic aspects is contained in a separate literature from that in which the flower is studied as a biological unit with its diverse functional activities. A system of ideas which can bring the several aspects of floral development into some valid relationship is very much needed at the present time. To this end the basis of a possible general theory is indicated and examined in the present chapter.

GENETICAL FACTORS IN AXIS AND LEAF FORMATION

When we examine inflorescences and flowers the basic organizational phenomena seem to be referable to the physiological-genetical determination of axial and lateral members. Many of the problems of floral morphogenesis are closely comparable with those of the vegetative shoot, although the ultimate developments are usually very different.

As we have seen, the reaction system in the vegetative shoot apical meristem gives rise to growth centres which usually develop into leaf primordia. In the further development of primordia in the subapical and maturing regions, the effects of specific genetical factors can usually be observed, e.g. in the presence of a discrete or a clasping petiole base, the formation of stipules, petiole development, the size and shape of the lamina, and so on. In brief, the physiological-genetical factors which determine taxonomic characters are active at a very early stage in leaf ontogenesis. Comparative studies of related varieties have shown that a relatively small genetical difference may determine more or less conspicuous differences in the shape of the adult leaf. The laciniate and broad (almost entire) types of leaf in *Gossypium arboreum* illustrate this point (Hammond, 1941). This investigator showed that although the shape of a cotton leaf may change continuously throughout its development, the effect of the related gene determining its differential growth does not. In short, there appear to be 'shape-determining' genes. On this aspect, information has been given by Sinnott (1935), based on studies of pure lines of *Cucurbita pepo* (Fig.4.2). He showed that highly varied fruit forms may be obtained in different crosses; and he inferred that there must be genes which directly control shape, these being independent of other genes which determine volume and weight. Supporting evidence was obtained by Kaiser (1935) in hybridization studies of *Capsicum annuum* in which inbred, homozygous varieties, with contrasted fruit shapes and sizes were used. Houghtaling (1935) also contributed information on specific genic effects on fruit shape in pure breeding types of tomato. These effects of individual genes, or of small groups of genes, on leaf shape, etc., may be largely attributed to the control which they exercise on differential growth.

SOME GENERAL ASPECTS OF FLORAL DEVELOPMENT

The inception and development of the inflorescence and the flower probably afford the most convincing evidence of the sequential activity of genes in the Plant Kingdom. Indeed, it is difficult to see how an adequate account of these major developmental phenomena can be given without making the basic assumption that the shoot, and subsequently the floral, meristem is the site of a reaction system in which the sequential evocation and activity of gene-determined substances take place (Wardlaw, 1957, 1961).

As an introduction to the relevant problems, it is advantageous to begin with the vegetative shoot apical meristem and its regular formation of growth centres and leaf primordia.

Metabolism in Growth Centres. Although all the growth centres formed at the vegetative shoot apex are probably similar in many respects, they are not necessarily metabolically identical: hence some of the differences in leaf primordium morphology in species showing heteroblastic development. As Foster (1929, 1935) and Schüepp (1929) have shown for particular species, important differences in the total, and in the differential, growth potential of growth centres can be detected from the outset, these resulting in such conspicuous morphological differences as those seen in cataphylls and foliage leaves. The writer (Wardlaw, 1949, 1950, 1957) and Cutter (1954, 1955) have shown that the development of growth centres and very young leaf primordia can be modified by surgical and chemical treatments. The latter are of special interest in the present context. Thus, when various physiologically-active substances were applied directly to the apical meristem of *Dryopteris dilatata*, the novel effects included (a) the failure of growth centres to develop into primordia, (b) the inception of double primordia, and (c) the formation of vegetative buds in leaf sites. The position may be summarized by saying that, during the vegetative phase, growth centres in the apical meristem usually give rise to leaf primordia; but the activity of a growth centre is subject to modification as a result of changes in some of its metabolic components, and these may have significant and sometimes very conspicuous effects on the ensuing organogenesis.

The Onset of the Reproductive Phase. The vegetative shoot apical meristem may, according to the species, develop into a single flower or into an inflorescence. As judged by external appearance, the showy, often brightly coloured, inflorescence or flower seems to bear little relation or resemblance to the antecedent vegetative leafy shoot. Indeed, some botanists have regarded inflorescences and flowers as organs of a completely different category from those formed during the vegetative phase. This, of course, is very different from the classical concept in which the flower is regarded as an axis of limited growth bearing variously modified lateral members which are homologous with leaves.

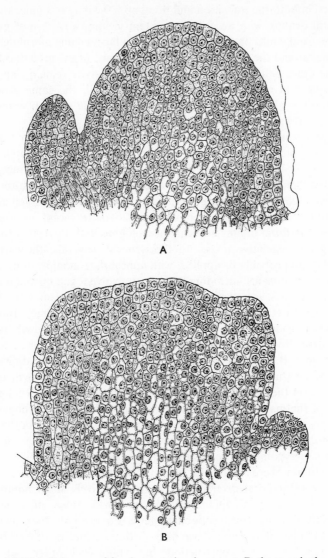

Fig.11.1 *Rubus rosaefolius* A, vegetative shoot apex. B, the same in the course of transition to a floral apex (× 410). (After C. J. Engard. *Univ. of Hawaii Publ.*)

In fact, in both the transition and floral apex we may recognize that we are still dealing with an apical meristem yielding a pattern of growth centres; and while, on the one hand, certain far-reaching morphogenetic changes attend the further development of some of the growth centres, on the other hand, certain aspects of apical activity remain singularly unchanged in any fundamental sense. After all, the same genetical constitution underlies all development in both the vegetative and the reproductive phase (Fig.11.1 and Plates 2, 16, 17).

Organogenesis in 'simple' and more complex flowers. In a 'simple' or 'prototypic' flower, i.e. exemplifying polypetaly, hypogyny, apocarpy, etc., as in *Ranunculus* spp., all the organs can be referred to the inception and development of lateral growth centres, these usually constituting a pattern of considerable regularity. As earlier workers had noted and as Tepfer (1953) has clearly demonstrated in more recent ontogenetic studies, the floral organs are truly homologous with the leaves formed during the vegetative phase. In the writer's view this, the classical, concept can probably be applied, with appropriate modifications, to all floral development, including the most evolved gamopetalous and epigynous types, as well as highly condensed and reduced ones (Fig.11.1).

At the onset of flowering, as the result of a 'florigenic' stimulus, important changes take place in the distribution of growth in the vegetative shoot apex (Fig.11.1 and Plates 16, 17) (for review, *see* Hillman, 1962). If we begin with the prototypic flower, it is not difficult to understand that certain changes in the distribution of growth in the apex, i.e. in the vertical and transverse components, could account for some of the major differences in floral construction, e.g. hypogyny to epigyny, polypetaly to gamopetaly, actinomorphy to zygomorphy, etc. But within any particular kind of floral development, e.g. syncarpy, epigyny or zygomorphy, or inflorescence category, e.g. the spike, umbel or capitulum, there is scope for great variation in detail. In short, much of the evident floral diversity is due to a relatively small number of major morphological differences and to a wide range of variations within the different constructional patterns. For example, the Cruciferae and Orchidaceae exemplify two very distinctive and readily recognizable 'types' of floral construction; but within each order there is a considerable range of relatively minor variation.

In the transition from the vegetative to the floral phase, closely comparable changes in apical growth and morphogenesis occur in species from groups not closely related. For example, zygomorphic flowers are usually lateral, the plane of zygomorphy being very commonly that of the axis and the subtending bract (Goebel, 1900, 1913). This suggests that certain genetically-determined adaxial/abaxial growth relationships, established at an early stage in floral ontogenesis, are of general occurrence; and similarly for other major features.

SERIAL GENIC ACTION IN FLOWER FORMATION

As the vegetative apical meristem becomes a transition meristem, the first group of growth centres may develop as evident foliar organs, i.e. smaller leaves and bracts, exhibiting heteroblastic development (Fig. 11.2). Where the apex gives rise to a flower, the next group of growth centres yields the outer perianth members, and later-formed centres the inner perianth, the stamens and the carpels. Even in highly modified, condensed, epigynous flowers, this conception of the basic nature of floral organogenesis is probably still applicable, attention being also paid to the distribution of growth in the receptacle and to correlative developments, especially during the earliest stages. Vegetative and transition apices of *Rubus* are illustrated in Fig.11.1; stages in the formation of the capitula of Compositae are illustrated in Plates 2, 16, 17; characteristic stages in the formation of a Ranalean flower are shown in Plate 16; a generalized scheme of floral development is indicated in Fig.11.3; and examples of the heteroblastic leaf development, which is often a concomitant of the transition to flowering, are shown in Figs. 11.5, 11.6 and 11.7.

The ontogenetic approach has already been effectively used by many workers, mostly in comparative studies; but it is no less essential in causal investigations. What is now required is an examination of characteristic floral developments in terms of the underlying physiological-genetical and other factors. To this end, the writer (Wardlaw, 1957) has suggested that, at the onset of flowering, the shoot apex continues to give rise to a succession of regularly spaced growth centres, the further development of which as primordia, with the distinctive characters of sepals, petals, stamens and carpels, is the result of the serial evocation and action of particular genes (or groups of genes), together with the other factors at work in the meristem. The existence of metabolic differences in growth centres, already mentioned, is an important part of the theory; for, as Engard (1944) noted, there are no real transitions at the morphological level between homologous organs; but, as we now see, there can be important changes and differences in the metabolism of growth centres.

The inception of the flower is stimulated by the entry of a new metabolic

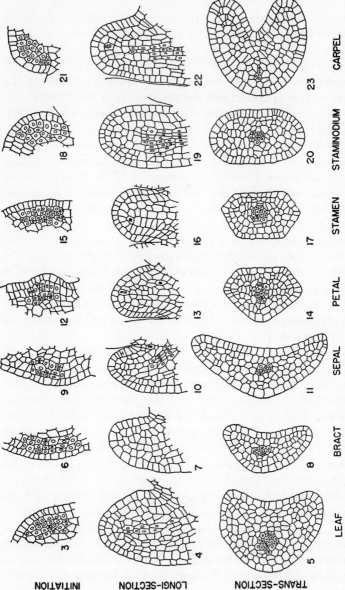

Fig.11.2 Camera lucida drawings of *Aquilegia formosa* var. *truncata*, showing early stages in the formation of leaves, bracts, and floral organs at the apical meristem. As judged by the usual criteria – i.e. position and mode of inception – all these organs are homologous. (After S. S. Tepfer, *Univ. Calif. Publ. Bot.* 1953.)

substance(s), not yet specified or isolated, into the reaction system of the apical meristem, with consequential effects on the metabolism and development of its growth centres. Other important, usually irreversible, changes also ensue. The allometric growth pattern of the apex is modified to a more or less marked extent, the elongation of the axis being usually conspicuously diminished or arrested. As a result, the growth centres, and the lateral organs to which they give rise, are now formed in closely associated groups, either whorls or condensed helices, on an abbreviated axis; and the meristem typically loses its former capacity for indefinite growth.

In normal floral ontogenesis the apical reaction system passes through a sequence of distinctive phases, these being determined and controlled by specific genes, and also by physiological correlations and environmental factors. The fundamental pattern in flower inception, which usually exhibits remarkable stability and constancy, is primarily referable to the genetical constitution; but during the elaboration of this pattern extrinsic factors may sometimes exercise important morphogenetic effects. J. and Y. Heslop-Harrison's (1956–59) studies of the morphogenetic effects of temperature, light and applied auxin on the development of the androecial and gynoecial regions of the floral meristem illustrate this point.

The action of specific genes in flower formation is essentially serial in character. As the florigenic stimulus begins to affect the apical reaction system, the specific action of certain genes, hitherto inert or non-specific in their effects, is induced. The changes thereby effected in the system lead to further specific genic action; and so on in a chain, or serial fashion, until flower formation terminates with the utilization of all, or practically all, of the residual distal meristem; and it is to the action of particular genes, as components of the reaction system, that the clear delimitation of the several organogenic phases, i.e. the formation of calyx, corolla, androecium and gynoecium, must be attributed.

The foregoing conceptions afford a basis for explaining some of the main features of floral ontogenesis and organization, such as (1) that the several floral organs are homologous with leaves; (2) that they originate in a characteristic pattern on the meristem; and (3) that the successive groups of growth centres, formed during the course of floral ontogenesis, have distinctive quantitative and qualitative growth properties, and accordingly give rise to groups of organs differing in form, structure and function. An important feature of the theory is that it envisages floral ontogenesis in terms of physiology, genetics and the

K*

dynamic geometry of the embryonic apical region. Moreover, several formerly important and highly controversial hypotheses, for example relating to homologous and non-homologous floral organs, to organs

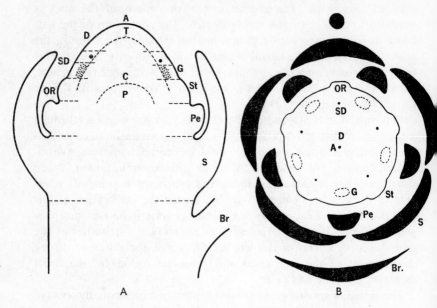

Fig.11.3 A, A diagrammatic representation of a theory of floral morphogenesis in a prototypic flower. The longitudinal section here shows, in acropetal sequence, a bract (Br); young sepals (S); young petal primordia (Pe); stamen primordia (St) at their inception; the positions of the next growth centres to become primordia (G); and the beginning of growth centres still closer to the summit of the apex (A). Tunica (T); corpus (C); and pith (P). The discontinuous transverse lines are intended to indicate a number of zones into which the organized apex is differentiated: the distal zone (D); the sub-distal zone(s) (SD), in which the reaction system is giving rise to a pattern of growth centres; the organogenic zone (OR), in which the active growth centres have given rise to very young primordia. The transverse lines also indicate the successive phases, or stages, through which the apex passes as floral morphogenesis progresses.

B, An apex similar to that in A as seen from above; indications as before. (From *Growth in Living Systems*, 1961.)

sui generis, to morphological 'transitions', etc., are seen in quite a different light as consideration of the relevant phenomena is transferred from the morphological to the physiological plane. Not least, the theory suggests opportunities for new observational and experimental work on floral ontogenesis, both in its general and more specific aspects.

In the theory as outlined above it is inferred that there must be differences in the metabolism, and therefore in the cytoplasm of the cells of growth centres at different levels on the floral meristem. The genetical literature provides supporting evidence for this view. To cite one common example, Mather (1944) showed that in a distylic species of *Primula*, in which the stamens in the 'pin' and 'thrum' flowers originate at different levels on the meristem, the incompatibility properties of the pollen cells cannot be understood by reference to their genotypes but to their cytoplasms. The tristylic species *Lythrum salicaria* affords another example of the same kind.

The factors involved in a complex reaction system (or perhaps system of systems), like that in a developing floral meristem, will evidently require much investigation before their effects are even partly understood. But the task, though difficult and complex, need not be regarded as impossible. Thus Tepfer *et al.* (1963), as also some earlier investigators, have shown that the flower buds of some species can be excised at various stages of development, e.g. from before sepal inception to later stages when young carpel primordia were present, and successfully grown in media of known composition. The media used for the culture of *Aquilegia* buds by Tepfer *et al.*, for example, contained basic and trace elements, sucrose, coconut milk, vitamins and hormonal substances. It was found that the addition of IAA, GA and kinetin to the basic medium extended bud development at nearly all stages and, in particular, enhanced carpel development. Cultured buds, on a medium containing these ingredients, typically formed the several groups of floral organs and grew to about the size of flowers at anthesis; but development did not take place unless the sepals had been removed – an engimatic and thought-provoking observation, suggesting the incidence of important correlative factors in the normal floral development (as suggested in the writer's scheme, Fig.11.3). Further work on the culture of flower buds in media of known composition may enable us, in time, to test the general theory of floral morphogenesis.

In floral development, genic action may be pervasive or specific, or both. An example of the first is afforded by the floral vascularization in *Mentha spicata*, *M. aquatica* and their F_1 hybrids (Hillson, 1963): on the basis of various comparisons, this author concluded that floral vascular structure, which is an integral part of the overall development, is a heritable character.

To summarize: a basis for explaining the major features in floral organization is afforded by the following concepts: (1) the several floral organs, like the antecedent vegetative leaves, originate from growth centres on the floral meristem; (2) in relation to the serial evocation of genes, the successive groups of growth centres have distinctive physiological properties and accordingly give rise to organs which differ in form, structure and function; (3) the floral meristem is also affected by these metabolic changes; (4) factors affecting correlative developments and various other factors are also important in determining the unified and harmonious floral development. With appropriate modifications the theory can also be applied to the inception of buds in inflorescences, e.g. capitula, the compact inflorescences of aroids, and so on.

THE DIVERSITY OF FLOWERS AND INFLORESCENCES

The diversity of inflorescences and flowers in Nature, and the array of varieties that have been produced by horticulturists and plant-breeders, afford unchallengeable evidence of the specific effects of genes and of changes in the genetic constitution, whether by mutation, hybridization, polyploidy or aneuploidy. Investigators such as Stebbins (1950) and Rensch (1959) regard these changes, together with the phenomena of selection, population genetics, isolation, etc., as being sufficient to account for taxonomic differences not only within the species and genus, but also, given sufficient time, between the higher taxonomic categories (*see* Chapter 5).

THE SOURCE OF ORDER

Geneticists have demonstrated that such features as the shape and colouring of flowers, doubling the number of floral parts, the transformation of petals into stamens, or *vice-versa*, peloria, fasciation, and the separation of the sexes in varying degrees, are all primarily and fundamentally referable to the action of genes, i.e. to the chemical activity of the specific substances which they control. These substances may be envisaged as active components of the floral reaction system at critical stages of development. Sometimes relatively small genetical differences result in quite considerable morphological differences, e.g. zygomorphy to peloria. Although many anomalous developments are known (Worsdell, 1916), the individual inflorescence or flower usually develops its characteristic features with a very considerable measure of constancy.

The flower, in fact, epitomizes the phenomena of orderly development and stability in a high degree. In attempting to account for this fidelity of organization, the sequential evocation and activity of gene-determined enzymes, as new substrates successively become available in the floral reaction system, seems to be the only answer in sight at the present time. But, we may ask, what is the nature of the ultimate ordering principle? How does each one of the many genes that are involved in a complex process like flowering take its proper place in the orderly developmental process? Since plants are not equipped with any central controlling agency or system, the answer to this question would seem to be that the order is inherent in, and a property or function of, the apical reaction system. And, as we have seen, this reaction system not only has great innate stability but also possesses a sufficient range of variability or plasticity to accommodate the various internal and external factors which may affect it during ontogenesis. However, when one considers what is involved morphogenetically in the formation of a fully developed flower, the importance of the flower in the life cycle and in the survival of the species, and its relationships to factors in the environment, it becomes evident how very inadequate any 'explanation' or interpretation of floral organization is likely to be.

INVESTIGATIONS RELATING TO HOMOLOGY

Goethe's classical view of the prototypic flower as a determinate shoot or axis, bearing the several floral organs, which are homologous with leaves (Eames, 1931; Arber, 1937), is supported by recent investigations (Fig.2.1). In an elegant histological demonstration (Fig.11.2), Tepfer (1953) showed that, at their inception in the meristem, the lateral organs, whether of leafy shoot or flower, in species of *Ranunculus* and *Aquilegia*, are closely comparable and truly homologous. Alternative theories of flower formation, e.g. those of Grégoire (1938), McLean Thompson (1937), etc., including that recently advanced by Plantefol (1948), Buvat (1952, 1955) and their adherents, do not seriously disturb the classical conception, though they have undoubtedly called attention to phenomena that require further investigation. The characteristic heteroblastic developments to be observed in the transition leaves, bracts and perianth in many species give realistic support to the classical concept. But the concept of homology should not be pushed too far; for while all the growth centres in a particular species have some properties and activities in common, they may differ in respect of other properties and activities, consequentially yielding organs so different

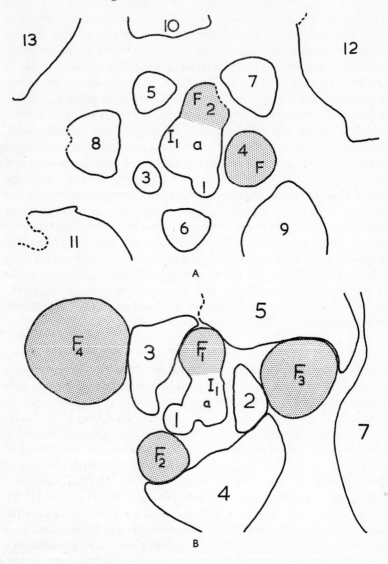

Fig.11.4 A, Transverse section (diagrammatic) of the apical meristem of a rhizome of *Nuphar lutea*, showing the sequence of primordia (1, 2, 3, etc., in the order of increasing age). Flower bud primordia (F) originate in leaf sites in the genetic spiral. a, centre of apical meristem; I_1, position of next primordium to appear.

(*Caption continued at foot of facing page*)

morphologically that excessive homologizing becomes absurd. In *Nuphar* and *Nymphaea*, for example, flower buds originate from growth centres which form part of the normal genetic, phyllotactic spiral and are therefore homologous with leaves in this particular respect; but it would be idle to attempt to push the homology further. Some inflorescences present similar difficulties (*see* below and Fig.11.4). The general position is that while all shoot apical meristems form growth centres, some of these, as in capitula and aroid inflorescences, may become flower buds and not leaves.

INVESTIGATIONS OF INFLORESCENCES

A conspicuous feature of many inflorescences is their almost geometrical regularity and the developmental harmony which they often exemplify in a high degree. The concepts discussed in Chapter 10 and in earlier sections of this chapter may also be applied to many aspects of inflorescence construction. In the formation of the capitula of the Compositae, for example, it can be seen that the inception of primary pattern, the elaboration of that pattern by differential growth, and regulated developments due to the serial action of genes, all contribute to the eventual organization (Plates 2, 16, 17, 18, 19, 20).

With the onset of the reproductive phase, in the common coltsfoot (*Tussilago farfara*), the vegetative shoot apical meristem changes considerably in size, form and morphogenetic activity. It gives rise to a large number of small bracts instead of a few large foliage leaves as hitherto; and it shows active radial but relatively limited vertical growth. On the dome-shaped nascent capitulum the primordia of the ray florets begin to be formed in acropetal sequence but the centre of the inflorescence meristem is still bare. Later, however, floret primordia – destined to become the male disc florets – are formed in the central, summit region of the capitulum. These are at first approximately the same size as the adjacent ray floret primordia but they rapidly outgrow them, indicating the incidence of genetical factors not actively involved in the earlier phase of floret formation (Wardlaw, 1960, 1961) (Plates 16, 17).

B, Transverse section of the apical meristem of a rhizome of *Victoria cruziana*, showing the positions of leaf and flower-bud primordia. The latter, like the former, originate in the apical meristem, but occupy interfoliar positions above leaf margins. Indications as in A. (Drawings by courtesy of Dr. E. G. Cutter; after C. W. Wardlaw, *Growth in Living Systems*, 1961.)

In the complex inflorescences of species of *Eucalyptus*, Carr and Carr (1959) noted that some of the characteristic features are comparable with morphological developments peculiar to the shoot system: for example, the outer bracts resemble the adult leaves in their asymmetry about the midrib. Leaf and bract primordia originate decussately at the shoot apex but in most species the leaves of each pair become separated by the development of a segment of axis (an 'intranode') between them. In certain species this growth distribution leads to the separation or 'disarticulation' of the unit inflorescence into two subclusters. Very complex inflorescences may thus result from the disarticulation of a simple inflorescence, followed by other developments. Carr and Carr concluded that inflorescences with few flowers and with free persistent bracts, the number of which is related to the flower number of the cluster, are phylogenetically primitive, whereas inflorescences with many flowers and fused bracts constituting a caducous involucre, in which the number of bracts is not related to the number of flowers, are advanced.

In *Nuphar* and *Nymphaea* spp. (Cutter, 1957–60), flower primordia originate as circular mounds on the surface of the rhizome apical meristem in positions on the genetic spiral which are normally occupied by leaf primordia, i.e. with the onset of flowering some growth centres become loci for the accumulation of the metabolic substances required in flower primordium formation, as distinct from leaf primordium formation. These important metabolic developments must take place high up on the apical meristem; but how adjacent growth centres become different metabolically is a problem in developmental physiology for which no adequate explanation has yet been advanced. In *Victoria* spp., alternative spirals of leaf and flower primordia can be traced from older regions of the rhizome upwards into the apical meristem (Cutter, 1960). The position of a young flower primordium is not axillary in the usually accepted meaning; it might be described as originating on the apical meristem above the anodic flange of an older tangentially extended leaf primordium, or as being interfoliar. Indeed, it is not unlike the interfoliar loci of bud rudiments in leptosporangiate ferns. In *Victoria*, as in *Nymphaea*, the phenomena of flower disposition and inception must also be sought in the apical meristem – a relatively small mass of embryonic tissue in which these definite but subtly distinctive patternized distributions of metabolites will have to be investigated. (For a full account of inflorescences, *see* Rickett, 1944.) (Fig.11.4).

EXTERNAL FACTORS IN FLORAL ORGANIZATION

Important effects of external factors in floral organization, some of which lend themselves to further exploration by experimental treatments, have been observed. For example, in studies of the physiology of sexuality, J. Heslop-Harrison (1959) has shown for different species that major changes can be induced in the structure and function of the floral organs by varying external factors such as temperature and light, and by the application of exogenous auxin. Y. Heslop-Harrison and Woods (1959) observed that when genetically male plants of dioecious *Cannabis sativa* L. are grown under short days and low night temperature, a high proportion of the flowers formed is intersexual, and a considerable amount of meristic variation, fusions and adnations, are found among the male flowers. The intersexuality in male flowers consists in a modification of stamens to carpellate and intermediate structures. In some species, one or other of the sets of reproductive organs can be more or less completely suppressed in what are normally hermaphrodite flowers (J. Heslop-Harrison, 1960). There are also interesting correlative changes in other floral members, e.g. the calyx and corolla. Figs. 11.5–11.7 illustrate heteroblastic effects associated with flowering.

By applying auxin exogenously to plants at a particular stage in ontogenesis, in fact, at an early stage in floral morphogenesis, J. Heslop-Harrison (1959) has shown that profound changes can be induced in the structure and function of the floral members. In species with hermaphrodite (or monoclinous) flowers, the corolla and androecium may be suppressed to a more or less marked extent, whilst the calyx and gynoecium become relatively enlarged; and in monoecious species like the cucurbits, the appearance of the first female flower may be advanced in time and the ratio of male to female flowers falls. In a dioecious species like the hemp plant (*Cannabis sativa*), male plants produce female or intersexual flowers. In these instances the auxin appears to be acting as a regulating rather than as a primary determining factor; i.e. its effects are restricted to changing the balance of growth between floral organs of different kinds (Heslop-Harrison, 1959). This view is in accord with the writer's thesis that the basic properties of the growth centres of any particular whorl or helix on the floral receptacle, e.g. of calyx, corolla, etc., are already determined as the result of serial genic evocation. In other words, when specific morphogenetic developments have once been initiated they can be suppressed but usually they cannot

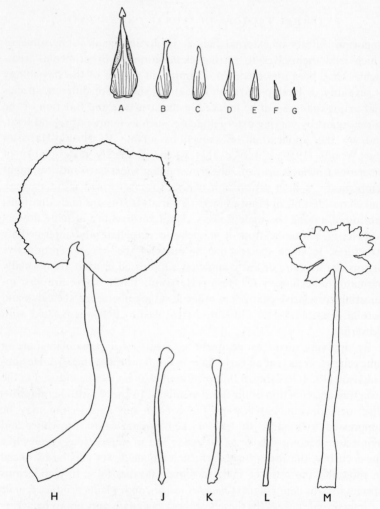

FIG. 11.5 *Petasites hybridus*. This species affords interesting evidence of heteroblastic development (i) in the normal ontogenesis of a lateral vegetative bud, (ii) in the transition from the vegetative to the floral phase, and (iii) in inflorescence meristems which have been induced to revert to the vegetative state.

A–G, Some representative foliar organs from the outside of an inflorescence bud (A) towards the small central bracts (G).

H–L, A leaf and various enlarged bract-like organs which have been induced by experimental treatment to develop from primordia which, in the normal development, would have become small bracts like C–G.

M, A deeply indented lamina of a kind that occasionally develops in experimentally-treated inflorescence apices ($\times \frac{1}{2}$). (Drawings by A. Walton.)

be fundamentally modified. However, instances of organs of intermediate or dual character are not uncommon, and these, it would seem, must be referred to particular metabolic properties of the growth centres. J. Heslop-Harrison has stated that no instance of a primordium of one prospective type being deflected into a quite different course of development as a result of auxin treatment has been recorded. In dioecious hemp, however, the auxin-induced intersexuality and sex reversal in genetically male plants 'seems to arise from a diversion of the ontogeny of the presumptive stamens from their normal path towards that characteristic of carpels'; that is to say, 'auxin may be influencing some determining process in the flower primordium'. These effects of applied auxin may be linked with the auxin changes now known to occur in plants variously exposed to different environmental factors. Further to these observations, Galun, Jung and Lang (1962) have been able to effect sex modification in male cucumber buds (*Cucumis sativus*), growing in aseptic culture, by direct applications to the buds of IAA. In this work the floral buds were taken into culture at a very early stage, i.e. when they were morphologically and physiologically still bisexual, or undetermined sexually, and IAA or gibberellic acid (GA₃), or a combination of the two, were applied directly to the bud surface. One aim was to discover if these substances exercise their effects indirectly, i.e. only when administered through the leaves or other organs of the plant, or if they can act directly. The results obtained showed that positive results can be obtained by direct application of IAA: what would normally have been male flowers developed a gynoecium while the anther primordia remained virtually unchanged at an early embryonic stage. In fact, ovaries only developed in media which had been supplemented by IAA. The presence of GA tended to reduce the effects of IAA when applied simultaneously, the stamens of buds treated with GA being more conspicuously developed than those receiving IAA only.

Certain fungal infections are known to cause remarkable changes in floral development, e.g. *Zea maiys* infected with *Ustilago maydis*, and *Melandrium rubrum* attacked by *Ustilago violacea*. In the former, female flowers appear in the normal male inflorescence and J. Heslop-Harrison (1959) noted that this effect is now understandable if the monoecism of maize is related to an auxin gradient, in that the fungus is known to produce IAA in the presence of tryptophane (Wolfe, 1952). In *Melandrium rubrum*, the pathogen induces the formation of stamens in genetically female plants (Schopfer, 1940; Baker, 1947 *a*, *b*; Wardlaw,

Fig.11.6 *Cannabis sativa.* Leaf sequences in hemp plants in long and short days.

A, Leaves from the first nine post-cotyledonary nodes from a plant grown in long days to an age of 3 months.

B, Leaves from the first ten post-cotyledonary nodes from a female plant of the same age grown under 8-hr. days from an age of 3 weeks.

C, Leaves from the first ten post-cotyledonary nodes from a male plant grown under the same conditions as B. All three plants grown during June-August.

In short-day races of *Cannabis sativa,* a dioecious species, the two sexes cannot be distinguished morphologically during

(Caption continued at foot of facing page)

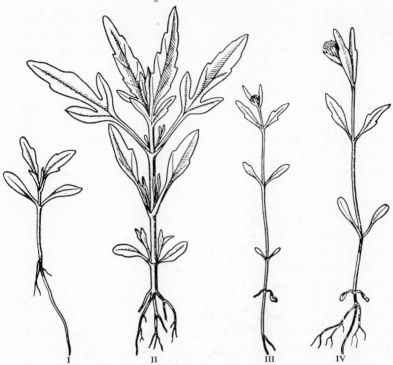

Fig.11.7 *Bidens radiatus*. I, II, Young and older seedlings, showing typical development, including leaf elaboration. III, IV, Leaf formation in two plants (of *B. perpusillus*) which had entered on the flowering phase at an early stage. (After Diels, from W. Troll, *Vergleichende Morphologie der höheren Pflanzen*.)

the vegetative phase; but major secondary sexual differences develop when flowering begins in short days: in both sexes the digitate leaves undergo a diminution in area from node to node and there is a reduction in the numbers of lobes and marginal serrations. These trends are much more pronounced in the male. These differences attend the differentiation of flowers and may be by-products of the primary sex-determining mechanism. Applications of auxin (α-naphthaleneacetic acid), which under some circumstances lead to sex reversal in male plants, also affect the trend of heteroblastic leaf development: they reduce the extent to which leaf-lobing and marginal serration decline following brief photoperiodic induction, so that male plants behave vegetatively more like female plants. In each sex, both the type of leaf primordium formed and the degree of expansion of the lamina depend upon prevailing day length; primordia initiated in one day length can be caused to develop in another, with a resultant production of leaves of anomalous types. (After J. and Y. Heslop-Harrison, *Proc. Roy. Irish Acad.* 59, B, 257–283 (1958).)

1961). These are only some examples of the effects of extrinsic factors in floral morphogenesis (literature in Heslop-Harrison, 1959). (For further observations on experimental chemical treatments *see* Chapter 14.)

Surgical treatments of the inflorescence or floral meristem afford a means of obtaining information on the interrelationships of its several regions and of the incipient and developing organs (Wardlaw, 1957). In experiments with *Primula bulleyana*, Cusick (1956) vertically bisected the meristem at different, known stages in floral ontogenesis, e.g. before perianth inception, and so on. By subsequently observing whether complete or half whorls of the several floral organs were formed, he was able to obtain information which supports the view that the meristem is a unified reaction system which undergoes a sequence of changes in its organogenic activities. For example, floral apices bisected up to the end of the primordial stamen stage continued their development as two growing regions, new organs being formed between them and the incision; bisections made at an earlier stage admitted of the formation of other groups of floral organs between the new flower centre and the wound. Surgical experiments along these lines might well be extended with interesting results to very young capitula, umbels, the corymb of *Iberis* spp., etc. in which the outer florets or flowers show characteristic zygomorphic developments.

Earlier, in a somewhat different type of surgical experiment, Murneek (1927) showed that, in the spider flower (*Cleome spinosa*), in which a phase of pistil formation is normally followed by a phase of stamen production, the excision of the very young pistils results in the formation of new ones for an abnormally long time.

ZYGOMORPHY

Only the simplest and commonest case of median zygomorphy, i.e. where the plane of dorsiventrality is that of the bract and shoot axis, will be considered here. Goebel (1900, 1913) has given an excellent survey of this phenomenon, especially with reference to possible causal factors (*see* Figs. 11.8, 11.9).

In some species with a racemose inflorescence and median zygomorphy, Goebel (1900) noted that if, as a result of some disturbance or injury, a flower primordium develops in a terminal position, it may be actinomorphic (Fig.11.8; Plates 22, 23). Such evidence – from one of

'Nature's experiments' – suggests interesting possibilities for the further exploration of the zygomorphic condition by surgical, chemical and

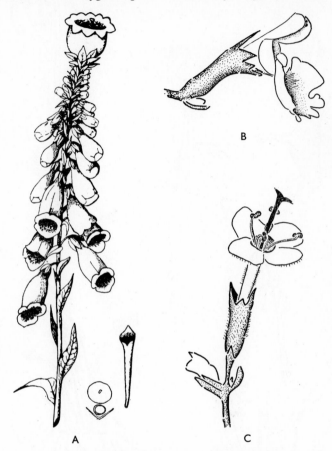

Fig.11.8 Peloria in A, *Digitalis purpurea* (Foxglove, Scrophulariaceae); and B, C, *Nepeta mussinii* (Catmint, Labiatae.) (*see* Plates 22, 23).
A, The terminal flower is of abnormally large size and is actinomorphic, the lateral flowers being normally zygomorphic (After Velenovsky).
B, Illustrates (diagrammatically) a normal lateral flower of *N. mussinii* and C, a terminal one which has developed with actinomorphic symmetry. (Drawings by courtesy of Dr. E. G. Cutter.)

other treatments, especially in materials which have been studied genetically. These investigations might be of special interest in families such as Orchidaceae and Zingiberaceae which show somewhat parallel, but not

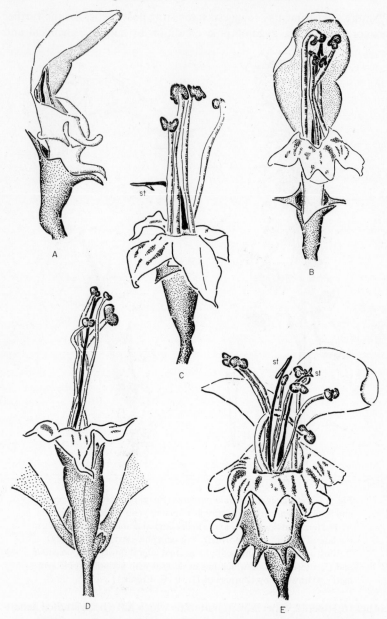

Fig.11.9 *Galeobdolon luteum* (Labiatae). A, B, Normal lateral zygo-
(*Caption continued at foot of facing page*)

identical, evolutionary trends in their reduced, dorsiventral flowers. In passing, the possibility that an incipient or transient dorsiventrality may be present at some stage in the ontogenesis of many flowers may also be noted (*see* Cutter, 1957). In comparative ontogenetic studies of the flowers in species of *Nymphaea* and *Nuphar*, Cutter observed that the 'subtending' bract in the latter, which is the first primordium to originate on the floral meristem, is homologous with the anterior sepal in *Nymphaea*, which has no bract. In both instances the position of the first floral organ suggests that there is some difference in growth in the anterior and posterior sides of the young floral meristem; but, on further development, radial symmetry is established. If, however, we suppose that the incipient, inherent growth difference between the anterior and the posterior (or abaxial and adaxial) sides of the floral primordium were to be accentuated, then the flower would be zygomorphic. This kind of relationship can perhaps be examined experimentally.

Zygomorphy is normally a genetically controlled phenomenon. The segregation which results when the peloric, i.e. actinomorphic, snap-dragon is crossed with the normal zygomorphic form has been related to a single pair, or to a very small number, of genes. In such instances we may conjecture that growth-regulating substances, proceeding from the inflorescence (shoot) apex, or from the bract, or from both, exercise particular effects on the relative rates of growth of the adaxial and abaxial sides of the young flower primordium. In some orders, in which this apparently takes place at a very early stage in flower formation, the zygomorphy is usually very strongly developed; in others, in which the growth differences take place at a relatively late stage in flower formation, the zygomorphy may sometimes be rather inconspicuous.

In a species in which the flower is normally actinomorphic, it may be assumed that growth rates on the adaxial and abaxial faces are approximately equal; i.e. such controlling or regulating effects as may be exercised by the axis, or inflorescence apex, above are equalled by those exercised by the bract below. If, now, the very young floral primordium were to be isolated from the controlling effects from above by a tangential incision, or to be given some appropriate chemical treatment,

morphic flowers. C, D, Terminal actinomorphic flowers. E, An axillary flower of large size, showing an increased number of parts (seven calyx lobes, seven petals, seven stamens, and two styles (*st*)). The symmetry is somewhat irregular and there may be partial fasciation. Stippling indicates the pattern of brownish spots normally present on the central lobe of the lower lip. (× ⅓). (Drawings by courtesy of Dr. E. G. Cutter.)

some degree of zygomorphy in the developing flower might be expected to follow.

Another approach to the phenomenon of zygomorphy is perhaps afforded by the classical case of meristic variation in *Stellaria media*, especially in the androecium (3–8 stamens). Matzke (1932) showed that the distribution of missing stamens is not entirely at random but is such as to approximate to an incipient dorsiventrality between the axis and the bract. It would be interesting to know if other instances of seemingly random meristic variation are also of this kind. In the extreme forms of androecial meiomery seen in Orchidaceae and Zingiberaceae, it is of interest to note that whereas the residual stamen of the former is in the anterior position, that of the latter is in the posterior position, both flowers showing median zygomorphic symmetry.

However conspicuous the departures from radial symmetry may be, floral development typically shows evidence of an overall balance and stability. This is what one would expect on the assumption that the floral meristem is a unified reaction system, producing new organs in a characteristic pattern at intervals, in accord with the laws of physical-chemistry, and with pervasive reciprocal relationships between the younger and the older organs throughout the floral ontogenesis.

The characteristic disposition of zygomorphic flowers, i.e. lateral and approximately horizontal, has long been associated with insect visitation and the biological advantages of cross-pollination. Already in 1819 A. P. de Candolle had noted that the position occupied by a flower has a great effect on its symmetry, the solitary, terminal, erect flower being usually of radial symmetry even when it belongs to a family characterized by zygomorphic flowers. Explanations of floral symmetry, reviewed by Goebel (1900), have tended to combine elements of both causality and teleology. Goebel summarized his views by noting that if zygomorphic flowers were entirely the result of variation in any direction, with selection and survival of the fittest, i.e. those best adapted to insect visitors, it is not evident why many terminal flowers should not also have become zygomorphic; and, moreover, he noted that dorsiventrality is found in many anemophilous plants, e.g. many of the grasses. It will be interesting to see to what extent the several views on zygomorphy accord with such results as may be obtained from critical morphogenetic investigations, undertaken without preconceived notions of biological advantage, etc. That certain characteristic morphological features of the adult flower may have an important selective advantage in relation to insect visitation and cross-pollination may be accepted; but these phenomena have still to be brought into some acceptable relationship with the factors which determine organization.

EXTERNAL AND INTERNAL FACTORS IN PARALLEL DEVELOPMENTS

In any general survey of the organization of inflorescences and flowers one cannot fail to be impressed by the abundant evidence of parallel development.

A number of common factors, some of which are purely extrinsic and others which are not closely and specifically genetical in character, seem to be involved in some of these developments. At least, this is a possibility that should be carefully considered. It is, however, to the genetical constitution of the individual species, and to differences in genetical constitution between species, that the distinctive floral morphology of a particular species, and the great diversity in floral morphology in species at large, must be primarily attributed. The question of the extent to which homologies of floral organization can be explained genetically has already been discussed in Chapter 5.

The morphological diversity of inflorescences and flowers is impressive but some simplification of our ideas concerning them begins to seem possible. If we begin with the generally accepted prototypic flower, i.e. hypogynous, apocarpic, etc., very extensive diversification could have resulted from genetical changes determining modifications in the distribution of growth in the floral meristem, or receptacle. But, in fact, only a relatively small number of major geometrical changes is possible, e.g. hypogyny may be replaced by perigyny or epigyny; polypetaly by sympetaly, and so on. It is therefore not so surprising that parallel developments have taken place in different, or seemingly different, phyletic lines as a result of cumulative genetical change. Moreover, as parallel developments have taken place in unrelated groups, it may be conjectured that the underlying genetical changes were those which had a high probability of taking place and of yielding floral constructions with survival value.

In considering the extensive, conspicuous and often confusing diversification which inflorescences and flowers have undergone during the course of evolution, it now appears, on the evidence and arguments outlined here, that only a comparatively small number of major growth and organogenic changes, in which both genetical and non-genetical factors participate, may have been involved. If this view can be validated by critical investigations, the hope may well be entertained that this complex mass of biological materials may eventually be understood and described in terms of simplifying and unifying concepts (*see* Chapter 16).

THE ORGANISM AS A WHOLE

As investigators like Bonner (1952), Sinnott (1960) and the writer have recognized and emphasized, it is a major task in botany, if not *the* major task, to comprehend and describe the development and organization of plants as whole, integrated, functional entities. Such accounts, which may eventually be enunciated as the Principles of Organization in Plants, should not only have a general application to the phenomena of order that become manifest during ontogenesis, but should suggest working hypotheses for further observation, analysis and experiment; and they should also include simplified concepts of an integrative character. The writer submits that, notwithstanding their admitted limitations and incompleteness, the three main propositions outlined and discussed in Chapter 10 and the present chapter contribute significantly to the desired end. Each of the concepts is undoubtedly susceptible of further investigation. But the full value of the results obtained for the several approaches will only become apparent when they are brought together and considered, not only in all their mutual relationships, but as these relationships affect the economy and survival of the organism, or its race, as a whole.

CHAPTER 12

Specificity of Organization

THE PHENOMENA OF SPECIFICITY

Perhaps the most distinctive and impressive features in the ontogenetic development of a higher plant are the increase in size and the progressive manifestation not only of organization but of *specific organization*. One could, of course, simplify the problems of specific organization by saying that the related phenomena all stem from, and should be referred back to, the genetical constitution. While this, no doubt, is true, it still leaves a great deal to be explained, since, as geneticists admit, genes are only known by their effects. In the present state of botanical science, it is doubtful if we are in a position to do more than assemble certain contributory ideas and fragments of information regarding the nature of specificity, often culled from zoology, and to indicate tentatively some major aspects of it on which further research and co-ordination or information may be fruitful.

The individual entities with which biologists are concerned are members of species, varieties and races, variously defined, each being recognizable because of its distinctive characters, i.e. by its specificity or organization. One cannot fail to recognize that, at all the evolutionary levels in the Plant Kingdom, there are very large numbers of specific organizations (*see* Chapter 16). To account for the differentiation of tissues and organs and for their integration as development proceeds, may be recognized as tasks of considerable difficulty. How much greater, then, is the task of accounting for the specificity of organization in the individual species or variety. This aspect needs no emphasis: the investigations of geneticists, experimental taxonomists and biochemists during recent decades have shown how numerous, complex and varied are the manifestations of specificity in plants.

SOME GENERAL FEATURES OF CELLULAR DIFFERENTIATION

Some general phenomena of cell growth in embryonic or meristematic regions may be examined with advantage at this point. In studies of root tips, Brown and Robinson (1955) showed that the expansion of an embryonic cell behind the apical meristem cells is a true process of growth, in that it involves (a) increases in all the components of the system, at least in certain stages, and (b) a succession of metabolic states. Their experimental evidence indicates that there is a continued development of the metabolic pattern and that this is the controlling factor in the growth process. Although the protein component is evidently of major importance, all the metabolic components must be considered in any analysis of development.

During cell expansion changes take place in the protein content, sustained synthesis and degradation taking place simultaneously. Increases or decreases in the protein content thus depend on the relative rates of the two processes: a constant protein content would indicate a steady state between synthesis and degradation. During its growth in an intact organ, the individual cell passes through a succession of states, each of which is probably characterized by a progressive change in protein, and each protein-stage sustaining a different enzyme pattern.

$$P_1 \rightarrow P_2 \rightarrow P_3 \rightarrow P_4$$
$$| \quad | \quad | \quad |$$
$$E_1 \quad E_2 \quad E_3 \quad E_4$$

According to Brown and Robinson, if P_1 represents the protein of a cell in the embryonic state and E_1 the enzyme complex corresponding to it, E_1 does not sustain growth, but the protein develops into P_2, and subsequently into P_3 and P_4. P_2 and P_3 involve the corresponding enzyme patterns, i.e. E_2 and E_3, which promote growth. When P_3 develops into P_4 the enzyme complex E_4 appears. As this complex does not sustain growth, cellular expansion ceases.

SEQUENTIAL INDUCTION PROCESSES

Growth and differentiation involve a chain of induction processes. On this topic, however, the general ideas have largely emerged from experimental and biochemical work on animal embryos. Thus, it has been ascertained that (a) embryonic development probably depends on the sequential activities of a large number of inductors, each of which typically becomes operative at some particular stage of development (Woerdeman, 1955); (b) several inductive agents may be successively at work in the development of a particular organ; and (c) several inductors may sometimes act simultaneously. It is probable that plant embryos are considerably more simple. However, if these ideas of development are generally accepted, one of the major problems is to explain how the activities of the several inductive agents are co-ordinated, culminating

in the formation of organs or tissues that are functionally effectiv
The concepts of successive changes in a reaction system, as outlined in
Chapter 11, may go some way towards an interpretation of this very
general but still quite remarkable phenomenon. That the competence of
cells to react to inductive agents is very important has long been
recognized (*see* Waddington, 1940). Botanists are familiar with this
concept, for it is known that the same auxin or hormone may produce
very different effects in different tissues; or, at different concentrations,
may produce different effects in the same tissue or organ. Also, some
inductors are not restricted to a particular species (but *see below*).
However, the effect produced by a general inductor may nevertheless be
specific since it is acting on a specific, gene-determined reaction system
(Woerdeman, 1955). Taken together, these several points indicate that
the specific organization of an organ or tissue is due to the specific
properties of the reaction system.

As knowledge of inductive processes advanced, the view developed
that, as well as the general inductors mentioned above, there must also
be many qualitatively different, i.e. *specific inductive* substances. In
floral organogenesis, for example, vegetative apices become transformed
into floral meristems, and these give rise to the successive floral parts –
sepals, petals, stamens and carpels. This is an acceptable *general*
statement. But, for any one species, these several developments are
specific and distinctive. Accordingly, it is reasonable to assume that
different specific substances or inductors enter and affect the reaction
system in a definite sequence; or we must attribute the specificity to the
system itself. From the different pigmentation of petals as compared
with sepals, and the very conspicuous structural and histological
differences between stamens and petals, it may be inferred that qualitative
as well as quantitative differences are involved at the successive stages of
floral development. Also, as between the varieties of a species, there
may be many differences in detail in the size and shape of the several
floral organs.

The more the problems of embryonic induction have been investigated, the more complex they seem to be. During recent years the view
has been elaborated that the structural differences between cells are
related to the presence of different specific substances, especially proteins,
in their protoplasm; and as the synthesis and degradation of proteins
are dependent on the presence of specific enzymes, differences in cellular
differentiation can be referred to differences in their content of particular enzymes (Woerdeman, 1955). In animal tissues the presence of

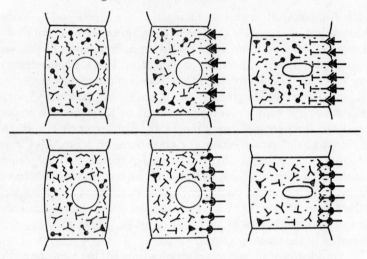

Fig.12.1 A model of induction. A conception of possible molecular rearrangements on contact with different organic substances. (After P. Weiss, *Quart. Rev. Biol.* 1950.)

When the cellular unit is envisaged as 'a highly organized population of interacting molecules and molecular aggregates, stereochemical properties, molecular structure, shape, orientation, alignment and, more generally, physical order', become decisively significant in determining biological events. The concept of 'molecular ecology' embodies this change of emphasis: 'it illustrates how interfaces, by selectively adsorbing, orienting, and aligning molecular key species from the cellular content, produce the physical conditions of spatial order which enable stereochemically complementary compounds, such as antibody-antigen or enzyme-substrate systems, to interact most effectively. According to this concept, the following would happen when a cell comes into contact with another body whose surface is settled with molecules with specifically formed end groups oriented toward the oncoming cell. As the agitated molecular population of the moving cell passes in review, as it were, before the stable molecular front of the outer surface, molecules of conforming configuration will be trapped by their correspondingly shaped counterparts. Thus, a specific fraction of the cell content will gradually become concentrated and segregated along the contact surface. Since these surface molecules, by virtue of their orientation, might serve not only as anchor points for the adsorption of additional molecules from the interior, but also perhaps as specific catalysts of reactions inside the cell, a whole train of events determining the further chemical history of the cell has thus been set into motion. It can readily be seen that the chemical fate of a cell on contact with another does not depend merely on what substances are

(*Caption continued at foot of facing page*)

19. *Petasites hybridus.* A, The autumnal condition of the terminal bud, when the withering, large foliage leaves of the current season have been removed; within the enclosing laminate bracts there is a large, complex inflorescence; lateral buds are beginning to grow out as rhizomes, one with small laminate leaves. B, A capitulum of 'male' florets (or sterile 'hermaphrodite' florets). C, A capitulum of female florets with a single conspicuous 'male' (or sterile) floret emerging through the involucre of bracts (× *c.*13). D, A similar capitulum with the bracts removed: the 'male' floret at the centre has greatly outgrown the older female florets (× *c.*13). E, F, Younger female capitula, showing variation in the number of 'male' florets at the centre. (× *c.*13).

20. *Petasites hybridus*. A, A fairly early transition apex: the outer bracts have been removed; those round the enlarging apical meristem have still a wide encircling base. This apex gives rise to a compound inflorescence of many capitula (× 50). B, An older transition apex, after removal of the outer bracts (× 50). C, The fasciated terminal capitulum of a female inflorescence: a row of 'male' flowers occupies the most distal region of the capitulum meristem (× 17). D, A bisected inflorescence meristem after some growth has taken place: the outermost, normally linear, bracts have developed as hirsute laminate foliage leaves. E, A later stage of a bisected inflorescence meristem: the foliar organs which would normally have developed as small, linear, non-laminate bracts have developed as large foliage leaves; the illustration shows that two leafy axes have been formed. (E, from *Nature*, 1963.)

a considerable number of specific proteins has now been detected by immunological methods. In a review of the evidence Woerdeman has shown that quantitative and qualitative differences can be demonstrated during development though their relation to morphogenetic processes has not yet been established. Some of the specific 'morphogenetic' substances which can be detected during embryogenesis are apparently of a transitory nature and subsequently disappear. A relevant hypothesis of Weiss (1947, 1949, 1955), supported by Tyler (1947), states that growth may be analogous to the mechanism of antibody formation, in which the presence of an antigen leads to the formation of a globulin of specific structure. Weiss's 'model of induction' is illustrated in Fig.12.1.

Woerdeman suggested that inductive processes which result in differentiation may be due to the incorporation of protein molecules into the cells of the reaction system; and, following the ideas of various investigators (*see* Horowitz, 1945) he stated: 'These may function as

present in it, but also on the strategic advantages given to one or another segment of the molecular population according to the chemical character of the contact surface.'

This condition is illustrated in the diagrams. These show two epithelial cells in three consecutive stages. Large molecules with specific end groups are indicated by various symbols. In the initial stage, both the upper and lower cells have identical chemical endowments (left-hand diagrams). If we assume that the upper cell makes contact with a system containing in its surface oriented molecules with arrow-shaped heads, while the lower cell confronts a surface with molecules with cup-shaped ends (middle diagrams), the notch-shaped molecules will be trapped and fixed in the upper cell, and the ball-shaped ones in the lower cell. In either case, the molecules adjust to the most nearly conforming surface configuration. The chemical composition of the two cells is thus still the same, but a segregation process has been initiated which is different in the two. If this process is allowed to continue it will lead to an increasing internal diversification, indicated in the right-hand diagrams, in which each cell is shown to have added a second macromolecular layer of fitting configuration to the first. 'As entirely different chains of chemical reactions are thus set going in the two cells, it will not be long until the composition of their contents will have become radically different; each will develop certain compounds not present in the other. The eventual consolidation (right-hand diagram) is irreversible and represents what we have called cellular differentiation, while the transition stage (middle diagrams) is still reversible, representing mere modulation. Permanent differentiation can, therefore, be regarded as merely an advanced stage of an initially reversible modulation.'

L

templates and impress a spatial configuration upon the molecules of the cells coming into direct physical contact with them, or act as models for moulds which would afterwards turn out more of the incorporated molecules.' The concept of adaptive enzymes may also have its place here, i.e. that certain enzymes are only formed when their specific substrate is present. Thus far, however, this phenomenon has only been definitely demonstrated for micro-organisms, though some experimental observations suggest that adaptive enzymes may also develop in the tissues of animals and higher plants. Woerdeman has also emphasized the importance of the spatial arrangement of enzymes and other substances in the functional activities of the individual cell. As already noted (*see* Chapter 8), 'messenger service' theory, attempts to explain how nuclear genes determine the synthesis of specific substances in the cytoplasm.

Although the ideas discussed above may provide an acceptable conception of cytological differentiation, they do not account for organization. To quote Woerdeman: 'We have to assume that in the inductor, as well as in the reacting system, there are patterns of distribution of material, of metabolic processes, and arrangements of molecules which interact in the processes which underlie the origin of an organ pattern.'

SPECIFICITY IN GROWTH CONTROL

According to Weiss (1947, 1955), biological specificity is a basic property of living systems and is especially manifested 'in drug responses, hormone actions, gene effects, immunological reactions, host-parasite relations, and developmental mechanisms', a common denominator in biochemical, presumably stereochemical, terms being indicated. Specificity in growth raises four different issues:

(1) the fact that the various cell strains of the body are different biochemically; (2) the possibility that biochemical distinctiveness may be not only a byproduct of differentiation but also an instrumental factor in growth; (3) the possibility that this may constitute a mechanism for the humoral co-ordination and regulation of growth processes throughout the organism; and (4) the hypothesis that this regulatory function presupposes the generation in each cell strain of paired compounds of complementary configuration, after the antigen-antibody scheme (Weiss, 1955).

Already in 1949 Weiss had stated that the embryonic cells of animals become differentiated, or 'speciated', into biochemically different strains, these cell-strains being more varied chemically than may be apparent histologically. The work of Van Fleet (1959) on the diversity of

enzyme distribution in closely comparable cells of the cortical parenchyma, and the localized effects of growth-regulating substances on
cells or cell groups, afford evidence of this phenomenon in plants.
According to Weiss, different organs in animals are composed of cell
strains that are specifically different in their biochemical constitution;
but to what extent this view is applicable to plants still requires close
consideration and a measure of caution (Fig.12.1). The general thesis
has, of course, long been accepted: Sachs held that different kinds of
organs developed on the same plant because of underlying chemical
differences.

Weiss's concept of specific growth control involves, among others,
the following assumptions:

(1) that during cell growth, and as a result of the catalytic activity of
    certain substances that are essential to, and characteristic of, the
    cell type, each specific cell type reproduces its own protoplasm;
    these specific catalysts have been described as 'templates';
(2) that each cell also produces substances, described as 'antitemplates';
    which can inhibit the templates by combining with them into
    inactive complexes;
(3) that as the concentration of antitemplates increases in the extra-
    cellular medium their intracellular density will also increase and
    bring about an inactivation of the corresponding templates; the
    general result will be a decline in the growth rate of all cells belonging
    to that particular strain 'bathed by the common humoral pool'.

When stationary equilibrium between intracellular and extracellular concentration
is reached, growth will cease. This mechanism results in a sigmoid growth curve for
the total mass of each organ system, and the familiar sigmoid curve for the whole
organism would essentially be an aggregate of similar curves for the individual
constituent organ systems.

Weiss considered that this concept offers a rational explanation for
both the self-limiting character of growth in a confined medium
(organism or culture) and the homologous organ-specific growth reactions after experimental interference; and he has shown, or has attempted
to show, how these conceptions are supported by experimental evidence.
An important inference is that when one organ of a pair is removed, the
compensatory or enhanced growth shown by the remaining one would
be interpreted in terms of the tendency towards regaining chemical
equilibrium rather than in terms of a response to the need for increased
functional activity. Weiss has emphasized two further points: (i) 'that

the existence of a cell-type specific chemical mechanism of correlating growth processes among homologous cell types . . . may be regarded as conclusively demonstrated'; and (ii) 'that the general idea of selective chemical communication among cells of identical types by direct exchange of protoplasmic type-specific compounds can hardly be questioned in view of the large evidence in its favour'.

MOLECULAR SPECIFICITY AND EPIGENESIS

From the foregoing analysis, specificity of organization is referable to molecular specificity, mediated through the reaction system in embryonic and developing regions. A conception of this kind may enable us to see how, in developmental physiology or morphogenesis, the phenomena of specificity, at all the levels at which they occur, may perhaps be accounted for; i.e., it is to the reactions in cells, tissues and organs that the manifestation of specific characters must be ascribed. If any justification be needed for probing into this subject more deeply, it is simply that specificity of organization, and viable changes in it, indicative of the inception of new molecular specificities and of new reactions, lie at the heart of evolutionary biology.

The problems of molecular specificity and differentiation have received considerable attention, especially at the hands of zoologists. As Schechtman (1955) has stated:

The patterns of molecular specificities, established by means as yet highly hypothetical, constitute the ground-work of differentiation and are expressed according to the means of analysis at our disposal: as morphological differentiation, biochemical change, specific physiological functions, embryonic competences, etc. With the assumptions as to the nature of differentiation, it is little wonder that immunological phenomena have become of greater interest to the embryologist as well as to others concerned with the creation of new features by living materials.

In immunological studies it has been shown that protein molecules which are chemically identical can be made to produce a large number of different specific molecules in the form of antibodies. Such processes may be not unlike those which are involved in the development of new features in growing organisms. In other words, the possibility may be envisaged that a process of molecular epigenesis may underlie the epigenetic development of an organism. Weiss (1950) and Ebert (1950) have applied techniques of immunology to causal aspects of development in animals; and, indeed, in the general physiology of animals the phenomena under consideration have already been explored in some detail (for a review, *see* Schechtman, 1955). But, thus far, botanists have done comparatively little in this direction.

Schechtman (1955) also entertained the idea that molecular epigenesis probably does occur during development in animals, the physico-chemical changes preceding, or being the concomitant of, the morphological or structural changes. Also, there is evidence that all the new macromolecules which appear in the developing embryo are not necessarily the products of its own synthetic activities but may be of maternal origin. This may have an application to plant embryos: for whereas older embryos, i.e. at or beyond the 'heart-shaped' stage can readily be cultured on synthetic media containing simple ingredients, younger embryos are difficult to culture and apparently need specific substances elaborated in the endosperm, e.g. coconut milk, or in the adjacent nucellar tissue. It is also known that whereas shoot apices of dicotyledons subtended on a plug of mature, or maturing, subapical tissue can readily be grown in simple culture media the strictly embryonic tissue at the tip of the shoot is difficult to culture, even in media containing various representative aminoacids, enzymes and growth-regulating substances. It thus appears that, in the growth and development of young embryos or angiosperm shoot apices, some molecular specificity is involved, the required molecules resulting from epigenetic processes in adjacent, older tissues in which differentiation has already progressed to a certain stage.

Studies of the embryonic blood and related antigens in animals afford evidence that new molecules make their appearance during ontogenesis, some being the result of synthesis in the developing embryo, others being elaborated by the maternal tissues. Somewhat similar relationships may obtain in plants. If an embryo or embryonic tissue requires certain essential molecules and is incapable of synthesizing them, its further growth and development may be limited in the absence of suitable older tissue in proximity. Considerations such as these may contribute towards explaining the limited growth and restricted morphological expression of a germinating fern spore, developing as a separate entity strictly on its own metabolic resources, as compared with the zygote which develops with all the resources of a tissue matrix (*see also* p. 337).

The assumption that only substances of a rather simple kind can pass through the plasma walls of adult cells of animal tissues no longer appears to be tenable. Should a revision of this view in respect of plant tissues become necessary, it will evidently have an important impact on experimental investigations. For, in plants as in animals (with some reservations), it has hitherto been generally accepted that, if they are provided with the basic materials for growth in relatively simple molecular form, the embryo, or the meristematic region, can elaborate its own specific macromolecules. In fact, such evidence as we have from the study of plants raises its own problems. Thus, as Wetmore (1954) has shown, if a fern shoot apex is excised on a very minute piece of tissue, comprising only the distal meristem, it can be successfully grown in simple culture media into adult plants. On the other hand, in such dicotyledons as have been investigated using similar techniques, comparable successful results have not yet been obtained. For animals, however, Schechtman (1955) stated, on evidence from serological and physicochemical studies, that the embryo admits complex macromolecules and that this takes place prior to and during the time when the basic differentiations of the vertebrate body are in progress. This is reminiscent of the situation in certain bacteria in which the addition of deoxyribonucleic acid to the culture media has resulted in permanent changes in their synthesizing capacities. In animals, however, it is not yet definitely known that the uptake of macromolecules is causally related to differentiation.

From the foregoing and other relevant observations, it appears that the specific differentiation of organs and tissues may be tentatively attributed to epigenetic, specific molecular differentiation, the phenomenon also reflecting the interaction of genes and other factors which become incident during ontogenesis. However, as Schechtman (1955) pointed out, although molecular differentiation has epigenetic aspects comparable with those of morphogenesis, it has not yet been demonstrated in any instance that 'the new antigens, or other chemical entities which appear in the course of development, are components of the mechanism of differentiation; where sufficient evidence is available the new molecular differentiations appear to be equivalent in character to the better-known morphological events – end products of differentiation'; and further that it remains to be seen whether the macromolecules of adult origin are merely end products of differentiation or take an active part as inductors or transformation factors in the actual mechanism of differentiation.

ENZYMES AND SPECIFIC PROTEINS

In discussing the basic factors in specific morphogenetic developments Shen (1955) suggested that enzyme development may constitute 'the ontogeny of specific proteins'. Since proteins are the principal components of embryonic and meristematic cells, the production and transformation of protein molecules and their aggregates must be more or less directly involved in primary morphogenetic developments. Accordingly, a major part of the task for the future is to bring specific morphological and histological developments into some proper relationship with the synthesis of specific proteins and these in turn with their specific enzymes; and so we work back to nuclear DNA and the orderly genetic basis of the nexus of processes. But whether specific organization can be adequately explained along these lines should, for the time being, be left an open question.

In attempting to relate the formation of specific proteins and morphogenetic processes in plants, several difficulties are encountered. The physiological and biochemical processes are exceedingly complex. Also, very little is yet known about the protein chemistry of plant embryos. And, not least, we do not know which particular physical and/ or chemical properties of the proteins are specially important in morphogenetic processes. As one approach to this problem, Shen (1955) examined the possible significance and relationship of the enzymological aspect of protein specificity to biological differentiation; i.e. on the assumption that the causal analysis of specific organization requires investigations of the sequence of processes which begins with gene action and involves enzyme development, protein elaboration, differentiation, morphological development and effective functioning. However, in Shen's view, there is a serious initial obstacle in that we do not yet know how enzymes function as regulatory factors during ontogenesis. Nevertheless, if we could detect specific enzymes at particular stages in development, this might afford useful indications of the chemical events which underlie the visible developments. Such *developmental enzymology* would, in fact, add to our description of the morphogenetic process rather than explain it; or, as Shen indicated, an account of chemical changes during development is not necessarily 'a chemical description of differentiation'. It has been suggested that enzymes may be among the principal structural proteins and may therefore constitute a substantial proportion of the total proteins in a cell or tissue. Engelhardt envisaged the possibility that all tissue proteins are both catalytically active and specific and, to quote Shen (1955): 'While all proteins are not necessarily enzymes, enzymatically active and specific proteins will undoubtedly become increasingly recognized as extensive and important constituents of living protoplasm. The developmental significance of enzymes as structural proteins may hence become increasingly apparent.'

As Shen (1955) also noted, it is unlikely that any enzyme is uniformly distributed in an embryo at any stage in its development from the zygote onwards. An increase in the heterogeneity of enzyme distribution, both qualitative and quantitative, as embryogenesis proceeds, is an essential characteristic of chemical differentiation; and the specificity in the pattern of enzyme distribution 'may be a significant expression of the specificity of structural and functional organization at a given level of differentiation'. If so, fuller information on enzyme localization may contribute substantially to our understanding of specific organization, especially if it can be directly related to visible features.

NUCLEAR-CYTOPLASMIC RELATIONSHIPS IN SPECIFICITY OF ORGANIZATION

Especially during recent years, much has been written about the nucleus as the gene-containing organizing centre of cellular activity. Substances determined by particular genes are envisaged as entering into the intra-cellular reaction system at particular times and, by controlling or modifying some aspect of metabolism, they eventually affect such processes as differentiation, functional activities, and so on. Adjacent cells may be affected by physiological processes which have their beginning in a single cell, the phenomena of induction and growth-regulation being of this kind. Some progress has been made in the study of nuclear differentiation during embryo development in animals; but in plant embryology such problems remain virtually untouched. (This is borne out by reference to recent symposia, etc., in which this subject is scarcely mentioned: *see* White 1957; Maheshwari, 1962; and Maheshwari and Ranga Swamy, 1963).

A problem that has been considered in some detail by zoologists is whether or not cell differentiation involves irreversible genetical changes in the nucleus, or in both nucleus and cytoplasm. In plants, the general evidence is against the view that such irreversible changes occur, though evidence of gene-changes in developing vegetative tissue has been reported.

In one of the earliest theories of differentiation and specific organiza-tion, that of Roux and Weismann, the zygote nucleus was assumed to contain a complete set of the determiners of differentiation which, in the course of the successive nuclear divisions during embryogenesis, became distributed, or 'parcelled out', in a regular way in different parts of the organism where they subsequently induced their characteristic and seemingly appropriate effects. This theory, however, was soon discarded, for it was shown in zoological experiments that, during the early embryonic divisions, nuclei could be interchanged at will without affecting the pattern of differentiation. There has accordingly been general acceptance of the view (Wilson, 1925) that, during the embryogeny, the nuclei are equivalent and that differential developments are properly to be attributed to the well-known localizations in the egg cytoplasm. This evidence of nuclear equivalence, however, relates only to early embryonic stages. That nuclei may show irreversible genetical changes during the later stages of development has been borne out by a considerable body of biochemical and cytological evidence. Chromosomal variations, for example, have been observed (*see* Huskins (1947) for a review of such changes in plant materials), some of which have effects on the activity of particular genes. McClintock (1951) described a case in maize where the mitotic mechanism is affected in such a way that a somatic segregation of certain genes results. Earlier Huskins and Steinitz (1948) reported that differentiation in the root-tips of *Rhoeo* (Commelinaceae) is accompanied by increases in chromosome number. In fact, instances are being recorded in increasing numbers, both in plants and animals, in which differences have been detected between somatic nuclei (Briggs and King, 1955). Biochemical observations show that there are functional, i.e. enzymatic, differences among somatic nuclei. Such differences are not necessarily to be related to a differential distribution of genes. On the basis of some elegant experiments on nuclear transplantation in animal embryos, Briggs and King (1955) concluded that 'the nuclei of animal hemisphere cells of late blastulae and early gastrulae are not differentiated – when transferred back to enucleated cells they can still participate in all types of differentiation'. Also, in later stages of the embryonic development, e.g. in the chick and mouse, in which the determination of organs occurs while the constituent cells are still undifferentiated, the experimental observations made by Briggs and King indicate that this phase of differentiation 'does not require specific irreversible changes in nuclear function nor does it involve the elaboration of cytoplasmic genetic units capable of directing differentiation when transferred back into uncleaved eggs'.

Light is shed on the problem of specificity of organization by a consideration of the time at which lethal effects develop in certain incompatible hybrids. Thus, in the hybrids between two species of frogs, the incompatibility between nucleus and cytoplasm becomes apparent

L*

just at the beginning of the principal morphogenetic developments and constitutes a block to further development. There is, apparently, 'a sudden development of specificity of nucleocytoplasmic interaction at the beginning of gastrulation' (Briggs and King), whereas a less specific relationship must have prevailed during the earlier stages.

In the postgastrula stages in animal embryogeny, nuclei may assume different forms and exhibit different biochemical properties, but it has still to be ascertained whether those variations are simply modulations or are indicative of irreversible genic changes (Briggs and King, 1955). In plant embryogeny, many instances have now been recorded in hybrids of early or later embryo abortion (for a review *see* Wardlaw, 1964). In these cases the biochemical incompatibility appears to be between the developing embryo and the endosperm or nucellar tissue, rather than between nucleus and cytoplasm. But, in fact, this topic has so far received comparatively little attention in plant embryology.

SPECIFICITY IN SEXUALITY

In a review of problems of specificity of sexuality in plants, J. R. Raper (1955) noted that these include the effects of specific inhibiting and other substances, aspects of physiological differentiation and so on. The fungi, for example, exhibit mating specificities which can be referred to sexual hormones. Here some examples will be selected from the flowering plants.

In a majority of angiosperms the stamens and pistils occur in the same 'perfect' flowers. Obligatory cross-breeding is imposed on many such hermaphroditic species by incompatibility mechanisms. These may prevent the germination of the pollen grains upon the stigma or the growth of the pollen tube through the style (*see* Lewis, 1949, for review). Raper characterized the basic types of heteromorphic and homomorphic incompatibility control as follows. In *heteromorphic incompatibility* the flowers are morphologically different, the differences being ascribed to two incompatibility alleles at a single locus or to two alleles at each of two loci. In the former, the population is equally divided into two self-sterile and cross-fertile classes, e.g. the 'thrum' (with short styles and long stamens) and 'pin' (long styles and short stamens) flowers in *Primula vulgaris*. Such species are termed *distylic*. In the two-allele two-locus incompatibility, four genotypes occur. However, on account of the epistatic masking of one dominant allele by the other dominant allele, only three self-sterile cross-fertile classes, each with a distinctive flower form, are phenotypically expressed. These are *tristylic* species. As

Raper pointed out, in this type of incompatibility the characteristic behaviour of the pollen 'depends upon the genotype of the diploid parent rather than upon the specific incompatibility allele(s) carried by the haploid pollen grain'. In *homomorphic incompatibility* multiple

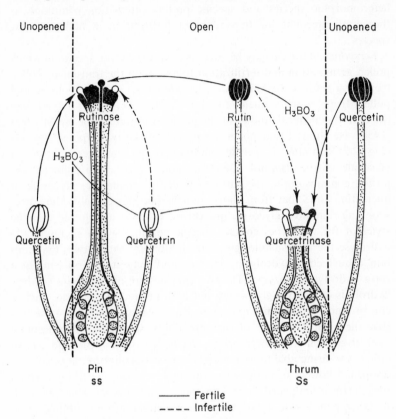

Fig.12.2 Diagram illustrating the mechanism of control of pollen-style incompatibility in *Forsythia intermedia*, summarizing data of Moewus. (After J. R. Raper, in *Biological Specificity and Growth*,1955.)

incompatibility alleles are present at a single locus. These determine a large number of self-sterile cross-fertile classes in the population. In this type of incompatibility, the capability of pollen grains to effect fertilization depends upon the specific allele carried by the haploid pollen; and fertilization can take place whenever the allele present in the pollen grain is different from both of those in the stylar tissue.

Raper noted that several distinct agents or terminal mechanisms may prevent pollen germination or subsequent developments in incompatible combinations: 'Specific nonproteinaceous inhibitors and physiological differentiation of pollen and styles are known to be involved in certain heteromorphic species and specific protein interaction commonly is thought to account for the failure of fertilization in homomorphic species'.

Forsythia intermedia may be cited as a typical distylic species in which pollen germination and fertilization follow upon the transfer of pollen from long stamens to long styles, i.e. *pin* (style) × *thrum* (pollen), and pollen from short stamens to short styles, i.e. *thrum* (style) × *pin* (pollen). Biochemical studies of the mechanism were made by Moewus (1950). He showed that pollen from each of the two types of flowers (Fig.12.2) contains a specific inhibitor of its own germination – a glycoside of the flavonol quercetin: pollen from long stamens (Ss, *thrum*) contains rutin, the rutinose (glucose+rhamnose) glycoside of quercetin, while that from short stamens (ss, *pin*) contains the corresponding rhamnose glycoside quercetrin. Moewus also found that the styles of the two types contain specific enzymes which preferentially hydrolyse the two flavonol-glycoside inhibitors: short styles (Ss) contain a quercetrin hydrolysing enzyme and long styles (ss) contain a rutin hydrolysing enzyme. The two enzymes are quite specific in their hydrolysis of the two glycosides, but both produce a common inactive end product, the flavonol quercetin. Raper called attention to the fact that the critical control of incompatibility specificity only becomes operative when the flower opens, the pollen of unopened flowers of either type being able to germinate and effect fertilization in opened or unopened flowers of both types. But pollen of opened flowers would only fertilize unopened flowers in those combinations which brought together pollen and stylar tissues of dissimilar incompatibility genotypes; i.e. 'the inhibitory constituents of the pollen, elaborated at anthesis, act as incompatibility-class-specific inhibitors of pollen germination and development'. It was ascertained that pollen of unopened flowers of both types contains quercetin but neither of the two inhibitory glycosides.

'Studies of pollen germination *in vitro* provided definite proof of the inhibitory nature of specific pollen constituents. Pollen of unopened flowers of both incompatibility classes germinates readily in sugar solution (20 to 30 per cent) but germination of both types is completely suppressed by either rutin or quercetrin in a concentration of $1 : 10^6$.

Pollen of opened flowers of neither type germinates in sugar solution, but pollen of each type germinates readily in an extract of the appropriate stylar tissue, i.e. *pin* pollen in extract of *thrum* styles and *vice versa*. The effectiveness of stylar extracts in removing the autoinhibition of pollen germination was in each case shown to result from the activity of a specific enzyme. The failure of germination of both types of pollen in sugar solution could also be overcome by treating the pollen with boric acid in a concentration of $1 : 10^4$' (Raper, 1955).

A different type of terminal mechanism which yields the same end results as do the specific inhibitors of *Forsythia* was observed by Lewis (1943) in *Linum grandiflorum*. In this species the osmotic pressure characteristics of pollen and style are such as to exclude in incompatible combinations the physical conditions necessary for pollen germination and development. 'The osmotic pressures of styles and pollen, as measured by plasmolysis and tissue tension and expressed as "sugar percentage equivalents", are as follows: *thrum* style, 10 to 12; *pin* style, 20; *thrum* pollen, 80; *pin* pollen, 50. The difference in osmotic pressures of the tissues in both compatible pollen-style combinations is approximately $4 : 1$, a differential which allows water uptake, germination, and normal development of the pollen. The differentials of osmotic pressure in the two incompatible combinations, however, are $7 : 1$ in *thrum*, which permits pollen germination but causes the young pollen tubes to burst, and $2 \cdot 5 : 1$ in *pin* $\times$ *pin*, in which combination the pollen grains do not even swell upon the stigmatic surface. In the latter case osmotic pressure difference can not explain the total effect and it was suggested that differences in protoplasm colloids were probably responsible for the lack of imbibition of water by the pollen.'

In other instances, the control of specificity may be similar to immunity reactions in animals (East, 1929), the product of a specific incompatibility allele in the pollen acting as an antigen to induce, in styles carrying the same allele, the production of an antibody which inhibits the growth of the antigen-producing pollen, but not that of pollen carrying any other allele. In *Oenothera organensis*, Lewis (1952) showed that the pollen contains incompatibility specific substances which act as antigens in serological tests; but corresponding antibodies were not demonstrated in the stylar tissues. As no enhanced inhibition was detected in successive pollinations, it was inferred that the observed effects should be ascribed to preformed stylar antibodies rather than to their induction by the pollen antigens. In further studies of interspecific hybrids between self-incompatible and self-compatible species, Lewis

(1949) indicated that the allele determining incompatibility consists of at least two distinct subunits. In studies of mutations he showed that in pollen subjected to X-rays prior to pollination in an incompatible combination, the pollen specificity of a given allele could be altered or lost without any corresponding change in the stylar specificity of the mutated allele as expressed in a subsequent generation. 'The absolute selection in this work of altered pollen characteristics possibly accounted for the failure to find alleles with altered stylar specificities' (Raper, 1955).

CONCLUSIONS

The differentiation of very large numbers of biotypes, strains, varieties and species, which the taxonomist assembles into higher taxa, is a central and pervasive feature of the evolutionary process. The detailed study of the factors which determine the evolution of specific organizations is, accordingly, essential to the advancement of biological science: it requires analytical observations and the formulation of concepts of an integrative character.

In the analysis of specific organization, we are closely concerned with the constitution and reactions in individual cells; for it is in them that particular sequences of gene-determined biochemical processes have their inception. An important concept is that the biochemical relationships of nucleus and cytoplasm are reciprocal. For example, an extraneous environmental stimulus, e.g. heat, light, nutrient supply, etc., or an intrinsic metabolic stimulus from a contiguous cell, e.g. diffusion of sugars, aminoacids, etc., will first affect some component of the cytoplasm. The stimulus, which we may assume to be duly transmitted to the nucleus, evokes the activity of a particular gene, or group of genes. Specific gene-determined molecules from the nucleus now enter the cytoplasmic reaction system and begin to react with other components. Characteristic syntheses or degradations follow, and the reaction system becomes modified in characteristic ways. This leads to the evocation of other nuclear genes, and new specific molecules enter the reaction system, and yet further chemical changes ensue; and so on. This hypothesis, if valid, would afford a basis for explaining, or interpreting in broad outline, (a) the genotypic/environmental control of development, (b) the inception of specific reactions and the eventual appearance of specific organizational features, and (c) the progressive change in the reaction system and the characteristic sequence of 'stages' which we observe in the ontogenesis of any particular species. The foregoing cannot be other than a vastly over-simplified and speculative account of an exceedingly complex system of interrelated processes. Nevertheless, even though assumptions have to be made at virtually every point, the general notion seems not unreasonable and at least some validating evidence is beginning to accumulate.

CHAPTER 13

Principles of Organization in Plants

DEFINITIONS

The term *principle* has a considerable range of usage but, following the *Oxford English Dictionary*, it can mean 'a fundamental source; a primary element, force or law which produces or determines particular results; the ultimate basis of the existence of something; a fundamental truth, law, or motive force; a highly general or inclusive theorem, or "law"; a general fact or law of nature by virtue of which a machine or instrument operates'. It is in the general sense of these several statements that the term *principle* will be used here.

One of the more evident difficulties in attempting to formulate principles of organization in plants is that, in many instances, all one seems to achieve is the statement of self-evident truths, e.g. that organisms manifest organization. Another difficulty is to state the 'principles' in such a way that the hypotheses relating to them can be validated by observation of their generality, or by analytical and experimental investigations. Some of the 'principles' indicated below admittedly apply more aptly to particular aspects of organogenesis and histogenesis than to the overall organization; for, indeed, it is largely from studies of morphogenesis that the relevant ideas and experience have been gained. It is also hard to avoid the difficulty of stating concepts, i.e. general ideas, rather than well-substantiated *principles*, as defined above, at this stage in the development of the subject.

These and other limitations and difficulties may be duly recognized but, even at the risk of an excessive discharge of aphorisms, a beginning should be made. If this chapter does no more than provoke someone with greater scholarly equipment and percipience to write a better account of the principles of organization in plants, something will have been achieved.

One of the more general aims of botanical science in the coming decades may well be to prepare a comprehensive classification not only of the morphological and other characters of plants, for that has already been done, but of the *processes* that have been involved in the evolution of both general and specific organization; since, in studying the *evolution of plants*, we are essentially concerned with *the evolution of organizations* (Wardlaw, 1963). This, indeed, may be specified as the central and most comprehensive phenomenon of plant life. It will require a knowledge of the principles of organization, operative at all levels, including the diverse conformations of unicellular organisms and other thallophytes, the organization of the primitive axis, the axis with appendages, and the elaboration of the leafy shoot by various innovations, differential growth, the elaboration of the reproductive organs, etc., all in relation to the general and specific action of factors in the hereditary constitution, to the self-ordering properties of organic and inorganic substances, and to factors in the environment.

SOME ESSENTIAL CONCEPTS

The interpretation of organization in plants calls for perception, analysis and synthesis of physical, chemical and physiological processes; of the relation of the organism and its environment; of the whole and its parts, and so on. Morphogenesis is sometimes described as being primarily concerned with answering the question: how does the observed form or structure come to be, in terms of the factors that are directly involved? Organization evidently covers much of the same ground; it comprises the same information; but one of its major aims is to understand the development of the organism as an integrated whole.

Among essential concepts,* the following may be indicated.

1. Organization involves order, stability, flexibility, continuity and specificity.

2. In the inception of organization in plants, the fundamental processes involve energy and matter, substances being brought together in characteristic spatial relationships, conformations or patterns, which are capable of hereditary perpetuation. Some simple aspects of organization, as in the formation of a crystal, are imminent in physico-chemical processes; but at more complex organismal levels – the result of chemical evolution and selection – organization both manifests and appears to transcend the laws of physical chemistry as presently understood and formulated. But *all* organizational features, whether

---

* At this early stage in the development of the subject, some overlapping between 'essential concepts' and 'principles' is difficult to avoid. (A *concept* is defined as a general notion or idea; an idea of a class of objects; the product of the faculty of conception.) The author regards his 'essential concepts' as providing further background for his 'principles'.

'structural' or 'physiological', must be due to innate properties of matter and energy. As molecules (with their associated energy relations) increase in size and complexity, new and often unexpected properties appear. Hence these properties seem to be 'emergent' and have been so described (*see below*).

3. As already noted, organization in plants is characterized by a high degree of constancy combined with a capacity for change. The hereditary constitution of the zygote or generative cell is relatively very stable and determines the developmental potentiality of the organism, i.e. its range of development and biological activity. But the actual reactivity of the developing organism may change in relation to environmental factors and the stage reached in ontogenesis; and both potency and reactivity may be different in different regions of the organism.

4. Organization is determined, or affected, by the spatial relationships of parts and their activities; e.g. contiguity is essential for certain reactions to take place. The spatial relationships of parts also affect the distribution of nutrients and therefore, together with other factors, the distribution of growth. In general, the nature of the spatial relationship determines how one part or organ may interact with another.

PHYSICO-CHEMICAL FACTORS, ORGANIZATION AND 'EMERGENT' PROPERTIES

While it is assumed that the laws of physics and chemistry apply to all biological activities, the reactions leading to organization typically take place in very complex systems, the bases of which are always transmitted in heredity. The 'hereditary substance' of any species is itself an exceedingly complex physico-chemical system, which has been elaborated as the result of cumulative irreversible changes during great spans of time.

At each successively higher level of evolution, or organization, the new properties or attributes which appear have often been described as being 'emergent', i.e. in the sense used in the concept of emergent evolution (Lloyd Morgan, 1922; Lillie, 1945). Some workers, e.g. Beckner (1959) and Waddington (1962), have denied that any properties are truly emergent: the new, 'emergent' phenomena could equally be regarded as the natural physicochemical attributes of systems which have attained to a high degree of complexity and organization as a result of hereditary changes and selection. Evolution may be recognized as a process in which chemical materials have become associated into progressively more complex, ordered, persisting systems; and different properties and functional activities will necessarily be associated with each new level of this ordered complexity, or organization. It is only because our ability to predict the properties and activities of complex systems is so limited that we regard them as being 'emergent'. This, of course, is not to deny generally that there can be anything 'new'; for it is undeniable that Mesozoic plants are 'new' relative to Palaeozoic ones. But can there be phenomena which truly transcend the inherent properties and potentialities of matter and energy? Phenomena in plants and animals are, presumably, only 'emergent' in the sense that they are still insufficiently explored by biologists, physicists and chemists. That certain phenomena impress us as being 'emergent' is not really so surprising when we consider how much we still have to learn about 'simple' things.* However, as Picken (1960) has noted, the attributes of organisms and their parts and, perhaps, indeed, the very existence of organisms, may be regarded as emergent, in the sense that they are due to properties which are the concomitant of the attainment of a particular level of molecular complexity. But these emergent properties 'can be "explained" as much or as little as we can explain the emergence of molecular from atomic attributes'. Indeed, there appear to be many biological phenomena with which contemporary physical chemistry is not equipped to deal. There are, moreover, many other phenomena, e.g. the reciprocal relationships of parts during development, which are essentially 'organismic' in category.

OTHER ACCOUNTS OF PRINCIPLES

Although in the section that follows the author has adopted a particular line in setting forth the 'principles of organization', i.e. based on his own working experience and personal convictions, this is by no means the first attempt of its kind. When, in 1868, Hofmeister wrote his *Allgemeine Morphologie der Gewächse* – the general morphology of growing things – he was quite evidently working towards a statement of the general principles relating to form and structure in plants; and in the great classical textbooks of Sachs, Strasburger, de Bary, Haberlandt, etc., we typically find orderly accounts of the Plant Kingdom either beginning with the cell and working upwards to tissues and organs, or beginning with the organs, as the more familiar and evident features, followed by analytical accounts of their tissues and individual cells. By implication, at least, all these authors were working towards

---

* *See* footnote on p. 437.

comprehensive and coherent accounts of the constitution of plants, i.e. of their organization. In the recent and contemporary periods, writers on philosophical aspects of biology, such as Woodger (1929, 1930–31) and Bertalanffy (1952, where many of his earlier views are summarized) have dealt explicitly with the topic of biological organization and its underlying principles. Bertalanffy, for example, in explaining his *organismic conception*, has affirmed that, fundamentally, organic processes are determined by the mutual interaction of all the factors and conditions in the system, i.e. by dynamic order; and that organisms are not simply reaction systems in the passive sense; i.e. they are not merely machines which operate under some external stimulus or control. An organism, on the contrary, is a basically active system. To quote:

We can therefore summarize the leading principles of an organismic conception in the following way: *The conception of the system as a whole* as opposed to the *analytical* and *summative* points of view; the *dynamic conception* as opposed to the *static* and *machine-theoretical* conceptions; the consideration of the organism as a *primary activity* as opposed to the conception of its *primary reactivity*.

The following quotations give a fuller impression of Bertalanffy's point of view (1952, p. 20):

It is not only necessary to carry out analysis in order to know as much as possible about the individual components, but it is equally necessary to know the laws of organization that unite these parts and partial processes and are just the characteristic of vital phenomena. Herein lies the essential and original object of biology. This biological order is specific and surpasses the laws applying in the inanimate world, but we can progressively approach it with continued research. It calls for investigation at all levels: at the level of physico-chemical units, processes, and systems; at the biological level of the cell and the multicellular organism; at the level of supra-individual units of life. At each of these levels we see new properties and new laws. Biological order is, in a wide measure, of a dynamic nature; how this is to be defined we shall see later on.

In this way the autonomy of life, denied in the mechanistic conception, and remaining a metaphysical question mark in vitalism, appears, in the organismic conception, as a problem accessible to science, and, in fact, already under investigation.

The term 'wholeness' has been much misused in past years. Within the organismic conception it means neither a mysterious entity nor a refuge for our ignorance, but a fact that can and must be dealt with by scientific methods.

The organismic conception is not a compromise, a muddling through or mid-course between the mechanistic and vitalistic views. As we have seen, the analytic, summative, and machine-theoretical conceptions have been the common ground of both the classical views. *Organization and wholeness considered as principles of order, immanent to organic systems, and accessible to scientific investigation, involve a basically new attitude* (My italics, C. W. W.).

In a chapter on 'Levels of Organization', Bertalanffy (1952) has a section entitled 'General Principles of Organization', in which the 'architecture envisaged in an organism' is perceived as a system of *hierarchical order*. In fact, the principles of hierarchical order had already been defined by Woodger, with the aid of mathematical logic, as early as 1930–31. Let the non-mathematical reader be reassured: this is not nearly as bad as it sounds! In the abstract sense, hierarchical order may be exemplified by a square divided into squares, each of which is also divided into squares; and so on. The hierarchical system is then expounded by Bertalanffy in terms of the *division hierarchy*, i.e. the four-dimensional order of cells which results from the division of a single cell; the *spatial hierarchy*, i.e. the consequences of the relationships of parts at different organizational levels; the *genetic hierarchy*, involving the relationships of successive generations; the *histo-system* of Heidenheim (1923), in which the organism is regarded as being constructed of an ascending order of superordinate systems, including subordinate systems; the morphological and physiological *hierarchy of parts*; and *hierarchical segregation*, as seen in embryonic development, and many other phenomena. Weiss's conception of hierarchical order in organisms is illustrated in Fig.2.10, p. 50.

In the section that follows, the author has set out his idea of the principles of organization in plants. These are, as far as possible, 'working principles', i.e. they are intended as a basis for further investigation towards a fuller validation of the 'principles'. Here, two pathways were open: (i) to set out the 'principles' as a coherent statement and (ii) to state each 'principle' with supporting evidence from observation and experiment. After due reflection the first of these choices has been selected, the possibility of the experimental investigation of organization being more fully considered in the following chapter.

PRINCIPLES OF ORGANIZATION IN PLANTS

The 'principles' which follow should be regarded as no more than a first approximation, to be improved as our understanding of organization advances. (The 'principles' are in *italics*, but additional statements, in brackets, are added in the interests of fullness of expression.)

1. *Organization in plants involves energy and substances so interrelated and structurally evolved as to constitute viable functional systems, capable of self-maintenance and of being transmitted in heredity.*

2. *The embryonic cell, an integrated entity comprising the nucleus, the organelles and other structural components (or their precursors), is the*

unit of biological organization and heredity. (Many organizational features, in addition to the nucleus, are transmitted during both sexual and asexual reproduction; i.e. all life from life, all cells from cells.)

3. *Both the 'chemical' and 'physical' attributes of metabolic processes make distinctive and important contributions to organization.* ('Chemical' processes may, purely as a matter of convenience for some purposes, be regarded as primary, and the related 'physical' processes as secondary and consequential; but the two aspects are inseparable. The statement could, for example, be reversed, since no movement, exchange, or recombination of substances can take place without energy; and the physical properties of organic substances, by contributing to the structural organization of the developing individual or biological entity, may profoundly affect all its activities.)

4. *Biological patterns and other manifestations of organization involve, and are an expression of, the attainment of dynamic equilibrium, or steady state, in complex individual (or unitary) physico-chemical systems, described as organismal reaction systems; or, for convenience, as reaction systems.* (Such reaction systems may consist of single cells, as in unicellular organisms; or they may comprise an associated group of embryonic cells, as in the apices of higher plants. Accordingly, all normal developments in plants, whether regular or seemingly irregular in their morphological or histological conformation, afford evidence of developmental harmony and holistic development, i.e. integrated wholeness. This principle could also account for the capacity of organisms for reorganization after injury or disturbance.)

5. *The way in which a particular cell becomes differentiated is not only related to its position in the plant, but also to its functioning as a component of a coherent tissue pattern which is characteristically determined as a whole. Organs such as leaves also originate as parts of a holistic pattern.* (Holistic tissue patterns are present in cross-sections of roots, petioles, etc. This pattern-forming function, or property, of reaction systems in embryonic regions is a basic phenomenon in organization; i.e. a characteristic distribution, or pattern, of metabolic substances precedes and determines the inception of organs and of tissue systems. This principle not only comprises the spatial aspects of organ and cell differentiation but also the changes in pattern which are correlated with changes in size.)

6. *However essential, or limiting, in morphogenesis and organization a particular substance may be, it can only produce its effects when it acts as a component of the integrated reaction system in an embryonic cell or region,*

or in a cell or region still capable of growth. (By effecting some characteristic change in a reaction system, at a particular stage in ontogenesis, certain substances may, with appropriate qualifications, be regarded as the proximate cause of important and distinctive organizational developments; e.g. certain gene-determined substances are known to act in this way. An organismal system comprises many complex reactions and interactions. In the reaction system in a shoot apex, and in the growth centres to which it gives rise, the components include general metabolites, specific gene products, environmental factors and organismal factors (e.g. gradients, correlation factors, etc.). Different genetical factors have different times of action: some are active as long as growth continues: others are evoked at particular stages in ontogenesis, often in characteristic sequence and in relation to the impact of environmental factors, e.g. light, heat, supply of water, nutrients, etc.)

7. *Differently constituted reaction systems may yield comparable primary patterns; and the same reaction system may yield different primary patterns at different stages in ontogenesis.* (In vascular plants, the reaction system in the vegetative shoot apex typically yields a *primary pattern* of regularly-spaced, discrete *growth centres* which typically develop as leaves during the vegetative phase; but vegetative buds, inflorescences or flower buds may originate from these and from other growth centres. As this primary pattern is usually elaborated in characteristic ways by differential growth in the subapical and maturing regions, similar primary patterns may give rise to very different adult forms.)

8. *The progressive organization which becomes manifest during ontogenesis is the result of many interrelated serial, or sequential, processes; genetical, organismal and environmental stimuli being involved in the induction and regulation of the successive phases of development.* (The harmonious development of the leafy and flowering shoot of an angiosperm can be analysed in terms of (i) pervasive, serial and specific genic activity; (ii) the establishment of polarity in the zygote and young embryo, and the inception of acropetal and basipetal gradients; (iii) sustained meristematic activity in the shoot apex and the inception of a primary pattern of organ primordia; and (iv) the effects of differential growth and of correlative and other factors in the subapical regions. The serial, or sequential, evocation of gene-determined substances, as components of the reaction system, by progressively changing the reaction system in characteristic ways, makes a major contribution to specific organization, e.g. in the formation of the distinctive and characteristic organs of a flower.)

9. *The physiological factors which determine reciprocal relationships of various kinds, e.g. between the whole and its parts,* between distal and proximal regions, between organ and cell, between contiguous cells of different kinds, etc., contribute significantly to the organization of the individual plant.* (While it is true that 'organs build cells, not cells organs', the substances which determine differential growth, and therefore the size and shape of an organ, proceed from the genetically- and environmentally-controlled metabolism of particular cells, or groups of cells. Although a biological relationship is not an agent, as Beckner (1959) pointed out, nevertheless the positional or spatial relationships of contiguous differentiating cells and nascent organs may affect organizational developments. This is seen (i) in various autonomous or self-ordering morphogenetic processes (*see* Chapter 7); (ii) in the translocation and distribution of metabolic substances; (iii) in the competition for nutrients, and in mutual stimulation, inhibition, etc.)

10. *Integration is an essential condition for the endurance of organismal reaction systems and for the development of adaptive features in organisms.* (Hence any viable gene mutation must be such that the specific substance which it determines must be capable of acting as a component of the system. A lethal gene is one which does not react compatibly with the other components of the system; a neutral gene is one which can persist in the system without specific activity other than self-reproduction. The adaptive characters of plants are equilibrium or steady state resultant effects of the interaction of hereditary and environmental factors, primarily in the reaction system.)

---

* Beckner (1959), in discussing biological statements such as 'the whole determines the part', has suggested that, on critical philosophical grounds, it would be more acceptable to say that 'the concept of the whole determines the concept of the part'.

CHAPTER 14

The Experimental Investigation of Organization

VALIDATION OF HYPOTHESES

It will be appreciated that many of the 'principles of organization' proposed in Chapter 13 have not yet been established: some of them, indeed, are little more than hypotheses for which, however, some measure of support can be adduced. What is needed, therefore, is validating evidence based on (a) a wide range of both general and particular observations on development in all classes of plants, and (b) analytical and experimental investigations of the inception and elaboration of organization. Some relevant information has already been presented in Chapters 7, 10, 11. Additional examples are now discussed, not in an attempt to cover the whole field, nor systematically to validate each of the 'principles', but rather to demonstrate that hypotheses relating to organization can be examined along the lines indicated above and that results have already been obtained.

It is held that the reaction system in an embryonic region, e.g. an embryo or shoot apex, normally gives rise to a pattern as a whole. Accordingly, if we wish to test this idea, we must interfere with the normal working of the reaction system in some characteristic way, e.g. by introducing new components, by changing the balance of the existing components, by modifying environmental factors, or by disturbing the system mechanically; and we must try to relate the induced changes in the system to the manifestation of organization. That changes can be induced in a reaction system may be inferred from the normal course of ontogenesis in any species; and many other observations in Nature support the general view. There is also a body of supporting experimental evidence, of which some examples may now be given.

GENERAL EVIDENCE OF PATTERN CHANGES AT THE SHOOT APEX

Of the changes in morphological pattern at the shoot apex, the simplest and most evident variations are those which accompany an increase or decrease in the size of the meristem. In ferns and flowering plants, the shoot apex undergoes an increase in size from the young sporophyte to the adult state. If the leaf arrangement is spiral, the phyllotaxis may change from a low value, e.g. $(1+2)$ to a high one, e.g. $(5+8)$; but no fundamental change in the organization of the apical meristem or in the functioning of its reaction system is involved. The principal factors involved are nutritional. In experiments in which the adult apex has been diminished in size by the removal of leaves and leaf primordia, changes in phyllotaxis, leaf morphology and vascular pattern have been induced.

Evidence of changes in the apical pattern are afforded by species with whorled phyllotaxis. For example, in some stellate Rubiaceae, the seedling has two cotyledons; but on proceeding upwards in the main shoot of an adult plant, or in a lateral branch, the number of leaves in the successive whorls increases till as many as nine may be present, as in *Galium aparine* L. The number of leaf primordia formed at any particular stage of development is probably directly related to the size of the apical meristem. Similarly, in the embryo of *Equisetum* three leaves are typically formed at the first node. As the young sporophyte grows, its apex enlarges and progressively larger numbers of primordia are formed at successive nodes till, in the adult shoot of some species, a very large number may be present. Other examples of this kind could be cited. Various algae, in which the branch filaments arise in whorls, also afford evidence of changes in pattern with increase in apical size. As already noted in Chapter 7 (p. 155), the number of cotyledons present in the embryo of *Pinus* spp. varies directly with the size of the apical meristem (*see also* Chamberlain, 1935).

EXPERIMENTALLY MODIFIED REACTION SYSTEMS

Selected examples of experimentally modified reaction systems will now be considered. Readers will appreciate that this can only be a small indication of what is indeed a very rapidly expanding literature.

EXPERIMENTS WITH EMBRYOS

In higher plants the embryo is encapsulated and is dependent for its nutrient supply on the gametophyte tissue and/or endosperm. The enveloping tissue, in fact, constitutes the immediate environment of the embryo and may accordingly be expected to have important effects on its reaction system. If, therefore, the embryo is removed from the gradients, pressures, and other effects proceeding from the maternal tissue, its reaction system and its resulting organization are likely to be modified. That this is so has been shown by Ward and Wetmore (1954), by Jayasekera and Bell (1959) and by DeMaggio (1963). They have reported anomalous developments after fern zygotes had been variously isolated, or excised, from the gametophyte tissue. In species of *Capsella*, *Datura* and other flowering plants, when young embryos have been removed from the embryo sac and grown in culture media of different compositions, many anomalous morphological developments have been recorded, such as the formation of double embryos, polycotyledons, etc. In some instances, the normal course of ontogenesis has been more or less radically modified. In *Capsella bursa-pastoris*, for example, Rijven (1952) found that as many as six cotyledons may be formed in some embryos; i.e. the distal region of the small club-shaped embryo, which *in ovulo* usually yields two centres of growth, may be modified experimentally so that a large number of growth centres is differentiated. Comparable observations have been made on excised embryos of other species; Sanders (1950), for example, has illustrated multiple and fasciated embryos of *Datura* in artificial culture. In experiments in which the fertilized ovules of *Eranthis* were injected with various growth-regulating substances, Haccius and Haccius *et al.* (1955–1960) found that the number of cotyledons was increased to three, four and some-times more. In other experiments by Haccius on *Eranthis* embryos, further evidence was obtained of changes in the working of the reaction system, with subsequent changes in the visible organization, as the result of introducing new components. (This and other relevant evidence has been reviewed by Wardlaw, 1964) (Figs. 14.1–14.5).

Maheshwari and Baldev (1962) have reported an interesting case of the induction of adventitious buds in cultured embryos of *Cuscuta reflexa*. In various other contemporary studies of embryos and organs, growing in culture media of known composition, it has been shown that, by changing the nutritional environment, more or less significant modifications of the normal morphogenetic developments can be induced, these being indicative of changes effected in the underlying organismal reaction system (*see* Mohan Ram, 1963; Reinert, 1963; Johri and Singh Bajay, 1963). In cultural studies of excised grass embryos Narayanaswami (1963) observed various induced anomalous developments, such as the formation of scutellar tumourous outgrowths, root formation from the scutellum, and other curious growth effects. These observations suggest that quite radical changes in the reaction system of the developing embryo can be effected by the addition of various regulative substances, adenine, IAA, maleic hydrazide, etc., to the basic medium.

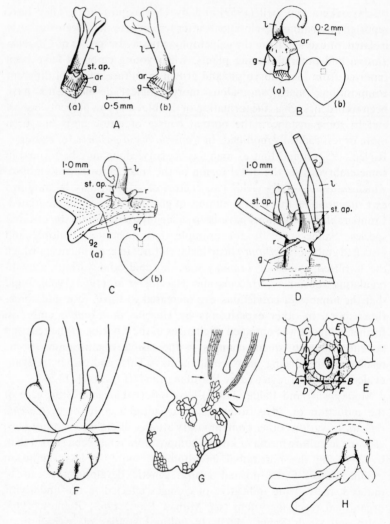

Fig.14.1 Experimentally modified fern embryos.

A–D, *Thelypteris palustris.*

A, Embryo 36 days old, excised from the gametophyte 5 days after fertilization; drawn as placed on the medium, ventral surface of the gametophyte uppermost: (a) from the side originally adjacent to the anterior of the gametophyte; (b) from the opposite side; *ar*, archegonium; *g*, gametophyte; *l*, leaf; *st.ap.*, stem apex.

(*Caption continued at foot of facing page*)

In a review of morphogenetic and other developments in tissue, organ and embryo cultures, Maheshwari and Ranga Swamy (1963) have shown how important is the impact of various growth-regulating substances on formative processes in embryonic regions. The new patterns which are induced afford evidence of changes effected in the reaction systems in embryonic tissues by particular metabolic substances, or combinations, present in the culture media.

B a, Embryo 27 days old, the archegonium excised from the gametophyte before fertilization. The dotted line indicates the position of the foot and stem apex determined by sectioning. Drawn as placed on medium, ventral surface of the gametophyte uppermost; indications as in A.

B b, Diagram showing original position of archegonium; distance between anterior margin of fragment of gametophyte and base of notch, 0·8 mm.

C a, Embryo 22 days old, the archegonium excised from the gametophyte before fertilization but with the apical notch attached and active. Drawn as placed on the medium, ventral surface of the gametophyte uppermost; n, original position of apical notch; g_1, original fragment of gametophyte; g_2, new growth of gametophyte.

C b, Diagram showing position from which fragment of gametophyte was removed.

D, Cylindrical body developing from zygote 70 days after fertilization following removal of the archegonial neck on the fifth day after fertilization. Drawn as placed on the medium, the dorsal surface of the gametophyte uppermost. (From R. D. E. Jayasekera and P. R. Bell, *Planta*, 1959.)

E–H, *Phlebodium aureum*.

E, Diagram to show position of incisions made on a prothallus in one of the experimental treatments. Dotted lines indicate the places where cuts were made to release the embryo from the restraint of the prothallial tissue.

F and G, Tuberous bodies resulting from single zygotes after surgical treatment. Massive growth in F is about 50 days old and bears three young shoots on the upper part, above the surface of the prothallus. In G, the vascular connections from two of the leaves (arrows) are shown diagrammatically from sections of tuber in E. Below the ends of the vascular trace is an arrangement of columnar tissue in the former foot region of the tuber. Variation in size and shape of the parenchymatous cells of the tuberous body is indicated in a few isolated areas. The apical notch is to the right in both figures.

H, Young leafy shoots on the under side of a tuberous body, becoming orientated towards the apical notch to the left. (From M. Ward and R. H. Wetmore, *Amer. Jour. Botany*, 1954.)

Embryo Transplants and Crossability. Readers may recall that the Russian plant-breeder Michurin made use of grafting in order to facilitate difficult sexual crosses. He described his method as 'vegetative approximation' (Michie, 1958). In fact, the same general idea had been to some extent explored as early as 1907 by Stingl. This worker excised embryos of various Gramineae and successfully implanted them in the

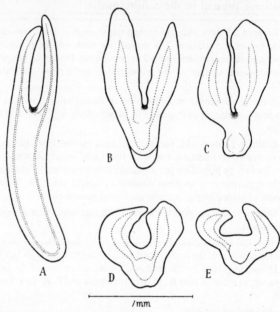

Fig.14.2 *Datura stramonium.* Effect of 1 mg/l 3-indoleacetic acid on embryos grown on a culture medium, after 9 days. A, control; B–E, embryos variously modified in medium to which IAA had been added. (From J. Rietsema, S. Satina and A. F. Blakeslee, *Amer. Jour. Botany.*)

endosperm of species of other genera. Later, Camara (1943) found that embryos of *Triticum vulgare* grew better when implanted in the endosperm of *Secale cereale* than in that of *Triticum durum* or *T. turgidum.* Further observations along these lines have been made by Hall (1954, 1956). This work, in fact, was undertaken primarily to verify results reported by Pissarev and Vinogradova (1944). These investigators had reported increases of the crossability of wheat and rye by transplantation of wheat embryos to rye endosperm. Hall repeated this work on an extensive scale and obtained, for example – in his largest experiment – 400 hybrid kernels from 2897 pollinations with rye when he used wheat plants raised from embryos which had been transplanted to rye endosperm, as compared with only 75 hybrid kernels from 2813 similar pollinations of wheat plants raised from wheat embryo/wheat endosperm transplants. Moreover, a further analysis of the data showed that 60 plants of the wheat/wheat group, when pollinated with rye, were entirely without kernel while only 28 of the wheat/rye group showed this condition. The results suggested that the rye endosperm from which the young wheat seedling had drawn its nutrients had an important effect on the subsequent capacity of the plant to intercross with rye. Hall (1956) also found that the endosperm of a Chinese wheat – which is known to offer virtually no crossing barrier to rye – behaved like rye endosperm as indicated above. These results are the more interesting and remarkable as the many reports of Soviet-Russian investigators of having increased the crossability between species, etc. by establishing a regular graft union between the partners, have not been confirmed by other scientists. It would be interesting to know whether the effect of the rye endosperm is specific, i.e. whether it increases only the crossability of wheat to rye or also to other species and genera.

Observations such as the above suggest that the reaction system in the young embryo can sometimes be changed in subtle but important ways. Exactly what happens biochemically in such experiments is still not known and may indeed be very difficult to discover. In this field of research, as it seems to the writer, one has to adopt an open-minded attitude, without being either imaginatively incautious, or over-credulous, whilst awaiting fuller information.

FERN GAMETOPHYTES AND SPOROPHYTES

The two alternating generations in the fern life cycle exemplify very different kinds of organization, even although the same genotype is present in both. Yet, both in Nature and by appropriate cultural treatments, apogamous and aposporous developments can be induced. Since, in certain fern species, reproduction normally takes place apogamously and aposporously, specific genetical factors as well as more general physiological factors are involved. It thus appears that some significant change can be induced in the reaction system, either by the presence of a particular gene or group of genes, or by some combination of environmental, nutritional or organismal factors; and this may lead to well-marked differences in the eventual visible organization. In other words, the same genotype can either determine different

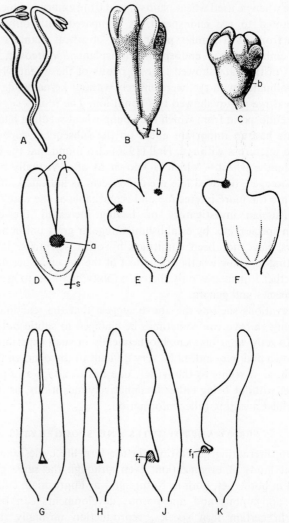

Fig.14.3 *Eranthis hiemalis*. Various effects produced in young embryos by treatment with 0·1 per cent 2, 4-dichlorophenoxyacetic acid. A, twin seedlings; B, C, twin embryos removed in September and towards the end of June (× 110 and × 220 respectively); D–F, longitudinal sections, showing common basal region (A × 110; B–K × 220). (From B. Haccius, *Nature*, 1955.)

Eranthis hiemalis. G, normal untreated embryo. H. embryo modified

(*Caption continued at foot of facing page*)

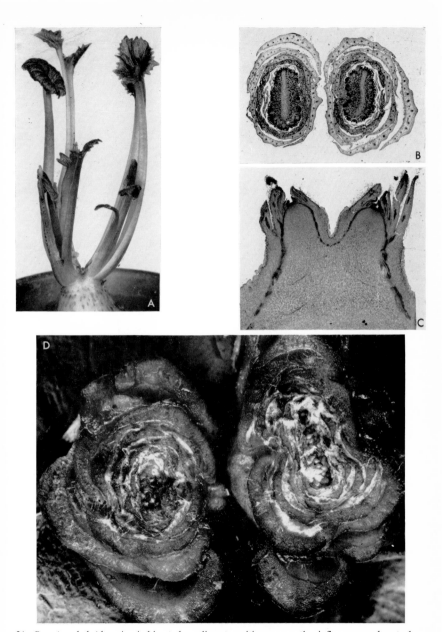

21. *Petasites hybridus*. A, A bisected medium-transition apex; the inflorescence bracts have developed into laminate foliage leaves; this stage is intermediate between those illustrated in Plate 20 D and E. B, Transverse section, after a period of growth, of a bisected late-transition apex: two new axes have been formed, each with an outer group of foliage leaves, with stem-encircling leaf-bases; more centrally there are inflorescence bracts and, at the centre, the inflorescence axis with young capitula (× 6·5). C, Longitudinal section, after a period of growth, of a bisected early-medium transition apex: two vegetative axes, with bulky foliage leaf primordia, have developed (× 6·5). D, Transverse section of a bisected medium-to-late-transition apex, after a period of growth, showing two axes, each with the encircling bases of fleshy foliage leaves—which in the normal development would have been narrow linear bracts—and a central inflorescence. The white material between the leaf-bases is the conspicuous hirsute development, characteristic of the vegetative but not of the inflorescence phase of development.

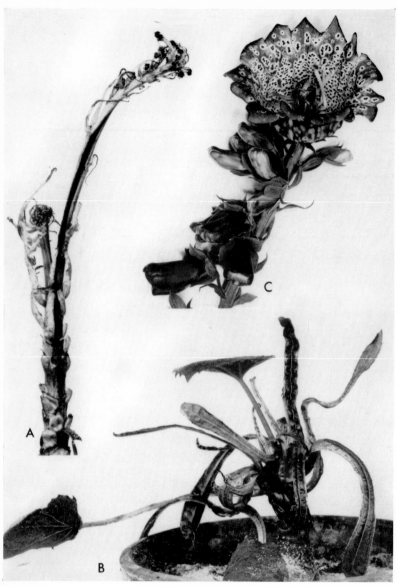

22. A, B, *Petasites hybridus*. A, A late-transition apex which had been laid bare, bisected and thereafter treated with 0.01 per cent gibberellic acid: this apex formed no foliage leaves but showed sustained development of the inflorescence, elongation of the inflorescence axis and precocious flowering, i.e. in September instead of the following spring (from *Nature*, 1963). B, A defoliated late-transition apex (i.e. in which the inflorescence meristem was more or less covered with capitula primordia) was bisected at the end of July; it was then treated with .001 per cent gibberellic acid; a few foliage leaves and a considerable number of large, spatulate, bract-like leaves have been formed. C, *Digitalis purpurea*. An inflorescence in which a large, actinomorphic flower has developed in the terminal position. The lateral flowers are of much smaller size and have the zygomorphic symmetry characteristic of the Scrophulariaceae. (Photo by courtesy of Professor J. Walton.)

kinds of reaction system, or essentially the same reaction system is markedly affected in its organizational manifestations by particular, but still unknown, metabolic substances. Once the character, or trend, of the reaction system is established it tends to persist.

Each of the two alternating phases in the fern life history begins as a single embryonic cell. It is not yet known if the two cytoplasmic

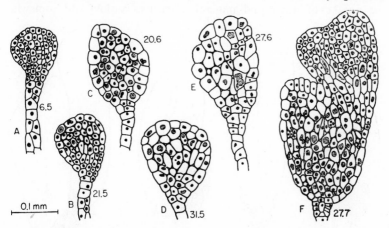

Fig.14.4 *Eranthis hiemalis*. Young embryos treated with antimitotic substances. A, untreated embryo at the beginning of the experiment; B–C, F, embryos treated with isopropyl-N-carbamate, and D–E treated with maleic hydrazide (MH), showing various histological and nuclear abnormalities. (From B. Haccius, *Beitr. Biol. Pflanz.*, 1957.)

organizations are fundamentally alike or different. As they show very different growth behaviour it is reasonable to assume that they differ metabolically. The fertilized ovum, which is surrounded and initially nourished by gametophyte tissue, soon begins to develop into a young sporophyte. The mature spore, on the other hand, has a thick outer wall of several layers, and storage reserves in the form of starch and oils. In some species there is no resting phase before germination. From the morphological evidence it seems probable that there are important initial differences in the respective reaction systems and, as development

as a result of treatment with 2, 4-D. J, embryo modied as a result of treatment with phenylboric acid: the embryo is monocotyledonous, f_1 being the first foliage leaf primordium. K, *Ranunculus ficaria*, a 'monocotyledonous dicotyledon' for comparison. (From B. Haccius and G. Trompeter, *Planta*, 1960.)

proceeds, further metabolic differences almost certainly develop. The young embryo soon becomes autotrophic as a result of its early development of functional leaves and roots and successive leaves show a progressive increase in size. The small filamentous gametophyte, on the other hand, soon exhausts the spore contents, and thereafter its growth, based on the small prothallial surface for photosynthesis and rhizoids for the uptake of water and mineral nutrients, is slow and somewhat

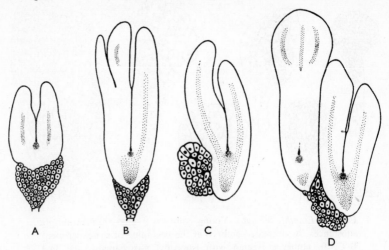

Fig.14.5 *Eranthis hiemalis.* Embryos, treated in May with maleic hydrazide, as seen in November; these have all shown a characteristic regeneration from the more basal tissue of the young embryo. A and C, dicotyledonous embryo; B, a tricotyledonous embryo; D, twin embryos. (From B. Haccius, 1957.)

limited in character, i.e. like green algae and moss gametophytes. However, in older gametophytes, young sporophyte plants may be formed apogamously, this being usually preceded by the formation of a tissue mass, or cushion, just behind the small notched apex. Aposporous prothalli are typically obtained when juvenile sporophyte leaves, or isolated pieces of older leaf margins, are grown under low illumination. These several observations are consistent with the view that there is a regulative relationship between the metabolic status of the zygote and its mode of development; and similarly for the spore. Evidence from other sources also indicates that nutrient supplies (in the comprehensive sense) may be of great importance in determining the size and level of organization attained in different organisms. This is true of the individual life and it may be, with appropriate reservations, extended to evolutionary developments.

With the facts of apogamy and apospory in mind, it does appear that, however different the reaction systems of the gametophyte and sporophyte may seem to be, some combination of factors, possibly relatively simple in character and action, may bring about the transition from one to the other. This finding, if valid, may evidently have an application to other organizational phenomena where more or less conspicuous 'transformations' take place (*see* section on Neomorphs).

The differences between the fern gametophyte and sporophyte have long engaged the interest of botanists. Thus Lang (1915) wrote: 'In one sense the fern-plant and the prothallus appear like two individuals, in another the two stages are like parts of the same individual. We seem almost forced to assume that the specific substance of a fern can, as it were, exist in two allotrophic modifications, the properties of which are revealed in the unlikeness of the two generations. Presented thus, the alternation of generations becomes a special aspect of the problem of individual development.' Earlier Lang had suggested that the two germ cells (spore and zygote) were 'essentially alike, the different products of their development depending on the different conditions'; and he noted that, in the simplest cases of direct apogamy, the young sporophyte is continuous with the thickened cushion of the prothallus but that otherwise its members are formed in the same relative position as those in a plant developed from a fertilized egg (*see* Wardlaw, 1955). He also remarked that when

we consider the strange cases of the perfect development of isolated members or tissues of the sporophyte on or in the prothallus, we seem forced to think further of special formative influences that are of the nature of substance rather than of a system of relations. We are confirmed in this by the fact that a number of cells may be simultaneously and collectively influenced, and that the influence may be reversed. This holds both for apogamy and apospory; in the latter when the prothalli develop upon leaves attached to the plant, it is difficult to see how either external or internal influences equivalent to the usual relations can come into play. There is no nuclear change, at least of the nature of meiosis, and there seems nothing for it but to assume some material modification involving the change to the alternative condition of the specific substance expressed in the prothallus. The interest of these considerations, tentative as they must be, lies in the way in which they associate two explanations of development, the influence of particular, unknown determining substances and the system of relation. The whole question is fortunately not complicated with adaptation or any gradual origin of these deviations from the normal, and affords a particularly clear example of a problem in causal morphology. The perfect development of isolated members without the usual relation to the rest of the plant-body has an important regulative bearing on the current assumption that every stage in development is determined by the preceding stage. In this connection a most interesting parallel can be traced between the appearance of perfectly formed roots, ramenta, sporangia, and vascular tissue in induced apogamy and the development of bones, teeth, and hairs in dermoid cysts occurring in the human ovary or testis. The further study of the conditions of development in such abnormal cases may do much to enlighten us as to the factors concerned in the normal ontogeny.

New Investigations. Recent years have witnessed a renewal of interest in these classical problems, and new experimental investigations have been undertaken, use being made of techniques taken from genetics and molecular biology. Some observations which are relevant to the present work may be briefly surveyed.

Wilkie (1963), in a genetic analysis of variation in the prothallus of *Pteridium aquilinum*, observed that, when single spores were grown in pure culture, some of them gave rise to small, male, ameristic prothalli; in fact, to a plate of cells of retarded growth, lacking an apical growing point. Some of these prothalli were stable, but others, after a time, developed into more or less normal heart-shaped prothalli. The genetical properties of the several types of prothallus were investigated by methods involving cross- and self-fertilization analysis. Although earlier investigators had held that ameristic forms were due entirely to environmental conditions, e.g. absence of nitrates from the culture medium, growth under low light intensity, etc., Wilkie's genetical analysis has led him to the view that his stable ameristic form can neither be attributed exclusively to environmental factors nor to the action of nuclear genes, but more probably to some unequal proportioning of the cytoplasm at cell division. 'No doubt a great deal of the cytoplasmic organization including particles, enzymes and metabolites is transmitted from spore mother cell to spore and it is feasible that spores will arise deficient in one or other of these units'. Under unfavourable growth conditions, a depletion of metabolites, or of available protein, might also result in diminutive, unorganized, ameristic forms; i.e. the bracken prothallus exemplifies the thesis that metabolism may change from one characteristic steady state to another and, in different instances, hereditary or environmental factors may be the more proximate cause. Along cognate though rather different lines, Morel (1963) and his colleagues are investigating, with the use of aseptic cultures, the biochemistry and morphology of parallel series of *n*, 2*n* and 4*n* gametophytes and sporophytes of *Todea barbara*, *Osmunda cinnamomea*, etc. Their problem, in fact, is to discover how the same nucleus controls the morphology of these different types of organisms; for as Morel has pointed out, in both a 2*n* gametophyte and a 2*n* sporophyte, with their very different organizational features, the 'information' coded in the chromosomes should be the same. With contemporary views on 'messenger' service as background (*see* Jacob and Monod, 1961), Morel and his colleagues are attempting, by very detailed analyses of all the forms of RNA occurring in the parallel series of gametophytes and sporophytes, to find if there are any significant differences and how the genes control the specific morphogenetic developments. To date, one of the interesting results reported, using *Adiantum pedatum*, is that

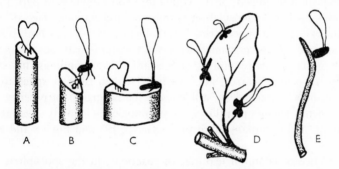

Fig.14.6 *Phlebodium aureum*. Diagrammatic representation of adventitious gametophytes and sporophytes grown in culture. A, adventitious (aposporous) gametophyte on petiole segment; B, sporophyte developing from filamentous outgrowth on similar petiole segment; C, gametophytic and sporophytic plants arising in proximity on section of rhizome; D, plants of sporophytic form on intact leaf of apogamous sporophyte; E, aerially-formed sporophyte on vertically extended three-dimensional outgrowth of apogamous sporophyte in sub-culture. (After M. Ward, *Jour. Linn. Soc. (Bot.)*, 1963.)

whereas juvenile leaves of young sporophytes regenerate gametophytes, adult leaves, from excised cultured apical meristems, regenerate sporophytes. It thus appears that during ontogenetic ageing, the factor which determines the formation of gametophyte tissue, which is apparently still present in the juvenile leaves, is lost. The hope is that, by using modern techniques of nucleic acid separation, it may be possible to identify this factor and thus 'open a new way of understanding the process of differentiation in plants' (Morel, 1963).

In a study of adventitious sporophytes in *Phlebodium aureum*, Ward (1963) cultured pieces of petiole, rhizome and apogamously-formed leaves under appropriate conditions and obtained: (i) adventitious, aposporous gametophytes from cut petiole surfaces; (ii) sporophytes which began as filamentous outgrowths from similar cut petiole surfaces; (iii) gametophytes and sporophytes growing in contiguity from the cut surface of the rhizome; (iv) sporophytic plants growing from the margins of intact leaves of an apogamous sporophyte; and (v) aerially-formed sporophytes, originating on a vertically extended cylindrical outgrowth of an apogamous sporophyte in subculture (Fig.14.6). These observations have led Ward to question the validity of an earlier conclusion of Ward and Wetmore (1954) that the characteristic morphological development of the young fern sporophyte is in part due to the pressures of encapsulation within the archegonium (*see* p. 322). On the evidence, it appears that metabolic factors, perhaps both general and specific, are the proximate causes of these enigmatic developments. These observations remind us of Steward's (1958) findings that small groups of cells of carrot, not closely related in time or space to the zygote, may, nevertheless, still possess meristematic totipotency and may yield young plantlings, morphologically closely resembling embryos, and eventually adult plants (*see* p. 198 and Fig.9.8 and Plate 11).

Evidence of common features, or reactions, in the sporophyte and gametophyte of ferns is afforded by recent observations made by De Maggio, Wetmore and Morel (1963). In *Todea barbara* they showed that vascular tissue can be induced at will in prothalli by growing them on a mineral solution to which sugar and auxin, at appropriate concentrations, have been added. The differentiation of numerous elongated tracheids in the prothallus is in direct relation to the composition of the medium and not to the formation of apogamous sporophytes.

Bell (1959) suggested that the differences in organization between the two generations in the fern life cycle may be due to factors at work in the respective cytoplasms of spore and zygote. DeMaggio and Wetmore (1961) criticized this approach on the grounds that it did not afford a sufficiently definite working approach to a major problem in causal morphology. However, in further investigations of *Pteridium aquilinum*, Bell (1963) has been able to demonstrate, by the use of contemporary techniques, that the ovum in ferns is cytochemically and cytologically not only a rather peculiar cell but is very different from a spore, the latter, in Bell's assessment, having the usual organizational features found in an unspecialized potentially meristematic cell. Thus, by means of staining techniques and autoradiography, he has demonstrated that the cytochemistry of the ovum is very different from that of somatic gametophyte cells. DNA is present in a stable state in both the nucleus and the cytoplasm of the mature egg; in fact, a high concentration of DNA surrounds the nucleus. Also the egg cytoplasm, by comparison with the cytoplasm of a somatic cell, contains large amounts of RNA especially in outer peripheral regions; there are also large amounts of basic proteins. Further, by using the electron microscope, Bell has shown that the unfertilized ovum of *P. aquilinum* has a number of ultrastructural peculiarities. As the egg matures the nucleus appears to evaginate or forms 'blebs' into the cytoplasm, this coinciding with the outward movement of nuclear DNA. There is evidence that many of the mitochondria and other organelles derived from those of the gametophyte degenerate and are replaced in the mature ovum by new sets, these possibly having been formed as a result of the direct participation of the nucleus; some of the nuclear 'blebs' may develop into mitochondria. Although it has not yet been possible to correlate in detail the cytochemistry of the ovum with its unique ultrastructure, Bell has suggested that the evidence so far obtained admits of the interpretation that the mature egg has a cytoplasm which is transformed under nuclear influence and that the presence of new organelles in the ovum may account for the differences in the complexities of the structures generated by the zygote and spore respectively. A further possible inference is that, in sporogenesis, there is some mechanism whereby the number of organelles is diminished or their functions impaired, this having its counterpart in the various 'starvation' and other techniques which have been successfully used for many years to obtain gametophytes from the leaves of sporophytes.

Reference should also be made to studies of fern prothalli by Sossountzov (1954, where earlier work is cited). This investigator observed that the shape and growth of prothalli was markedly affected by the presence of glycine and other aminoacids in the culture medium.

All of the foregoing shows that, to some extent, metabolic processes and organizational phenomena in ferns are being brought into a more tangible relationship. It will be interesting to see how all this looks in the course of the next five to ten years.

THE ANGLE MERISTEM IN *Selaginella*

The rhizophores of *Selaginella*, which normally develop from the angle meristems, have been described as being morphologically indeterminate organs. They afford an unusually good example of the experimental modification of an apical reaction system under known conditions. In the normal development, an angle meristem grows out into a leafless, downwardly directed root-bearing organ, the rhizophore. But if the main shoot is cut off, the angle meristem, or very young rhizophore,

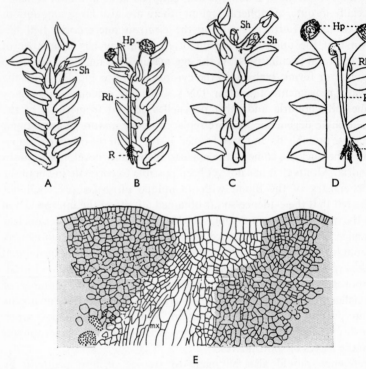

Fig.14.7 A–E

develops as a negatively geotrophic leafy shoot, If, however, the cut end of the decapitated shoot is smeared with lanoline containing indole-acetic acid, a root-bearing rhizophore is usually obtained (S. Williams, 1937). Here we have a clear indication of a very considerable known modification in a reaction system with attendant changes in the sub-sequent morphological and histological organization (Fig.14.7).

NEOMORPHOSIS IN SEED PLANTS

Developments which could perhaps be regarded as having something in common with the very different manifestations of growth in the fern life history, and which are also reminiscent of the variable growth

effects obtained in tissue cultures, have recently been described by
Waris (1957, 1959, 1962) and Miettinen and Waris (1958) in species of

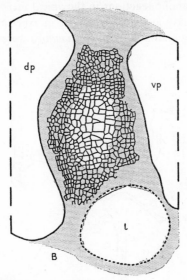

Fig.14.7 F

Fig.14.7 A–D, *Selaginella Martensii.* A, Decapitated, chemically-
untreated length of shoot: a shoot (sh) has developed from one of the
angle meristems; B, Decapitated length of shoot, treated with indoleacetic acid in lanoline paste: a rhizophore (Rh) giving rise to a
root (R) has developed from the angle meristem; C, *S. Lobbii,* decapitated but untreated, has given rise to a shoot; D, *S. Lobbii,* decapitated
and treated with indoleacetic acid, has given rise to a rhizophore
(× 1½). (After S. Williams, *Nature,* 1937.)

E, F, *Selaginella Willdenovii.*

E, Vertical section through a dormant ventral angle meristem. Apex
and stelar tissue unstippled; on either side of the meristem are raised
areas – the dorsal and ventral rims; *mx,* metaxylem; coarse stippling,
lacunae (× 150.)

F, Surface view of young ventral angle-shoot; *dp, vp,* cut bases of
dorsal and ventral prophylls; *l,* primordium of first lateral leaf; apical
meristem, unstippled (× 150). (After F. Cusick, *Annals of Botany,*
1954.)

Oenanthe (Umbelliferae). Waris (1957) entertained the idea that, since
aminoacids are essential constituents of proteins, morphogenetic
changes might be expected to occur when the normal balance of protein

M*

synthesis was intentionally upset by an excess of a particular aminoacid. In other words, it might be possible to interfere in some characteristic way with metabolic reactions in the apical meristem.

Aquatic plants have evident advantages in experiments of this kind.
Accordingly, young plants of *Oenanthe aquatica* were grown aseptically

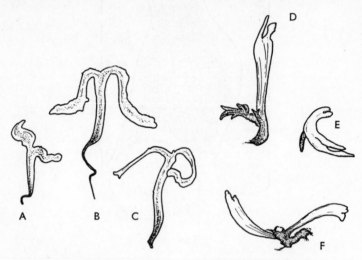

Fig.14.8 *Oenanthe aquatica*. Neomorphs induced by aminoacids in
culture media.

A, B, C, Seedling-like neomorphs (× 3) formed from plants grown in a
medium containing 0·4 per cent glycine.

D, E, Neomorphs obtained in a medium containing 0·01 per cent
glycine.

F, A broad-leaved neomorph grown in a medium containing 0·00063 M
of arginine nitrate. (After H. Waris, *Physiol. Plantarum*, 1959.)

from seed in a basic nutrient medium containing in addition 10 g sucrose
and 1–4 g glycine per litre. At first the plantlings were of normal
appearance but within three to four months they ceased to grow and
were seemingly moribund. However, some time later, a number of
fresh green plants of a *Vallisneria*-like appearance developed in the
culture flasks and grew vigorously. These plantlings were so different,
and of such reduced differentiation, that they would not have been
recognized as belonging to *O. aquatica*. It was ascertained that the new
type of plant, or 'neomorph', had originated from small bodies, or
nodules, constricted and detached from lateral root tips of the original

morbid plant. These nodules showed polarity with evidence of distinct shoot and root poles. At some concentrations of glycine, thalloid structures were formed. The further reproduction of the neomorphs took place from cell groups which were spontaneously detached from colourless, epidermal outgrowths of the green leaves. These cell groups gave rise to colourless embryo-like structures which subsequently became green and developed a configuration like a normal seedling, though sometimes more than two 'cotyledons' were present. On further development, narrow leaves, a few millimetres wide and a few centimetres long appeared, but the final size of the individuals was only a few centimetres. A feature of the neomorphs was their ability to grow submerged. When these neomorphs were transferred to nutrient solutions containing sucrose but no glycine, the new conformation was maintained for several months, there being some evidence of growth promotion, especially in the roots (which was poor in the presence of glycine). However, after about four months normal leaves began to be formed in some plants; but transfer to inorganic solutions was unsuccessful (Fig.14.8).

Waris has tentatively interpreted these results as evidence of physiological adaptation of this species to glycine, but without involving any irreversible change in the genotype. But however the results may be understood, it is apparent that significant metabolic changes in embryonic tissues must have taken place. This was borne out in biochemical investigations by Miettinen and Waris (1958) in which they found that the neomorphs contained much larger quantities of free aminoacids than normal plants. Similar changes were subsequently induced with aminoacids in *Oenanthe lachenalii* and *Daucus carota* (Waris, 1959, 1962). Waris also reported that the transition of neomorphs to normal growth was considerably accelerated by ribose, although this sugar inhibits growth in size.

Morphogenetic effects of aminoacids had previously been demonstrated in both higher and lower plants, e.g. by Virtanen and Linkola (1946, 1957). They found that pea plants show increased branching, reduced leaves and tufty roots, if nitrogen is supplied in excess as certain aminoacids and amines which are tolerated only at low concentrations. The 'frenching' of tobacco also seems to belong to this category of neomorphs (Steinberg 1947, 1949, 1952; Steinberg, Bowling and McMurtrey 1950). In this disease the symptoms include inhibition of stem elongation and a profuse development of narrow, even strap-shaped, leaves. These curious developments are accompanied by an accumulation of aminoacids in the leaves. They can also be induced by aminoacids in aseptic culture.

Waris's comment on his observations may well be cited, having in mind the comparisons with phenomena in ferns to which the present writer has already referred.

In the above-mentioned examples of pea and tobacco the morphogenetic effects of aminoacids do not exceed the range within which the characters of the species or of the genus are still recognizable, while in the present case (i.e. in *Oenanthe*), termed neomorphosis, the effects are so profound that even the family characters are hardly recognizable. Moreover, in the former case it is the organs of the original seedlings which appear modified, while in the present case the original seedlings undergo a long period of morbidity after which a new pattern of development initiates from the growing points. From these, embryonic units become detached and multiply and may reach a differentiation level comparable to cotyledon-stage seedlings but adapted to submerged growth, all development stages being able to form new embryonic units from their outgrowths. Thus neomorphosis implies a cycle of development which is restricted to a more or less embryonic stage.

In this connexion it is of interest that Steward and his collaborators succeeded in deriving embryonic stages direct from vegetative cells which were disassociated from carrot roots by a very promising method (Steward and Pollard, 1957, 1958; Steward, Mapes and Smith, 1958). The embryonic stages could be reared to mature plants, but the cultures could also be continued at a cellular level. It may be pointed out that coconut milk was added to the nutrient medium, and that considerable amounts of hydroxyproline were found in the tissue cultures of carrot and potato. As the authors say (Steward and Pollard, 1958), the question arises how far the events of embryology in the ovule are determined by nutrition and how far they presuppose fertilization.

All the above-mentioned data are compatible with the view that aminoacids are closely concerned with differentiation. The morphogenetic effectiveness of aminoacids has proved so strong that it can well be compared with hormonal action; this Steinberg (1947, p. 88) has done, focusing attention on the rôle of the ordinary metabolic products in growth correlations. *Evidently differentiation depends on changes in equilibria between the many substances involved in metabolism.** Illustrative examples of the equilibria between growth substances have been cited by Skoog and Miller (1957). In the present case the morphogenetic significance of the equilibria between the major intermediary metabolites becomes more pronounced.

In these equilibria a competitive interaction seems to play an important rôle. This appears as a physiological antagonism between various aminoacids, between various sugars, and between these two groups of substances. The antagonism between various sugars has recently been dealt with in detail by Stenlid (1959). In the present work it is represented by the morphogenetic antagonism between ribose and sucrose, ribose promoting the transition of the neomorphs to normal growth, in particular when a small proportion of the total sugars was present as sucrose. In spite of inhibiting growth in size, ribose thus promoted differentiation, which shows that growth in size and differentiation do not necessarily run parallel. The antagonism between amino-acids and sugars appeared from the fact that, in the absence of sucrose, glycine proved much more toxic to the seedlings of *Oenanthe aquatica*.

Since the equilibria between intermediary metabolites have a morphogenetic significance it may reasonably be assumed that their antagonism is displayed at definite sites in the cellular structure. These sites may well reside in the cellular organelles, nucleus, plastids, mitochondria and microsomes. A tentative interpretation of the morphogenetic antagonism between aminoacids and sugars can be based on the theory that nucleic acids are concerned with protein synthesis which, in turn, affects, and is affected by, carbohydrate synthesis. It may be remembered that in the neomorphs both kinds of syntheses seem to be affected (Miettinen and Waris, 1958). The present results with ribose could be taken to mean that syntheses involving ribonucleic acid-containing bodies are concerned. This focuses attention on the mitochondria and microsomes. In this connexion it is interesting that Bonner has recently attributed a particular significance to the microsomes, for he suggests that *differentiation may consist merely in enrichment or impoverishment of the cell in particular kinds of microsomes, which differ in their ribonucleic acids and synthesizing power*;* the microsomes, in turn, are supposed to receive their ribonucleic acids and proteins from the nucleus. In the case of mitochondria, it has been shown that they are subject to changes in number and in content of ribonucleic acids during metabolism and development (Lindblad, 1959).

The present work offers some evidence for the hypothesis that various organs are differently affected by aminoacids. Thus in *Oenanthe aquatica* there appears a difference in the nutritional requirements between hypocotyl and epicotyl, and between cotyledons and foliage leaves. On the other hand, the meristems exhibit a surprising degree of plasticity.

In further studies, Waris (1962) showed that *Oenanthe lachenalii* yielded irreversible neomorphs, morphologically rather different from those already described for *O. aquatica*, in media in which 4-leucine was present at a critical concentration (about 0·01 M). In this species the callus-like nodules were abstricted from shoot apices. These neomorphs retained their characteristic features when transferred to normal nutrient solutions. Also, they appear to have lost their capacity for root formation. Cytological studies showed that an (unspecified) increase in chromosome number had been induced. Reversible neomorphs were again obtained in media in which glycine was present in excess.

THE VEGETATIVE APEX

Although analytical chemical studies are now beginning to yield information about the aminoacids, carbohydrates, hormonal substances, etc., which are present in the vegetative apices of ferns and angiosperms, we do not yet know how these and other substances, moving upwards into the apex, or produced there, enter into reactions which eventually lead to the inception of growth centres, organ formation,

* My italics, C. W. W.

tissue differentiation and the eventual manifestation of integrated development. Nor is much yet known about the more specific genetically-determined substances in the reaction system in the apical meristem. However, by increasing or restricting the supply of general metabolites to the apical meristem, or by inhibiting or promoting the activity of any of the special components of the apical reaction system, e.g. enzymes, hormonal substances, antagonists, etc., changes may be effected in the concomitant manifestations of organization. Thus, by direct applications of various physiologically-active substances to the large apices of *Dryopteris dilatata*, for example, substances which are known to affect enzymic activity, characteristic disorganizations of the apical meristem were induced (Wardlaw, 1957); and Wardlaw and Mitra (1958) showed that the direct application of kinetin to the apical meristem resulted in the disappearance of the youngest primordia and failure of new primordia to be formed (Figs. 9.3–9.5 and Plate 8).

ASEPTIC CULTURE OF APICES

In studies of excised fern apices in culture, it has been shown that by modifying the composition of the medium, either in respect of its main nutrients or of its content of vitamins, growth regulators, etc., the rate of growth and the size and complexity of the shoot, its lateral members and tissue pattern can be modified, sometimes over a very considerable range (Allsopp, 1952, 1953, 1954, 1955, 1956, 1964; Wetmore, 1953, 1954, 1956, 1959; Wetmore and Morel, 1949; Wetmore and Wardlaw, 1951). But, thus far, in the several cultural studies, the basic morphogenetic pattern at the shoot apex has remained essentially unchanged: the size of the apex and the organ and tissue patterns to which it gives rise, may be contracted or expanded, according to the nutrients and growth conditions provided, but the basic specific pattern undergoes no radical modification. The results obtained by culturing leaf primordia have been discussed on p. 231 (*see* Plate 15).

ORGAN FORMATION IN TISSUE CULTURE

In tissue culture investigations, as distinct from organ culture, some points relevant to the theme of organization are beginning to emerge. Skoog (1950, 1954) reviewed the accumulating evidence on the importance of the nucleic acids in the regulation of growth and demonstrated that, in some tissue cultures, bud formation may be promoted by, and is ultimately dependent on the presence of, adenine: he suggested that, in the intact plant, the auxin produced in the terminal bud may exert an inhibiting effect on the ability of the embryonic cells of a bud rudiment to produce desoxypentose nucleic acid and to undergo mitosis and cell division. Indeed, the experiments of Skoog and his co-workers on the effects of adenine, IAA and kinetin on the formation of buds and roots have, with some reservations, opened up new vistas in the study of organogenesis.

Adenine and IAA in Organization. In 1948 Skoog and Tsui successfully demonstrated the action of adenine in bud formation. When callus and stem internode segments of tobacco were grown in White's nutrient medium, with and without the addition of adenine, adenosine and 1-naphthaleneacetic acid (NAA), buds were formed in the presence of adenine; but NAA, whilst stimulating callus growth and root formation, inhibited bud formation. Additional phosphate (KH_2PO_4) and sucrose in the basic medium increased bud formation and to some extent counteracted the inhibitory effect of NAA. These results afford evidence of the 'organizing' effect of chemical substances in some tissue cultures.

In further investigations of tobacco callus and stem tissue in culture, Skoog and Tsui (1951), Miller and Skoog (1953), Skoog (1954), and Skoog and Miller (1957), confirmed that the type of growth and organ formation obtained, stand in a close relationship to the existence of a delicate *quantitative* balance between IAA, adenine and other factors. Thus spontaneous bud formation on stem segments was inhibited by the addition of 5 mg/l IAA to the culture medium, but was restored if 40 mg/l adenine was also present (15,000 molecules of adenine are apparently required to offset the effect of 1 molecule of IAA). Both of these substances seem to be essential for the several types of growth tested, including cell elongation. Their interaction is not considered to be one of competitive inhibition.

Kinetin in Organization. Jablonski and Skoog (1954) reported the important observation that excised tobacco pith tissue responds differently to IAA according to whether vascular tissue is present or not. In its absence, only some cell enlargement takes place; but, in its presence, cell division and, later, root formation occur. So it was inferred that a 'morphogenetic substance' was present in vascular tissue. This led to the discovery and synthesis of 6-furfurylaminopurine, or *kinetin* (Miller *et al.*, 1956; Strong, 1958, pp. 98–157; Skoog and Miller, 1957). Various adenine derivatives exhibit similar activities. Both IAA and kinetin must be present in excised tobacco pith for the continuous active synthesis of DNA, mitosis and cell division (Patau et al., 1957). According to Skoog and Miller (1957), the organizing effects of the two substances together are numerous and subject to modification by various factors and conditions.

Kinetin-auxin Interaction in Organogenesis. Kinetin is important in bud formation in tobacco callus and stem segments, its action being particularly affected, among other factors, by the concentration of auxin in the culture medium (Skoog and Miller, 1957). For example, on a modified White's medium, with IAA maintained at 2·0 mg/l, the control cultures chiefly showed cell enlargement and formed a few short roots. But with added kinetin, at 0·02 mg/l, abundant root formation took place. At 0·2 mg/l, undifferentiated callus growth was mainly effected. At 0·5 and 1·0 mg/l there was bud formation but not root formation. In other experiments, the interaction of kinetin and IAA at certain concentrations resulted in abundant bud formation, this formative process being repressed at higher concentrations of IAA. High IAA promoted root development, its inhibiting effect on root elongation being counteracted by the presence of kinetin; and, at the higher concentrations of kinetin, bud development was increased, the inhibitory action of IAA being counteracted. These remarkable results indicate that particular organizing effects can be associated with the interaction of certain substances in embryonic tissues.

Casein hydrolysate in the medium stimulated growth and bud formation but only when kinetin and IAA were present. Tyrosine was regarded by Skoog and Miller as the ingredient of casein hydrolysate which is most effective in promoting bud development. These and other observations led these workers to the important conclusion that 'no sharp distinction except in a quantitative sense can be made between growth-factor requirements for buds and roots'.

Organizing Effects of Kinetin-adenine Combinations, etc. Conspicuous growth and organ formation, including buds, were obtained when adenine and kinetin were present together in tissue culture media. It was noted that different tissue cultures, derived originally from the same parent stock, may show different responses to growth-regulating substances in the medium. Some strains of Turkish tobacco (*Nicotiana tabacum*) studied by K. Tryon (cited by Skoog and Miller, 1957), yielded undifferentiated tissue masses whereas others formed buds; and yet others showed abundant root formation. By the addition of suitable quantities of IAA and kinetin, under conditions of favourable phosphorus and nitrogen supply, both bud and root formation could be repressed at will. A 'non-differentiating' strain formed buds when the medium contained suitable combinations of kinetin, adenine and tyrosine; but with either of the latter two substances alone, buds were not formed, indicating that in organ formation, i.e. in organizing processes, there is a multiple growth-factor requirement in the reaction system.

Various other investigators have also examined the effects of adenine, kinetin and other substances on bud and root formation in different plant organs and tissues. Kinetin restored bud formation in excised *Isatis tinctoria* roots which had lost such capacity in the course of several subcultures (Danckwardt-Lillieström, 1957) and promoted this process in excised roots of *Convolvulus arvensis* (Torrey, 1958). Schraudolf and Reinert (1959) found that, in leaf discs of *Begonia*, kinetin did not increase bud formation but abolished the polarity of this process; and buds and roots, which are usually formed at the distal ends of veins in this species, were induced at any point on the surface of treated discs. In the same material, Wirth (1959) observed that adenine promoted bud formation and reduced root formation, while auxins (IAA, naphthaleneacetic acid, 2·4-dichlorophenoxyacetic acid) had the opposite effect.

In a comprehensive study, Paulet and Nitsch (1959) used leaf discs of *Cardamine pratensis* which did not include the preformed, undifferentiated meristems which are known to be present in certain regions. They found that bud formation was promoted by a whole series of compounds, including gibberellin. All the other substances tested were known to be associated with nucleic acid metabolism, e.g. purine and pyrimidine bases (adenine, guanine, cytosine, thymine), certain precursors (orotic acid, glycine, ammonium compounds), nucleic acid derivatives or analogues (kinetin and 6-succinylaminopurine) and substances involved in nucleic acid biosynthesis (nicotinic acid, folic acid). Even close analogues with no such relationship (alanine and other aminoacids) were altogether inactive.

From observations of the kind briefly indicated above Skoog and Miller reached the important conclusion *that growth regulation and organogenesis are dependent on the quantitative interactions rather than on the qualitative actions of growth factors.* In other words, they rejected the concept of *specific morphogenetic substances* advanced by workers like Bouillenne (1950) and Gautheret (1950). In their view, both auxin and kinetin are probably involved in nucleic acid metabolism and there may be 'an essentially nuclear mechanism of growth regulation which possesses recognized means for interaction with the cytoplasm and which is also considered to be represented rather directly in the synthesis of large molecular structural units of the cell wall'. The importance of nucleic acid metabolism in bud formation is borne out by the results of Paulet and Nitsch.

The importance of the discoveries outlined above and their relevance to the topic of organization need no emphasis. To the author, at least, it seems evident that, however much we may discover about the particular substances that are required in organ formation, we have yet to discover why an embryonic tissue, under one set of conditions, assumes the characteristic configuration and structure of a bud while, under another set, it assumes those of a root. The observations submitted both support the concept of reaction systems and show the need for it. Also, it is salutary to recall that the morphogenetic developments are only obtained in some materials; i.e. there is an important specific genetical aspect.

Skoog and Miller's principal thesis is that organogenesis is primarily determined by quantitative interactions, i.e. by the ratios rather than the absolute amounts of growth substances. However, this does not seem to hold in all cases. Mayer (1956) and Stichel (1959), for example, found that additions of adenine or guanine affected the number of organs regenerated by *Cyclamen* tuber tissue but that the type of the organs (buds or roots) was exclusively determined by the auxin (naphthaleneacetic acid) concentration of the medium, quite regardless of the presence and quantity of the other materials, i.e. of the adenine (or guanine)/auxin ratio.

In discussing the importance of such metabolic substances as adenine, kinetin, auxin and phosphates in bud formation in the leaf axil, Audus (1959b) indicated a possible mechanism both for bud inception and positioning. He suggested that leaf primordia might supply one metabolic component, the apical meristem another, and the developing axis perhaps yet a third. From these sources an intricate pattern of gradients might be set up yielding the proper balance of the necessary factors for bud initiation in the leaf primordium axil.

THE TRANSITION TO FLOWERING

According to the stage reached in ontogenesis and its nutritional status, the vegetative shoot apex gives rise to a more or less elaborate pattern of leaf primordia, but one which is essentially of the same kind throughout. In the vegetative phase, therefore, we might regard the supplies to the apical reaction system as only changing *quantitatively*.

In the development of an angiosperm, however, a stage in development is reached when the vegetative apex undergoes radical changes: it becomes a floral apex and gives rise to new patterns of organs, e.g. the groups of sepals, petals, stamens and carpels. When this transformation takes place it may reasonably be assumed that the supplies of nutrients, or of some special metabolic substance(s) to, or in, the apex, have changed *qualitatively* and perhaps also quantitatively; i.e. new and important substances are introduced into the reaction system. Notable changes in the patternized distribution of metabolites now follow: the reaction system undergoes well-defined, critical but interrelated changes (*see* Chapter 11); and further manifestations of specific organization become apparent.

The transition to flowering is, accordingly, a phase which lends itself to experimental modifications of the normal working of the apical reaction system. Some relevant evidence has already been given in Chapter 11. This may now be supplemented by further examples.

Substances are known which, if not actually 'florigenic' in any strict sense, nevertheless promote the onset of flowering; e.g. gibberellic acid, if applied to many plants which are still in the vegetative phase, typically advances the onset of flowering and may even be a flower-inducing agent (*see* below p. 359).

Effects of TIBA. It is known that 2,3,5-triiodobenzoic acid, (TIBA), whatever its basic biochemical action may be, can induce far-reaching changes in the shoot apices of certain dicotyledons. Thus, Zimmerman and Hitchcock (1942, 1949, 1951) reported that when TIBA and related synthetic substances were applied to tomato plants still in the vegetative condition, flower buds were induced, i.e. apparently by the transformation of what would normally have been vegetative buds. They pointed out, however, that 'since the tomato is photoperiodically indeterminate, it is not clear whether TIBA acts to initiate floral primordia or merely to accentuate the development of already differentiated flower buds'. They also found that 2-chloro-3,5-diiodobenzoic acid was very active and resembled TIBA in its effects. Galston (1947) concluded from an investigation, in which short-day varieties of soya-bean were used, that 2,3,5-triiodobenzoic acid does not possess florigenic properties, i.e. it does not bring about the transformation of vegetative apices into floral ones: it does, however, greatly increase the flowering response to the photoperiodic treatment. A point that emerged from Galston's investigations, as also from those of Reece, Furr and Cooper (1946) on the mango, is that the transformation of the vegetative apex is associated with low concentrations of auxin. Thus, some of the histological and other changes in the vegetative apex, which are of special interest in morphogenesis, are apparently associated with low auxin concentrations, though other metabolites are also likely to be affected. Various possible explanations of the biochemical action of TIBA have been indicated (Skoog, Schneider and Malan, 1942; Galston, 1947; Thimann and Bonner, 1948; de Waard and Florschütz, 1948). The last authors, for example, suggested that both indoleacetic acid and TIBA combine irreversibly with other metabolites within the cell. If they act competitively, the antagonistic effect of TIBA on auxin would be explained.

Perhaps the most interesting effects of TIBA on apices, from the standpoint of organization and morphogenesis, are those described by de Waard and Roodenburg (1948) and by Gorter (1949, 1951). The former authors found that when newly germinated tomato seedlings, or even still ungerminated seeds, were treated with TIBA, flower buds were induced prematurely: two or three small leaves were first formed and then the terminal stem appeared. Some very curious developments then followed. Instead of forming leaf primordia, the growing point of the shoot became convex, and was elevated on a stalk-like structure by the rapid elongation of the shoot immediately below it. By the repeated division of the elevated meristem a cluster of crowded partially-formed flower buds resulted. Stalked apices, also eventually producing flower buds, were likewise obtained from axillary buds which would normally have grown into vegetative side shoots. Some of the stalk-like structures bore a few small leaves, e.g. six, before the inception of the flower buds. Thus, as a result of treatment with TIBA, de Waard and Roodenburg observed (i) a change in the shape of the vegetative apex, (ii) the suppression of leaf formation and growth, (iii) a marked subapical elongation, yielding a stalk-like structure, and (iv) the premature induction of flower buds, though not of normal flowering.

Gorter (1949) has provided excellent illustrations of vegetative apices as modified by applications of TIBA (Plate 24). Both in the main shoot and axillary buds, the normal rounded growing point becomes flattened; it no longer forms lateral members, but undergoes growth in the subapical region, and is seen as a leafless, truncated-cone-like object. These cones grow into long stalks bearing flower buds and occasional small leaves as already described. Gorter (1951) also found that ring-fasciations – a phenomenon relatively rare in Nature – were sometimes induced by TIBA applications. These ring-fasciations which result from the growth of a ring-like, distal meristem, have a hollow stem and an internal epidermis. Occasional, irregularly disposed leaves and bracts are formed on the outside of the stem and within the cavity, with axillary buds in the latter; the orientation of these foliar members is towards the apical ring. The upper regions of the tube usually separate into band-shaped fasciated segments. In these ring-fasciated stems a double vascular ring is differentiated, the outer and inner ring having a normal orientation towards the outer and inner surfaces respectively. The inner stem surface is characteristically thrown into folds. A small, compact, but otherwise normal shoot is usually present at the base of the tube (Plate 24).

According to Gorter, the first activity of TIBA is to modify the cells at the summit of the apex. These cells undergo a thickening of their walls and lose their regular arrangement, the normal two-layered tunica being transformed into an 'epidermis dividing anticlinally', and the underlying cells also showing irregularity in their divisions. During its further development, this modified growing point (described as being of a peculiar pale-green colour) becomes broader and, depending on the concentration of the TIBA and environmental factors, it may develop into one single flower, or into a hollow stem with a distal, ring-like, active meristem. After some elongation of this stem has taken place, buds (mostly flower buds) may be formed on the inner and the outer flanks of the ring-like meristem. A ring-fasciated inflorescence with many flowers is thus formed.

Effects induced by Gibberellic Acid. A copious and expanding literature deals with the effects of gibberellic acid (GA) on flowering (*see* A. Lang, 1957; Lang *et al.*, 1957; Lang and Reinhard, 1961; Michniewicz and A. Lang, 1962, where bibliography is cited; Zeevaart and A. Lang, 1962, etc.). Thus, in a review, Lang and Reinhard (1961) have indicated that in some, though not in all, species which have received GA applications, the onset of flowering may be more or less notably promoted and, in some instances, may even be induced. The latter claim is, however, still tentative though, as Lang and Reinhard have emphasized, 'the gibberellins are the first class of compounds which cause flower formation in numerous plants grown under strictly non-inductive temperature or light regimes, this effect, in any given species, being consistent and reproducible'. However, these authors also noted that, not only is the biochemistry of the flowering process still obscure – although there is considerable information on various other physio-logical aspects – but that 'the precise function of gibberellin in flower formation is by no means clear and may be indirect in nature.' Evidence and inference of this kind seem to the writer to support his contention that 'morphogenetic substances', however important they may be in some organizational process, must exercise their effects as components of a reaction system in an embryonic region. Moreover, as we have seen, if certain effects are to be induced, the inducing substance must be a compatible component of the reaction system. In this connection it may be noted that not all of the several gibberellins that have now been tested experimentally promote or induce flower formation. Michniewicz and Lang (1962) examined the effects of GA_1 to GA_9 on stem elongation and flower formation in five species of flowering plants.

The plants were *Myosotis alpestris* and a biennial strain of *Centaurium minus* (cold-requiring plants), *Silene armeria* and *Crepis parviflora* (long-day plants), and *Bryophyllum crenatum* (a long-short-day plant). The two former plants were maintained on non-inductive temperatures and long days, the three latter on short days. In *Myosotis*, flower formation was only obtained with GA_7 and GA_1, the latter being relatively less active. In *Centaurium*, GA_3 was the most effective, followed by GA_1, GA_4 and GA_7 and perhaps GA_5 and GA_9. In *Silene*, flower formations were induced only by GA_7. In *Crepis*, the most effective gibberellins were GA_4 and GA_7, in *Bryophyllum*, GA_3, GA_4 and GA_7. Thus, the different gibberellins exhibited considerable differences in their activity with respect to flower induction, and different plants exhibited in this respect certain specific differences in their sensitivity to the various gibberellins. Except in *Crepis*, flower initiation as a result of gibberellin treatment was always preceded by substantial stem or internode elongation; however, the correlation between the effect of the different gibberellins on stem elongation and flower induction was not in all cases complete. No correlation of the flower-inducing and elongation-promoting activity with the chemical structure of the different gibberellins could be recognized.

Lona (1962), in emphasizing the importance of GA in organizational processes – he refers to some developments in terms of 'G-morphosis' – pointed out that the physiological activities of this group of substances occupy an important position, linking genetical and ecological aspects of plant phenology (defined as the study of the times of recurring natural phenomena). As this and other investigators have noted, GA, or GA-like manifestations may occur at different points in ontogenesis, e.g. seed germination, hypocotyl elongation, bud sprouting, the grand period of growth, sustained growth in climbing and twining plants, stem and peduncle elongation and the inception of flowering. There are also some notable exceptions in which the gibberellins appear to be absent, or almost completely so; e.g. in truly dwarf plants. From comprehensive studies, Lona reached conclusions which are of considerable importance in the present context. To begin with, it is interesting to note that one of his basic concepts is that 'each species or variety has its own peculiar biochemical development (parallel to the organographic one), nothing but similarities existing among the various entities. The G-morphoses caused by the predominance of activity of a stimulant (such) as gibberellin, are distributed in the ontogenetical cycle in different ways, according to the peculiarity of the entity. There are frequently some G-morphoses correlated with flowering and neighbouring phenomena, in different degrees (Fig.14.9). To quote Lona:

> We selected cases in which the G-morphosis is distinctly preceding and other cases in which it is clearly subsequent to flower primordia formation. We supposed that the first case (vegetative bolting) is very congruous for G-application (on rosette plants) in order to obtain flowering, because of the accordance with the natural biochemical sequence. In fact we were able to see this in a horticultural variety of *Cichorium intybus*, which is a biennial requiring vernalization to bolt and then to initiate flowering morphological processes. GA substitutes completely for cold requirement – in this case – producing vegetative bolting followed by flowering.
>
> The congruousness here demonstrated may lead (us) immediately to conclude that GA (or a substitutive gibberellin) is the flowering substance in *Cichorium*, or that in *Cichorium* the real flowering substance derives from a biochemical evolution of GA.
>
> On the other hand GA is not capable of inducing flower primordia formation in plants in which natural G-morphosis is intervening long after flower bud formation or does not intervene at all. In these plants, GA may – however – be a stimulant for another phase of flowering. This was demonstrated in a widespread group of alpine and montane perennial species (*Saxifraga* spp., *Draba aizoides*, *Androsace carnea*, *Primula* spp., etc.). The vegetative branches of these plants, treated with GA during August-September-October, elongated and produced many leaves; sometimes they produced new branches, but no flower buds were formed.
>
> A first conclusion was achieved: GA florigenic activity (flower primordia formation) is easily detectable in plants in which it naturally takes place in the biochemical ontogenetical sequence just before and during flower primordia formation, but not in plants in which gibberellins do not apparently intervene at all or intervene after flower bud formation. Indeed in the first type of plants (such as *Cichorium*) G-morphosis takes place before the real flower primordia formation, while in the second type (many perennials above mentioned such as *Saxifraga* spp., *Primula*, *Draba*, *Douglasia*, *Silene*, *Alsine*, etc.) there is a G-like morphosis – if any – long after flower buds or flower formation.

Lona's scheme of GA action at different stages in the ontogenetic development of different species is illustrated in Fig.14.9. The effects are evidently very varied and need not be discussed in detail here. But in each instance where the GA has a significant morphogenetic effect, Lona sees it as a 'congruous' component of the reacting metabolic substances in a growing or formative region.

DNA and RNA in Flower Inception. As indicated in Chapter 11, the onset of flowering is characterized by changes in the organogenic pattern produced by the shoot apical reaction system and by a close sequence of specific genic activities. Accordingly, it is a reasonable expectation that the synthesis of DNA and RNA may be of critical

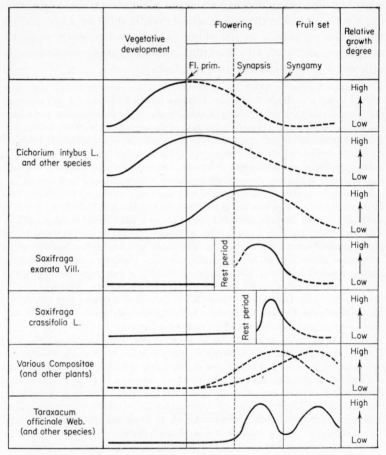

Fig.14.9 Gibberellic acid effects. Schematic representation of shoot or flower-peduncle elongation, correlated with GA–phases during the ontogenesis of different species. (After F. Lona, in *Eigenschaften und Wirkungen der Gibberelline*, 1960.)

importance at this stage in ontogenesis. This, in fact, has been appreciated by various investigators, a typical experimental approach being to examine to what extent the induction of flowering by appropriate photoperiodic exposures can be arrested or modified by applications of substances known to interfere with nucleic acid synthesis. Thus Salisbury and Bonner (1958, 1960) showed that photoperiodic induction of the cocklebur (*Xanthium pennsylvanicum*) is inhibited by applications of the pyrimidine 5-fluorouracil (5-FU), to the plant; this inhibitor being most effective if applied directly to the bud at the beginning of the inductive dark period. The evidence obtained indicates that the 5-FU interferes with metabolic processes basic to flowering which normally take place in the apex during the inductive dark period. In a further study, Bonner and Zeevaart (1962) showed that the critical process which is affected by 5-FU is the synthesis of RNA in the apical bud. They were able to demonstrate that C^{14}-labelled 5-FU is incorporated into bud RNA, the extent of this process being reduced by simultaneous applications of orotic acid. The synthesis of DNA is also inhibited by 5-FU, but it is the inhibition of RNA synthesis which is of critical importance in offsetting the photoperiodic induction of flowering. Bonner and Zeevaart have also ascertained that 5-fluorodeoxyuridine (5-FDU), a specific inhibitor of DNA multiplication, inhibits the development of floral primordia. But if thymidine is also applied, even at the end of the photoinductive period, the 5-FDU effect can be reversed. Heslop-Harrison (1960), working with *Cannabis sativa*, observed that the pyrimidine 2-thiouracil inhibits flowering, apparently by causing the apices to become unresponsive to the floral stimulus proceeding from the leaves; and Moore and Bonde (1962) have reported that 2-thiouracil inhibits flowering in peas (*Pisum sativum*).

REVERSIBLE CHANGES IN THE REACTION SYSTEM

The effects of 'disbudding', if not of defoliation, of plants approaching the onset of flowering, have long been known to horticulturists; i.e. the plant tends to remain in the vegetative phase for a longer period, indicating some critical change, or absence of change, in the constitution of the apical reaction system. More recently this topic has begun to receive attention from physiologists and others interested in the problems of floral inception and morphogenesis. Lam and Leopold (1960, 1961) have described disbudding experiments using *Xanthium* and *Perilla* (in both of which species the photoperiodic needs for flower induction are now well known), which resulted in a return to the vegetative phase. In *Xanthium* they found that if plants have received an insufficient number of the appropriate inductive cycles, they will return to the vegetative state without further treatment (Lam and Leopold, 1960). In *Perilla crispa*, a short-day species, Lam and Leopold (1961) observed an eventual return to the vegetative state in plants in which appropriate photoperiodic exposures had not been maintained for a sufficient number (about 20) of cycles of short photoperiods. But in plants which had had 35 cycles, reversion to the vegetative state was markedly affected by disbudding. However, such reverted plants could then be re-induced twice by subjecting the originally induced leaves to appropriate photoperiodic treatment. In timing experiments, in which the aim was to measure 'the flow of flower stimulus' from treated leaves to potential floral meristems, the evidence tentatively indicated a gradual loss of the stimulus. The basis for these observations was in the increased time required for flower formation and the decreased number of flowers. Lam and Leopold concluded that, when the inductive treatment is withdrawn, the effectiveness of the stimulus to flowering, coming from treated leaves, declines with time; and where reversion to the vegetative state is observed, there has been a decline in the stimulus proceeding from the induced leaves. Such observations lend themselves to interpretation in terms of reaction system theory.

In somewhat similar experiments the writer (Wardlaw, 1963) observed that, in *Petasites hybridus* (Compositae), if early transition apices have their bracts removed, or are otherwise injured, they return to the vegetative state. In this species, with experience, early transition apices can readily be distinguished from vegetative apices. In the latter, very young leaf primordia occupy large sectors of the periphery of the apical meristem and, by tangential growth, soon encircle it entirely. With the onset of flowering, that is, during early transition, the apical meristem enlarges and the leaf primordia which originate near its periphery are conspicuously smaller both in relative and actual size and thus occupy progressively smaller sectors of the meristem. These primordia develop into the various small scale-like bracts of the compound inflorescence. In brief, there is a transition from the large, hirsute, clasping foliage leaves of the vegetative phase to the small, glabrous, non-laminate bracts of the reproductive phase (*see* Figs. 11.5–11.7 and Fig.14.10; and Plates 19–23).

In preliminary experiments with *P. hybridus* and other species of Compositae, it was found that if an early transition apex was bisected, it reverted to the vegetative state (Fig.14.10). This phenomenon was more fully explored in a considerable series of experiments (Wardlaw, 1963). Early transition apices begin to be available in Cheshire and Lancashire from about mid-June. From this time onwards, batches of suitable plants were collected at frequent intervals, potted in soil, defoliated and their apices laid bare. This was continued until late transition, when the primordia of numerous bracts and nascent capitula were present round the base of the now considerably enlarged apex. These batches of apices were consistently treated as follows: (1) the meristem was laid bare, all bracts and larger bract primordia round the apical meristem being excised (controls); (2) apices prepared as in (1) were either (a) bisected by a vertical incision, or (b) punctured at the centre, or (c) isolated

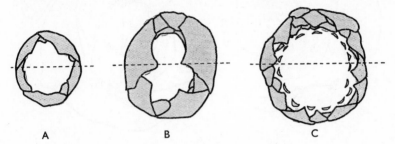

Fig.14.10 *Petasites hybridus*. Experimental treatments. When shoot apices at various stages of transition from the vegetative to the reproductive (or early inflorescence) state were subjected to different surgical treatments, such as (a) removal of all the basal bracts, (b) bisection, (c) puncturing at the centre and (d) isolation by four vertical incisions, they have usually grown on and all have shown the same characteristic responses. A, B, and C show apices, as seen from above, at different stages of transition. The broken line indicates the bisecting incision. The following results were obtained:
(1). A, early transition apices returned to the vegetative condition, with production of typical hairy foliage leaves. In the normal development these would have remained as very small glabrous bracts (*see* Fig.14.11 and Plates 20, 21).
(2). B, C, Successively older (or later) transition apices also showed a substantial development of large foliage leaves, then some small foliage leaves encasing an inflorescence of reduced size.

from adjacent subapical tissues by four vertical incisions. Each apex was borne on a substantial piece of rhizome and rapid growth was usually obtained. In all, nine series of apices, with 2–5 apices per treatment, were examined between June 30 (when apices were in early transition) and July 21 (when apices were in late transition) (*see* Figs. 14.10–14.12 and Plates 20–23).

Although the several treatments yielded many interesting morphogenetic observations, only one major result will be considered here. This was that, in all the treatments and in the several batches, there was

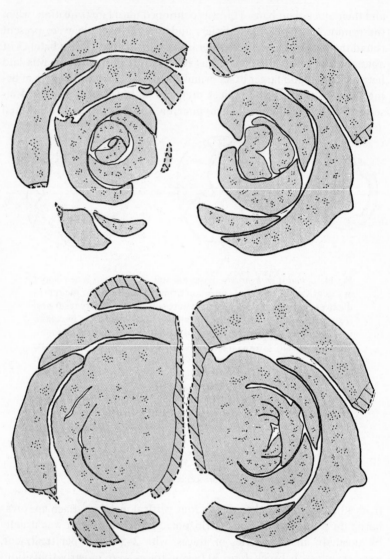

Fig.14.11 *Petasites hybridus.* Early and mid-transition apices which were defoliated and bisected returned to the vegetative state. The illustrations show a bisected transition apex at two levels: the foliar development is that of a normal vegetative apex.

an evident and conspicuous return to the vegetative condition. Primordia which would normally have become small glabrous bracts with simple venation, developed as hirsute, petiolate, normal laminate leaves up to 10 cm in width. Fig.14.11 shows the foliar development in the two shoots formed from a bisected middle transition apex after two months. In the earlier series all the apices also reverted completely to the vegetative state. In later transition apices, the outermost bract primordia also developed into conspicuous vegetative leaves as in Plates 20, 21, with vegetative buds in their axils; but in many specimens a small inflorescence, surrounded by typical small inflorescence bracts, was present. Plate 21 illustrates a cross-section of a bisected late transition apex with outer, encircling, foliage leaves, central capitula primordia and small bracts. In many specimens, including later transition apices which had been defoliated but not incised in any way, a fragmentation of the large apical meristem, with formation of a group of terminal vegetative buds or inflorescences, was observed (Fig.14.12 and Plate 23B).

These observations indicate important reversals of the normal development of the apical reaction system after the onset of flowering. Now, as we have seen, a considerable body of evidence indicates that gibberellins, when applied to the still vegetative shoots of many species, may promote, or perhaps even induce, the onset of flowering. It was therefore a matter of some interest to see if the experimentally induced return of transition apices to the vegetative phase, described here, could be prevented by applications of gibberellic acid. Accordingly, groups of early and of successively later transition apices were (a) defoliated, and (b) defoliated and bisected, as already described. Of these, some received no further treatment (controls), but others in each group were treated with 0·01 and 0·001 per cent gibberellic acid solution, applied directly to the exposed apex at the rate of one drop twice per week for about four weeks.

The control plants confirmed the findings of the previous experiments. In the plants treated wih gibberellic acid the following observations were recorded. (1) Some early transition apices formed large vegetative leaves only; others had leaves with conspicuously broad petioles and more or less well-developed inflorescences; these were evident externally as conspicuous swellings in the rosette of foliage leaf-bases, and were surrounded by large, broad, strap-like, glabrous scales. (2) Somewhat more advanced transition apices formed fewer vegetative leaves; glabrous, fleshy scale-leaves were conspicuous in many specimens and more or less well-developed, sometimes fasciated, inflorescences had been formed. (3) Late transition apices formed few or no foliage leaves; they showed sustained development of the inflorescence and elongation

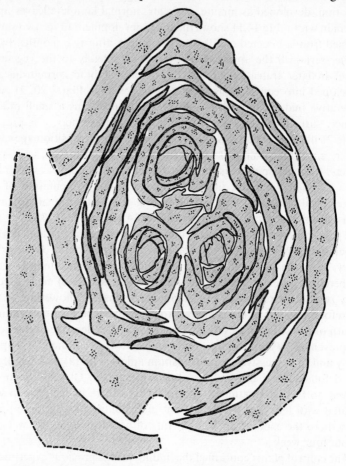

Fig.14.12 *Petasites hybridus.* A mid-transition apex which had been bisected. On further growth, the half-meristems have undergone fragmentation and have formed several vegetative apices; three are shown in this half-section. It can be seen that the leaf-bases are fleshy and of large size, partly encircling the axis. The profuse covering of cottony hairs has been omitted (*and see* Plates 21 and 23).

of the inflorescence axis (from 4 to 22 cm in different specimens), and flowering occurred precociously during September instead of the following spring. Plate 22A shows the record made on October 9, 1962, of a bisected late transition apex, treated with 0·01 per cent gibberellic acid. Vegetative apices of *P. hybridus* have consistently shown no response to GA applications.

However the effects of gibberellic acid on the induction and/or promotion of flowering may eventually be interpreted, these observations indicate that this substance has important regulative effects on the development of both foliar and floral organs of *Petasites hybridus* if it is applied during the transition from the vegetative to the reproductive phase. The effects are mediated through the functioning of the reaction system in the apical meristem.

Summary. The foregoing information supports the views (i) that a reaction system as here envisaged is present in vegetative and flowering shoot apical meristems; (ii) that it can be more or less radically modified, though still remaining actively functional, by the introduction of new reactants, i.e. metabolic ingredients, or by changing the balance or rate of utilization of the metabolic components; and (iii) that its organization is thereby modified, this becoming apparent in the concomitant morphological developments.

DIFFERENTIAL GROWTH

The importance, in organization, of the distribution of growth, especially in the subapical and maturing regions of the shoot, has already been discussed in some detail (Chapters 10 and 11). In different instances, genetical, nutritional and environmental factors may be of particular importance. Accordingly, those aspects of organization which result from differential growth can be explored by appropriate analytical and experimental techniques (*see* Wardlaw, 1963). On the fundamental problem of how differential growth is brought about we still have little information.

SUMMARY

A considerable body of evidence of an experimental character shows that when various metabolic substances are introduced into embryonic regions, they may modify the reaction system with concomitant changes in organization. Some substances may cause loss of organization, or active disorganization. The many teratologies and monstrosities in floral development, resulting from excessive manuring, the application of growth-regulating substances, herbicides, etc., afford further evidence of the same kind. Certain genetical changes, virus infections, and ionizing radiations may also have profound effects on the reaction system in apical meristems and on the resulting morphological developments. In practice, it is difficult to devise methods whereby the reaction system can be altered at will in some particular way. But that, in the writer's view, is largely due to the subtlety, complexity and stability of the system and the difficulty of introducing new substances into it. However, it is apparent that reaction systems, though stable, can be modified experimentally. They are, moreover, constantly being modified in Nature.

23. A, *Digitalis purpurea*. An enlarged view of the peloric terminal flower illustrated in Plate 22 C; the number of petals and stamens is greatly increased. (Photo by courtesy of Professor J. Walton.)

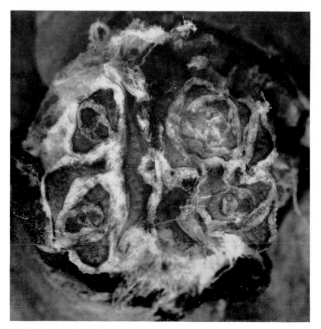

23. B, *Petasites hybridus*. A medium-transition apex which had been laid bare and punctured at the centre: the tensions set up during the ensuing growth have resulted in a disruption of the apical meristem, here seen in transverse section. Each of the pieces of meristem has regenerated and has given rise to a vegetative axis, bearing typical fleshy, hirsute, foliage leaves.

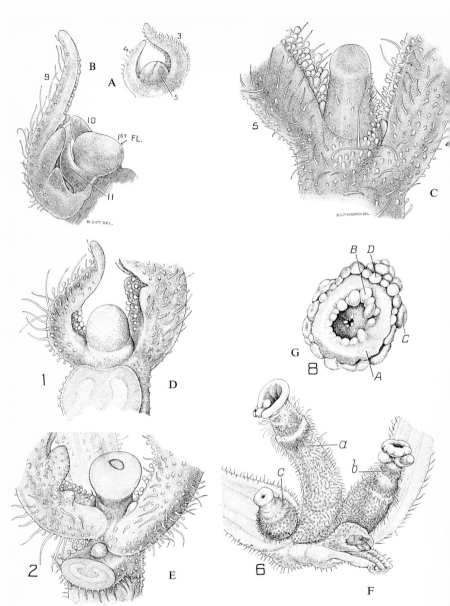

24. Tomato plants, with variously transformed apices, after treatment with 2,3,5-triiodobenzoic acid (TIBA). (The ascending numbers refer to leaves or leaf primordia of decreasing age). A, Normal vegetative apex giving rise to leaf primordia (× 40). B, Normal flower-forming apical growing point: the enlarging apex divides, one part giving rise to the terminal flower of the inflorescence, the other part growing on and, after some time, giving rise to the second flower; and so on. C, A vegetative apex after treatment with TIBA: no new leaf primordia have been formed (i.e. after the leaf indicated as 5), whereas control plants formed ten leaves during the same period. The apex has grown out into an elongated, truncated conical organ. Axillary meristems were similarly transformed.

D-G, Other modifications in the apical reaction system: tomato plants treated with TIBA (applied as lanolin-paste, with 50 mg TIBA, 5 ml water and 5 g lanolin, applied to the cotyledons). D, A vegetative apex 19 days after the application (× 30). E, Ditto, 23 days after the application: the formation of a ring-fasciation has begun (× 30). F, Later stages in the formation of ring-fasciations: tubular organs have developed by the transformation of shoot apices (× 10). G, An older ring-fasciation as seen from above (× 33): buds are being formed on both the outside (C) and inside (B) surfaces of the ring-like apical meristem (A). (After Chr. J. Gorter, *Koninkl. Nederl. Akad. Wetens.*)

CHAPTER 15

General Discussion and Summation

'The synthetic study of the different aspects of evolution is perhaps the salient feature of the present period.' J. S. Huxley, 1954.

ORGANIZATION A *CONTINUUM*

Long ago Lyell noted that ancient fossils were generally like contemporary living organisms in their basic organization. This he described as the principle of continuity. One may now recognize that some aspect of organization can be perceived in *all* the materials with which science is concerned – the elements, inorganic crystals, organic macromolecules, and progressively up the scale of increasing biological diversification, from a virus to the most highly evolved angiosperm. In this general sense, organization is a *continuum* in the physical world. Organization is also a *continuum* in the ontogenesis and reproduction of the individual organism and in the phyletic line of which it is a component.

Since metabolism, growth and structural development are fundamentally physico-chemical processes, it would be surprising if living entities did not manifest organization, since many of these processes have organizing effects. In some instances it is possible to indicate the physico-chemical factors, or the mathematical relationships, that are directly or indirectly involved in, or indicative of, organizing processes; but, in others, the developmental situations are so complex, and our knowledge of the kinetics and reactions of large organic molecules in the protoplasm and between cells so inadequate, that reasoned conjecture must still take the place of validated interpretation. Such difficulties led earlier workers to formulate vitalistic hypotheses, concepts of the 'emergent' properties of more complex substances, emergent evolution, and so on.

While some problems of organization are yielding to the direct application of physico-chemical ideas and techniques, and many others may be expected to do so in the coming decades – especially if biophysics and biochemistry become established in biology departments, as they ought to be – *the higher levels of organization call for concepts of an organismic kind*. The concepts of 'organismic biology', as distinct

N

from 'molecular' or 'atomistic biology', are not only justifiable: they are essential. The development of an organism as an integrated whole, the relation of its parts to the whole and to each other, its co-ordination and functional unity, and many aspects of its life history, all require concepts that lie outside, or beyond, the physical sciences as presently formulated. Thus while biologists should make the fullest use of the ideas, techniques, results and criteria of the physical sciences, they must go further: they must formulate their own distinctive and necessary concepts. The aim should be to work towards a philosophy of biology; i.e. a philosophy of *organisms* as distinct from, but in addition to, the analysis of molecular processes that take place in them. These views are in no sense new but a re-emphasis of them seems timely. Some contemporary botanists, e.g. J. Bonner (1963), consider that, if botany is to remain 'alive', the traditional areas of research in systematics, anatomy, mineral nutrition, photosynthesis, ecology, etc., should give way to an intensification of work in molecular biology. 'New and deepening insights on the molecular level', as he says, are undoubtedly needed. It will be evident from this book that the author is in agreement with much of Bonner's outlook, i.e. that we are basically concerned with the nexus of genetical, biochemical and biophysical factors in relation to all aspects of the life of plants. But let us be wary of casting aside the accumulated scholarship of botanical science, or of forgetting that our real concern is with *organisms* in *all* their aspects.

In this connection it is interesting to note Waddington's conclusion (1962, p. 234) that while genetic analyses of patterns have yielded important information about the fundamental units involved, they have been 'much less informative about the intermediate steps between the genes and the final patterns'; and he adds that many of the relevant problems 'must be tackled at the level of complex components rather than of the basic genetic elements'. He has also indicated that although the contemporary phase of molecular biology or molecular genetics, largely based on the study of micro-organisms, is yielding new and invaluable information, it 'needs to be enriched by the addition of some metazoan embryology'.

ORGANIZATION A HERITABLE 'CHARACTER'

Organization in plants is a *continuum* in the sense that its basis is heritable. At some stage during the phase of chemical evolution, a persisting arrangement of substances that could be specified as 'living', in contrast to 'non-living', was attained. For convenience, we may accept this stage as the beginning of biological organization. The essential features were that the 'living substance' had considerable stability, that it could increase quantitatively, and that it could reproduce itself so that its distinctive features, the cumulative result of the previous phase of chemical change and selection, were perpetuated. In other words, the nascent organization was heritable; the 'living substance', or entity, consisted of a compatible system, or 'consociation', of molecules, capable of growth and self-reproduction; and it was in equilibrium with its environment.

In considering the phenomena of organization in plants, we are typically concerned with the development of a zygote, a spore or other reproductive cell, or with the apices of shoots, buds, leaves or roots. Since there is no evidence that runs contrary to the aphorism: 'all cells from cells, all life from life', every cell or tissue region possesses some characteristic organization from the outset. Accordingly, the processes of metabolism, growth, development and progressive organization which may be observed during the ontogenesis of a moss or a vascular plant, and which involve sequences of chemical reactions, all take place in embryonic cells in which some organization is already present.

INTEGRATION AN ESSENTIAL CONDITION

Integration is an essential condition for organization. It presents itself as a logical necessity, in that organization could scarcely result from the action of forces causing disintegration. Even in the simplest living system, certain physico-chemical and biological conditions must be satisfied. Thus the molecules and macromolecules in the system must tend to cohere rather than disperse in the particular environment; their reactions must be such as to impart stability and equilibrium, or steady state, to the system; and they must be disposed in some characteristic spatial or geometric arrangement so that they can maintain and reproduce themselves and react with each other. All this is as much as to say that, collectively, the molecules must constitute a system which has functional efficiency. In more complex organismal systems, it may be assumed that similar physico-chemical relationships also obtain; for organisms in general are characterized by functional efficiency, by stable relationships with the environment, and by the arrangement and compatibility of their components, making for harmony of development. At the highest evolutionary level, i.e. that of *Homo sapiens*, Le Gros Clark (1958) has used the concept of 'total morphological pattern' connoting the integrated combination of all the unitary characters, this making for a complete functional design. Mayr (1954) discussed in some detail (with citation of the relevant literature) the importance of coadapted selective changes in chromosomes and gene-complexes. A well-integrated gene-complex may be regarded as a genetical description of part of what is involved in the writer's concept of an organismal reaction system.

ORGANISMAL REACTION SYSTEMS

Theoretical considerations together with observations and experiments support the general idea that the primary organizational features, or patterns, in plants are due to the functioning of *organismal reaction systems*. These cannot yet be defined with any precision, but they are held to be present in individual cells, as in zygotes and spores, and in the integrated groups of cells that constitute embryonic or meristematic regions, e.g. the shoot apex. In each instance, an inherited cellular organization determines the nature and potentiality of the reaction system. The functioning of the reaction system is affected by all its components, i.e. by the specific physico-chemical properties of its various substances and by external factors such as heat, light or nutrient supply. The reaction system, in fact, admits of continuity and interaction between organism and environment.

The idea that reaction systems in embryonic cells and regions can yield patterns* makes possible at least a tentative approach to some of the more fundamental aspects of organization and evolution in plants. Among the things we can say, tentatively but with factual support, are: (i) that the basis of the reaction system is transmitted in heredity, i.e. in the protoplasmic organization of the ovum; (ii) that individual components of the system include specific gene-determined substances and nutrient and other substances obtained from the environment or from contiguous cells or tissues; (iii) that the reaction system admits of the interaction of genetic factors, factors in the environment, and organismal factors; (iv) that the reaction system in a shoot apex typically gives rise to a patternized (or patterned) distribution of metabolites, this process preceding and underlying the visible organogenic developments and tissue differentiation; (v) that, since the reaction

---

* Le Gros Clark (1958), in a discussion of the descent of man, and with reference to the integrated unity of organisms, has emphasized the importance of the concept of *pattern*; he has referred to 'the inheritance of a mechanism conferring a common potentiality to develop the same pattern'.

system is physico-chemically an open system which tends towards a steady state, and is the primary locus for the interaction of the several categories of factors indicated above, the organization which results is typically characterized by unity, integration, specificity and adaptation; (vi) that as the reaction system in a shoot apex becomes more complex during ontogenesis, so also does the pattern of organs and tissues to which it gives rise; but the transition from one morphological 'stage' to another is usually characterized by physical and developmental harmony; (vii) that the specific substance determined by a mutant gene must be compatible* with the other components of the reaction system; otherwise the system may be disrupted to a greater or less extent, i.e. the gene will be lethal; (viii) that, in relation to (vii) above, selection begins in the reaction system of the ovum, zygote, or embryonic tissue; and that, however random gene mutation may be, the selection of mutants is to an unknown extent canalized by the constitution of the reaction system; (ix) that evolutionary concepts, including those of orthogenesis and the inheritance of acquired characters of adaptive value, may be re-examined in the light of reaction system theory; (x) that although each species or variety has its own specific reaction system, and gives rise to many specific characters, the number of basic kinds of pattern in plants is quite small. Reaction system theory may thus contribute to a better understanding of differences in specific organization on the one hand and of the prevalence of homologies of organization on the other.

THE INTERPRETATION OF PHYSIOLOGICAL PROCESSES

In theories of correlation in plant development, e.g. the inhibition of lateral buds by the main apex, it cannot be said that definitive and truly satisfying 'explanations' have yet been proposed, though the reality of the phenomenon itself is not in doubt. The general idea in correlation is that an auxin, or a hormonal substance, moves from one region of the plant into another, e.g. from the shoot apex to an axillary bud or bud site, and there exercises some characteristic effect on growth and organogenesis. It is not unusual in such studies to find that the state of the tissue acted upon is not specified, e.g. in respect of its biochemical constitution, histology or other aspects of its initial organization. Such information is now seen to be essential. Again, studies of organ formation in undifferentiated tissue cultures, e.g. the induction of buds and/or

---

* This does not exclude antagonistic or inhibitory reactions or the presence of so-called non-reactive genes.

roots, suggest that certain growth-regulating substances, alone or in combination, have definite organizing and morphogenetic effects. Such substances are certainly essential to the observed developments. Nevertheless, explanations of specific developments in terms of metabolism alone are inadequate (*see* p. 26): they usually tell us nothing of the actual inception of organization. It is now suggested that a growth-regulating, 'organizing' or 'morphogenetic' substance can only exercise its characteristic effects by becoming a component of the reaction system of the meristematic tissue or nascent organ acted upon. It may then affect the further development in characteristic ways, the concomitant organization being due to *all* the factors in the situation, biophysical factors being important among the proximate causes of structural developments.

EXTERNAL AND INTERNAL FACTORS

As J. B. S. Haldane (1952) remarked: 'It is hard to disentangle the effects of nature and nurture.' At any particular stage in development, e.g. of an angiosperm, the manifestations of organization are due to genetic, organismal and environmental factors. This is well illustrated by the transition from the vegetative to the reproductive phase in flowering plants: hereditary factors fundamentally determine the nature and scope of the general and specific morphological developments; but the stage reached in ontogenesis, and the incidence of external factors such as day-length or temperature, are usually closely involved in the inception of the flowering process. One of the results of experimental taxonomy has been to show how important both genetic and environmental factors can be in different circumstances (Illustrations in Chapter 4).

SPECIFICITY AND HOMOLOGY OF ORGANIZATION

In studying any considerable range of organisms, either within the same circle of affinity or in different major groups, one becomes aware of the dual nature of organization. On the one hand, the evolution of plants, in all groups and at all levels, has been marked by active differentiation of new varieties from the parental stock, yielding abundant specificity of organization. On the other, the Plant Kingdom is characterized by much homology of organization (*see* p. 56). Specificity of organization, e.g. in related varieties or species, can be referred to genotypic differences. Homologies of organization, by contrast, raise problems of a different order of magnitude. In the simplest case, i.e. that of genetical homology, comparable features may be expected in plants which have originated from the same ancestral stock and have many genes in common. On the other hand, more or less closely comparable organizational features may be produced by what are usually regarded as quite differently constituted genetical systems. Other homologies of organization may be ascribed to the action of self-organizing factors which may not be closely gene-controlled, to extrinsic factors, to size-and-form correlations, and to other mathematical relationships.

In the search for general ideas relating to organization, it becomes evident that while the number of specific genetical systems in the Plant Kingdom is very large, the number of basic organizational patterns or plans, indicating major evolutionary innovations, is quite small. For example, viewed as geometrical constructions, all vascular plants are essentially alike, i.e. they consist of an axis with regularly-disposed lateral appendages. In addition to genetical homology (*see* below), the prevalence of homologies of organization may perhaps be accounted for on various grounds: (i) that all heritable organizational changes must obey physico-chemical laws; (ii) that, in terms of probability, the successive organizational innovations which mark the course of evolution were those which were most likely to take place;* these may include the evolution of important parallelisms in genetical systems; i.e. some kinds of system will tend to have been perpetuated and others to have been eliminated; and (iii) that environmental factors and certain limiting factors have tended to canalize development.

Genetical Homology. Since (a) the cell organelles which have been investigated and (b) the principal metabolic processes seem to be *common to all green plants*, the reaction systems of different species may be expected to have features in common and to yield some similarities of pattern. This may account, to an unknown extent, for some aspects of parallel or homoplastic development. As we have seen, certain general configurations or patterns are common to all the classes of higher plants. But within any one kind of pattern, there may be more or less extensive variations. These may be attributed to specific gene-controlled metabolic substances acting as components of the reaction system at particular stages in ontogenesis.

On closer inspection, the topic of genetical homology proves to be

---

* It is not difficult to think of exceptions to this statement, e.g. *Welwitschia, Rafflesia, Drosera*, or a hundred other 'improbable plants'.

complex and difficult. Thus De Beer (1958) has written that since gene-complexes have constantly been undergoing changes by mutation, recombination, etc., 'it is impossible to imagine that the gene-complex of any living organism contains any unchanged "old" genes capable by themselves of controlling the development in the descendant of "stages" representing the finished products of the gene-complexes of the ancestors that were built up under very different conditions of selection'. On the other hand, Le Gros Clark (1958), in a discussion of evolutionary convergence and parallelism, has followed Simpson (1950) in the view that the parallelisms which the biologist recognizes depend on an initial similarity of structure and on 'the inheritance of a common potentiality for reproducing similar (or homologous) mutations, and that, this being so, the initial similarity and the homology of mutations themselves imply an evolutionary relationship. Thus "closeness of parallelism tends to be proportional to closeness of affinity" ' (Le Gros Clark, 1958, p. 183). It is evident that we are still far from definitive solutions of some of these evolutionary problems: in biology, as it seems, we never reach an end but only a new beginning.

Reaction System Criteria. If we accept as valid hypotheses (i) that primitive living entities resulted from an antecedent phase of chemical evolution, and (ii) that active embryonic cells and regions are complex physico-chemical reaction systems (or the loci of such systems), it follows that, in biological evolution, our primary concern is with the nature and activity of such systems. Reaction system theory and concepts, in fact, provide us with new criteria for re-examining the merits of the several theories of evolution and of views on evolutionary parallelisms, the nature and action of mutant genes, adaptation, etc.

Biochemical Homology. In the nineteenth century the theory of evolution was largely based on morphological evidence. In the contemporary view, since development in organisms is the result of physico-chemical processes, a knowledge of the existence of closely comparable, specific processes is probably the best guide to genetic affinity and homology. It is now becoming possible to investigate some aspects of physiological or biochemical evolution (*see* Haldane, 1954; Dobzhansky, 1955). Haldane suggested that the theory of evolution may eventually be envisaged as an extensive system of biochemical processes. As we have seen, many of the basic processes in living cells are of very general occurrence, perhaps considerably more so, indeed, than might have been considered possible by earlier biologists. Dobzhansky (1955), for example, referred to them as 'most striking biochemical homologies which attest that the whole living world is really a large family adapted to subsist in different manners in different environments'.

ASPECTS OF VARIATION

The variations in form, structure and biochemistry that have been studied genetically usually relate to differences within a close circle of affinity, i.e. in strains, varieties and much more occasionally, in species, which can be intercrossed. With some notable exceptions, only relatively minor characters are affected: the basic morphological and structural patterns remain fundamentally unchanged. However, the occurrence and selection of small variations, over sufficiently long periods of time, was regarded by Darwin – and is affirmed by contemporary geneticists – as accounting for the more considerable differences that distinguish the higher taxonomic categories, i.e. families, orders and classes (*see* Fisher, 1930, 1954; Huxley, 1942; Stebbins, 1950, and Chapter 5). This is certainly a reasonable inference or conjecture, for it is well supported on general grounds. Nevertheless, genetical studies of differences in varieties and species have not yet yielded the kind of information we require concerning the inception of the principal organs and tissues of plants or the organizational features that distinguish the major phyletic lines. It seems improbable that these problems will yield to the techniques of genetics alone; but they may yield to the collective techniques of botany.

Haldane (1952) indicated how exceedingly complex, difficult and enigmatic are the problems of variation, selection and evolution: 'Variation is extremely hard to study, and we still know remarkably little about it.' If natural selection were unopposed, it would 'give rise to a species all of whose members were of the genotype that was fittest in the given environment'. He also pointed out that certain important characters may have little survival value and that relatively conspicuous morphological characters may be neutral from a selective point of view. There are, moreover, many instances where variation is of no importance in natural selection. 'For only genes which affect survival or fertility can furnish the raw materials for natural selection, and natural selection is a reality.' By eliminating the extreme types, natural selection tends to reduce the variation in a population. To summarize: Haldane recognized an element of conflict in genetical variation in that genetical diversity results from mutation and 'is preserved by a conflict in which natural selection is opposed by other processes'. Beckner (1959), in a philosophical review of selection theory, concluded that the important

N*

factor in evolution is differential reproduction; and that the adaptation of an organism to its environment 'is relevant to evolution only in so far as it is necessary for reproduction at all' (p. 169). Botanists, however, are familiar with the wonderfully successful vegetative reproduction of many species of plants which are not particularly well equipped in the matter of their sexual reproduction. Some suspension of judgment on, and critical re-examination of, Beckner's statement is indicated.

The phenomenon of *homologous variation* has long been recognized. Darwin (1878, p. 123) referred to it, quoting B. O. Walsh's 'law of equable variations', and stated that 'Distinct species present analogous variations' (*see* Haldane, 1952). The underlying idea was reformulated by Vavilov (1922) as the Law of Homologous Variation (*see* Chapters 3, 5). Studies in comparative genetics indicate that similar characters are often inherited in the same way in related species, the genes involved being often located on homologous chromosomes. Haldane (1927) initially considered that 'homologous variation occurred in related species simply because they had similar sets of genes which could mutate in corresponding ways, giving the same sort of variation'; in other words, that chemically-based genic homology underlies structural homology. However, as noted in Chapter 5, Harland (1933) found that homologous features in related cotton species were controlled by quite different genes. This suggests, or indicates, that different genes may sometimes have approximately the same physico-chemical and morphogenetic effects as components of a reaction system. In some of these instances it may be that the main effect of the gene-determined substance is to participate in a common category of chemical reaction, such as oxidation, reduction, etc. And while it may be a convenience to regard genes as functional units, as Pontecorvo (*see* Waddington, 1959), Benzer (1959), Watkin Williams (1962) and others have done, their action is chemical and they must basically possess structural specificity. But how this will eventually be defined is for the future.

In some groups of animals, a particular developmental process may be altered without markedly affecting other developmental processes; but, in other groups the whole developmental process is so integrated that this is not possible. From such facts Haldane (1952) concluded that the possible range of variation in a group is determined both by the genes which can mutate and by the developmental physiology – an important organismic concept to which the author has tried to give due emphasis in this book. The fact that many effects, usually associated with the action of particular genes, can also be produced by cultural treatments, supports this conclusion.

Community Evolution. A somewhat different aspect of variation may also be indicated at this point. Genetical studies are concerned with the investigation of the variation manifested by individuals and populations of a species, variety or race, usually growing under more or less closely controlled conditions. But in Nature, wherever growth conditions are generally favourable, considerable numbers of different species of plants and animals occur together, so that their variation, competition, symbiosis, selection and evolution all take place on a mixed community basis. The prime examples of such evolutionary or genetical ecology are afforded by tropical forests. Corner (1949, 1954) has developed a general theory – described as the 'Durian Theory' – on the probable course of evolution in an ecological complex such as a tropical forest. He has also contributed an unusually graphic account of how changes in physical or biological environmental factors, together with mutations, necessarily beget other changes, and these further and still further changes, and so on. In fact, the whole ecological system, or community of systems, is, as it were, on the move, with a multiplicity of concomitant evolutionary and adaptive changes. The culminating state, as in a tropical rain forest, presents a truly astonishing, not to say fantastic, array of strange and unexpected morphological developments and curious ways of life. But, in all the components of this complex system, i.e. the different species, small heritable and environmental changes have determined the course of the evolutionary development.

REACTION RANGE

Sinnott, Dunn and Dobzhansky (1950) stated that what a genotype determines are the reactions and responses of an organism to a particular environment. The distinctive forms which develop in different environments, and others which might develop in appropriate circumstances, give a measure of the range of reaction, or plasticity, of the phenotype. The limits of this range are probably seldom defined, but general observation indicates the very wide tolerance of some common species. Thus *Pteridium aquilinum*, in varietal forms, is pan-temperate and pan-tropical. Other species, again, are of very limited range: Willis (1914) recorded that, in the same river, different species of *Castelnavia* (Podostemaceae) were found localized at different cataracts. As genetical studies have shown, virtually every possible intermediate condition exists between characters which are closely gene-determined and those which respond so markedly to different environments that the basic genotypic effects may be more or less completely obscured. In brief, genotypic and environmental effects may overlap and be difficult to separate. In the individual development, environmental factors are components of the functioning reaction system – the *genotype* being an abstraction from the actual biological totality.

NEO-DARWINIAN EVOLUTION

In the contemporary genetical view, sometimes described as Neo-Darwinian or Neo-Mendelian, the fundamental aspects of development, organization, adaptation and evolution in plants are referred primarily (i) to the action of nuclear and cytoplasmic genes, the former being of paramount importance; (ii) to random genic mutations and chromosome changes, and to genetical segregation and recombination in populations; (iii) to pervasive or omnipresent natural selection and adaptation; (iv) to the isolation of new taxonomic entities by barriers of various kinds. In this book a cognate but somewhat different line of thought has been developed, largely based on morphogenetic investigations. Here the general phenomenon of evolution is envisaged as the result of the progressive elaboration and differentiation of enduring, specific physico-chemical organizations. What is passed on from generation to generation is not only an ordered complement of genes, but a specific, physico-chemical organization at the cellular level, many features of which are common to the cells of all green plants. This comprehensively organized cell is the locus of many interrelated and co-ordinated physico-chemical activities and may accordingly be regarded as a reaction system. At a higher level of organization, the group of cells which constitutes an embryonic region may also be regarded as the locus of a reaction system.

No attempt will be made to comment on plant evolution as a whole. Indeed, the exposition of Lamarckian, Darwinian, Neo-Darwinian, Neo-Lamarckian and Neo-Mendelian ideas and relevant controversies has now become so voluminous, complex and tangled that, short of an encyclopaedic effort, any orderly treatment is virtually impossible to achieve. Huxley (1954) has given a short graphic account of the many curious ups and downs in views regarding the efficacy of Darwinian selection, adaptation, etc., as evidence of past selective changes, and related topics. At this date, to decide with detachment what truly pertained to Darwin that did not previously pertain to Lamarck and others, would call for more scholarly assiduity, not to say leisure, than most of us have at our disposal. Accordingly, what the author has tried to do is to discuss selected aspects of evolutionary fact and theory in terms of the general thesis of this book.

GENES, MUTATIONS AND THE EVOLUTION OF MAJOR ORGANIZATIONAL FEATURES

Contemporary geneticists have elaborated Darwin's general idea that the variations and mutations which are important in evolution usually produce relatively small effects and that natural selection may operate in every phase of development.* Genic mutations are considered to take place entirely at random. However, in terms of organization theory, as now presented, a mutant form will only survive provided the new substance determined by the mutant gene is not incompatible with the other components of the zygotic or embryonic reaction system; or, as Waddington (1958) stated, all the genes in an interbreeding population show a certain 'concordance'. This still leaves plenty of latitude for random mutation, since the effect of the gene-determined substance may be neutral. Although a mutant gene usually exercises comparatively small effects, more considerable mutational effects are not precluded in reaction system theory, the essential criterion for gene survival being the aforementioned physico-chemical compatibility. The larger mutational changes of the kind discussed by de Vries (1901, 1905), Willis (1940) and others, and which may have been important at periods of 'explosive' evolutionary change, could perhaps be accounted for by reaction system theory along these lines.† An obligatory physico-chemical compatibility of mutant genes may also account for some of the many unexplained orthogenetic trends in plant and animal evolution. If natural selection, on the basis of compatibility, begins in the zygotic reaction system, one can also envisage a basis for explaining some of the seemingly, and perhaps actually, useless or non-adaptive structural developments to which various writers have referred, e.g. Willis (1940), Haldane (1954).

---

* Waddington (1939) defined *natural selection* as 'an inevitable consequence of genetical variation in fitness'.

† The large 'mutations' of de Vries are mostly interpreted in other ways by contemporary geneticists (*see* Huxley, 1942, p. 204). However, perhaps this is a door which should not be completely closed.

On the evidence to date, it appears that it is impossible to convert one kind of protein directly into a completely different kind of protein: only closely related proteins are interconvertible (Pollock, *see* Waddington, 1959). This may have an important bearing on the nature and extent of the changes associated with mutant genes. It may be that only closely related proteins can function as components of a viable reaction system.

The adaptational aspects of mutant forms and progressive adaptational trends can also be considered in relation to the reaction system concept (*see also* next section). Since a viable mutational change must be compatible with *all* the components of the reaction system, including environmental factors, and since the modified systems will also tend towards dynamic equilibrium, some measure of adaptation may be expected to result as a natural concomitant; i.e. *compatibility and equilibrium at the physico-chemical level may be the basis of adaptation at the organismal level*. If this is a valid inference, all structural features at all stages of morphogenesis may be regarded as having an adaptational aspect;[*] but the question of the close, direct adaptiveness of all features needs fuller examination (*see* p. 403). On this subject, Barnett (1958, p. xiv) pointed out that it is 'easy to talk about "adaptation" in a general way and to leave the content of this notion exceedingly vague'. Specific, detailed statements justifying the assumed adaptation are required in each particular instance. On close examination, the subject is seen to be a rather difficult one, particularly when, as in the 'sickle-cell' gene affecting the shapes of the red blood cells, one aspect of the mutation is to produce harmful effects, i.e. causing anaemia, whereas another aspect is adaptive in that it confers some degree of resistance against malaria. The discovery of the unexpected adaptive advantage of a trait such as this may well lead some biologists to conclude that all features are adaptive.

Reflection on the many parallelisms and sometimes close similarities in physiological activity, form, structure and function in taxonomically unrelated organisms suggests that, if metabolism in general is due to genic action, or is under direct genic control, the effects of many gene products in the reaction system, including those of mutant genes, are

---

[*] Contemporary exponents of evolution tend more or less completely towards the view that all characters are adaptive in that natural selection makes for the perpetuation of the adaptively more efficient organisms or characters; or, as Dobzhansky (1955) put it, populations respond to the selective forces in their environment by the retention or improvement of their adaptedness.

general rather than specific. This does not, of course, exclude the induction by gene-determined substances of specific effects at particular stages of development, or in particular circumstances. In fact, this has been demonstrated in many plant and animal materials. The general conception stated above may perhaps help to account for the genetical conclusion that, in some phyletic lines, characteristic morphological features of the organisms are maintained even although the relevant genes have changed during the evolutionary process.

Support for the view that much genic action is general rather than specific, or both general and specific, i.e. pleiotropic, emerges from a survey of the Plant Kingdom. On the one hand, we find ourselves confronted with a vast number of different taxa, of seemingly endless morphological and structural diversity (*see* Chapter 16). On the other hand, an examination of plants in their more general morphological aspects shows that the number of fundamental kinds of constructional plan – *Bauplan** – is really quite small. In all vascular plants, there is only one *major* type of construction, namely, the leafy-shoot, i.e. an axis with regularly disposed lateral members. And, as we have seen, in all the constituent species, as also in the mosses and some of the larger algae, the polarity, which leads to this *Bauplan*, is determined in the zygote or even in the ovum. In brief, more or less closely comparable organizational features have been evolved in species with, as is generally assumed, quite differently constituted genetical systems. It thus appears that if genes are the primary determiners of these features, different collocations of genes produce very much the same *main* effects. It may be, of course, that genetical systems in different major groups have much more in common than is usually thought.

There remains the possibility that the basic cell organization, which is common to all green plants, rather than the genes, is the main determiner of basic organizational features at higher levels. But, to be adequate, such a proposition would also have to include all the modulating effects of evolving genetical systems. These are very difficult problems and, in the writer's view, it would be idle to suggest that definitive solutions, contributed by any branch of biology, are yet in sight. In this connection, Waddington (1962, p. 239) has considered whether the genetic determination of development can best be understood in terms of (a) the integration of syntheses by typical chemical processes, e.g. by competition or interaction between the various synthesizing systems;

---

* *See* Woodger (1929–48).

or of (b) the ultrastructural organization of cells, i.e. comprising the several kinds of organelles:

This organization involves the entities which we believe to be part of the genetic effector system, in particular, the nucleus and the microsomes. It is, to my way of thinking, most unplausible to suggest that any widespread characteristics of this effector system will turn out to be not of significance. It seems to be much more likely, though this is admittedly a guess, that the structural organization will be found to be an essential part of the mechanism by which the genes become effective.

As to the morphogenesis or configuration of organelles such as mito-chondria, chloroplasts, etc., this, in Waddington's view, is a problem to which genetical methods can make little contribution but which may perhaps be resolved by a new 'supra-molecular' chemistry.

Within the axial plan of construction in vascular plants several distinctive patterns are evident, e.g. the microphyllous type in *Lyco-podium* and *Equisetum* and the megaphyllous type in ferns and flower-ing plants. One of the still unsolved problems in the evolution of plants is to account for these distinctive types. Here it is pertinent to recall that, once a main organizational type has been evolved, the further evolution within the phyletic line usually consists of relatively small variations of the basic organization. Thus, with the exception of a small number of genera, e.g. *Ophioglossum, Aneimia, Marsilea, Azolla,* etc., the general affinity of virtually all fern species, whether small or large, presents no problem: they are all quite evidently ferns. Similar remarks could be made of the several hundred species of *Lycopodium,* and of *Selaginella.* And again, with some exceptions, the mosses, both in their gametophytic and sporophytic phases, are very evidently mosses. And so on, for other great classes of plants.

The flowering plants are not only quite outstanding numerically: they are also the most highly evolved and highly differentiated of all the subdivisions of the Plant Kingdom.* Yet the main organizational features of the vegetative phase are those of the axis-with-appendages. Holttum (1960), for example, has described the very diverse vegetative features of monocotyledons as variations of a central type of configura-tion. Even the seemingly endless diversity in floral morphology can be considered in terms of a relatively small number of basic constructional plans, suggesting that, as well as specific genetical factors, certain physiological processes of general occurrence are also involved (*see* Chapter 11).

---

* According to Good (1956), they have been seriously neglected from the point of view of close evolutionary study.

In a philosophical discussion of evolutionary theories, Grene (1958) has compared the outlook and main conclusions reached by two palaeontologists, Simpson (1953) and Schindewolf (1950); the former being taken as an exponent of contemporary orthodox Neo-Darwinism, i.e. evolution by small genic changes, selection and universal adaptation; the latter as a critic of such views, in that Schindewolf considered that there are important evolutionary developments which are non-adaptive and do not lend themselves to interpretation by selection theory. Indeed, other palaeontologists have shared, in some degree at least, the kind of critical doubt expressed by Schindewolf. According to him, some common structural features are not necessarily, of themselves, adaptations in the first instance: they are simply new types of organization; but they may be capable of numerous further evolutionary changes and elaborations which have adaptive value. Furthermore, once a new type or *Bauplan* has appeared, it may undergo a progressive orthogenetic development, reach a climax of successful structural and functional development, and eventually decline and persist tenuously, or become extinct. As Grene has cogently written (p. 113): 'Whereas for Simpson it is a question of particular small changes adding up to big ones, for Schindewolf the big changes in structure come first, the new general structures breaking down thereafter into more special adaptations.' Both exponents are in general agreement about the facts; but they derive very different inferences and conclusions from them. According to Schindewolf, life can originate novelty. In relation to genetical and reaction system theory, two points may be made here: (i) the new evolutionary developments, or innovations, must have their inception as compatible and viable changes in reaction systems; and (ii) relatively small genetical changes may sometimes result in what a phylogenetic or comparative morphologist would regard as very considerable structural changes, e.g. actinomorphy to zygomorphy, or *vice-versa*. It seems not improbable, to the author at least, that some of these conflicting views may disappear, or be seen to be unnecessary, as progress is made in the comprehension of organization in its many aspects and at its several levels; for, as Polanyi (1958), in his theory of personal knowledge, has stated, the exponents of the two contrasted views appear to be thinking on opposite sides of a *logical gap*.

In a considerable study of evolution in the flowering plants, Good (1956) reached the following main conclusions: (i) although the members of this very large and varied group provide little positive evidence in favour of the concept of orthogenesis, they show little evidence against it; (ii) they yield 'no evidence that natural selection has played an important part in their evolution', but afford many contrary indications; and (iii) they suggest that mutation, connoting evolutionary changes of more or less considerable magnitude, has been a frequent and important factor in their history.

THE PERVASIVENESS AND APTNESS OF ADAPTATION: PRELIMINARY OBSERVATIONS

In the Neo-Darwinian view, in which the concepts of population genetics occupy an important place, organisms with new gene-determined characters which are more closely adapted to the environment, or to the conditions of life, than their parents tend to be selected. Selective forces are at work in every phase of development and of the life history; and adaptation is a pervasive phenomenon, underlying all aspects of living things. In other words, genetically-determined variations, with adaptive features possessing survival value, tend to be selected.

It may be recalled that Herbert Spencer's phrase for *natural selection* was the *survival of the fittest*. But as Dampier (1929) asked: What is the fittest? His definition was that the fittest 'is that which best fits the existing environment'. But J. M. Thoday (1958) considered that this is probably less than the whole truth and has supplied a contemporary definition in the form that 'the fit are those who fit their existing environments and whose descendants will fit future environments'. In Thoday's view, the ability of organisms to accommodate themselves to environments, which are always undergoing both physical and biological changes, is essential to an understanding of the nature of fitness and biological progress. Elsewhere the author has referred to the essentially reciprocal relationships of organisms and environments: neither is static; each affects the other, their interaction being mediated during development through the organismal reaction system. Herbert Spencer (1898) defined life as 'the continuous adjustment of internal relations to external relations'.

The importance attached to the hereditary constitution is well supported by the facts of every-day observations. Thus, if one considers the numerous and varied forms of plants in a tropical rain forest or, indeed, in any other situation supporting abundant plant life, it is apparent that environmental factors cannot be the *primary* determiners of form, or of the inception of biological pattern, though they may have important effects on the ultimate phenotypic expression of the primary form. A particular formal or organizational type or pattern is not necessarily associated with a particular environment. It is true that *extremes* of environment, e.g. xerophytic environments, yield similar formal and structural features in unrelated phyletic lines, e.g. succulent stems, diminished leaf surface, thick cuticles, sunken stomata, water-storing tissues, etc.; but many morphological differences of greater specificity still remain; and non-xeromorphic forms are also found in these same environments. The very varied forms of phytoplankton in lakes, etc., where the life conditions for the different organisms must be closely comparable and, on the whole, rather uniform, support the foregoing conclusion. Some environmental conditions are no doubt much more exacting in the matter of selection than others. Some, indeed may exercise very little selective effect; i.e. as far as organizational features are concerned; or it may be that many species have consider-able flexibility, or range of tolerance, *vis-à-vis* the main environmental factors.

In the Neo-Darwinian (Neo-Mendelian) view, variation may take place in any direction and since selective forces are ever-present, and even the smallest selective advantage may be important (Fisher, 1954), more highly evolved organizations inevitably result. Furthermore, the characters developed are usually deemed to be in the nature of useful adaptations, or were so at the time that they became 'fixed'. No quite useless characters could persist, though not all contemporary biologists share this view, e.g. Haldane (1954). Closely associated with the earlier concept of adaptiveness was that of economy of material; i.e. many structural features, especially those with rather specialized or advanced differentiation, were considered to be more or less *precisely adapted* for their particular functions in the economy of the organism in relation to its particular environment. (This is a topic which has been discussed at great length (*see* Huxley, 1942); it can only be touched on here in the most sketchy manner.) In contrast to these views, Nägeli regarded the progressive evolution of organisms as being determined by factors or conditions in the living protoplasm, i.e. by inner or inherent tendencies. That being so, the struggle for survival would ensure the removal of useless or harmless characters. Useful features, in Nägeli's view, were the result of direct adaptation. But, in circumstances where the struggle was absent or not acute, useless as well as useful characters might well be perpetuated, since both were determined by inherent factors. This and related aspects were cogently discussed by Haberlandt (1914). Considerations such as these prompt us to look more closely at (i) the validity of the concept of *the omnipresence and pervasiveness of adaptation* in *all* aspects of development, for example, as advocated by Huxley (1942); (ii) the validity of the *principle of economy of material*; and (iii) the assumed *precision of adaptations* in relation to the seeming needs of the plant.

There are, it need hardly be said, many other facets of evolution which merit further examination; but because of the limitations of space, the foregoing may serve as focal points for discussion, partly to indicate the ebb and flow of scholarly views, partly to test the cogency of the views developed in this book, and, not least, to see where we now stand in this most comprehensive of biological topics.

THE OMNIPRESENCE OF ADAPTATION

That adaptation in plants and animals is pervasive, or omnipresent (Huxley, 1942, 1954), may be accepted as being *generally* true, without necessarily asserting that *every* morphological, structural, and physiological feature is closely adaptive at every stage in development.* For example, many organs and tissues only become adaptively functional when they have attained to the adult state: if so, the many remarkable processes of the antecedent morphogenesis will have to be 'explained' on other grounds. Also, in all classes of plants, one can observe structural features to which no special adaptiveness can readily be attributed; and even where we attribute adaptiveness, because it seems to be self-evident, we often do not know, on the basis of comprehensive observation and experiment, that our idea is justified. In brief, notwithstanding the great volume of information, conjecture, effective argument and discussion, the whole question of adaptation in plants should still be treated critically, cautiously, and with suspension of final judgment. Of course, there is little doubt that many structural features are

---

* 'There is a universal process of adaptation, though this may take very various forms, from material adjustment of the parts of the gene-complex to the development of the elaborate organs serving particular biological ends' (J. S. Huxley, 1954). This is a very definite and comprehensive statement and is no doubt accepted in its entirety by many biologists. Yet, one may perhaps enquire, how many of these biologists have ever subjected any single assumed adaptation to rigorous validating tests. As an example of the full acceptance of the adaptiveness of floral constructions, reference may be made to Grant (1951), in which he stated: 'In the long course of evolution the flowers of plants have become adapted through natural selection to the characteristics of their pollinators. Thus the various species of flower owe their structure, shape, colour, odour and other attributes to the particular agents that cross-pollinate them.' That this statement contains part of the truth may be accepted: that it is the whole truth seems to the writer to be open to question.

highly adapted to the function to be performed in the life economy of the individual plant or animal and the survival of the race, e.g. eyes for seeing, wings for flight. Floral constructions that ensure cross-pollination by insects are among the commonest and best known examples of more or less precise adaptations, e.g. in Leguminosae, Scrophulariaceae, Orchidaceae and many other families; and their effectiveness can scarcely be doubted. Yet we may note that members of the Gramineae, which are mainly anemophilous and in which numerous varieties and species have been evolved all over the world, are a very successful group, occupying a not inconsiderable share of the earth's surface. Then, again, we have the curious fact that many, though not all, of the flowers visited by insects are horizontally disposed and of zygomorphic construction. Darwin, in fact, regarded floral zygomorphy as an adaptation to insect visitation. Yet many anemophilous plants have also zygomorphic flowers. Examples of these paradoxes could be multiplied. Adaptation, in fact, has many aspects and may be of very different kinds. In brief, one can accept the general concept of omnipresent adaptation but also recognize that there is still a great deal about it, perhaps especially in plants, that we do not know with the precision that engenders conviction. It should be said, with due emphasis, that the author does not take a pessimistic view of the situation. Quite simply, because of his experience in the fields of embryogenesis and morphogenesis, he thinks that a great deal has still to be done – perhaps a new beginning, characterized by new thinking and objectivity rather than partisan argument, has to be made – and that a more comprehensive understanding of organization may provide a basis for further insight into the evolution of plants.

Criticism of Adaptation Theory. By way of illustrating aspects of recent and contemporary thought on adaptation, some criticisms and counter-criticisms may be briefly considered. It is probably true to say that adaptation has been so much discussed during the past hundred years that there is an understandable tendency for biologists to take it for granted, as if all the seemingly evident or alleged adaptations had been rigorously examined. This is certainly not true of plants. Thus, we have the generally-expressed view in standard texts, e.g. Huxley (1942), that adaptation pervades all development (*but see* below); and hence, by implication, all structural features are deemed to be in some degree adaptive. It is, of course, self-evident and practically a truism that many structural features are highly adaptive: it would be idle to deny the functional effectiveness of the main organs of plants and animals.

Many complex and highly evolved structural features impress us as being precisely adapted to the function to be performed; and hence follows the view that all specialized structures are highly adapted. Nevertheless, there are biologists who have seriously doubted the utility and adaptiveness attributed to certain special or unusual structural features in plants. There are also a great many subtle and still unsolved problems as to how any particular adaptive feature has been brought about, whether in the individual development or the race.* Huxley (1942), in his very fair and objective discussion of these and other problems, pointed out that, although most evolutionary trends are definitely adaptive, there are some trends 'for which no adaptive meaning has yet been discovered'; and Holmes (1948, p. 102), referred to the numerous non-adaptive features of the living world'.

We may recognize that, rightly or wrongly, there are biologists who lack full conviction, or have serious doubts, about the body of doctrine and 'explanation' on adaptations elaborated by Darwinian and post-Darwinian exponents. The theory of natural selection was essentially based on the concept of the adaptation of organisms to their environments and of organs to their functional activities. Nowadays we perhaps hear more of selection, and of selective pressures, etc., the greater adaptation in the successful mutant forms that are preferentially selected being taken for granted. It is pertinent to note at this point that much of the Darwinian and immediate post-Darwinian view of evolution was based on the observation of morphological and structural features. The 'Phyletic Period' in botany, for example, was the great period of comparative morphology. The visible structural features, as Willis (1940) noted, were regarded as the expression of the adaptation that had taken place; i.e. it was thought that morphological and structural features had, in themselves, adaptational value. As Willis (1940, p. 52) wrote:

Once this was fully realized there was a great rush into the study of adaptation, especially during the eighties and early nineties of last century. But in spite of all the work that was put into it, no one ever succeeded in showing that even a small percentage of the structural characters, that were the reason why plants were divided into so many families, genera and species, had any adaptational meaning or value whatever. No value could be attributed to opposite as against alternate leaves (or *vice versa*), to dorsal against ventral raphe, to opening of anthers by pores or by slits, and so on.

---

* The morphogenetic investigation of special adaptive features may be indicated as affording almost unlimited scope for new work.

Willis affords an example of an observer of great experience who began as a confessed adherent of Darwinian adaptation theory and finished up with serious doubts about the whole doctrine. Today, many of his views have been denied, disregarded, or superseded (*see* below); but he undoubtedly made some telling points.

A vast amount of energy was put into the study of adaptation (he wrote) and the imagination was pushed to the extreme limit to find some kind of adaptational value in even the least important features of plants, such as a few hairs in the mouth of a corolla, an unpleasant smell (to some human beings), and innumerable other characters.

Willis concluded that, in general, adaptation in plants must relate to their physiological rather than to their morphological attributes: 'adaptation has far more to do with the physiological than the morphological characters, if indeed it has anything to do with the great bulk of these'. On general biological grounds, Huxley (1942, p. 204) regarded the sharp distinction between structural and functional adaptations as being unjustified. From observations of the proportions of monocotyledons to dicotyledons in particular ecological groups of plants, e.g. in bogs, woodlands, etc., Willis concluded that although the structural differences between monocotyledons and dicotyledons are probably the most important differences that occur, 'there is no evidence to show that they have any adaptational value whatever'; and similarly for many morphological and structural features that are basic to the systematic classification of plants. He also pointed out that although plants growing in extreme environments, e.g. hydrophytes or xerophytes, may show common adaptive characters, which may, admittedly, greatly change the appearance of the plant, they also possess many other more specific and distinctive characters, e.g. those by which they are separated taxonomically, the adaptive aspect of which is unknown.

Willis's general contention was that the concept of adaptation has become accepted in biology on insufficiently critical evidence. In particular, he pointed out that the Podostemaceae* and Tristichaceae (two related families of flowering plants, sometimes treated as one, on which Willis (1914, 1940) was an authority) include some 40 genera and 160 species, all of which are tropical aquatic plants growing submerged in more or less swiftly-running water. The Podostemaceae are, in fact, an

---

* The Podostemales are treated by J. Hutchinson, in *The Families of Flowering Plants*, as *Order* 16, and are placed between the Saxifragales and Sarraceniales, on the one hand, and the Caryophyllales, on the other.

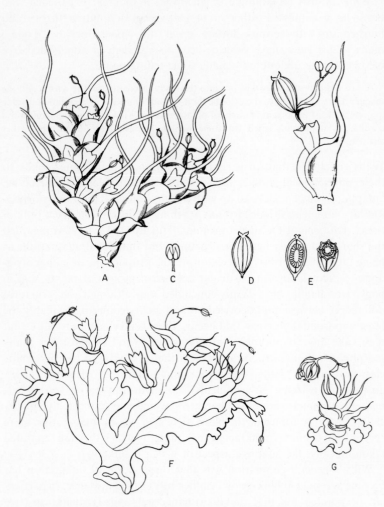

Fig.15.1 A–E, *Podostemon subulatus*. A, Portion of plant. B, Flower.
C, Stamen. D, Pistil. E, L.s. and T.s. ovary.
F, G, *Griffithella hookeriana*. F, Plant. G, Portion of plant enlarged.
(After K. Subramanyam, *Aquatic Angiosperms*, 1962).

exceedingly odd assemblage of flowering plants, resembling various algae, hepatics and mosses in their vegetative development (*see* Figs. 15.1, 15.2). To quote Willis:

All live upon the same substratum of water-worn rock (or anything firm, like timber, that may be caught in the rock) in rapidly flowing water. They are annuals, flowering immediately that the spathe comes above water in the dry season, and then

Fig.15.2 A, *Dicraea dichotoma*; plant.
B–E, *Zeylanidium johnsonii*. B, Plant. C, Portion of plant enlarged.
D, Flower. E, Stamens on a common axis with staminodes on either side. (After K. Subramanyam, *Aquatic Angiosperms*, 1962).

dying. If accidentally laid bare by an unusual fall of water in the vegetative season, they soon die without flowering. All the food comes from the water, and they have no competition for place, except among themselves. Enormous quantities of minute seeds are produced, which have no adaptation at all (except in *Farmeria*) for clinging to their place in the swift current. At most one in a thousand or two may be caught in some fragment of old plant, or in some other place where it can germinate.

At the period when this study was undertaken, the Podostemaceae, with their strange look of lichens or seaweeds, their peculiar mode of growth, their great variety of form, were looked upon as obviously showing adaptation in the highest degree, and it was for this reason that the work was undertaken. But among the conclusions drawn from it was this, that apart from those adaptations which they showed in common with all water plants, such as the lack of strengthening tissues and of stomata, there was in them little evidence of any special adaptation whatever. The conditions under which they lived were the most uniform that it was possible to conceive – the same mode of life, no competition with other forms of life, the same substratum, the same light (varying from day to day with the depth of water), the same temperatures, the same food, everything the same. Yet in spite of this, the plants showed an enormous variety of form, greater than that of any other family of flowering plants whatsoever, while water plants as a rule show little variety in form, and have but few genera and species. Still more remarkable was it that their morphology differed for each continent, flattened roots in the Old World, flattened shoots in the New, so that it was usually possible to say by a simple inspection what was the probable habitat of a species never seen before. It was hard to believe that natural selection, working upon structural modifications that have never been shown to have any functional value, could do this. The linking genus, *Podostemon* itself, covers an immense area, including that of many of the smaller genera, and is less dorsiventral than they are, though all show a highly dorsiventral flower, which stands erect, and is commonly wind pollinated, an unexpected combination of characters for the selectionist to explain.

As it now appears, Willis was probably wrong in many of his views and conclusions. But it is evident that he suffered from honest doubt regarding the concepts of precise and omnipresent adaptation; and at least some of his arguments about the Podostemaceae, and similar points that might be raised regarding other highly specialized morphological structures, still await adequate consideration.

Criticisms of Willis's Views. Arber (1920), while agreeing with Willis (1914) that the concept of natural selection does not explain the origin of the specific and distinctive entities that we call species, urged caution in accepting Willis's assertion that natural selection is unimportant in contributing to adaptation. The Podostemaceae, as it seems, afford an example of evolution unhindered by the limiting, or canalizing, effects of competition and natural selection. In relation to this freedom, a considerable group of well-defined species evolved, these being remarkable for their wide morphological diversity and seeming lack of some well-defined adaptation to their particular and relatively uniform conditions of life. On the contrary, they appear to have varied in all sorts of curious ways. Arber surmised that the absence of adaptation may in part be attributed to the absence of competition and therefore of natural selection. In other words, a study of the Podostemaceae yields important negative evidence of the general effectiveness of natural selection in the inception of adaptations, since, in this group, the absence of competition and natural selection is correlated with the absence of special adaptations. Huxley (1942, p. 491) noted that a greater degree of differentiation in some groups was made possible by reduced competition from other types. In the context of this book, the author would say that the Podostemaceae exemplify a phyletic line in which there has been uncanalized morphogenesis in evolving reaction systems, the end products of many curious pathways of development having survived in the exceptional circumstances already indicated. Now, if this argument is valid, it could be inferred that, in particular circumstances, relatively useless (or non-essential) structures, as assessed on strictly adaptational criteria, could have been evolved. This argument could also apply to many other seemingly non-adaptive morphological features, i.e. evolved in circumstances where selection pressure was low or absent. However, it may be recognized how readily, in discussions of adaptation, as in the present one, one moves from a modest basis of observation into the wide realms of conjecture. One may also note that, while selection pressure is an entirely rational concept, it may be difficult to measure in particular instances. Arber (1920) summarized her views by saying: 'If we can no longer whole-heartedly accept the facile Darwinian explanation, *we must be content to confess that adaptation remains one of the outstanding mysteries of biology.*' (My italics, C. W. W.)

Huxley (1942, p. 204), too, was critical of many of Willis's conclusions, partly because Willis had failed to take note of contemporary cytogenetical findings, and partly because he tended to over-emphasize the importance of the de Vries concept of large mutations.

Omnipresent Adaptation. Huxley (1942) stated that adaptation is in some degree omnipresent – a conclusion with which the present writer cannot be other than in general agreement; for, as he has argued, organismal reaction systems afford the opportunity for the interaction of organismal and environmental factors and are always tending towards a state of equilibrium; i.e. *towards reciprocal, steady-state relationships between organism and environment*; and this, after all, must be the essential basis of adaptations. Huxley has rather deplored the tendency of some biologists to consider adaptations chiefly in terms of very specialized structural developments, such as those seen in insectivorous plants, pollination mechanisms in orchids, etc. Concentration on the study of 'the wonders of nature' (he says) tends to deflect our attention from 'the bedrock fact that some degree of adaptation is omnipresent in life, and that this fact demands its evolutionary explanation'. The tenor of this book indicates that the author is in agreement with this view, subject to the provisos: (i) that while some of the commonplace aspects of adaptation may be accepted as truisms, the factual basis of such adaptations may be difficult to validate; (ii) that, as a fact, the Plant Kingdom includes a great many specialized structures, usually deemed to have

adaptive value, that need to be much more fully investigated and interpreted (*see* Good, 1956); and (iii) that, as well as the evolutionists'
somewhat general interpretations of adaptations, we also need valid,
detailed interpretations in terms of ontogenesis and organization, *since
each individual, throughout its development, is in the very act of becoming
organized and adapted.* This last point brings us back to the concepts of
reaction systems and progressive organization, without which, as it
seems to the author, it is impossible to penetrate more deeply into the
phenomena of adaptation. This view, indeed, seems to be in accord
with one expressed by T. H. Morgan as long ago as 1932, namely, that
the general problem of adaptation is to be found, not so much in the
occasional instances of highly specialized structures, but rather 'in the
totality of the relations of the organism to its environment which makes
the perpetuation of the individual and of the species possible'. If,
however, we can interpret the more general, or common, phenomena of
adaptation, it should also be possible to gain a better understanding of
the more specialized instances, since all of them result from the functioning of reaction systems during ontogenesis.

Evolutionary Trends. In Huxley (1942) there is a long and comprehensive chapter on this and related topics. With some qualifications,
he has come down heavily in favour of a selectionist interpretation of
such trends as against an orthogenetic one, i.e. one in which a trend in
some particular direction is predetermined by intrinsic factors irrespective of selective disadvantage; or in which evolutionary change takes
place without adaptive improvement (Fisher, 1954). Most of his arguments relate to evolutionary developments in animal groups. Adaptations in nature (said Huxley) require natural selection to explain their
origin, the degree of adaptive specialization being correlated with the
intensity of the selection pressure. Adaptation and selection, however,
are not always beneficial to the species: 'We find that intraspecific
selection frequently leads to results which are mainly or wholly useless
to the species or type as a whole' (p. 483).

Most, though not all, of the long-range evolutionary trends are
considered by Huxley to be adaptive, though he noted that some trends
are known for which 'no adaptive meaning has yet been discovered'
(p. 486). Many major trends appear to have been established as a result
of adaptive radiation. Thus, in large systematic groups, it is usual to find
different members adapted to ways of life which are mutually exclusive;
or, as in the phylogenetic discussions of comparative morphologists, a
common ancestral group may have given rise to a number of divergent

phyletic lines; e.g. the Psilophytales are regarded by some botanists as having given rise to the several classes of more advanced vascular plants. Some biologists, however, have held that certain trends are non-adaptive and that the evolutionary progression in a particular direction, i.e. orthogenesis, is determined by inherent tendencies. Where there is apparent orthogenesis of adaptive trends, Huxley has been at pains to show that the phenomena can be explained in other ways, usually in terms of adaptive radiation and selection; and he has cited T. H. Morgan (1925, p. 148) to the effect that when 'a variation in a new direction becomes established, the chance of further advance in the same direction is increased'. Examples of what seem to have been non-adaptive and orthogenetic trends, chiefly in animals, have been cited by Watson (1926) and Haldane (1932). These are very difficult to understand, though, as Huxley pointed out, trends which are in themselves useless may perhaps be correlated with adaptive trends in other characters. So the position seems to be that some structures are adaptive and others are not. We have to distinguish one kind from the other; but we have to account for both.

If the present author is somewhere near the truth in his views on the inception of organization, it may be inferred that, whereas some organismal reaction systems may be so constituted as to 'accommodate' mutational changes in various directions, others may only admit of the incidence of new factors – the effects of mutations – which work in particular directions. In other words, while the general thesis of adaptive radiation may be accepted as being strongly supported by the evidence and by reasoned conjecture to date, the concept of orthogenesis need not be excluded. Indeed, the reflective botanist may be forgiven if he feels that, although part of the evolutionary tangle has now been unravelled, our insight into the many perplexing problems of evolutionary trends, especially in the flowering plants, is still very limited.

ADAPTATION AND THE PRINCIPLE OF ECONOMY

Many instances are known which appear to justify the conception of development with economy of materials. For example, the disposition of the mechanical tissues in plants, whereby maximum strength combined with flexibility is achieved with minimal formation of fibres and other mechanically effective tissues, bears out this point. The mechanical arrangements in some tall grasses have been compared favourably with the structural features of the Eiffel Tower; and so on. All this may be admitted. Nevertheless, the 'excess' and the 'wastefulness' of Nature, though they can perhaps be justified as having survival value, or as conferring biological advantage – e.g. the large dispersal of seeds by orchids to which Darwin referred; or the prodigious discharge of pollen from gymnosperms, anemophilous angiosperms, etc. – are very general features. To cite a commonplace example: many angiosperms typically form axillary buds or bud rudiments, many of which never develop further, or become functional in the adult state, unless the main shoot apex is injured. Now, in plants, buds are organs of major importance. In Darwinian evolution, the formation of such organs would almost certainly be regarded as an important adaptive development! Again, it is a commonplace of experience that species producing tubers, storage rhizomes, etc., typically form far more of them than is in any way essential for competitive survival.

In plant anatomy, the amount of vascular tissue differentiated tends to be regarded as being closely related to the translocational needs of the plant or organ. But how good is the evidence for this view? Undoubtedly, the poor development of vascular tissue in aquatic plants affords affirmative evidence. But other evidence must also be examined. For example, the underground rhizomes of some ferns, e.g. of *Dryopteris dilatata* and *Matteuccia struthiopteris*, eventually become elongated organs, five to ten inches in the former, and several feet in the latter, with well-developed dictyostelic vascular systems, the diameter of the stele being related to the cross-sectional area of the rhizome. Yet all the organic materials required in the formation of these rhizomes come from the maternal main rhizome through a protostele of very small diameter at the point of attachment. The diameter of the dictyostele is directly related to the size of the rhizome apex; but we do not know that it is closely related quantitatively to translocational needs; i.e. that it exemplifies the close adaptiveness implied in the principle of economy. And for all we know, this may also be true of other major developmental features in plants (*see* Fig.10.10).

In the instances already mentioned, where the 'provision made by the plant' vastly exceeds all normal requirements, it may reasonably be asked if the impact of natural selection has been as acute as is sometimes assumed. The apparently 'excessive' development which one may recognize in tuberous and rhizomatous species could, perhaps, be referred to random variation in environments where competition was not severe; or simply to the sheer efficiency of photosynthetic processes. But inherent trends, related to unidirectional changes which alone may be possible in some reaction systems, and including the impact of

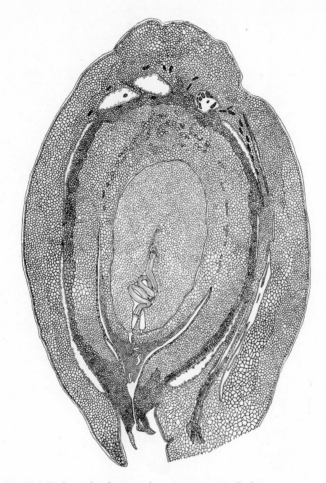

Fig.15.3 Embryo development in a gymnosperm. *Podocarpus totarra.* Longitudinal section of an ovule, showing the long, slender, filamentous embryo (often showing polyembryony), which grows into the richly-stored tissues of the prothallus ('endosperm') and ovule, the suspensor becoming greatly compressed and convoluted during development. (After J. T. Buchholz from C. J. Chamberlain, *Gymnosperms*, 1935).

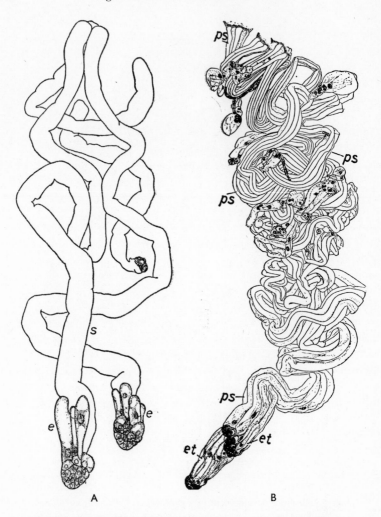

Fig.15.4 Embryo development in gymnosperms. A, *Sequoia semper-virens*: two embryos (*e*) with very long, convoluted, filamentous suspensors (*s*). (Redrawn from J. T. Buchholz, *Amer. Jour. Botany*).
B, *Podocarpus urbanii*: three embryo systems with massive secondary suspensors; *et*, embryonal tube; *ps.* prosuspensors. (After J. T. Buchholz).

It is hard to accept that the embryogenesis of gymnosperms epitomizes either precise adaptation or the principle of economy.

environmental factors, could also afford a possible interpretation. Tuberous and rhizomatous organs may, and probably often do, confer an important biological advantage – they are often, indeed, essential to survival – but, one may ask, in relation to the concept of precise adaptiveness: how closely is the structure developed and perpetuated in heredity commensurate with functional needs?

Numerous instances could be cited of elaborate developments in plants which do not at all appear to be in conformity with the principle of economy of materials or to exemplify precision of adaptation. One particular example may be illustrated here (Figs. 15.3, 15.4). Many gymnosperms are characterized by: (i) the provision of elaborate food reserves for the developing embryo; (ii) the phenomenon of cleavage polyembryony; and (iii) the formation of very long, filamentous, complex suspensors before the embryo proper begins to develop (*see* Wardlaw, 1955, for a fuller account). These developments, which are of general occurrence in a coherent, major group, are considerably more suggestive of the effects of inherent, unidirectional trends than of random variation and selection; they certainly do not suggest economy of materials or precision of adaptation.

Holmes (1948) has called attention to the peculiar problems in adaptation presented by gall-formations caused by insects, fungi, bacteria, etc. Structural features, often characterized by their distinctive and specific morphology and sometimes by their considerable anatomical complexity, are formed by the host-plant. In oaks, for example, recognizably different galls are induced as reactions to the specific chemical stimuli secreted at egg-laying by different insect invaders. Also, the same organism may induce different kinds of galls in different plant species. Now these galls are undoubtedly useful adaptations in the life of the insect invaders; but they are usually regarded as being injurious or at least as gratuitous and uneconomic developments as far as the plant is concerned. One may recognize in gall-formation a kind of tolerance on the part of the plant. No doubt it could be argued that, by forming galls, the plant achieves a measure of protection, i.e. by localizing the deleterious effects of the insect secretion, and that the galls are therefore in the nature of adaptations. However, it is hard to reconcile the considerable structural complexity, and the development of regular tissue patterns in some galls, with an explanation along these lines. It is simpler to recognize that plants may react to specific, localized, chemical stimuli by characteristic morphogenetic developments which may be neither useful nor adaptive. Some of them can be tolerated but others may prove very

o

damaging or even lethal, e.g. bacterial crown gall of many herbaceous plants, caused by *Bacterium tumefaciens*, or Witch's Broom of cacao, caused by *Marasmius perniciosus* (*see* Fig.15.5).

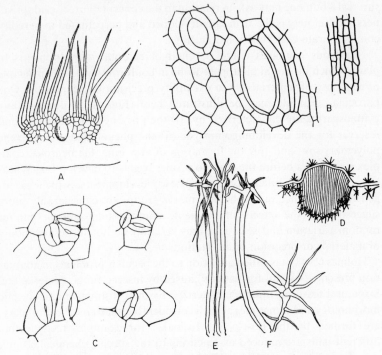

Fig.15.5 Gall formation in plants: some examples of changes in histological organization induced by fungal and insect agents.

A, *Potentilla tormentilla*. Hair development and tissue proliferation due to infection by the fungus *Synchytrium pilificum*; the enlarged cell (centre) contains the fungal cyst.

B, *Populus pyramidalis*: Abnormally large epidermal and stomatal cells in petiole-galls caused by *Pemphigus bursarius*: normal tissue (on right) at same magnification.

C, *Salix* sp. Anomalies in stomatal formation and distribution in galls caused by *Pontania proxima*.

D, E, F, *Phlomis samia*. D, Gall formation, and E, deformed hairs due to the felt-gall; F, normal hairs. (After Rubsaamen).

(After E. Küster, *Pathologische Pflanzenanatomie*, 1925).

THE PRECISION OF ADAPTATIONS

Some adaptations in plants impress us by their sheer functional precision and biological aptness, but others raise problems because they appear to combine different mechanisms which serve the same general biological ends. Thus, in some Leguminosae, the floral construction is of such a nature that when the flower is visited by a bumble bee, cross-pollination is assured (a) by the position of the stigma relative to the pollen with which the bee has been dusted from previous visits to other flowers, and (b) by a motor mechanism which then flicks the insect with the ripe anthers. However, the floral morphology is also such that, should cross-pollination not take place, self-pollination is assured. Since the two adaptive mechanisms are different in kind and, as it were, in 'aims', one may enquire what genetical variations occurred and how the selective forces acted during the evolution of the flower. In this and in other instances, it appears that organizational features may have both specific and more general functional properties or attributes. Whether these developments can be adequately interpreted in terms of random variation and selection, or of inherent trends directed by environmental factors, or in terms of both of these processes, in different degrees in different instances, seem to be questions on which there is scope for new work and critical re-examination.

Special adaptive features such as those exemplified by the plants of special habitats, climbing plants, insectivorous plants, the vegetative and floral developments in the Rafflesiaceae, the numerous cunning floral arrangements that ensure cross-pollination, and so on virtually *ad lib.*, seem to the writer to be difficult to account for *adequately* in terms of a sequence of small random variations, correlative developments, and natural selection, though all of these considerations are admittedly relevant. Geneticists have assiduously sought validating evidence for their views and have been active in the pursuit of reasoned inference and in the expression of imaginative conjecture. But relevant morphogenetic aspects, especially in the flowering plants – the largest and most important group with which the botanist has to deal – have received considerably less attention. When one tries to account for the ontogenesis and phylogenesis of some special adaptive feature, one has no conviction that any *adequate detailed explanation* has yet been advanced. Huxley (1942), as already noted, deprecated the tendency to discuss adaptations mainly with reference to special cases (*see* p. 397). Nevertheless, it is a simple inescapable fact that there are indeed very large numbers of these special cases both in the Plant and Animal Kingdoms which are not satisfactorily accommodated in the omnibus of evolutionary doctrine. But, to be fair, neither are they satisfactorily accounted for by any other scientific doctrine or thesis. We may recognize the

Darwinian 'explanations' as being valid inferences and reasoned conjectures based on a great body of careful observation and experiment. But, even so, the organismal systems under consideration are complex and still very incompletely understood. Some new and additional system of ideas, based on integrated studies of genetical changes, morphogenetic processes, ecological factors and organization seems to be required.

INSECTIVOROUS PLANTS

Insectivorous species, such as those of *Nepenthes*, *Sarracenia*, *Drosera*, and *Dionaea* (or the Venus fly-trap, which Charles Darwin (1875, p. 231) described as one of the most wonderful plants in the world), exemplify some of the most remarkable and complex adaptations in the Plant Kingdom. In them, special structural features and particular physiological activities are closely linked in a combined operation that results in the attracting, trapping and digesting of insect visitors. These plants typically grow in situations in which mineral nutrition is poor. The additional nitrogenous nutrition obtained by catching and digesting insects is thus likely to be important in the growth of the plant, and to confer on it some biological advantage. So, one may ask, as others have done (*see* Kerner and Oliver, 1894), if, in the absence of this ancillary source of nitrogen, the growth, reproduction and survival of these species is greatly affected. One may further ask what kind of variation – random or inherent – was involved in the evolution of these complex new structures and how the selective forces worked on relatively small variations during the intermediate stages. These are very difficult questions, especially when one considers the extent and delicacy of the adaptational developments. It is understandable that the answers given often tend to be rather general. But, in the first place, let us see how Charles Darwin dealt with these problems.

In his fascinating book on *Insectivorous Plants* – to the present author delightful because of its comprehensive and ingenious factual content and its engaging modesty and lucidity of presentation – Darwin, with appropriate citations of contemporary literature, demonstrated beyond any reasonable doubt that the common and well-known insectivorous species *Drosera rotundifolia* derives *several* very considerable advantages from its adaptational features. By measuring various differences between 'starved' plants, i.e. deprived of insects, and those which had been 'fed' with minute pieces of roast meat, Darwin showed that the latter had greater vegetative development, a larger number of flowers, a greatly increased seed production, and much heavier winter buds. Darwin cited contemporary work by Büsgen on the effects of 'starving' and 'feeding' young *Drosera* plants grown from seed. In this case even more marked differences were obtained, as might be expected. Darwin described in detail the very considerable number of experimental observations made by himself and contemporary workers; and by way of summary, after 223 pages of exposition, he wrote: 'I have now given a brief recapitulation of the chief points observed by me, with respect to the structure, movements, constitution, and habits of *Drosera rotundifolia*; *and we see how little has been made out in comparison with what remains unexplained and unknown.*' (My italics, C. W. W.) Darwin concluded that 'most or probably all the species of *Drosera* are adapted for catching insects by nearly the same means' (*ibid.*, p. 229). In this book, as in the *Origin*, he used the method of comparative study in support of his thesis of adaptation. Thus he pointed out that the species of the six known genera of Droseraceae, to all of which he had given some attention, all capture insects. In *Drosophyllum*, *Roridula* and *Byblis*, the more primitive genera from the standpoint of this adaptational development, insect capture is effected solely by the viscid fluid secreted by glands on the leaves; whereas in *Dionaea* and *Aldrovanda* there is a rapid closing of the leaves 'which makes up for the loss of viscid secretion'. In *Drosera*, the most highly adapted and most successful genus, comprising about 90 species (Hall, 1961), there are both viscid secretions and the trapping movements of the so-called 'tentacles'. Leaves of all six genera are apparently able to dissolve animal tissues by means of acid secretions and thereafter to absorb the digested matter. Darwin thought that the small root development in some genera – *Aldrovanda* is rootless – was correlated with this additional source of nutrition; but other observers, e.g. Kerner and Oliver (1894), questioned this view and pointed out that the limited root formation is associated with their boggy or aquatic habitat, as in other non-carnivorous aquatic species.

The *Drosera* species apart, Darwin regarded the other five genera as failing groups. In particular, of *Dionaea muscipula*, the only species of this genus, he wrote: 'It is a strange fact that *Dionaea*, which is one of the most beautifully adapted plants in the vegetable kingdom, should apparently be on the high road to extinction. This is all the more strange as the organs of *Dionaea* are more highly differentiated than those of *Drosera*. . . . ' From comparative studies, Darwin concluded that the parental stock of the Droseraceae might be inferred from the characters of *Drosophyllum*, *Roridula* and *Byblis*, the leaves of the ancient form being 'almost certainly linear, perhaps divided, and bore on their upper and lower surfaces glands which had the power of secreting and absorbing'. By widening the basis of comparison, he then proceeded to show that many plant species have morphological features in which water and insects tend to collect, e.g. in the troughs of many leaf axils; and that many species, e.g. some species of *Saxifraga*, have secretory glands which can also absorb salts, including matter from insect tissue. 'There is, therefore, nothing anomalous in the Droseraceae having acquired the power of absorption in a much more highly developed degree.' And so his argument was cautiously and skilfully built up. He then went on to note that 'it is a far more remarkable problem' that species of quite different taxonomic affinity, such as *Pinguicula* and *Nepenthes*, 'could all have acquired the power of secreting a fluid which dissolves or digests animal matter. The six genera of the Droseraceae have probably inherited this power from a common progenitor, but this cannot apply to *Pinguicula* or *Nepenthes*, for these plants are not at all closely related to the Droseraceae.* But the difficulty is not nearly so great as it first appears'. With references to contemporary physiological studies, Darwin then discussed the fact that many plants have acid juices that serve for digestion. In particular instances, where captured insects were involved, as this secretory and digestive process 'would be of high service to plants growing in very poor soil, it would tend to be perfected through natural selection. Therefore, any ordinary plant having viscid glands, which occasionally caught insects, might thus be converted under favourable circumstances into a species capable of true digestion. It ceases, therefore, to be any great mystery how several genera of plants, in no way closely related together, have independently acquired this same power' (p. 293). Using the comparative method, Darwin also gave evidence and reasoned views as to how the power of movement in leaves and 'tentacles' could have been evolved. Indeed, in his earlier work on *Climbing Plants* (1865, 1906), he had shown that the tendrils of different plants are variously stimulated by contact with different kinds of surfaces. In the case of *Drosera* and *Dionaea* he made the important

---

* *Taxonomy of Carnivorous Plants.* Hutchinson (1926) included the Nepenthaceae in Order 6, Aristolochiales; Droseraceae and Sarraceniaceae in Order 15, Sarraceniales; and *Utricularia* and *Pinguicula* in the Lentibulariaceae, Order 75, Personales. Hall (1961) has included Sarraceniaceae, Nepenthaceae and Droseraceae in the Sarraceniales.

point that their sensitive organs are specialized 'so as not to be uselessly affected by the weight or impact of drops of rain, or blasts of air'; and all this 'perfection of sensitiveness' is the more remarkable in that, unlike animals, these plants have no central nervous system.

Darwin's treatment of insectivorous plants affords a good indication of his general approach to the problems of evolution. He assembled, with painstaking care, all the *facts* available to him, and then, in cautious and modest but direct statements, he brought in his broadly-based verdict – that certain kinds of adaptive developments were biologically advantageous and were likely to persist and be enhanced through natural selection. His arguments, as it were, strode forward in 'seven-league boots'. Indeed, their broad factual basis and immense, simple plausibility make them very difficult to gainsay. Yet, while admiring what Darwin achieved, one may ask if adequate *detailed* investigations of these phenomena in plants have, in fact, been made, whether by morphologists, physiologists, Darwinians, Lamarckians or geneticists. The whole of the causal, morphogenetic aspect, for example, is still relatively untouched, though electron-microscopic studies of the glandular hairs in *Drosophila* may be expected to reveal not only new patterns of organic development but new patterns of thought. When one considers how difficult it is to explain some of the simpler phenomena in plants (*see* p. 413), it becomes evident how slender is our knowledge and understanding of any of the more elaborate 'adaptations'. To quote Lloyd (1942) who reviewed the extensive literature on carnivorous plants: 'About the origin and evolution of the carnivorous plants, however, much as these questions may intrigue the mind, little can be said, nor have I attempted to discuss them' (p. 7). And again: 'How the highly specialized organs of capture could have evolved seems to defy our present knowledge' (p. 7). Because of their wide distribution and the permanence of their curious morphological and physiological features, Peirce (1926) was inclined to regard them as descendants of ancient forms. But, as Lloyd noted, only some of them are widely distributed: others may be very restricted indeed.

It is pertinent to enquire if reaction system theory is likely to assist us in interpreting these special cases of adaptation which exemplify, as it were, some of the curious by-ways of Nature. If, as a starting point, we take the system of an unspecialized ancestral dicotyledon, it is still difficult to see, notwithstanding the many cogent and persuasive arguments advanced by Darwin and contemporary geneticists, how *purely random* mutational changes and selection could have resulted in some of the more complex adaptive mechanisms. Since these mechanisms necessarily involve a number of closely correlated developments, organismal as well as genetical factors must be considered. However, according to geneticists, e.g. Fisher (1954), Huxley (1942), even the most complex and highly adaptive features are not impossible provided there is (i) a sufficiently large amount of random gene mutation, (b) correlative development within the organism at each new evolutionary stage, and (c) a sufficient lapse of time. On the other hand, it could be argued that there are a great many physiological and morphogenetic processes that we do not yet understand and that a reaction system may be so constituted that only certain developmental pathways can be followed; i.e. evolution is limited to advances in certain directions. Provided the action of selective forces is not too severe, this would admit of evolutionary trends, sometimes of a curious and unexpected character and not necessarily useful or adaptive in a high degree at all stages of the trend. So we may ask: at what stage did the ancestors of *Nepenthes* or *Pinguicula* spp. begin to be insectivorous? The same argument could be applied to other remarkable examples of adaptation, e.g. the highly specialized floral organization in the Orchidaceae, etc. Here, as Stebbins noted, the type of development that has been produced during the course of evolution is of an exceptional kind; but, once attained, there has been a vast amount of minor variation round the central type.

Many structural features in plants, which would normally be described as adaptations, e.g. the small leaves of xerophytes, the nectaries in many flowers, the formation of wound cork, etc., occur in quite different environments. Sinnott (1960) regarded such characters as 'being deeply embedded in the genotype'; they probably originated as a result of natural selection and hence their adaptive character. But 'explanations' along these lines do not convey much information. The whole question of adaptation in plants, especially the flowering plants (Good, 1956), is exceedingly difficult and, as it now seems, has been only superficially investigated. Quite simply, and without in any way supporting vitalistic or mystical concepts, the present writer recognizes, from his personal studies of morphogenesis, that in the phenomena of adaptation (some of which seem so precise and apt to the need as to suggest that they are the result of purposeful evolutionary change), there may be processes or reactions – basically physico-chemical in an organismal setting – which so far have not been investigated, have escaped attention, defied analysis, or need to be re-examined from a new point of view.

FISHER'S VIEWS ON 'SPECIAL CASES'

Fisher's studies (1930, 1954), based on a mathematical examination of what is involved in mutation rates, selection, duration of evolutionary trends, etc., have led him to some important and helpful, though not necessarily definitive, conclusions relating to 'cases of special difficulty'. In view of the doubt which the author and others have expressed about the adequacy of the interpretation of special cases, Fisher's ideas and inferences must now be examined. His thesis is that a very large, indeed inconceivably large, amount of variability has been available for recombination and selection in the very numerous generations of organisms throughout the long span of geological time; and that a better understanding of the quantitative efficacy of selective processes enables us to understand that even seemingly improbable evolutionary changes may be brought about. He pointed out that Darwin, with his very cautious approach, consistently tended to underrate the rapidity with which evolutionary changes might take place in favourable circumstances. He also indicated that some of our difficulties, e.g. regarding the evolution of special and highly perfected structures such as the human eye, the organs of flight, etc., are psychological and self-induced: our imaginative faculties simply cannot cope with all that is involved in the splendid spectacle and sheer magnitude and subtlety of evolutionary change. Yet, as he noted, the very difficulties which we experience, like those discussed in the previous section, afford 'the strongest corroboration of the view that evolutionary change was caused by, or rather consisted in, the improvement of adaptations'.

A special difficulty with which Fisher dealt in some detail is that of an organ which is evidently closely adapted to perform some rather trivial function in the economy of the organism, e.g. as in the insectivorous plants already discussed. 'In these cases it may be asked, how can the efficiency of this trifling function have ever been a matter of life and death to the organism, and so have determined its survival in the struggle for existence?' (Fisher, 1954, p. 89). In Fisher's view, if the various special adaptive features are not to be understood in terms of evolutionary selectionist concepts, it virtually becomes necessary to postulate 'a creative power in living matter equivalent to the ingenuity of a benevolent creator'. And he adds that the problems of special cases of adaptation are all, in different ways, 'difficulties less of the reason than of the imagination' (*ibid.*, p. 89). Posterity, perchance, may have other ideas!

The difficulty of accounting for organs of extreme perfection, such
o*

as the human eye, have been discussed by Fisher (1954, p. 90) as follows:

Examples of this difficulty, however, if for the moment, we assume the paradox that examples of extremely minute and intricate adaptation can be regarded as difficulties of a theory, which makes adaptation the mainspring of evolutionary change – could now be easily multiplied. For not only have morphological structures showing such adaptation been described in greater detail, but the study of the regulation and development of organisms has brought to light physiological mechanisms which rival them in the perfection of their aptitude. Darwin clearly recognized in this case that the principal difficulty lay in the limitations of the imaginative faculty. In the *Origin* he writes (Chapter VI): 'Reason tells me, that if numerous gradations from a simple and imperfect eye to one complex and perfect can be shown to exist, each grade being useful to its possessor, as is certainly the case; and if such variations should be useful to any animal under changing conditions of life, then the difficulty of believing that a perfect and complex eye could be formed by natural selection, though insuperable by our imagination, should not be considered as subversive of the theory.'

It would be impossible to add to the cogency of this sentence, yet we may perhaps attempt to probe the difficulty more closely by examining it under the aspect of the improbability of chance variations ever conspiring to achieve what we should naturally regard as a finished triumph of design. This aspect is the better worth examining since, in the writer's opinion, it was Darwin's chief contribution, not only to Biology but to the whole of natural science, to have brought to light a process by which contingencies *a priori* improbable, are given, in the process of time, an increasing probability, until it is their non-occurrence rather than their occurrence which becomes highly improbable.

With regard to adaptive organs which appear to be of small importance to the organism, Fisher pointed out that difficulties of explanation only arise when we have conviction that the organ under consideration is truly adapted to the assumed specific function; after all, we might be in error in this matter.

If the adaptation itself is in question the criticism we are concerned with here cannot be developed. The selectionist is bound by no obligation to show that all characters are adaptive. Anyone, however, who rejects the alternative methods by which adaptation might conceivably have been acquired, i.e. by Lamarckism, or by the special intervention of the Creator, must be prepared to claim that all genuinely adaptive characters have become so through selection.

In a notable passage, Fisher referred to encounters among animals resulting in injury or death. In these dramatic events, he pointed out that although natural selection acts by life or death, i.e. by the destruction of the less fit, 'all modifications that confer advantages, however slight, or which avert injuries, however apparently trivial, will be favoured by natural selection in proportion to the magnitude of their actual effects upon survival and reproduction.'

We may, nonetheless, in so far as our judgment can be relied on, make a broad distinction between characters of great apparent importance to the life of the individual and those the apparent importance of which is much less considerable. *In the case of characters of great importance, such as acuteness of vision, and of the other chief senses in the higher animals, we may infer that any appreciable differences in adaptation will be favoured by selections of a high numerical intensity, leading to a proportionately rapid progress in the species.* (My italics, C. W. W.)

Intricate adaptations, involving a great complexity of genetic substitutions to render them efficient would only be established, or even maintained in the species, by the agency of selective forces, the intensity of which may be thought of broadly, as proportional to their complexity.

The difficulty of high adaptation of unimportant organs may therefore be genuinely felt in cases where we have substantial reasons for believing, (i) that the bionomic function is in fact unimportant, and (ii) that the adaptation is so intricate and has required so many gene-substitutions to build it up, that it could only have come into existence through the agency of selective intensities more powerful than any that our knowledge of the bionomics of the species permits us to postulate (Fisher, 1954, p. 96).

Summation. The writer's attitude to, and summation of, the interpretation of special adaptations may be indicated as follows. Over the years many workers, not undistinguished, have attempted to account for the common phenomenon of the inhibition of lateral buds by the shoot apical meristem. But, notwithstanding all their efforts, no definitive and generally accepted account of this phenomenon has yet been given. The phenomenon itself is not in doubt; but something still escapes us! Again, since the discovery of auxin (indoleacetic acid), continuous efforts have been made by able physiologists all over the world to explain how this substance produces its several important effects. One or other of the contemporary theories is probably close to the truth; but *we still do not know for certain.* And again, during the past three decades, there have been numerous studies of the physiology and biochemistry of the inception of flowering; but students in the classroom still await a satisfying account of the mechanism of this common organizational phenomenon. Many other instances of unexplained common features in plants could be cited. Now, if we still cannot 'explain', in reasonable detail, the more commonplace organizational features in plants, including some which have been investigated at very considerable length, can it really be said that the numerous special adaptive features, with all their subtleties and unexpected and sometimes surprising complexities, have in any sense been adequately investigated? The value of the body of *general* evolutionary doctrine, as now elaborated, can hardly be questioned: it affords an acceptable *general* conception of how the living world could have come to be as it is. But many factual aspects of the inception of form and function still await close investigation. Accordingly, as we attempt to fill in the details and to validate working hypotheses by more thorough studies of adaptational organization, it will indeed be strange if new interpretations, based on the new facts and on new patterns of thought, do not emerge. How these new interpretations will affect the well-established Neo-Darwinian concepts remains to be seen; but they can hardly fail to deepen and widen our comprehension of organizational aspects of adaptations. For, as Darwin and Fisher so well understood, our percipience regarding evolutionary changes has been limited or inhibited by the sheer magnitude and intricate aptness of the phenomena. We must, as it seems, develop a new imaginative insight, and seek help from a 'neo-physical-organic chemistry'* and from much fuller investigations of what is involved in cell organization, if we are to understand in any close fashion what are popularly, but not erroneously, described as the 'wonders', or the 'miracles', of Nature. Although there is undoubtedly widespread acceptance of Neo-Darwinian views among biologists, there are some, like Holmes (1948, p. 103), who have asked: 'Will so simple a theory suffice to explain all the manifold and seemingly purposive contrivances in the world of life?'

THE INHERITANCE OF ACQUIRED CHARACTERS

Views on the inheritance of acquired characters range widely from those of Lamarck and Neo-Lamarckians, who have attributed major evolutionary changes primarily to the capacity of organisms to respond directly to the stress of environmental factors and to the inheritance of the new characters thus acquired, to those who deny absolutely that such essentially phenotypic characters can ever be inherited. Darlington (1950), for example, referred to Lamarck's theory as being discarded and disreputable, embodying the 'ancient superstition of the inheritance of acquired characters'. However, many contemporary geneticists would probably prefer Haldane's (1952) more detached and

---

* Waddington (1962) has discussed aspects of morphogenesis in a somewhat similar vein and has called attention to a paper by Platt (1961) on the 'Properties of large molecules that go beyond the properties of their chemical subgroups'. The forces involved in the organization of very large molecules and organelles are probably of a kind not dealt with by conventional chemistry; i.e. there is scope for what Waddington has described as 'supramolecular chemistry'.

temperate view that the effects of 'nurture' are very seldom inherited but that no one with any knowledge of genetics would say that they are never inherited. As is well known, Darwin (1859, 1878) himself thought that variation was due, to some extent at least, to the constant action of environmental differences in provoking the appearance of new characters and that some of these were inherited.

As already noted, contemporary geneticists affirm that abundant random gene mutation provides the basic materials on which natural selection can work. Haldane (1952), for example, enumerated nine 'distinct reasons why genetic variation can exist in a population', persistent genetical diversity being maintained when the heterozygote *Aa* is fitter than the homozygotes *AA* and *aa*; for in these circumstances neither gene will disappear. Waddington (1957, 1961) has used the fact of abundant genetic variation as the basis for a genetical interpretation of the *apparent* inheritance of acquired characters (*see below*, p. 426).

During recent years, the late H. Graham Cannon (1956, 1957, 1958, 1959) emphasized the importance of Lamarck's contribution to our understanding of evolution and attacked the views of contemporary Neo-Darwinian geneticists.

NEO-LAMARCKIAN EVOLUTION

Cannon (1956, 1957, 1958, 1959) restated and expanded Lamarck's thesis to the effect that the significant evolutionary changes have been responses by plants and animals to *directly felt needs* ('*besoins*') in particular environments. He maintained that variations do not take place at random, as a matter of pure chance, with natural selection ensuring the survival of the fittest: there must be a directive force within the organism which controls its evolution. That force resides in the capacity of the living substance to respond appropriately to stresses imposed by the particular environment, or by the circumstances of life. It was Cannon's contention that a view of this kind affords a more acceptable interpretation of the many marvellous adaptational features of plant and animal life than one based on random variation and selection. (A similar view had previously been expressed by men of letters such as Butler, Shaw and others.) The stress or *need* felt by an organism in particular circumstances affords the stimulus or mechanism which, as it were, triggers-off the series of changes which results in the appearance of an appropriately adaptive new character; and he maintained that the basis of this new character can be transmitted in inheritance.

Here, too, it is appropriate to note that some thinkers, e.g. Waddington (1958), who would probably not describe themselves as Neo-Lamarckians, have expressed themselves in terms that come fairly close to the Lamarckian position. Although 'acquired characters' are not inherited, 'one would expect the *capacity* to undergo such appropriate modifications of the development system to be a hereditary character' (Waddington).

THE ATTEMPTED RE-INSTATEMENT OF LAMARCK

Cannon's aim was to show that, notwithstanding the faults, confusions and inconsistencies which appear in Lamarck's numerous writings, he was the true founder of modern evolutionary theory; that he has been left unread, misrepresented and gravely misunderstood by the world of scientific scholarship; and that there has been undue emphasis on the least important part of his thesis, i.e. the inheritance of acquired characters. In pungent phrases, Cannon indicated how much Darwin's theory owed to Lamarck, and he asserted that Lamarckian views of acquired characters permeate both Darwinian and contemporary Neo-Mendelian theory. For a pro-Lamarckian account of 'what Lamarck really said', and a discussion of the contributions made to evolutionary theory by Lamarck, Erasmus Darwin, Charles Darwin, Mendel and contemporary geneticists, the reader is referred to the writings of Cannon mentioned above. Our concern here is with the impact of new facts and views about organization on some of the classical concepts of evolution.

Lamarck's Laws. In the first place it will be helpful to examine briefly Lamarck's main ideas. These were expounded as *laws*. In 1809 in his *Philosophie Zoologique*, and in 1815, in his *Invertebrate Zoology*, Lamarck published different accounts of his laws of evolution (for the documentation of a somewhat confused situation, *see* H. G. Cannon, 1959). The later version of these laws is as follows (after Cannon):

First Law

Life, by its own force, tends continually to increase the volume of every living body and to extend the dimensions of its parts, up to a limit which it imposes.

Second Law

The production of a new organ in an animal body results from a new need (*besoin*) which continues to make itself felt, and from a new movement that this need brings about and maintains.

Third Law

The development and effectiveness of organs are proportional to the use of those organs.

Fourth Law

Everything acquired or changed during an individual's lifetime is preserved by heredity and transmitted to that individual's progeny.

Cannon regarded the first law as following from the third and as redundant. The writer does not agree: this law seems to be valid and important; and both logic and life are contrary to Cannon's interpretation. The earliest holistic organizations cannot have been other than small. Pre-genetic and subsequent genetic changes, making for increase in size, and therefore admitting of increased assimilation and differentiation, but inevitably involving the principle of similitude, have almost certainly had biological advantages. In a competitive plant population, rapid growth of an individual to some considerable size is usually advantageous; but this is not necessarily determined by 'use'. Furthermore, there is evidence from many sources that living entities have evolved from small to large size, i.e. from unicellular to multicellular organisms; and, without going into details, there is abundant evidence that genetical changes do determine size increases. Single genes, for example, are known to determine the difference between tall and dwarf forms in a strain. Also, with increases in size, various formal and structural changes necessarily follow in conformity with the principle of similitude; and various morphogenetic innovations become possible.

The second law was regarded by Cannon as being of paramount importance; for it says that 'if the relation between the organism and environment demand the appearance of a new organ then the organ will appear. *This is the essence of real Lamarckism*' (Cannon, 1959, p. 53). His discussion of this law is in the following terms:

Lamarck states that 'The foundation of this law derives its proof from the third', which he says cannot be disputed. But this is not so. The third law states that organs increase in size and effectiveness with use, and so, says Lamarck, one can be sure that the same forces which control this increase in size 'would necessarily give birth to the organ adapted to satisfy' the new need. But can one be sure of this? Surely this is the stumbling-block for most people, at least those who take Lamarckism seriously. Everybody appears to accept this third law because it is easy to envisage how an acting organ can increase itself. The works are there, and so by use they can become more powerful and efficient. But when the works are not there it is harder to picture how new organs can originate, and to many of our present-day geneticists the whole idea smacks of mysticism or at least vitalism. But let us remember that such a process does not involve any greater stretch of the imagination than is required to accept the modern orthodox theory which leaves everything to chance!

Cannon argued that the third law is dependent on the second, and not *vice-versa* as Lamarck had thought. The third law is one with which botanists who have studied, for example, the development of mechanical or vascular tissues in plants, are familiar. Some of the developments are phenotypic effects relating to functional activity; but others seem to be closely determined by constitutional factors.

The fourth law, which deals with the inheritance of acquired characters – 'the cause of all the trouble' – was regarded by Cannon as being unnecessary. The essence of his argument is that, since the environment does not change appreciably from one generation of plants or animals to the next, the effects induced in the parent will equally be induced in the offspring; so the acquired phenotypic character need not be inherited. While this argument enables one to avoid having to propose a physiological-genetical mechanism for the inheritance of a character, acquired during the lifetime of an individual, it is not really acceptable. The findings of experimental taxonomy in plants are contrary to Cannon's interpretation. Clones of the same variety taken to contrasted environments often show more or less conspicuous phenotypic divergences; but clones from different localities grown under the same conditions may, or may not, show more or less close parallelisms. However, in each instance the range of response is determined by the genetic constitution. Moreover, the primary morphogenetic patterns in the embryo and in the shoot apical growing point are not directly related to environmental factors, though these are necessarily involved. It is during the elaboration of the primary patterns in the subapical and maturing regions that the effects of environmental factors become important and sometimes conspicuous. There is also the inescapable fact that, in stable and uniform environments, a large amount of genetical differentiation takes place at the biotype, strain, variety and species levels. Both phenotypic and genetical diversity may be recognized as major phenomena.

Lamarck's fourth law impresses one as an over-statement and is not proven. In view of the various findings regarding adaptive enzymes, however, it cannot be dismissed as being inherently improbable.

Cannon maintained (p. 56) that if a particular structure is required in the adult life, therefore it will appear, i.e. in terms of Lamarck's second law. The fact that such a structure must originate at some earlier stage in ontogenesis, i.e. before it has become functionally necessary, was regarded by Cannon as being beside the point, since 'it is reasonable to deduce that the precocious appearance is an advantage and even a necessity, in which case it will be Lamarck's second law which controls the phenomenon and not the fourth'. Botanists who have studied the formation of organs and the differentiation of tissues at the shoot apex are familiar with this seeming anticipation of subsequent functional needs. It is a commonplace in the development of plants. As a *jeu d'esprit*, Bower described it as prolepsis, or as 'intelligent anticipitation'. One of the aims of morphogenesis is to seek epigenetic explanations of these phenomena. The value of reaction system concepts in this connection is evident. However, when viewed with detachment, it does not appear to the writer that satisfying Lamarckian or epigenetic explanations have yet been advanced relating the inception of organogenic patterns to the subsequent functional efficiency of the adult structure.

Criticisms of Darwin and Others. Cannon contended that Lamarck anticipated Darwin in proposing the theory or principle of natural selection and that he envisaged Nature as one dynamic system tending towards equilibrium, 'well balanced and in order', and controlled by the interactions of many different organisms.

In discussing what he regarded as the shortcomings of Darwin and the Neo-Mendelians, Cannon cited various authors as supporting the propositions: (i) that the characters studied by geneticists often differ fundamentally from those which appear to be most important in evolution under natural conditions; (ii) that the arguments of Neo-Mendelians allow for virtually all eventualities, including the inheritance of acquired characters;[*] (iii) that natural selection, which in any case is a simple truism, will act on variations however they may be deemed to have arisen, whether by 'Neo-Mendelian' or 'Lamarckian' processes; (iv) that, in natural selection, it is not only the unfit that die but, wherever there is competition, the fittest that survive; i.e. there is a whole gamut from features which make for unfitness at one end, through features which are neutral in selection or even useless to the organism, to those which make for survival because of their fitness; (v) that, notwithstanding the neo-Mendelian view of the importance of spontaneous, random, heritable variations in evolution, Darwin himself

---

[*] Waddington (1958, p. 18) wrote as follows: 'Darwin may not have been so wrong as many have since thought him in feeling that there was something – he was never quite sure what – in Lamarck's views.'

had noted a tendency on the part of offspring 'to vary again in the same manner as their parents', i.e. he recognized the existence of orthogenetic trends; and (vi) that Darwin failed to realize that the correlation of characters is quite essential in all adaptive innovations.

Cannon then asked, as others have done, if genes, which admittedly can alter existing structures, also bring about the appearance of new functional structures and effect their correlation with the organism as a whole. In fact, this point has been considered at some length by geneticists. Stebbins (1950), for example, regarded the concept of correlation as being essential to the system of genetical changes involved in the differentiation of the species and higher taxa of flowering plants (*see* Chapters 5, 11). In emphasizing his view that when a gene mutation takes place, the whole of the organism reacts in a Lamarckian manner (p. 121), Cannon apparently failed to appreciate that many geneticists have stated explicitly that *no gene ever acts in isolation* but only through the genetical system as a whole, due allowance also being made for the incidence of environmental factors (*see* p. 43). Finally, Cannon blamed the Neo-Mendelians for their failure to distinguish between the relatively minor characters, which readily lend themselves to genetical experimentation, and the major features on which the essential functioning of the organism is based; for (he said) it is among these major functional characters that adaptation is most manifest, and 'adaptation is the essence of evolution'. Biologists who are interested in the wider aspects of evolution and in organisms as organisms may well find themselves, to some extent at least, in sympathy with this outlook.

Two Aspects of Inheritance. In his book on *The Evolution of Living Things* (1958), Cannon affirmed that the evolutionary process has two manifestations, namely, *organismal inheritance* and *Mendelian inheritance*. Organismal inheritance is concerned with the major morphological and structural features that are involved in the adequate functioning of an organism and has been brought about by 'balanced evolution' affecting the whole integrated organism in its relation to its environment. In brief, it epitomizes the close and purposive adaptiveness of the organism to its functional needs, along the lines envisaged by Lamarck. Mendelian inheritance, on the other hand, often seems to deal with relatively trivial characters of little functional or selective significance. While it is a fact that geneticists often work with relatively trivial characters, a subdivision of the kind proposed by Cannon is unacceptable to those who hold holistic views.

Le Chatelier's Principle and Homeostasis. In stating the case for balanced, organismal inheritance and evolution, based fundamentally on a system of physico-chemical reactions between organism and environment, Cannon invoked Le Chatelier's principle and W. B. Cannon's (1939) concept of homeostasis.

Le Chatelier's principle arises from a consideration of chemical equilibrium and the law of mass action and may be stated as follows (Lowry and Sugden, 1929, p. 253):

> *If one of the conditions of a system in equilibrium be altered, the system will adjust itself in such a direction as partially to neutralize the change in condition.* According to the law of mass action, the velocity of a homogeneous chemical change is proportional to the concentration of each of the reacting substances. In 'incomplete' reactions, the reaction does not continue until one or other of the reacting substances has disappeared but stops short at an equilibrium point at which both the product of change and the original substances are present in a state of equilibrium in the reaction system. Such reactions are reversible.

The concept of homeostasis is an application of Le Chatelier's principle and relates to the power or ability of an organism as a whole to readjust itself appropriately to a change in one of its parts. 'Any change in the body (wrote H. G. Cannon, 1959, p. 131) must be followed by adjustments in all other parts of the body.' The Lamarckian adaptation is thus seen as an active and purposeful reaction of the organism in relation to its environment. The absence of a holistic conception of change and adaptation in an organism, was indeed, one of Cannon's principal objections to modern genetics – one in which, however, he was not justified. As the writer has shown at several points in this book, geneticists do envisage the working of the genetical system as a whole and have emphasized that, in development, environmental and correlative factors are of great importance. But there are also geneticists who have overemphasized what Waddington (1961) has described as the *atomistic* aspect, at the expense of the *continuum* or *organismic* aspect.

Cannon contended that, where organisms were exposed to some considerable change in an environment to which they could respond, the new equilibrium between organism and environment would 'mean a new type of living thing'. In other words, evolutionary changes, essentially adaptive and purposeful in character, would take place in the organism 'by virtue of a power within itself. Purposive constitution in fact is a fundamental property of living matter'. It must be said that the botanical evidence is against this view. Studies of experimental taxonomy during the past few decades have shown clearly that many species of flowering plants have remarkable flexibility for growth and reproduction over a wide range of environment, without undergoing any permanent, i.e. genotypic change. These studies have also shown that if specimens of a species or variety are collected in the same or in different localities and grown under uniform conditions, evidence is often obtained of the existence of a considerable amount of genetical variability which, in particular circumstances, could have adaptive or selective value. (For a useful summary and discussion *see* Heslop-Harrison, 1953). The many expeditions in search of relatives of cultivated species of plants have had as their aim the improvement of agricultural and horticultural varieties in respect of yield, heat or cold resistance, etc. The success of this work is beyond dispute.

Purposive or Purposeful Changes. Apart from the disadvantages of its unavoidable teleological implications or undertones, the use of the term *purposive* or *purposeful* in connection with adaptive features may not be strictly necessary. If organism *plus* environment constitute a holistic physico-chemical system, always tending, like any such system, towards a state of equilibrium or steady state, certain results must follow as a natural consequence. These may appear to us to be *purposeful*, and may be so described as a handy, comprehensive, biological statement. But strictly speaking, this kind of expression is not necessary. If physico-chemical principles are pervasive in Nature – as we believe them to be – the effects of environmental changes in an organismal reaction system will be unavoidable. As these will be 'equilibrium' or 'steady state' effects, it is not surprising that they may appear to the observer as adaptations with seemingly purposive structural and functional attributes.

Much of the argument reviewed above is largely a matter of semantics and personal approach, and seemingly divergent attitudes may perhaps be reconciled. Thus, we may perhaps equate 'purposive structure', by some regarded as 'a fundamental property of the living being' (Berg, 1926, p. 8), or 'adaptive structure', with resultant equilibrium or steady state effects.

A Further Note on Adaptive Features and Purposiveness. When we speak of *purpose* in biology, we refer, according to the *Oxford English Dictionary*, to the object in view; to 'the action or fact of intending to do something; the object for which anything is done or made, or for which it exists'. And when, in biology, we use the term *purposive* or *purposeful*, we mean 'serving or tending to serve some purpose in the animal or vegetable economy'.

Although the concept of *purpose* is teleological (*see* Chapter 1, p. 9 *et seq.*), some biologists find it difficult to exclude. A common argument, which they use in support of this view, is that it is highly improbable that a complex and efficient organ like the human eye could have come into existence by purely random variation and selection. Hence the support by Cannon and others of the Lamarckian view that new characters evolve in direct relation to the needs of the organism. The exactitude of some adaptations, often involving many components, depends on a system of correlated and integrated developments of 'the right kind', the collective effect of which still awaits adequate detailed explanation. When one reflects on the evolution of the insect-trapping and digesting pitchers – modified foliar organs – of *Nepenthes*, the numerous floral mechanisms to ensure cross-pollination by insects in the Leguminosae, Orchidaceae, and many other families, the various devices of climbing and parasitic plants, etc., to mention only a few of 'the wonders of the Plant Kingdom', one may well ask if, after all, anything more than partial and very incomplete interpretations have so far been advanced. On the other hand, whether we can 'explain' them or not, the prevalence of special mechanisms supports the general thesis that evolution and adaptive change, effected by selection, are general, pervasive phenomena.

Now, in a 'purposive' or other development, the organism, envisaged as a physico-chemical entity, may be regarded as being in a state of dynamic equilibrium with its environment at every stage; i.e. the attainment of this state is due to both extrinsic and intrinsic factors. Accordingly, on a thesis along these lines, all ontogenetic developments must be characterized by an element of pervasive adaptiveness. Moreover, since ontogenesis usually exemplifies developmental harmony – which is also an equilibrium effect – any viable evolutionary change will, through correlation, become part of that harmony. But even although the development of ideas along these lines, which are, admittedly, a vast over-simplification, may eventually admit of a *generalized* neo-physico-chemical interpretation of adaptive features, the difficulties of accounting *in detail* for any of the numerous instances of special adaptation in plants seem likely to remain with us for a long time to come.

An insuperable difficulty in considering *purpose* in biology is to suggest a mechanism whereby a *purpose* could act on the organismal reaction system. A *need* does not present this difficulty, for it could, for example, be envisaged as a stress or stimulus of some kind, i.e. as a physical or chemical factor, capable of affecting the reaction system. Also, in a particular environment, a plant might experience and react to a need without necessarily having a purpose – although *we* might say anthropomorphically that the fulfilment of the need was essential to, or for the purpose of, survival. At the level of organization attained by plant life, then, it may be doubted if the general question of purpose can be pursued further to any advantage.

In considering the nature of adaptations, Thomas *et al.* (1956, p. 439) stated that, in analysing growth phenomena, our concern is with *proximate* causes and not with final or *purposeful causes*. Plant structures are seen as 'the inevitable end products of the reactions between inherited internal factors and significant environmental factors'; and the end products 'may or may not be adaptations', i.e. making the plant specially fit to survive in a particular environment. 'Even when the use of the term adaptation is justifiable, it is not justifiable to assign as the cause of the formation or occurrence of any structure its importance to the plant as is so often done in sentences such as "the *reason* for the production of chlorophyll is that plants require light energy for photosynthesis".' Thomas's view of the evolution of adaptive features is that 'such adaptations towards a given environment as are inevitably formed during the development of a given individual will have survival value for the race to which that individual belongs'. In brief, *interaction* between environmental and inherited factors, and the intense competition for space, light, nutrients, etc., are seen to be the key to adaptation.

The Inheritance of Major Organizational Features. While Cannon was on insecure ground at several points, there is substance in his contention that many of the major morphological and organizational features in plants and animals have been left relatively untouched by Mendelism, whether classical or 'neo'. For example, we know from genetical investigations that there are genes which determine whether a shoot shall be tall or short; and, in some instances, we know what some of the related chemical processes are. But so far there is virtually no genetical information or theory regarding the factors which determine the organization and morphogenetic activity of the shoot apex or the shoot type of construction. Yet, as we have seen, this is a very important and distinctive feature in higher plants. Again, genetical studies have yielded very interesting information on genes which affect leaf shape and size; but they have not shed any light on the origin and morphological nature of leaves as such. To cite a recent example, Lamprecht (1963) has found, in a detailed genetical analysis of *Pisum*, that the difference in pod length in parental lines is mainly due to a single gene; and also that in one of the parent lines the further reduction of the already small stipules can be ascribed to a single gene. But do we know anything about the genes that determine the morphogenesis of pods or stipules?

In short, although we assume that genes are closely involved in all organogenic processes, there do not appear to be adequate genetical explanations of any of the major organizational features in plants.

Genetical studies indicate that very large numbers of genes are involved in the organization of any higher plant or animal. Yet, in various developmental situations, many genes have little perceptible *specific* effect; i.e. they behave as 'general purposes' physiological units in the protoplasm and in the growth of the plant as a whole. In particular developmental situations, however, specific genic effects may become of critical importance. For example, particular genes may 'block' or accelerate a major system of reactions, or they may modify the differential growth pattern, and so on.

Reaction System Concepts and Neo-Lamarckism. If we consider the Neo-Lamarckian theory of evolution in terms of reaction system concepts as developed in this book, the *need* or *stress* experienced by an organism in a particular environment may be envisaged as a physical or chemical factor making its impact on the reaction system. An increase in the temperature or light intensity of the environment, for example, would modify the activity of the system and related developments in characteristic ways. So, if there is a middle road between Neo-Lamarckism and Neo-Mendelism, it may well be found in reaction system concepts. The organizational and adaptive features which we see in plants at large seem likely to include both random and directed changes. Neither need be excluded on reaction system theory. In fact, the more one contemplates some of the highly adaptive features in plants, the more difficult it becomes to suggest mechanisms whereby they could have come into existence. The adaptation of plants in general to their environment does not present this difficulty, if only because many common species seem to have a considerable range of tolerance.

The present study of organization has indicated the need for recognizing: (i) that given energy, substance and circumstance, autonomous combinations and organizations of CN compounds can take place – a physico-chemical concept; (ii) that the number of possible combinations of C, N, O, H, and other elements is very great; hence the large number of metabolic substances recognized by physiologists and the diversity of genes and gene-mutants revealed by genetical study; (iii) that organism and environment are inseparable; (iv) that environment, which is ever present, mediates important phenotypic developments in the individual life, some of which may be heritable – a Lamarckian view; (v) that natural populations are characterized by a large amount of variation, the result of gene mutation, segregation and recombination, and that this variation provides the materials on which selective forces may work – the central Neo-Mendelian concept.

THE CONTEMPORARY GENETICAL APPROACH TO THE INHERITANCE OF ACQUIRED CHARACTERS

With Cannon's restatement of Lamarck's views before us, with its emphasis on environmental factors and life conditions, it is a matter of some interest to consider the views of geneticists who have seriously examined the Lamarckian position. For, as Harland (1958) stated: 'Any biologist knows that if genetics succeeds in postulating a way of bringing Lamarckian effects within its framework, science will be well served, and all geneticists will welcome the new synthesis.' Waddington (1942, 1957, 1961), an exponent of this topic, has stated:

> There is also a second cyclical system which has to be considered in relation to evolution. The environment influences the nature of the adult organisms which grow up within it. When organisms reproduce and leave offspring, the characters which enable some to be more successful than others depend only in part on their hereditary constitution, but in part also on the environmental circumstances under which they develop. The older discussions of the Lamarckian problem of 'the inheritance of acquired characters' usually missed the point that all characters of all organisms are to some extent directive* in their formation, and that equally all characters are to some extent inherited, since an organism cannot form any structure for which it does not have the hereditary potentialities. The question we need to ask is not whether acquired characters are inherited, but whether, as we should expect, *the ability to acquire the character*† differs hereditarily in different individuals in a population, and if so what will be the effect of natural selection on the potentialities of later generations. Once the problem has been formulated in this way it is easy to carry out experiments which will give us at least the first answers in this field.

In any population, different individuals have different *hereditary* potentialities for adaptation to new, or abnormal, environmental conditions and stresses. These are the individuals, which are likely to persist when natural selection operates, and the potentialities of the next generation for acquiring the *seemingly* Lamarckian character will be increased. Thus, in experiments with *Drosophila* grown on a medium

---

* It seems to the author, as a matter of logic, that environment must always have directive effects in adaptational phenomena.

† My italics, C. W. W.

containing an almost lethal amount of salt, Waddington found that most of the grubs were killed but some survived and became slightly modified during their development. There was an enlargement of the two papillae on either side of the anus, these organs being probably involved in regulating the salt content of the body fluid. The importance of this experiment was to show that, in a population, some individuals already existed which had the inherent property of resisting the effects of high salt concentrations. These, of course, were selected and gave rise to the next generation, all the others being killed. The experimental treatment, which was maintained over some twenty generations, eventually yielded populations in which a much higher proportion of the individuals were salt-tolerant. Further studies of the 'acquired character', i.e. the selected existing genetic variation, showed that selection had led to (i) an increase in the capacity of individuals in populations to form enlarged papillae, and (ii) a general, permanent increase in the size of the anal papillae. The seeming inheritance of a Lamarckian acquired character was thus put on a genetical basis. The normal developmental pathway had been deflected from its usual course by unusual environmental conditions and the new modification, being useful, tended to be selected and increasingly perpetuated in subsequent generations. Even when a population was returned to its original environment, some of the 'acquired' effects persisted. This phenomenon has been described by Waddington (1957, 1961) as *genetic assimilation*.

In terms of the 'feed-back', or *cybernetic*, concept of developmental canalization, Waddington (1957, 1961) has considered a feed-back type of mechanism, or system, which may act in conjunction with mutation.

Consider a population of animals in which there has been natural selection for the ability to acquire some character when they are subjected to a particular environmental stress. In time the hereditary constitution of the individuals will be such that their development is very easily modified by an environmental stress to produce the acquired character. They are set, as it were, on a hair trigger and aimed to hit the target. But once this state has been reached, it will be relatively easy for other things besides the environment to pull the trigger. If genes are changing at random all the time, it will be by no means unlikely that a new mutation will turn up which suffices to pull the trigger, and thus to produce the same acquired character which originally required an environmental stimulus to bring it into being.

Waddington's general conclusions from his consideration of the possible inheritance of acquired characters are: (i) that random mutation is still the only known way in which new hereditary variation comes into existence; and (ii) that natural selection is the only known process which is effective in changing the hereditary constitution of a population in successive generations. And while these basic processes in evolution are not in themselves finalistic, they may interact with one another in such a way as to yield a biological mechanism with some quasi-finalistic attributes. (One may be permitted to wonder how the substance of this section will appear to readers in twenty, or even ten years' time.)

Environment and Genotype. With regard to the effects of environmental factors on hereditary constitution, Waddington (1959, p. 164) expressed the view that a genotype formed under natural selection will have tendencies to be resistant to environmental factors making for less fitness and other tendencies 'to be labile in a manner appropriate to the environmental stresses which the animal tends to meet. So the developmental system will be tuned in to respond to the environment in a suitable manner'. Moreover, the phenotypic effect of new gene mutations

will be dependent on the way the developmental system is stable or unstable. In this way you will reach, rather at second-hand, a relation between the organism and the environment which is rather more close than one has usually envisaged. We reach the view that the environmental stresses impinging on an organism do in fact have something to say about the nature of the phenotypic variation that will be submitted to natural selection, not at first hand but at second hand, by building-in these stabilities and instabilities of the developmental system, and in that way influencing the type of phenotypic effects which random changes in the nuclear proteins of the chromosomes may produce.

Adaptive Changes in Bacteria. Dean (*see* Waddington, 1959) has cited evidence from the chemical kinetics of bacteria to the effect that adaptive changes in response to the environment are possible. After stating three kinetic principles he has derived a fourth principle, namely that, in particular systems which can be specified, 'the proportions of constituents tend towards those which give a maximum rate of growth in the given environment. That is to say, under new conditions a new quantitative scheme of reactions will gradually replace other quantitative schemes with smaller resultant reaction rates. In this way adaptive changes in response to the environment are possible.'

Dean further stated that these kinetic considerations have been shown to apply to systems in which alternative metabolic pathways exist. 'In general, the route chosen will be the one leading to the optimum rate of growth in the given environment although considerable time may elapse before this condition is fulfilled since the route leading to the best rate of growth may be inhibited by the operation of a less effective alternative route already in operation.' In short, it is now possible to indicate a kinetic scheme of bacterial adaptation as an automatic adjustment in response to the environment. Dean considered that a mechanism of this kind explains the observed experimental results better than does a theory involving mutation and selection. The following quotation from Dean is of rather special interest.

The question is often asked whether these adaptations represent stable heritable changes. It is our experience that in general the longer the training process has been continued the more stable does the adaptation become until eventually it appears to a cursory sort of test to be stable. But the stability is never absolute and so what we are dealing with are not stable heritable changes but sluggishly reversible adaptations. Kinetic theory in its simplest form predicts easy and complete reversibility on removal of the inducing agent but there are good physico-chemical reasons why reversibility may on occasion be slow.

MONOPHYLETIC AND POLYPHYLETIC VIEWS

One of the great controversial issues among an earlier generation of botanists was the monophyletic or polyphyletic origin of the several classes of vascular plants. Both concepts still have their adherents. Some taxonomic and fossil botanists regard the problem as being incapable of any final solution but consider that a polyphyletic origin of the vascular plants from an algal ancestry is more probable and more in keeping with the evidence. But they, too, accept that all the more advanced classes of vascular plants probably passed through a *Psilophyton*-like phase of development, i.e. as independent evolutionary progressions, though much earlier than the Middle Devonian times of *Rhynia*, *Psilophyton*, etc. Accordingly, the Pteridophyta, formerly regarded as a great coherent subdivision of the Plant Kingdom, has been replaced by four separate, independent phyletic lines, namely Psilopsida, Lycopsida, Sphenopsida and Pteropsida (comprising the Filicineae, the Gymnospermae and the Angiospermae). Stewart (1959), however, considered that there is no 'irrefutable evidence which supports the polyphyletic origin of vascular plants', and maintained that the Tracheophyta should continue to be recognized as a natural group of green plants. That rather general view is, of course, supported by the evidence submitted by the author. It may now be asked if the study of organization in plants has shed any new light on this old controversy. Does it enable us to accept one view and reject the other? Or does it, perhaps, afford some new vantage point from which to assess the merits of both concepts?

Among relevant facts and inferences the following may be noted: (i) all zygotes, including those of the more advanced Algae, manifest polarity from the outset and give rise to a filamentous structure with a distal growing point; (ii) apical meristems are pattern-forming, and typically yield an axis with regularly-disposed lateral members; (iii) in their mode of origin at the shoot apex, there is no *essential* difference between megaphylls and microphylls; (iv) differently constituted reaction systems in embryonic regions, i.e. with different gene-determined components, may nevertheless yield comparable organogenic patterns; and correlative and physical factors and spatial relationships are important in the eventual assumption of form.

It does not, in fact, appear that the study of organization has as yet enabled us to resolve the problem of monophyletic or polyphyletic origins. Fundamentally the problem is concerned with the origin and evolution of genetical constitutions. It may be, as some workers maintain, that what cannot now be decided on the morphological evidence may yet be resolved by studies of chemical phylogeny, though there, too, definitive conclusions may be impeded by the existence of parallel evolutionary trends. But sooner or later, with the expansion of enquiries to plants in different systematic groups, and with refinement of technique, it may be possible to indicate phylogenetic relationships based on specific, or unique, metabolic processes and trends. So, even if the present study of organization has not enabled us to distinguish between the merits of monophyletic and polphyletic views, there may still be new ways in which decisive information may yet be obtained. However, in comparative studies, it is still mandatory that the fullest use should be made of *all* possible criteria.

Comparative Chemistry. The comparative chemistry of plants, though of evident importance, still commands the attention of a relatively small proportion of professional botanists: witness the very small group of papers contributed to the IXth International Botanical Congress (Montreal, 1959). The subject, in fact, may well pass into the competent hands of organic and biochemists. Moritz (1959) discussed the point of view and procedures in the new phase of comparative serology. Hegnauer (1959) has demonstrated that cyanogenetic glycosides are of wide occurrence in the Plant Kingdom, indicating that it is a character of some considerable antiquity; indeed, a substance in this category occurs in *Degeneria*, one of the most ancient genera of dicotyledons according to I. W. Bailey. Gibbs (1959) showed that Hutchinson's further subdivision of the great group of the Tubiflorae into 28 families, as compared with the 22 families in Engler-Diels' grouping, is not justified on the basis of a rigorous chemical examination. The close study of the chemical characters of plants is evidently a vast subject. One may safely predict that its further development, as in all other biological topics, will bring its own problems and difficulties. That this is appreciated by its adherents is apparent from a statement by Hegnauer (1959) to the effect that 'nothing may be more noxious to chemotaxonomy than an over-valuation of the possibilities it offers for taxonomic work'. Contributors to a recent symposium (*see* Swain, 1963), have also adopted a cautious attitude regarding the conclusions that may be expected from studies of comparative chemistry or chemical phylogeny.

General Affinity of Chlorophyta. The general affinity of green plants can scarcely be doubted. As we have seen, *all* green plants have major features of cellular organization in common; they are closely comparable in their general physiology; and their life processes are broadly, and sometimes closely, comparable, even where no close genetical affinity is considered to be involved. These shared attributes strongly suggest that the several classes of Embryophyta originated from green algal ancestors in which the basic and stable features of cellular organization had already been established. A further inference might be that many of the common genes or gene-complexes of the 'algal phase' were transmitted relatively unchanged during the differentiation and evolution of the several phyletic lines. This, however, is not the view of some geneticists who hold that genetical systems may undergo very considerable changes even though the related morphological manifestations may only be slightly changed (*see* Chapter 5). On the other hand, there are biologists who consider that too much emphasis has been placed on gene action and mutation in determining some of the major aspects of morpho-genesis and evolution.

Divergences and Phyletic Gaps. One of the main questions in phylogeny is concerned with the points at which the divergences of the major phyletic lines from the parental stock took place, i.e. at the algal phase, or at various later evolutionary stages, as some comparative mor-phologists have suggested. It is now recognized that some criteria based on morphological and structural similarities are considerably less depend-able as evidence of natural affinity than was formerly thought. However, this is the kind of evidence that is most readily accessible at the present time: and it is still *the* most comprehensive evidence, can we but assess it correctly! In the Embryophyta, from the first division of the zygote onwards to the adult state, it now appears that many of the principal organizational features cannot be directly and closely related to specific genetical factors. Nevertheless, the basic affinities of organisms, however different they may appear morphologically, are essentially genetical phenomena. Yet, who among us, if he had no previous knowledge of the fern life cycle, would ever guess that the small simple gametophyte and the large, complex sporophyte shared the same genetical constitution? The fullness of knowledge, whether of the individual organism or the phylogeny of its race, clearly requires morphological, taxonomic, genetical, biochemical and biophysical observations, all brought together and seen in their proper relationships.

In phylogenetic studies, particularly in those in which the aim was to construct a monophyletic 'genealogical tree' of the Plant Kingdom, an almost insuperable difficulty lay in the wide 'gaps' that separate algae and bryophytes, bryophytes and pteridophytes, and so on up to the angiosperms. 'Phyletic gaps' have bedevilled the efforts of comparative morphologists at virtually every critical point. Even today, there is no clear and generally accepted view of the origin and relationships of the dicotyledons and monocotyledons. Gaps in the fossil record are unavoidable; the plant remains have simply disappeared, or have not yet been found. But there are other gaps in genealogical constructions which may not be due to the incompleteness of the fossil record. Such gaps should be capable of being 'explained', or perhaps 'explained away'! Some of the real gaps may possibly be filled as the earth's crust becomes more completely explored; but it may be doubted if many fossil botanists seriously think that this will ever amount to very much, though no doubt there are those who live in the hope of finding 'key' materials. Where the gaps are not real gaps in the sense of the fossil botanist, much still remains to be done, both in the reorientation of our thinking and in new discovery in living species. Comprehensive studies of organization seem likely to contribute to these and other desirable ends.

IN CONCLUSION

From the observations and discussions which have been submitted in this book it seems clear that organization, at every evolutionary level in the Plant Kingdom and in the individual organism, is due to the integrated actions of both intrinsic and extrinsic factors. To neglect either category, or to over-emphasize it, does no service to botanical science. Just as the hereditary constitution of a species persists from generation to succeeding generation, usually with only minor viable mutations, so also, with some fluctuations, does the complex of environmental factors remain relatively unchanged; while the inherent physical and chemical properties of the substances utilized in growth, and autonomous properties of the systems in which they act as components, remain immutable.

As we have seen, many features of cell physiology and organization are of universal occurrence in green plants and are transmitted in heredity. We know that they may be modulated by genic action, but to what extent they are closely and specifically *gene-determined* has in no sense been definitively explored. It has been argued that the forms of plants can be referred to a few basic types of geometrical construction or pattern. The elaboration of these patterns is only possible if there are changes in the size of the organism. Thus an enlargement of a polarized unicell could have resulted in a filament; an increase in all the dimensions of a segmented filament could have resulted in an axis consisting of a tissue mass, this admitting of differentiation between the outer and inner regions; further size increases, with concomitant differentiation, could have resulted in a vascularized axis with appendages; and so on. In the successive evolutionary advances, it may be inferred that genetical changes which made for increased efficiency in photosynthesis, in the uptake of minerals and water from the environment, in protein synthesis, etc., and adaptation to environment, were of paramount importance; for increases in size admit of increased differentiation of organs and tissues, a wider range of functional activities, division of labour, and of special adaptations. Also, as the size of organisms increased, physical factors such as gravity, mechanical stresses, etc., and the whole system of physico-chemical factors and changes in form and structure that we associated with the Principle of Similitude and differential growth, would become incident. As the range and intensity of functional activities increased, so also would the impact of environmental factors become more important. From the foregoing it can be seen that, in attempting to analyse what constitutes organization in plants, it is not only a question of separating 'nature' and 'nurture' which, as Haldane (1952) indicated, is already a sufficiently difficult exercise, but of understanding ever-present effects that are due to the physico-chemical 'organizing' properties of both general and more specific metabolic substances. Wetmore (1959), Wetmore and Rier (1963), and Allsopp (1963), for example, have shown how important different concentrations of a simple metabolic substance such as sugar may be in morphogenesis. Although we do not usually think of simple metabolic substances in this way, sucrose and aminoacids sometimes exercise just as much 'morphogenetic' effect as the more specific growth substances.

The genetical control of size and of differential growth has rightly been given an important place in the literature of genetics. Thus, a genetically-determined increase in the potential size of a shoot apical meristem – the locus of the reaction system – will inevitably bring various physical and chemical factors into action, as well as the complex of physiological factors associated with size-and-form correlations. So, on the one hand, the genetical constitution is primary and fundamental; on the other, many important organizational factors and manifestations are non-genetical; and when we speak of adaptations, it is evident, as Henderson (1913) long ago pointed out, that organism and environment quite unavoidably stand in a reciprocal relationship. For each organism, 'nature' and 'nurture' are essential complementary components of a holistic system.

With regard to the potentiality for growth to larger size, it is evident that comparable or parallel changes in genetical systems have taken place independently in different phyletic lines. For the reasons given above, such size changes alone may account for some of the homology of organization in species of different taxonomic affinity. Other hereditary changes, especially in genes which act in a close complementary relationship with environmental factors, are also likely to result in organizational parallelisms. Mention should also be made of the numerous homologies of organization which are referable to what may be described as evolutionary 'refinements' in the organization of the shoot apical meristem. This is seen in comparisons of eusporangiate and leptosporangiate ferns and in the inception of elaborate organogenic patterns in the small apices of many angiosperms.

As a phenomenon of physical chemistry, it appears that certain of the larger molecules in the protoplasm have an inherent instability, i.e. they have a tendency to mutational change. However, since any particular molecule has a definite structure or configuration, it may be asked if mutational changes can be *entirely* at random: it seems more probable that they can only take place in certain ways, or in particular directions. If this is so, comparable mutational changes in certain molecules of common occurrence in protoplasm could take place in organisms of different affinity. This again would contribute towards parallel organizational developments. However, one must recognize that, in large molecules, the number of possible mutational changes is still very considerable.

Where, in an evolutionary line, different genes appear to be closely involved in a particular morphological or other development, i.e. where the form remains unchanged although the genes are known, or considered, to have changed (*see* Harland, 1933; Haldane, 1952), it could be argued that the genes in question are mainly concerned with some relatively simple and common function such as oxidation or reduction. Certainly, from the genetical literature, it does appear that many different genes have closely comparable effects in the reaction system.

P

CHAPTER 16

The Evolutionary Diversification of Organization

THE SUPERABUNDANCE OF SPECIES

Every species and variety of plant is recognizable because of its distinctive organization. A major result of the long-continued evolutionary process has been the differentiation, from simple beginnings, of a vast number of new specific entities, so much so that the contemporary botanist finds himself suffering from what the author has described as 'a surfeit of species' (Wardlaw, 1963). For most of us, if we are to be frank, there are far more species than we can conveniently cope with. Even for the most gluttonous of taxonomic appetites, there is a vast over-abundance of biological materials. At one end of the evolutionary scale, there is the large and varied array of the flowering plants, up to a quarter of a million of them, according to some authorities: at the other end, there is the populous world of micro-organisms, viruses, bacteria, flagellates, algae, fungi and so on. And between the two there is a substantial assemblage of archegoniate plants. There are, or have been, surprising numbers of species at almost every evolutionary and organizational level. And the taxonomists are still hard at it! Every year sees many new accessions and records, from viruses to angiosperms.

Although it may bring him little comfort, the botanist is by no means alone in this *embarras de richesses*: he is not even ahead of the field! Upwards of three-quarters of a million insect species have been described and named, while the yearly record of new accessions exceeds six thousand species and the end is not even remotely in sight. The total number of named animal species is roughly estimated at a million. In a quite different realm of order and magnitude, astronomers, with their new techniques, are finding that there is not only the very large number of individual heavenly bodies already revealed by optical means, but also very numerous assemblages of such bodies. One might also refer to the vast and ever increasing encyclopaedia of compounds with which the organic chemist has to cope. In brief, a superabundance of materials for study exists in every branch of science. As scholars, we cannot escape the fact that, in different material categories, the numbers of specific entities are very, very large.*

Our special concern here is with the fact that large numbers of species and varieties are typically found in different taxonomic groups. Many botanists, like the author, who have gone to the moist tropics equipped with a reasonable working knowledge of their own temperate flora, must have been repeatedly humiliated by their limited and entirely inadequate knowledge of the superabundance of flowering plant species, to mention only one group. In a particular region, an order may comprise up to a thousand or more species; in the Caribbean mainland, for example, more than 1400 species of Bromeliaceae have already been named, and new accessions are daily coming to hand. But this is to mention only a single order, and by no means one of the largest. On every side, the observant botanical neophyte in the tropics is liable to be overwhelmed. But even if one's scholarship were encyclopaedic, one could still not hope to know well all the families of the flowering plants, let alone their botanical significance. These comments apply no less to other groups, e.g. the microfungi or the ferns. In discussing the classification of the ferns, which comprise some 300 genera and 10,000 species – a relatively small group as compared with the flowering plants – a leading authority has recently stated that no one person could hope to have a critical knowledge of all of them, even in the matter of assigning some of them to their proper genera (Holttum, 1949).

THE MULTIPLICITY OF SPECIES – A MAJOR PHENOMENON

So we may very properly ask ourselves: as scholars, scientists and teachers, how are we to handle these great masses of varied biological materials – the outcome of the long process of evolution, characterized by the differentiation of specific organizations. For example, how much systematic botany should one know and how much should we try to teach our students? And what are the essential things that they should be taught? These questions must often have been discussed. Botanists of

---

* In an essay on 'The fundamental structure of matter', B. H. Flowers (*Mem. and Proc. Manchester Lit. and Phil. Soc.*, **103**, p. 41, 1960–61) pointed out that physicists in recent decades have become aware of 'the existence of no less than thirty different kinds of particles in which matter is able to manifest itself in an apparently fundamental way. The mere description of so many different forms of matter, comparable in number with the number of chemical elements, is an embarrassment which stretches our understanding of physics to the utmost; the reason for their existence defies all our understanding at the present time'.

different outlook and interests would no doubt express very different views such as: (i) that, whatever our special interest may be, we ought to have a general knowledge of the Plant Kingdom, implying a reasonable working knowledge of systematic botany, in much the same way that a biochemist must have a good knowledge of systematic organic chemistry; or (ii) that, as specialist workers, fully occupied with our own particular problems and materials, we just do not have the time, nor perhaps the energy or inclination, to widen our general knowledge of plants; but, nevertheless, we really ought to know 'some' plants; or (iii) that a knowledge of systematic botany is quite unnecessary: all we need is an appropriate label for the species on which we are working.

These several views can no doubt be defended. Intensive work in particular fields is quite essential if botanical science is to advance and such work can be completely absorbing and satisfying. It has also been argued that the day of the general scholar is ended; and it is generally agreed that no one can cover the whole field of botany in the way that was still possible during the latter part of the nineteenth century. Specialization is the order of the day: the specialist is entitled to live at peace in his own selected niche.* But, viewed philosophically, i.e. in terms of the wider aims of botanical science, is this good enough? This great mass of taxonomic material, like Mount Everest, is there; it exists. The very existence of the numerous and varied flowering plant species is itself a major natural phenomenon – one of the greatest with which the botanist has to deal.

That flowering plant species show interrelationships in different degrees, and that, collectively, they exemplify the ever-present, pervasive phenomenon of evolution, is beyond dispute, even though many major problems still await elucidation; and so also for other major groups. If botanical science is to develop a coherent philosophy, based on the cumulative experience of its adherents, botanists cannot afford to neglect this wealth of material. To do so would be to indulge in a kind of ostrichism, an attitude that surely falls well below the scholarly attainments of the past. So, recognizing the magnitude of the problem, we must try to come to terms with it, however ponderous and intractable it may seem. For in this matter we are still concerned with problems of organization and evolution.

---

* It is appreciated that specialization is not all a 'narrowing' process: on the contrary, it often results in opening up important new contacts with other branches of science.

A PHILOSOPHY FOR BOTANICAL SCIENCE

In referring to the need for a coherent *philosophy* for botanical science, the word is being used in one of the commonly accepted senses; i.e. the knowledge or study of natural objects and phenomena and their causes – now usually called science; also, that department of knowledge or study which deals with the most general causes or principles of things (*Oxford English Dictionary*). The main biological themes, expressed in very general terms, include (i) the inception of 'living' from 'non-living' substance and the organization of primordial organisms; (ii) the variation, adaptation, survival, reproduction and dispersal of primitive organisms, and their progressive genetical and somatic elaboration and organization; (iii) the characteristic growth, morphogenesis and functioning of different kinds of living entities; and (iv) the differentiation and diversification, during vast spans of time, of the numerous varieties and species which the taxonomist groups into higher taxa, i.e. genera, families, orders, etc. These several topics are all interrelated, our information concerning them constituting, as it were, a kind of *continuum*. Each aspect has its own particular interest and attraction, with the result that, allowing for the diversity of the human mind, more or less acute specialization is inevitable. But there are undoubtedly many who share the writer's view that we should try to keep botanical science comprehensive, yet coherent and unified; and that we should make a sustained effort to develop a philosophy of botany.

Notwithstanding all the wonderful cosmic explorations that are now afoot, the tremendous achievements in telecommunication, the miracles of chemical synthesis, and the almost inconceivable resources of nuclear energy that, for good or ill, are daily being released, all flesh is still grass and it seems probable that *Homo sapiens* will have to occupy, live on and in, and try to understand, his own green world for some very considerable time to come. That being so, it must surely be a sustaining aim among botanists to make their science grow in strength and dignity and so take its proper place in the public regard no less than in what Francis Bacon long ago described as the 'Advancement of Learning'.

TOWARDS COHERENT SCHOLARSHIP

How is this desirable level of scholarship to be achieved? In each major branch of the science, we must consciously work towards the formulation of simplified, coherent, general concepts, laws or principles, especially those which relate to converging or closely related branches.

Among other tasks, this means coming to terms with the superabundance of species. For, unless there is due appreciation of the fact that the abundance and variety of plant life are major and ever-present phenomena, the underlying causes of which must be continuously explored, the general laws which we try to formulate will lack full validity.

In fact, over the centuries, taxonomists have been gradually coming to terms with the numerous flowering plant species, i.e. by identifying them and arranging them into hierarchical groups which, on the evidence, probably indicate genetical affinities and evolutionary trends. They have brought at least preliminary order into a vast and complex mass of materials, though, as is proper in any lively branch of science, plant taxonomy is constantly undergoing revision. Using a different approach, involving the cytogenetic analysis of small groups of selected materials, experimental taxonomists and geneticists have been exploring the nature of the processes that are involved in the origin of species. The many contributors to what has been described as *The New Systematics* (ed. J. H. Huxley, 1940; *see also* Turrill, 1938; Stebbins, 1950; Heslop-Harrison, 1953, etc.) have now been able to advance a reasoned if still incomplete account of the differentiation of varieties and species and to extend their findings to higher taxonomic categories.

The Importance of the Species. In botany, the biological unit or entity is the species, connoting a group of plants having certain common and permanent characteristics which clearly distinguish it from other groups. Basically the word species means the appearance, visible form, or kind (*Oxford English Dictionary*). So, in classifying the higher plants, we are essentially concerned with their form, the latter term being used here in its more comprehensive, Aristotelian sense. And, as we have seen, it is the apparently endless diversity of form that constitutes our seemingly intractable problem.

Similitude and the Diversity of Form. Now, there is no denying that flowering plants are exceedingly diverse in form and structure; and hence even the simplest classification is still very complex. Hutchinson (1926), for example, enumerated 105 orders (or cohorts) and 332 families. So, even at the higher taxonomic levels, we still have a surfeit. Some simplification is desirable and may indeed be possible. Studies of morphogenesis have enabled us to recognize that many seemingly quite unlike adult forms may fundamentally be essentially alike. As an example from plane geometry, a circle is simply a special case of a whole family of ellipses, some of which might be very greatly extended along one axis. Again, as D'Arcy Thompson (1917) showed, the same basic form can be greatly diversified if it is projected on to variously distorted Cartesian co-ordinates; and we now recognize that identical or closely comparable primary patterns in embryonic tissues may develop into very different adult forms as a result of genetically-determined differential growth. Some phyllotactic systems are very simple, others are more complex and yet others are highly complex. Yet they may all be related mathematically, i.e. in so far as they all belong to the same Fibonacci series. In fact, they may all occur during the ontogenesis of certain species. Even decussate and simple spiral systems are by no means as unlike as they seem to be: indeed, the former may be transformed into the latter by a simple experimental treatment. Here, too, we may note that, in floral morphogenesis, the number of basic patterns is quite small; i.e. the floral organs typically occur in groups of two, three or five, with occasional instances of higher or irregular numbers. And many other instances of similitude could be cited. It thus appears that if plants show great morphological diversity, they also yield abundant evidence of similitude. But whereas the differences are usually evident, the similitude may have to be sought.

These and cognate observations hold out the hope that, eventually, although the need for the full taxonomic treatment of our wealth of species will remain, it may be possible to formulate simplified general statements which will enable botanists in general, and not only specialists in taxonomy, to gain a fuller insight into the main features that have characterized the evolution of this great group of plants.

Evolutionary Trends and Parallelisms. In any considerable group of related organisms it is usually possible to perceive some characteristic evolutionary trend, or trends. Most of them are upgrade but some, as it seems to us, are downgrade, though they still possess survival value. Such relationships can be distinguished not only in the families and orders of flowering plants but in all major groups. The more evident and distinctive trends have long been discussed by students of phylogeny. In the flowering plants, although the number of trends is considerable, it is not large; for essentially the same kinds of evolutionary change appear to have taken place independently in different families. Even although the causes of these evolutionary trends and parallelisms are still not understood – although genetical and cognate studies are beginning to reveal some of the probable mechanisms – it is possible to specify and classify the relevant morphological data. As these tend to be encyclopaedic, some new system of nomenclature and/or codification is needed to give simple expression to them. Moreover, many special cases may be encountered which can not be readily assimilated to a simplified scheme. Nevertheless, with the help of computing apparatus and techniques, to which taxonomists are already having recourse, it should be possible to obtain more precise information and to formulate more valid general conceptions of what has been involved in the differentiation of the flowering plants.* In time, this effort may result in a system of principles, or laws, which will admit of a deeper insight into the evolution of any particular group.

A New Taxonomy: The Classification of Processes. The essence of what is being suggested is that botanists should work towards a *classification of evolutionary processes*, to supplement and simplify the comprehensive systematic classifications. The latter will, of course, be retained, extended and modified as knowledge increases. It is pertinent to recall that taxonomy in biology is not only concerned with the principles and practice of classification, usually based on morphology, with the aim of indicating the true natural affinities between plants: it is also, by definition, concerned with the arrangement or classification of materials or entities *in relation to general laws or principles* (*Oxford English Dictionary*). In a contemporary publication, Linsley and Usinger (1961), in defining the comprehensive objective of taxonomy, have included: 'to devise and perfect a scheme of classification in which the named taxa can be arranged in a meaningful manner, preferably one which will demonstrate at once the unity and diversity of organic life, contribute to an understanding of organic evolution, and provide a convenient and useful basis for recording, analysing and interpreting the data of the biological sciences'. This definition comes very close to what the author has in mind in suggesting a new approach to the manifold materials of the Plant Kingdom.

In the proposed new taxonomy the aims will be to specify, classify and, if necessary, to *codify*, not only the morphological or other characters, but the major *processes* that are, and have been, involved in the evolutionary trends and morphogenetic parallelisms in representative taxa. The findings both of classical and experimental taxonomy, and of other branches of botany, will all be contributory. Ultimately we may hope to formulate the laws or principles that determine these processes, though these are, admittedly, ambitious aims. But already in physics, e.g. in the laws of motion, and in chemistry, e.g. the laws of

---

* For example, *see* J. L. Crosby, 'Evolution by Computer'. *New Scientist*, **17**, 415-17.

thermodynamics, it has been possible to bring together and express in relatively simple terms many seemingly very different phenomena. (It is appreciated that neither the physicist nor the physical chemist considers that his labours in these fields are in any sense at an end; but the general analogy is still valid.) Biological systems are admittedly much more complex than those with which the physicist or chemist has to deal; but, if we can recognize and state a problem, it is usually possible also to make some progress towards its solution. Like the physicist working towards the formulation of simplified general laws, to achieve what Newton described as the perfection of simplicity, the botanist must also, in appropriate ways, come to terms with his superabundance of species. If something along these lines can be achieved, one begins to see the possibility not only of reducing the major phenomenon of organization, species differentiation, etc., to manageable proportions, but of effecting a vital integration of all the branches of botanical science.

ENVOI

To the world at large, and especially in the rapidly expanding realms of applied science, this is *par excellence* the age of physics and chemistry. In the effulgent light of these energetic disciplines, botany tends to be regarded, perhaps by many, including professional botanists, as a shrinking, Cinderella-like science, which is only likely to attract interest in so far as its problems are tackled by those with competence in the physical sciences. Many of the new advances will almost certainly be made in this way. In fact, this is happening at the present time.

Are we, then, to envisage a time, perhaps not very distant, when the basic philosophy of botany will, in effect, be seen as merely an extension of the philosophy of the physical sciences? The writer has no objection to this, *provided* that the physicists and chemists who propose the new concepts are as well informed about organisms *as organisms* as they are about the physico-chemical properties of organic materials. Under these conditions, botany is likely to be enriched and advanced in many desirable ways. On the other hand, if purely physico-chemical concepts of some of the processes in plants were permitted to displace and to supervene upon the comprehensive synthetic biological concepts, which are essential to any adequate understanding of plants as integrated functional entities, botanical science will almost certainly suffer a severe setback. It will cease to be botany.

As we have seen, organization exists at all levels, and a kind of
P*

organizational *continuum* can be traced from the physico-chemical constitution of simple substances to the complex and highly adapted organs of the higher plants. Accordingly, it is logical to suggest that biochemistry and biophysics should now be established *within university departments of botany or biology*, cognate with the other branches which are typically represented at the present time; for *all* of them are essential.* It is evident, however, that there are levels of organization in plants, and many other essentially 'biological' phenomena, with which the chemist or physicist as such is not equipped to deal, though they may obviously make contributions of very great importance. Nor will a veneer, 'a little learning', of botany meet the situation. The ideas and techniques which botanists can and should acquire from the physical sciences should properly be regarded as servants: they should not be allowed to become masters. If there is to be a philosophy of botany, let it come primarily from the well-informed botanist.

Botany may be one of the less considerable of the natural sciences at the present time. But it need not be; and it should not be. If the aim of education is to prepare the young for a fuller appreciation and understanding of life and of the world, it seems evident that the study of botany – the science of plants – should be part of any education described as liberal; for plant life is everywhere around us and essential to us. Primitive man was of necessity 'a botanizing animal'; and agriculture, based on the green plant, is still the world's most historic and most essential industry. These elementary facts are often forgotten, or imperfectly understood, in our highly urbanized civilization. But however important these economic matters may be, they are only one aspect of botany. From the equator to the poles, the earth is clothed with such a richness and diversity of plant life, personifying the phenomena of organization and evolution, that only the blind or the uneducated can fail to be stirred to a sense of curiosity, wonder and delight. To appreciate these things, whether at the general level or as a basis for more specialized study, a liberal education in botany is essential. It is the author's hope that this book may contribute to this end.

---

* This, of course, is without prejudice to such approaches as chemists and physicists may see fit to make from their points of view.

Bibliography

ABBE, E. C., and STEIN, O. L. (1954) The growth of the shoot apex in maize: embryogeny. *Amer. J. Bot.*, **41**, 285–93.

AGAR, W. E. (1943, 1951) *A Contribution to the Theory of Living Organism.* Melbourne Univ. Press.

ALBAUM, H. G. (1938) Inhibitions due to growth hormones in fern prothallia and sporophytes. *Amer. J. Bot.*, **25**, 124–33.

ALLFREY, V. G. and MIRSKY, A. E. (1961) How cells make molecules. *Scientific American*, **205**, 3, 74–82.

ALLSOPP, A. (1948) Chromatographical study of meristematic plant tissues. *Nature, Lond.*, **161**, 833.

ALLSOPP, A. (1952) Experimental and analytical studies of pteridophytes. 17. The effect of various physiologically active substances on the development of *Marsilea* in sterile culture. *Ann. Bot., Lond.*, N.S., **16**, 165–83.

ALLSOPP, A. (1953a) Experimental and analytical studies of pteridophytes. 19. Investigations on *Marsilea*. 2. Induced reversion to juvenile stages. *Ann. Bot., Lond.*, N.S., **17**, 37–55.

ALLSOPP, A. (1953b) Experimental and analytical studies of pteridophytes. 20. Investigations on *Marsilea*. 3. The effect of various sugars on development and morphology. *Ann. Bot., Lond.*, N.S., **17**, 447–63.

ALLSOPP, A. (1954a) Experimental and analytical studies of pteridophytes. 24. Investigations on *Marsilea*. 4. Anatomical effects of changes in sugar concentration. *Ann. Bot., Lond.*, N.S., **18**, 449–61.

ALLSOPP, A. (1954b) Juvenile stages of plants and the nutritional status of the shoot apex. *Nature, Lond.*, **173**, 1032–5.

ALLSOPP, A. (1955) Experimental and analytical studies of pteridophytes. 27. Investigations on *Marsilea*. 5. Cultural conditions and morphogenesis, with special reference to the origin of land and water forms. *Ann. Bot., Lond.*, N.S., **19**, 247–64.

ALLSOPP, A. (1956a) Apical dominance in *Marsilea* with particular reference to the effects of 3-indolylacetic acid, 3-indolylacetonitrile and coumarin on lateral bud development. *J. Exp. Bot.* **7**, 14–24.

ALLSOPP, A. (1956b) Morphogenetic effects of 3-indolylacetonitrile on sporelings of *Marsilea* in aseptic culture. *J. Exp. Bot.* **7**, 1–13.

ALLSOPP, A. (1964) *Handbuch der Pflanzenphysiologie.* Springer, Heidelberg.

ALSTON, R. E. and TURNER, B. L. (1963) *Biochemical Systematics.* Prentice-Hall, New Jersey.

ANDERSSON-KOTTÖ, I. (1929) A genetical investigation in *Scolopendrium vulgare*. *Hereditas, Lund.*, **12**, 109–78.

ANDERSSON-KOTTÖ, I. (1938) Genetics, in Verdoorn's *Manual of Pteridology*, Chap. IX, 284–302.

ARBER, A. (1919) On heterophylly in water plants. *Amer. Nat.*, **53**, 272–8.

ARBER, A. (1920) *Water Plants*. Cambridge Univ. Press.

ARBER, A. (1930) Root and shoot in the angiosperm: a study of morphological categories. *New Phytol.*, **29**, 297.

ARBER, A. (1937) The interpretation of the flower: A study of some aspects of morphological thought. *Bot. Rev.*, **12**, 157.

ARBER, A. (1950) *The Natural Philosophy of Plant Form*. Cambridge Univ. Press.

ARIYANA YAGAM, D. V. and STEBBINS, G. L. (1962) Developmental studies of cell differentiation in the epidermis of monocotyledons. III. Interaction of environmental and genetical factors on the stomatal differentiation in three genotypes of barley. *Develop. Biology*, **4**, 117–33.

ASHBY, E. (1948) Studies in the morphogenesis of leaves. 2. The area, cell size and cell number of leaves of *Ipomoea* in relation to their position on the shoot. *New Phytol.*, **47**, 177–95.

ASHBY, E., and WANGERMANN, E. (1950) Studies in the morphogenesis of leaves. 4. Further observations on area, cell size and cell number of leaves of *Ipomoea* in relation to their position on the shoot. *New Phytol.*, **49**, 23–35.

ASHBY, E., and WANGERMANN, E. (1951) Studies in the morphogenesis of leaves. 7. Part 2. Correlative effect of fronds in *Lemna minor*. *New Phytol.*, **50**, 200–9.

ASIMOV, I. (1954) Potentialities of protein isomerism. *J. Chem. Educ.*, **31**, 125–7.

ASTBURY, W. T. (1957) Some master plans of molecular biology. *The Listener*, 21 Feb., 300–2.

AUDUS, L. J. (1953, 1959a) *Plant Growth Substances*. First and Second edns., London, Hill.

AUDUS, L. J. (1959b) Correlations. *J. Linn. Soc. Lond. (Bot.)*, **56**, 177–87.

AUDUS, L. J. and QUASTEL, J. H. (1947) Toxic effects of amino acids and amines of seedling growth. *Nature, Lond.*, **160**: 222.

AVERY, G. S., JR. (1935) Differential distribution of a phytohormone in the developing leaf of *Nicotiana* and its relation to polarized growth. *Bull. Torrey bot. Club*, **62**, 313–30.

BAILEY, I. W. (1954) *Contributions to Plant Anatomy*. Waltham, Mass.

BAIN, H. F. and DERMEN, H. (1944) Sectorial polyploidy and phyllotaxy in the cranberry (*Vaccinium macrocarpon* Ait.). *Amer. J. Bot.*, **31**, 581–7.

BAKER, H. G. (1947a) Infection of species of *Melandrium* by *Ustilago violacea* (Pers.) Fuckel and the transmission of the resultant disease. *Ann. Bot., Lond.*, **11**, 333.

BAKER, H. G. (1947b) Sex in *Melandrium. Nature, Lond.*, **159**, 34.

BALL, E. (1946) Development in sterile culture of stem tips and subjacent regions of *Tropaeolum majus* L. and *Lupinus albus* L. *Amer. J. Bot.*, **33**, 301–18.

BALL, E. (1948) Differentiation in the primary shoots of *Lupinus albus* L., and of *Tropaeolum majus* L. *Symp. Soc. exp. Biol.*, **2**, 246–62.

BALL, E. (1955) On certain gradients in the shoot tip of *Lupinus albus. Amer. J. Bot.*, **42**, 509–21.

BARNARD, C. (1961) The interpretation of the angiosperm flower. *Australian J. Sci.*, **24**, 64–72.

BARNETT, S. A. ed. (1958) *A Century of Darwin*. Heinemann, London.

BARON, W. M. M. (1963) *Organization in Plants*. Arnold, London.

BASFORD, K. H. (1961) Morphogenetic responses to gibberellic acid of a radiation-induced mutant dwarf in groundsel, *Senecio vulgaris* L. *Ann. Bot., Lond.*, N.S., **25**, 279–302.

BATE-SMITH, E. C. (1962) The phenolic constituents of plants and their taxonomic significance. *J. Linn. Soc. Lond. (Bot.)*, **58**, 95–173.

BECKNER, M. (1959) *The Biological Way of Thought*. Columbia Univ. Press, New York.

BELL, P. R. (1959) The experimental investigation of the pteridophyte life cycle. *J. Linn. Soc. Lond. (Bot.)*, **56**, 188–203.

BELL, P. R. (1963) The cytochemical and ultrastructural peculiarities of the fern egg. *J. Linn. Soc. Lond. (Bot.)*, **58**, 353–9.

BENZER, S. (1959) On the topology of the genetic fine structure. *Proc. Nat. Acad. Sci. U.S.*, **45**, 1607–20.

BERG, S. (1926) *Nomogenesis–Evolution Determined by Law*. London.

BERNAL, J. D. (1951a) *The Creation of the Universe*. Viking Press, New York.

BERNAL, J. D. (1951b) *The Physical Basis of Life*. London.

BERNAL, J. D. (1954) The origin of life. *New Biol.*, **16**, 28–40.

BERNAL, J. D. (1962) Is there life elsewhere in the universe? *The Listener*, 26 Apr., **67**, 723–4.

BERNAL, J. D. and FRANKUCHEN, I. (1937) Structure types of protein 'crystals' from virus-infected plants. *Nature, Lond.*, **139**, 923.

BERSILLON, G. (1955) Recherches sur les Papaveracées. Contribution à l'étude du développement des dicotylédones herbacées. *Ann. Sci. Nat., Bot.*, XI, **16**, 225–443.

BERTALANFFY, L. (1952) *Problems of Life*. London.

BERTRAND, P. (1947) *Les Végétaux Vasculaires*. Masson, Paris.

BINDLOSS, E. (1942) A developmental analysis of cell length as related to stem length. *Amer. J. Bot.*, **29**, 179–88.

BIRCH, A. J. (1963) Biosynthetic pathways: in *Chemical Plant Taxonomy*, ed. T. Swain; Academic Press, London and New York, 141–66.

BLIXT, s. (1961) Quantitative studies of induced mutations in peas. V. Chlorophyll mutations. *Agric. Hort. Genetica*, **19**, 402–47.

BÖCHER, T. W. (1951) Studies on the morphological progression and evolution in the vegetable kingdom. *Kong. Danske Vidensk. Selsk. Biol. Medd.*, Copenhagen, **18**, 1–51.

BÖCHER, J. W. and LEWIS, M. C. (1962) Experimental and cytological studies on plant species. *Biol. Skr. Kong.* Danske Vidensk. Selsk. 11, 5, 1–25.

BONNER, J. T. (1952) *Morphogenesis. An Essay on Development.* Princeton University Press.

BONNER, J. (1959) Protein synthesis and the control of plant processes. *Amer. J. Bot.*, **46**, 58.

BONNER, J. (1963) The future welfare of botany. *AIBS Bull.*, **13**, 20–1.

BONNER, J. and ZEEVAART, J. A. D. (1962) Ribonucleic acid synthesis in the bud an essential component of floral induction in *Xanthium. Plant Physiol.*, **37**, 43–9.

BOUILLENNE, R. (1950) La rhizogénèse. *Année biol.*, **26**, 597–628.

BOURNE, G. H. (1951) *Cytology and Cell Physiology.* Second edn., Oxford, Clarendon Press.

BOWER, F. O. (1914) Presidential Address. Sect. K, Brit. Assoc. Advancement of Science. Rept. Brit. Assoc., 560–72.

BOWER, F. O. (1916) On leaf-architecture as illuminated by a study of Pteridophyta. *Trans. Roy. Soc. Edinb.*, **51**, 657–788.

BOWER, F. O. (1919, 1947) *Botany of the Living Plant.* Macmillan, London.

BOWER, F. O. (1921) Size, a neglected factor in stelar morphology. *Proc. Roy. Soc. Edinb.*, **41**, 1–25.

BOWER, F. O. (1923–8) *The Ferns* (Filicales) I. (1923) Analytical examination of the criteria of comparison. II. (1926) The eusporangiate and other primitive ferns. III. (1928) The Leptosporangiate Ferns. Cambridge Univ. Press.

BOWER, F. O. (1930) *Size and Form in Plants.* London.

BOWER, F. O. (1935) *Primitive Land Plants.* London.

BOYDEN, A. A. (1953) Comparative evolution—with special reference to primitive mechanisms. *Evolution*, **7**, 21–30.

BRACHET, J. (1961) The living cell. *Scientific American*, **205**, 3, 51–73.

BRAITHWAITE, R. B. (1953) *Scientific Explanations.* Cambridge Univ. Press.

BRAY, H. G. and WHITE, K. (1954) Organisms as physico-chemical machines. *New Biol.*, **16**, 70–85.

BRIAN, P. W. (1959) Effects of gibberellins on plant growth and development. *Biol. Rev.*, **34**, 37–84.

BRIGGS, R. and KING, T. J. (1955) Specificity of nuclear function in embryonic development: in *Biological Specificity and Growth*: ed. E. G. Butler; Princeton Univ. Press, 207–28.

BRIGGS, W. R. and STEEVES, T. A. (1958) Morphogenetic studies on *Osmunda cinnamomea* L. The expansion and maturation of vegetative fronds. *Phytomorph.*, **8**, 234–48.

BRIGGS, W. R. and STEEVES, T. A. (1959) Morphogenetic studies on *Osmunda cinnamomea* L. The mechanism of crozier uncoiling. *Phytomorph.*, **9**, 134–47.

BRINK, R. A. (1958) *Cold Spring Harbor Symp. Quant. Biol.*, **23**, 379.

BRINK, R. A. (1960) *Quart. Rev. Biol.* **35**, 120.

BROWN, R. (1958) Cellular basis for the induction of morphological structures. *Nature, Lond.*, **181**, 1546–7.

BROWN, R. and ROBINSON, E. (1955) Cellular differentiation and the development of enzyme proteins in plants: in *Biological Specificity and Growth*, ed. E. G. Butler; Princeton Univ. Press, 93–118.

BUCHHOLZ, J. T. (1946) Volumetric studies of seeds, endosperms, and embryos in *Pinus ponderosa* during embryonic differentiation. *Bot. Gaz.*, **108**, 232–44.

BÜNNING, E. (1948) *Entwicklungs- und Bewegungs-physiologie der Pflanzen.* Springer, Berlin.

BÜNNING, E. (1952) Morphogenesis in Plants. *Surv. biol. Progr.*, **2**, 105–40.

BUTLER, L. (1952) The linkage map of the tomato. *J. Hered.*, **43**, 25–35.

BUTLER, L. (1963) Five genes located on chromosome 4 of the tomato. *Canadian J. Bot.*, **41**, 1159–64.

BUVAT, R. (1952) Structure, évolution et fonctionnement du méristème apical de quelques dicotylédones. *Ann. Sci. Nat. Bot.* **11**, **13**, 199–300.

BUVAT, R. (1955) Le méristème apical de la tige. *Ann. Biol.*, **31**, 595–656.

BUVAT, R. (1958) Recherches sur les infra-structures du cytoplasme, dans les cellules du méristème apical, des ébauches foliaires et des feuilles developpées de l'*Elodea canadensis. Ann. Sci. Nat. Bot.*, **11**, **19**, 121–61.

BUVAT, R. (1961) Le reticulum endoplasmique des cellules végétales. *Ber. Deutsch. Bot. Ges.*, **74**, 261–7.

CALVIN, M. (1956) Chemical evolution and the origin of life. *Amer. Sci.*, **44**, 248–63.

CALVIN, M. (1961) Chemical evolution. Condon Lectures, Oregon State System of Higher Education. Univ. of Oregon Press, 1–42.

CALVIN, M. (1962) Communication: from molecules to Mars. *AIBS Bull.*, **12**, 29–44.

CAMARA, A. (1943) Transplantacão de embryoes. *Agron. lusit.*, **5**, 375–86.

CAMUS, G. (1949) Recherches sur le rôle des bourgeons dans les phénomènes de morphogénèse. *Rev. Cytol. et Biol. Vég.*, **9**, 1–199.

CANDOLLE, C. DE (1868) Théorie de la feuille. *Arch. Sci. Bibl. Universelle*, **32**, 32–64. (In Arber, 1930.)

CANNON, H. G. (1956) An essay on evolution and modern genetics. *Jour. Linn. Soc. Lond. (Bot.)*, **43**, 1–17,

CANNON, H. G. (1957) What Lamarck really said. *Proc. Linn. Soc. Lond.*, **168**, 71.

CANNON, H. G. (1958) *The Evolution of Living Things*. Manchester Univ. Press.

CANNON, H. G. (1959) *Lamarck and Modern Genetics*. Manchester Univ. Press.

CANNON, W. B. (1939) *The Wisdom of the Body*. Revised edn. London.

CARR, D. J. and CARR, S. G. M. (1959) Developmental morphology of the floral organs of *Eucalyptus*. *Austr. J. Bot.*, **47**, 109.

CATCHESIDE, D. G. (1956) Genes—their nature and function. *C.R. Labor. Carlsberg, Ser. Physiol.*, **26**, 31–9.

CATHEY, H. M. (1958) Mutual antagonism of growth control of *Chrysanthemum morifolium* by gibberellin and Amo-1618. (Abstr.) *Plant Physiol.*, xliii Suppl., 33.

CHAMBERLAIN, C. J. (1935) *Gymnosperms*. Univ. of Chicago Press.

CHANTRENNE, H. (1961) *The Biosynthesis of Proteins*. Oxford Univ. Press, London, New York, Paris.

CHAPMAN, J. A. and SALTON, M. R. J. (1962) A study of several blue-green algae in the electron microscope. *Archiv. für Mikrobiol.*, **44**, 311–22.

CHAUVEAUD, G. (1921) *La constitution des plantes vasculaires révélée par leur ontogénie*. Paris.

CHEADLE, V. I. (1956) Research on xylem and phloem—progress in fifty years. *Amer. J. Bot.*, **43**, 719–31.

CHILD, C. M. (1941) *Patterns and Problems of Development*. Chicago Univ. Press.

CHURCH, A. H. (1919) *Thalassiophyta and the Subaerial Transmigration*. *Oxford bot. Mem.*, 3.

CLARK, W. LE GROS (1958) The study of man's descent: in *A Century of Darwin*, 173–205, ed. S. A. Barnett, Heinemann, London.

CLUTTER, M. E. (1960) Hormonal induction of vascular tissues in tobacco pith in vitro. *Science*, **132**, 548–9.

COLLYER, D. M. and FOGG, G. E. (1955) Studies on fat accumulation by algae. *J. Exp. Bot.*, **6**, 256–75.

COLVIN, J. R., SMITH, D. B. and COOK, W. H. (1954) The microheterogeneity of proteins. *Chem. Revs.*, **54**, 687–711.

COOPER, R. S. (1950) Antigens of frog embryos and of adult frog serum studied by diffusion of antigens into agar columns containing antisera. *J. Exp. Zool.*, **114**, 403–20.

COPELAND, J. J. (1936) Yellowstone thermal myxophyceae. *Annals N.Y. Acad. Sci.*, **36**, 1–232.

CORNER, E. J. H. (1949) The durian theory or the origin of the modern tree. *Ann. Bot., Lond.*, N.S., **13**, 367–414.

CORNER, E. J. H. (1954) The evolution of tropical forest: in *Evolution as a Process*, edit. Huxley, Hardy and Ford; Allen and Unwin, London, 34–46.

CRICK, F. H. C. (1960) Genes and atoms. *The Listener*, 4 Aug., 188–9.

CRICK, F. H. C. (1961) Macromolecules and natural selection: in *Growth in Living Systems*, 3–8 (ed. M. X. Zarrow). Basic Books Inc., New York.

CRICK, F. H. C. (1962) Towards the genetic code. *Discovery*, **23**, 8–16.

CRICK, F. H. C. and HUGHES, A. F. W. (1950) The physical properties of cytoplasm. A study by means of the magnetic particle method. *Exp. Cell Res.*, **1**, 37–80, 505–33.

CRICK, F. H. C., BARNETT, L., BRENNER, S. and WATTS-TOBIN, R. J. (1961) General nature of the genetic code for proteins. *Nature, Lond.*, **192**, 1227–32.

CROSBY, J. L. (1963) Evolution by computer. *New Scientist*, **17**, 415–17.

CROSS, G. L. and JOHNSON, T. J. (1941) Structural features of the shoot apices of diploid and colchicine-induced tetraploid strains of *Vinca rosea* L. *Bull. Torrey Bot. Club.*, **68**, 618–35.

CROTTY, W. J. (1955) Trends in the pattern of primordial development with age in the fern *Acrostichum danaeafolium*. *Amer. J. Bot.* **42**, 627–36.

CUSICK, F. (1956) Studies of floral morphogenesis, I: Median bisections of flower primordia in *Primula bulleyana* Forrest. *Trans. Roy. Soc. Edinb.*, **63**, 153.

CUSICK, F. (1959) Floral morphogenesis in *Primula bulleyana* Forrest. *J. Linn. Soc. Lond. (Bot.)*, **56**, 262.

CUTTER, E. G. (1954) Experimental induction of buds from fern leaf primordia. *Nature, Lond.*, **173**, 440–1.

CUTTER, E. G. (1955a) Anatomical studies on the shoot apices of some parasitic and saprophytic angiosperms. *Phytomorph.*, **5**, 231–47.

CUTTER, E. G. (1955b) Experimental and analytical studies of pteridophytes. XXIX. The effect of progressive starvation on the growth and organization of the shoot apex of *Dryopteris aristata* Druce. *Ann. Bot., Lond.*, N.S., **19**, 485–99.

CUTTER, E. G. (1956) Experimental and analytical studies of pteridophytes. XXXIII. The experimental induction of buds from leaf primordia in *Dryopteris aristata* Druce. *Ann. Bot. Lond.*, N.S., **20**, 143–65.

CUTTER, E. G. (1957a) Studies of morphogenesis in the Nymphaeaceae. I. Introduction: some aspects of the morphology of *Nuphar lutea* (L.) Sm. and *Nymphaea alba* L. *Phytomorph.*, **7**, 45–56.

CUTTER, E. G. (1957b) Studies of morphogenesis in the Nymphaeaceae. II. Floral development in *Nuphar* and *Nymphaea*: bracts and calyx. *Phytomorph.*, **7**, 57–73.

CUTTER, E. G. (1957c) Experimental and analytical studies of pteridophytes. XXXVI. Further experiments on the developmental potentialities of leaf primordia in *Dryopteris aristata* Druce. *Ann. Bot., Lond.*, N.S., **21**, 343–72.

CUTTER, E. G. (1958) Studies of morphogenesis in the Nymphaeaceae. III. Surgical experiments on leaf and bud formation. *Phytomorph.*, **8**, 74–95.

CUTTER, E. G. (1959) Studies of morphogenesis in the Nymphaeaceae. IV: Early floral development in species of *Nuphar*. *Phytomorph.*, **9**, 263.

CUTTER, E. G. (1961) The inception and distribution of flowers in the Nymphaeaceae. *Proc. Linn. Soc. Lond.*, **172**, 93.

CUTTER, E. G. (1964) Observations on leaf and bud formation in *Hydrocharis morsus-ranae*. *Amer. J. Bot.*, **51**, 318–324.

CUTTER, E. G. and VOELLER, B. R. (1959) Changes in leaf arrangement in individual fern apices. *J. Linn. Soc. Lond. (Bot.)*, **56**, 225–36.

DAMPIER, W. (1929) *History of Science*. Cambridge Univ. Press.

DANCKWARDT-LILLIESTRÖM, C. (1957) Kinetin induced shoot formation from isolated roots of *Isatis tinctoria*. *Physiol. Plant.*, Copenhagen, **10**, 794–6.

DARLINGTON, C. D. (1939, 1958) *Evolution of Genetic Systems*. Cambridge and Edinburgh.

DARLINGTON, C. D. (1950) In the Foreword to a reprint of the first edition of Darwin's *Origin* etc. (1859), Watts, London.

DARLINGTON, C. D. (1957) On being descended from a molecule. *The Listener*, 14 Mar., 419–20.

DARLINGTON, C. D. and MATHER, K. (1949) *The Elements of Genetics*. London.

DARWIN, C. (1859) *On the Origin of Species by Means of Natural Selection, or the Preservation of the Favoured Races in the Struggle for Life*. First edn., London.

DARWIN, C. (1865, 1906) *The Movement and Habits of Climbing Plants*. *Jour. Linn. Soc. Lond. (Bot.)*, 1865, popular edn., 1906, London.

DARWIN, C. (1875, 1888, 1908) *Insectivorous Plants*. Popular edn. revised by Francis Darwin, 1908. London.

DARWIN, C. (1878) *Origin* etc. Seventh edn.

DASANAYAKE, M. D. (1960) Aspects of morphogenesis in a dorsiventral fern, *Pteridium aquilinum* (L.) Kuhn. *Ann. Bot. Lond.*, N.S. **24**, 317–29.

DE BEER, G. R. (1951) *Embryos and Ancestors*. Clarendon Press, Oxford.

DE BEER, G. R. (1958) Darwin and embryology: in *A Century of Darwin*, 153–72, ed. S. A. Barnett, Heinemann, London.

DEAN, H. L. (1963) Further variations in style number and other gynoecial structures of *Lychnis alba* Mill. *Phytomorph.*, **13**, 1–13.

DEMAGGIO, A. E. (1963) Morphogenetic factors influencing the development of fern embryos. *J. Linn. Soc. Lond. (Bot.)*, **58**, 361–76.

DEMAGGIO, A. E. and WETMORE, R. H. (1961) Morphogenetic studies of the fern *Todea barbara* (L.) Moore. III. Experimental embryology. *Amer. J. Bot.*, **48**, 551–65.

DEMAGGIO, A. E., WETMORE, R. H. and MOREL, G. (1963) Induction de tissue vasculaire dans le prothalle de fougère. *C.R. Acad. Sci.*, **256**, 5196–9.

DERMEN, H. (1945) The mechanism of colchicine-induced cytohistological changes in cranberry. *Amer. J. Bot.*, **32**, 387–94.

DERMEN, H. (1947) Periclinal cytochimeras and histogenesis in cranberry. *Amer. J., Bot.* **34**, 32–43.

DERMEN, H. (1951) Ontogeny of tissues in stem and leaf of cytochimeral apples. *Amer. J. Bot.*, **38**, 753–60.

DERMEN, H. (1953) Periclinal cytochimeras and origin of tissues in stem and leaf of peach. *Amer. J. Bot.*, **40**, 154–68.

DE VRIES, H. (1901) *Die Mutationstheorie*, etc. Leipzig; 1905. *Species and Varieties; Their Origin by Mutation*, etc. Chicago.

DOBZHANSKY, TH. (1955) *Evolution, Genetics and Man.* New York.

DRIESCH, H. (1908) *The Science and Philosophy of the Organism.* Gifford Lectures. London.

DUNN, L. C. (1951) *Genetics in the 20th Century.* New York.

DURRANT, A. (1958) *Proc. Tenth Intern. Congr. Genetics.*, **2**, 71.

EAMES, A. J. (1931) The vascular anatomy of the flower with refutation of the theory of carpel polymorphism. *Amer. J. Bot.*, **18**, 147.

EAMES, A. J. (1936) *Morphology of Vascular Plants. Lower Groups.* McGraw-Hill, New York.

EAST, E. M. (1929) Self-sterility. *Bib. Gen.*, **5**, 331–68.

EBERT, J. D. (1950) Analysis of the effects of anti-organ sera on the development, in vitro, of the early chick blastoderm. *J. Exp. Zool.* **115**, 351–77.

EDWARDS, P. ST. J. and ALLSOPP, A. (1956) The effect of changes in the inorganic nitrogen supply on the growth and development of *Marsilea* in aseptic culture. *J. Exp. Bot.*, **7**, 194–202.

ENGARD, C. J. (1944) Organogenesis in *Rubus. Res. Publ. Univ. Hawaii*, **21**, 1.

ESAU, K. (1953) *Plant Anatomy.* New York, Wiley; London, Chapman and Hall.

ESAU, K. (1954) Primary vascular differentiation in plants. *Biol. Rev.*, **29**, 46–86.

ESAU, K. (1963) Ultrastructure of differentiated cells in higher plants. *Amer. J. Bot.*, **50**, 495–506.

ESAU, K., CURRIER, H. B. and CHEADLE, V. I. (1957) Physiology of phloem. *Ann. Rev. Plant. Physiol.*, **8**, 349–74.

FISCHBERG, M. and BLACKLER, A. W. (1961) How cells specialize. *Scientific American*, **205**, 3, 124–140.

FISHER, R. A. (1930) *The Genetical Theory of Natural Selection.* Oxford Univ. Press.

FISHER, R. A. (1954) Retrospect of the criticisms of the theory of natural selection: in *Evolution as a Process*, ed. Huxley, Hardy and Ford; Allen and Unwin, London, 84–98.

FOSTER, A. S. (1928) Salient features of the problem of bud-scale morphology. *Biol. Rev.*, **3**, 123–4.

FOSTER, A. S. (1929) Investigations on the morphology and comparative history of development of foliar organs. I. The foliage leaves and cataphyllary structures in the horse-chestnut (*Aesculus hippocastanum* L.). *Amer. J. Bot.*, **18**, 243–9.

FOSTER, A. S. (1932) Investigations on the morphology and comparative history of development of foliar organs. III. Cataphyll and foliage-leaf ontogeny in the black hickory (*Carya buckleyi* var. *arkansana*). *Amer. J. Bot.*, **19**, 75–99.

FOSTER, A. S. (1935) A histogenetic study of foliar determination in *Carya buckleyi* var. *arkansana*. *Amer. J. Bot.*, **22**, 88–147.

FOSTER, A. S. (1939) Problems of structure, growth and evolution in the shoot apex of seed plants. *Bot. Rev.*, **5**, 454–70.

FOWDEN, W. (1962) The non-protein amino-acids of plants. *Endeavour*, **21**, 35–42.

FOX, S. W. (1953) A correlation of observations suggesting a familial mode of molecular evolution as a concomitant of biological evolution. *Amer. Naturalist*, **87**, 253–6.

FOX, S. W. (1956) Evolution of protein molecules and thermal synthesis of biochemical substances. *Amer. Sci.*, **44**, 347–59.

FOX, S. W. (1960) How did life begin? *Science*, **132**, 200.

FOX, S. W., HARADA, K. and VEGOTSKY, A. (1959) Thermal polymerization of aminoacids and a theory of biochemical origin. *Experientia*, **15**, 81.

FRANKHAUSER, G. (1955) The role of nucleus and cytoplasm; in *Analysis of Development*, by Willier *et al.*, Saunders, Philadelphia, Pa., 39–69.

FREY-WYSSLING, A. (1948) *Submicroscopic Morphology of Protoplasm and its Derivatives*. Elsevier Publishing Co., Inc., New York, London.

FREY-WYSSLING, A. (1953) *Submicroscopic Morphology of Protoplasm*. Second Eng. edn., Elsevier, Amsterdam.

FRIES, N. (1951) The influence of aminoacids on growth and lateral root formation in cotyledonless pea seedlings. *Experientia*, **7**, 378.

FRITSCH, F. E. (1935) *The Structure and Reproduction of the Algae*. Vol. 1 (1935), vol. 2 (1945). Cambridge Univ. Press.

FRITSCH, F. E. (1939) The heterotrichous habit. *Bot. Notiser*, Lund.

FRITSCH, F. E. (1945a) Studies in the comparative morphology of the algae. IV. Algae and archegoniate plants. *Ann. Bot., Lond.*, N.S., **9**, 1.

FRITSCH, F. E. (1945b) Observations on the anatomical structure of the Fucales. 1. *New Phytol.*, **44**, 1–16.

FRITSCH, F. E. (1952) The evolution of a differentiated plant: a study in cell differentiation. *Proc. Linn. Soc. Lond.*, (1950–1), 218–33.

GALE, E. F. (1957a) The role of nucleic acids. *The Listener*, 7 Mar., 381–2.

GALE, E. F. (1957b) The problem of protein synthesis. *The Listener*, 28 Feb., 344–5.

GALSTON, A. W. (1947) The effect of 2,3,5-triiodobenzoic acid on the growth and flowering of soybeans. *Amer. J. Bot.*, **34**, 356.

GALUN, E., JUNG, Y. and LANG, A. (1962) Culture and sex modification of male cucumber buds *in vitro*. *Nature, Lond.*, **194**, 596–8.

GARRISON, W. M., HAMILTON, J. G., MORRISON, D. C., BENSON, A. A. and CALVIN, M. (1961) The reduction of carbon dioxide in aqueous solutions by ionizing radiations. *Science*, **114**, 416.

GAUDICHAUD, C. (1841) Recherches générales sur l'organographie, etc. Paris. [In Arber, 1930].

GAUTHERET, R. J. (1950) La culture des tissus végétaux et les phénomènes d'histogénèse. *Année biol.*, **26**, 719–44.

GERARD, R. W. (1957) Units and concepts of biology. *Science*, **125**, 429–33.

GIBBS, R. DARNLEY (1959) Comparative chemistry of plants as applied to problems of systematics. *Recent Advances in Botany*, IX Internat. Bot. Congr. Montreal, **1**, 67–71.

GIFFORD, E. M., JR. (1954) The shoot apex in angiosperms. *Bot. Rev.*, **20**, 477–529.

GOEBEL, K. (1900) *Organography of Plants*. Eng. trans. Clarendon Press, Oxford.

GOEBEL, K. (1905) *Organography of Plants*. Part II. Clarendon Press, Oxford.

GOEBEL, K. (1908) *Einleitung in die experimentelle Morphologie der Pflanzen*. Teubner, Leipzig.

GOEBEL, K. (1913) *Organographie der Pflanzen*, Gustav Fischer, Jena, Second edn., Pt. 1, 181.

GOEBEL, K. (1928a) Morphologische und biologische Studien XIII. Weitere Untersuchungen über die Gruppe der Drynariaceae. *Ann. Jard. bot. Buitenz.*, **39**, 117–26.

GOEBEL, K. (1928b) *Organographie der Pflanzen*, pt. 1: Allgemeine Organographie. Third edn., Gustav Fischer, Jena.

GOEBEL, K. (1930) *Organographie der Pflanzen*. Third edn., Gustav Fischer, Jena.

GOETHE, J. W. (1790) *Versuch die Metamorphose der Pflanzen zu erklären*. Gotha.

GOLDACRE, R. J. (1958) Surface films; their collapse on compression; the shapes and sizes of cells, and the origin of life: in *Surface Phenomena in Chemistry and Biology*. Pergamon Press, London, 278–98.

GOLDSCHMIDT, R. B. (1927) *Physiologische Theorie der Vererbung*. Berlin.

GOLDSCHMIDT, R. B. (1938) *Physiological Genetics*. New York.

GOLDSCHMIDT, R. B. (1940) *The Material Basis of Evolution*. Yale Univ. Press.

GOLDSCHMIDT, R. B. (1946) Position effect and the theory of the corpuscular gene. *Experientia*, **2**, 1–40.

GOLDSCHMIDT, R. B. (1951) Chromosomes and genes. *Cold Spring Harbor Symp. Quant. Biol.*, **16**, 1–12.

GOLDSCHMIDT, V. M. (1952) Geochemical aspects of the origin of complex organic molecules on the earth, as precursors of organic life. *New Biol.*, **12**, 97–105.

GOOD, R. (1956) *Features of Evolution in the Flowering Plants.* London.

GOODWIN, R. H. (1937) The role of auxin in leaf development in *Solidago. Amer. J. Bot.*, **24**, 43–51.

GORTER, C. J. (1949) The influence of 2,3,5-triiodobenzoic acid on the growing points of tomatoes. *Proc. Acad. Sci. Amst.*, **52**, 1185.

GORTER, C. J. (1951) The influence of 2,3,5-triiodobenzoic acid on the growing points of tomatoes. II. The initiation of ring-fasciations. *Proc. Acad. Sci. Amst.*, **54**, 181.

GORTER, C. J. (1961) Dwarfism of peas and the action of gibberellic acid. *Physiol. Plant.*, **14**, 332–43.

GOTTLIEB, J. E. (1958) Development of the bracken fern, *Pteridium aquilinum* (L.) Kuhn. 1. General morphology of the sporeling. *Phytomorph.*, **8**, 184–94.

GRANT, V. (1951) The fertilization of flowers. *Scientific American*, June, 2–6.

GRÉGOIRE, V. (1938) La morphogénèse et l'autonomie morphologique de l'appareil floral, I: Le carpelle. *Cellule*, **47**, 285.

GREGORY, F. G. (1928) Studies in the energy relations of plants. II. The effect of temperature on increase in area of leaf surface and in dry weight of *Cucumis sativus. Ann. Bot., Lond.*, **42**, 469–507.

GREGORY, F. G. and VEALE, J. A. (1957) A reassessment of the problem of apical dominance. *Symp. Soc. exp. Biol.*, **11**, 1–20.

GRENE, M. (1958) Two evolutionary theories, I and II. *Brit. J. Phil. Soc.*, **9**, 2–28.

GUPPY, H. B. (1906) *Observations of a Naturalist in the Pacific.* London.

GURWITSCH, A. (1922) Über den Begriff des embryonalen Feldes. *Arch. Entw. Mech.*, **51**, 383.

GURWITSCH, A. (1927) Weiterbildung und Verallgemeinerung des Feldbegriffes. *Arch. Entw. Mech.*, **112**, 433.

GUTTENBERG, H. V. (1960) *Grundzüge der Histogenese Höheren Pflanzen.* I. Die Angiospermen. Encyclo. Plant. Anatomy. Gebrüder Borntraeger, Berlin.

HABERLANDT, G. (1914) *Physiologische Pflanzenanatomie.* Leipzig: Engelmann 1884; Sixth edn. 1924. Eng. trans.: *Physiological Plant Anatomy.* London: Macmillan.

HACCIUS, B. (1955a) Experimentally induced twinning in plants. *Nature, Lond.*, **176**, 355–6.

HACCIUS, B. (1955b) Versuche zur somatischen Beeinflussung der Organbildung pflanzlicher Embryonen. *Experientia*, **11**, 149–152.

HACCIUS, B. (1956) Uber die Beeinflussung der Morphogenese pflanzlicher Embryonen durch Lithium-Ionen. *Ber. dtsch. bot. Ges.*, **69**, 87–93.

HACCIUS, B. (1957a) Uber die Regenerationsfähigkeit junger Embryonen von *Eranthis hiemalis* nach Colchicin-Behandlung. *Naturwissenschaften*, **44**, 18–9.

HACCIUS, B. (1957b) Regenerationserscheinungen an pflanzlichen Embryonen nach Behandlung mit antimitotisch wirksamen Substanzen. *Beitr. Biol. Pflanz.*, **34**, 3–18.

HACCIUS, B. (1959a) Morphoregulatorische Beeinflussung pflanzlicher Embryonen durch Phenylborsaure. *Naturwissenschaften*, **46**, 153.

HACCIUS, B. (1959b) Uber die unterschiedliche Antimitotica-Empfindlichkeit der Zellen noch undifferenzierter Embryonen von *Eranthis hiemalis*. *Z. Naturforsch*, **14b**, 206–9.

HACCIUS, B. (1960) Experimentell induzierte Einkeimblättrigkeit bei *Eranthis hiemalis*. II. Monokotylie durch Phenylborsäure. *Planta*, **54**, 482–97.

HACCIUS, B. and MASSFELLER, D. (1959) Durch Phenylborsäure induzierte Reduktion der Petalen von *Cucumis sativus*. *Naturwissenschaften*, **46**, 585–6.

HACCIUS, B. and REINHOLZ, E. (1953) Somatisch induzierte Veränderung der Keimblattzahl bei *Eranthis hiemalis* durch Röntgenstrahlen. *Naturwissenschaften*, **40**, 533.

HACCIUS, B. and TROMPETER, G. (1960) Experimentell induzierte Einkeimblättrigkeit bei *Eranthis hiemalis*. I. Synkotylie durch 2,4-Dichlorphenoxyessigsäure. *Planta*, **54**, 466–81.

HALDANE, J. B. S. (1927) The comparative genetics of colour in rodents and carnivora. *Biol. Rev.*, **2**, 199–212.

HALDANE, J. B. S. (1929) The Origin of Life. *Rationalist Annual*. Reprinted in *The Inequality of Man* (London, 1932); reprint in Pelican series, 1937. Published as *Science and Human Life*, New York, 1933.

HALDANE, J. B. S. (1932a) The time of action of genes, and its bearing on some evolutionary problems. *Amer. Nat.*, **66**, 5.

HALDANE, J. B. S. (1932b) The part played by recurrent mutation in evolution. *Amer. Nat.*, **67**, 5.

HALDANE, J. B. S. (1932c) *The Causes of Evolution*. Longmans, Green and Co., London.

HALDANE, J. B. S. (1941) *New Paths in Genetics*. London.

HALDANE, J. B. S. (1952) Variation. *New Biol.*, **12**, 9–26.

HALDANE, J. B. S. (1954) *The Biochemistry of Genetics*. London.

HALDANE, J. B. S. (1954) The origin of life. *New Biol.*, **16**, 12–27.

HALL, B. A. (1961) Sarraceniales: in *The Encyclopedia of the Biological Sciences*, ed. P. Gray, Reinhold, New York, 902.

HALL, O. L. (1954). Hybridization of wheat and rye after embryo transplantation. *Hereditas, Lund*, **40**, 453–8.

HALL, O. L. (1956) Further experiments on embryo transplantation. *Hereditas, Lund*, **42**, 261–2.

HAMMOND, D. (1941) The expression of genes for leaf shape in *Gossypium hirsutum* L. and G. *arboreum* L. Parts I and II. *Amer. J. Bot.*, **28**, 124–50.

HARLAND, S. C. (1933) The genetical conception of the species. *C.R. Acad. Sci. U.S.S.R.*, **4**, 181–6.

HARLAND, S. C. (1936). The genetical conception of the species. *Biol. Rev.*, *Camb. Phil. Soc.*, **11**, 83–112.

HARLAND, S. C. (1958) Review. *Ann. Human Genetics*, **23**, 79–80.

HARRIS, G. P. (1953) Amino-acids and the growth of isolated oat embryos. *Nature, Lond.*, **172**, 1003.

HARRISON, B. F. (1937) Histological responses of *Iresine lindenii* to indole-acetic acid. *Bot. Gaz.*, **99**, 301.

HARRISON, R. G. (1936) Relations of symmetry in the developing embryo. *The Collecting Net*, **2**.

HEGNAUER, R. (1959) Taxonomic value of cyanogenesis in higher plants. *Recent Advances in Botany*, IX Internat. Bot. Congr., Montreal, **1**, 82–86.

HEGNAUER, R. (1962–63) *Chemotaxonomie der Pflanzen*. Birkhäuser, Basel.

HEIDENHAIN, M. (1923) *Foremen und Kräfte in die lebenden Natur*. Berlin.

HENDERSON, L. J. (1913) *The Fitness of the Environment*. New York.

HERSH, A. H. (1941) Allometric growth: the ontogenetic and phylogenetic significance of differential rates of growth. *Growth*, Third Suppl., 113–45.

HESLOP-HARRISON, J. (1953) *New Concepts in Flowering-Plant Taxonomy*. Heinemann, London.

HESLOP-HARRISON, J. (1956) Auxin and sexuality in *Cannabis sativa*. *Physiol. Plant.*, **9**, 588.

HESLOP-HARRISON, J. (1957) The experimental modification of sex expression in flowering plants. *Biol. Rev.*, **32**, 38.

HESLOP-HARRISON, J. (1959) Growth substances and flower morphogenesis. *J. Linn. Soc. Lond. (Bot.)*, **56**, 269.

HESLOP-HARRISON, J. (1960a) Suppressive effects of 2-thiouracil on differentiation and flowering in *Cannabis sativa*. *Science*, **132**, 1943–4.

HESLOP-HARRISON, J. (1960b) The experimental control of sexuality and inflorescence structure in *Zea mais* L. *J. Linn. Soc. Lond. (Bot.)*, **172**, 108.

HESLOP-HARRISON, J. and HESLOP-HARRISON, Y. (1957a) Studies on flowering-plant growth and morphogenesis, I: Morphogenetic effects of 2,3,5-triiodobenzoic acid on *Cannabis sativa*. *Proc. Roy. Soc. Edinb.* B, **66**, 409.

HESLOP-HARRISON, J. and HESLOP-HARRISON, Y. (1957b) Studies on flowering-plant growth and morphogenesis, II: The modification of sex expression in *Cannabis sativa* by carbon monoxide. *Proc. Roy. Soc. Edinb.* B, **66**, 424.

HESLOP-HARRISON, J. and HESLOP-HARRISON, Y. (1958a) Photoperiod, auxin and sex balance in a long-day plant. *Nature, Lond.*, **181**, 100.

HESLOP-HARRISON, J. and HESLOP-HARRISON, Y. (1958b) Long-day and auxin induced male sterility in *Silene pendula* L. *Portug. Acta Biol.*, **5**, 79.

HESLOP-HARRISON, Y. and WOODS, I. (1959) Temperature-induced meristic and other variation in *Cannabis sativa*. *J. Linn. Soc. Lond. (Bot.)*, **56**, 290.

HILLMAN, W. S. (1962) *The Physiology of Flowering*. Holt, Reinhart and Winston, New York.

HILLSON, C. J. (1963) Hybridization and floral vascularization. *Amer. J. Bot.*, **50**, 971–8.

HODGE, A. J., MCLEAN, J. D. and MERCER, F. V. (1956) A possible mechanism for the morphogenesis of lamellar systems in plant cells. *J. Biophys. Biochem. Cytol.*, **2**, 597.

HOFMEISTER, W. (1857) Beiträge zur Kenntniss der Gefässkryptogamen. *Abh. kgl. sachs. Ges. Wiss.*, **3**, 603–82.

HOFMEISTER, W. (1862) *Higher Cryptogamia*. Eng. ed. Roy. Soc. Lond.

HOFMEISTER, W. (1868) *Allegemeine Morphologie der Gewächse*. Hdb. der Physiol. Bot., Leipzig.

HOLMES, S. J. (1948) *Organic Form and Related Biological Problems*. Univ. of California Press.

HOLTFRETER, J. (1951) Some aspects of embryonic induction. *Growth*, Suppl., **15**, 117–52.

HOLTTUM, R. E. (1949) The classification of ferns. *Biol. Rev.*, **24**, 267–96.

HOLTTUM, R. E. (1955) Growth-habits of monocotyledons—variations on a theme. *Phytomorph.*, **5**, 399–413.

HOROWITZ, N. H. (1945) *Proc. Nat. Acad. Sci.*, *Wash.*, **31**, 153.

HOROWITZ, N. H. (1960) On defining life: *in The Origin of Life on the Earth*. Internat. Union of Biochem, Biochemical Symposium Series 1, **106**. Pergamon Press, London.

HOUGHTALING, H. B. (1935) A developmental analysis of size and shape in tomato fruits. *Bull. Torrey Bot. Club*, **62**, 243.

HURWITZ, J. and FURTH, J. J. (1962) Messenger R.N.A. *Scientific American*, **206**, 41–9.

HUSKINS, C. L. (1947) The subdivision of the chromosomes and their multiplication in non-dividing tissues: possible interpretations in terms of gene structure and gene action. *Amer. Nat.*, **81**, 401–34.

HUSKINS, C. L. and STEINITZ, L. M. (1948) The nucleus in differentiation and development. I. Heterochromatic bodies in energic nuclei of *Rheo* roots. *J. Hered.*, **39**, 35–44. II. Induced mitoses in differentiated tissues of *Rheo* roots. *J. Hered.*, **39**, 67–77.

HUTCHINSON, J. (1926, 1934) *The Families of Flowering Plants*. Vols. I, II. Macmillan, London.

HUXLEY, J. S. (1932) *Problems of Relative Growth*. London.

HUXLEY, J. S. (1935) The field concept in biology. *Trans. Dynam. Development*, Moscow, **10**, 269.

HUXLEY, J. S. (editor) (1940) *The New Systematics*. Oxford University Press.

HUXLEY, J. S. (1942) *Evolution: The Modern Synthesis*. London.

HUXLEY, J. S. (1953) *Evolution in Action*. New York.

HUXLEY, J. S. (1954) The evolutionary process: in *Evolution as a Process*, ed. Huxley, Hardy and Ford, Allen and Unwin, London, 1–23.

HUXLEY, J. S., HARDY, A. C. and FORD, E. B. (1954) *Evolution as a Process*. Allen and Unwin, London.

HUXLEY, T. H. (1901) On the physical basis of life. *Collected Essays*, vol. 1. London.

JABLONSKI, J. R. and SKOOG, F. (1954) Cell enlargement and cell division in excised tobacco pith tissue. *Physiol. Plant.*, Copenhagen, **7**, 17–24.

JACOB, F. and MONOD, J. (1961) Genetic regulatory mechanisms in the synthesis of proteins. *J. Molec. Biol.*, **3**, 318–56.

JACOBS, W. P. (1952) The rôle of auxin in differentiation of xylem around a wound. *Amer. J. Bot.*, **39**, 301–9.

JACOBS, W. P. (1959) What substance normally controls a given biological process? 1. Formulation of some rules. *Develop. Biol.*, **1**, 527–33.

JACOBS, W. P. (1961) Auxin as a limiting factor in the differentiation of plant tissue. *Recent Advances in Botany*, Univ. of Toronto Press, 786–90.

JACOBS, W. P. and MORROW, I. B. (1957) A quantitative study of xylem development in the vegetative shoot apex of *Coleus*. *Amer. J. Bot.*, **44**, 823–42.

JACOBS, W. P. and MORROW, I. B. (1958) Quantitative relations between stages of leaf development and differentiation of sieve tubes. *Science*, **128**, 1084.

JACOBS, W. P., DANIELSON, J., HURST, V. and ADAMS, P. (1959) What substance normally controls a given biological process? 2. The relation of auxin to apical dominance. *Develop. Biol.*, **1**, 534–54.

JAMES, W. O. (1962) Plant respiration and the microstructure of plant cells. Presidential Address, Sect. K, British Assoc. Advancement of Science. Also *Adv. of Science* (1963), **19**, 375–82.

JAYASEKERA, R. D. E. and BELL, P. R. (1959) The effect of various experimental treatments on the development of the embryo of the fern *Thelypteris palustris*. *Planta*, **54**, 1–14.

JOHRI, B. M. and SINGH BAJAY, Y. P. (1963) *In vitro* response of the embryo of *Dendrophthoe falcata* (L.f.) Ettings: in *Plant Tissue and Organ Culture—A Symposium*, ed. Maheshwari, P. and Ranga Swamy, N. S., Univ. of Delhi. 292–301.

KAISER, S. (1935) The factors governing shape and size in *Capsicum* fruits; a genetic and developmental analysis. *Bull. Torrey Bot. Club.*, **62**, 433.

KEFFORD, N. P. and GOLDACRE, P. L. (1961) The changing concept of auxin. *Amer. J. Bot.*, **48**, 643–50.

KERNER VON MARILAUN, A. and OLIVER, F. W. (1894) *The Natural History of Plants.* London.

KLEIN, L. (1884) Vergleichende Untersuchungen über Wachsthum am Vegetationspunkt dorsiventraler Farne. *Bot. Zgt.,* **42,** 577–87.

KUYPER, CH. M. A. (1962) *The Organization of Cellular Activity.* Elsevier Publ. Coy., Amsterdam, New York.

LAM, S. L. and LEOPOLD, A. C. (1960) Reversion from flowering to the vegetative state in *Xanthium. Amer. J. Bot.,* **47,** 256–9.

LAM, S. L. and LEOPOLD, A. C. (1961) Reversion and reinduction of flowering in *Perilla. Amer. J. Bot.,* **48,** 306–10.

LAMPRECHT, H. (1960) Über Blattfarben von Phanerogamen. *Agr. Hort. Genetica,* **18,** 135–68.

LAMPRECHT, H. (1963) Zur Vererbung der Hülsenlänge bei *Pisum. Agr. Hort. Genet.,* **21,** 25–34.

LANG, A. (1957) The effect of gibberellin upon flower formation. *Proc. nat. Acad. Sci., Wash.,* **43,** 709–17.

LANG, A. (1959) The influence of gibberellin and auxin on photoperiodic induction: in *Photoperiodism and Related Phenomena in Plants and Animals* ed. R. B. Withrow; Amer. Assoc. Adv. Sci. Publ. **55,** Washington, 329–50.

LANG, A. (1960) Gibberellin-like substances in photoinduced and vegetative *Hyoscyamus* plants. *Planta,* **54,** 498–504.

LANG, A. (1961) Entwicklungsphysiologie. *Fortschr. Bot.,* **23,** 312–45.

LANG, A. (1964) *Handbuch der Pflanzenphysiologie.* Springer.

LANG, A. and REINHARD, E. (1961) Gibberellins and flower formation. *Adv. in Chem.,* **28,** 71–9.

LANG, A., SACHS, R. M. and BRETZ, C. (1959) Effets morphogénétiques de la gibbérelline. *Bull. Soc. franc. Physiol. végét.,* **5,** 1–19.

LANG, A., SANDOVAL, J. A. and BEDRI, A. (1957) Induction of bolting and flowering in *Hyoscyamus* and *Samolus* by a gibberellin-like material from a seed plant. *Proc. nat. Acad. Sci., Wash.,* **43,** 960–4.

LANG, W. H. (1915) Causal and phyletic morphology. Presidential Address, Rept. Brit. Assoc. Adv. Sci., Sect. K. (1915). 701–18.

LANKESTER, E. R. (1870) On the use of the term homology in modern Zoology and the distinction between homogenetic and homoplastic agreements. *Ann. Mag. Nat. Hist.,* **4,** Ser. 6.

LARSON, P. R. (1962) The indirect effect of photoperiod on tracheid diameter in *Pinus resinosa. Amer. J. Bot.,* **49,** 132–7.

LASHLEY, K. S. (1951) *Cerebral Mechanism in Behavior.* The Hixon Symp. ed. L. A. Jeffress. New York and London.

LEE, A. E. (1950a) The growth in culture of intact seedlings and isolated seedling organs. *Amer. J. Bot.,* **37,** 312–8.

LEE, A. E. (1950b) The influence of various sugars on the growth in culture of intact seedlings and isolated seedling organs. *Amer. J. Bot.,* **37,** 528–33.

LE FANU, B. (1936) Auxin and correlative inhibition. *New Phytol.*, **35**, 205–20.

LEMBERG, R. (1951) The Origin of Life. 2. A Critique of Bernel *Australian J. Sci.*, **14**, 3, 73.

LEVINE, R. P. and EBERSOLD, W. T. (1960) The genetics and cytology of *Chlamydomonas. Ann. Rev. Microbiology*, **14**, 197–216.

LEWIN, R. A. (1954) Sex in unicellular algae: in *Sex in Microorganisms*, Amer. Assoc. Adv. Sci., Washington, 100–33.

LEWIS, D. (1943) The physiology of incompatibility in plants. II. *Linum grandiflorum. Ann. Bot., Lond.*, N.S., **7**, 115–22.

LEWIS, D. (1949) Incompatibility in flowering plants. *Biol. Rev.*, **24**, 472–96.

LEWIS, D. (1952) Serological reactions of pollen incompatibility substances. *Proc. Roy. Soc.*, B, **140**, 127–35.

LILLIE, R. S. (1945) *General Biology and Philosophy of Organism.* Univ. Chicago Press.

LINDBLAD, K. J. (1959) The influences of growth conditions on the amount of ribonucleic acid content of wheat root mitochondria. *Physiol. Plant*, **12**, 400.

LINSLEY, E. G. and USINGER, R. K. (1961) Taxonomy. *The Encyclopedia of the Biological Sciences* ed. P. Gray. Reinhold Publishing Corporation, New York, 992–6.

LLOYD, F. E. (1942) *The Carnivorous Plants.* Chronica Botanica Coy., Waltham, Mass.

LOCKHART, J. A. (1956) Reversal of the light inhibition of pea stem growth by the gibberellins. *Proc. nat. Acad. Sci., Wash.*, **42**, 841–8.

LONA, F. (1962) Ontogenetical sites of gibberellin-like manifestations. From Symposium on *Eigenschaften und Wirkungen der Gibberelline*, 73–93. Springer, Berlin.

LOOMIS, W. E. (1953) Growth correlation: in *Growth and Differentiation in Plants* ed. W. E. Loomis, 197–217.

LOWRY, T. M. and SUGDEN, S. (1929) *A Class Book of Physical Chemistry.* Macmillan, London.

LUGG, J. W. H. (1943) Further studies of cryptogam tissue proteins: protein composition and tissue function in plants. *Biochem. Jour.*, **37**, 132–7.

LUGG, J. W. H. (1949) Plant proteins. *Adv. Prot. Chem.*, **5**, 229–304.

MADISON, K. M. (1953) The Organism and its Origin. *Evolution* **7**, 211–27.

MAHESHWARI, P. (1962) *Plant Embryology—A Symposium.* C.S.I.R., New Delhi.

MAHESHWARI, P. and BALDEV, B. (1962) *In vitro* induction of adventitious buds from embryos of *Cuscuta reflexa* Roxb. In *Plant Embryology*—A Symposium, ed. P. Maheshwari, C.S.I.R., New Delhi. 127–38.

MAHESHWARI, P. and RANGA SWAMY, N. S. (1963a) *Plant Tissue and Organ Culture—A Symposium. Intern. Soc. Pl. Morph.*, Univ. of Delhi.

MAHESHWARI, P. and RANGA SWAMY, N. S. (1963b) Plant tissue and organ culture from the viewpoint of an embryologist. In *Plant Tissue and*

Organ Culture—A Symposium, ed. P. Maheshwari and N. S. Ranga Swamy, Univ. of Delhi. 391–420.

MAJUMDAR, G. P. (1957) The shoot of higher plants: its morphology and phylogeny. *J. Asiatic Soc.*, **23**, 39–62.

MANTON, I. (1961) Plant cell structure: in *Contemporary Botanical Thought.* Oliver and Boyd, Edinburgh and London, 171–97.

MANTON, I. and CLARKE, B. (1952) An electron microscope study of the spermatozoid of *Sphagnum. J. Exp. Bot.*, **3**, 265–75.

MARINOS, N. C. (1963) Studies on submicroscopic aspects of mineral nutrition. II. Nitrogen, potassium, sulfur, phosphorus and magnesium deficiencies in the shoot apex of barley. *Amer. J. Bot.*, **50**, 998–1005.

MARSDEN, M. P. F. and WETMORE, R. H. (1954) *In vitro* culture of the shoot tips of *Psilotum nudum. Amer. J. Bot.*, **41**, 640–5.

MARTH, P. C., PRESTON, W. H., JR. and MITCHELL, J. W. (1953) Growth controlling effects of some quarternary ammonium compounds on various species of plants. *Bot. Gaz.*, **115**, 200–4.

MATHER, K. (1944) Genetical control of incompatibility in angiosperms and fungi. *Nature, Lond.*, **153**, 392–4.

MATHER, K. (1948) Nucleus and cytoplasm in differentiation. *Symp. Soc. exp. Biol., Growth*, **2**, 196–216.

MATHER, K. (1955) Biological Organisation. Presidential Address, Brit. Assoc. Adv. Sci., 1955. *Advancement of Sci.*, XII, 250–7.

MATHER, K. (1961) Nuclear materials and nuclear change in differentiation. *Nature, Lond.*, **190**, 404–6.

MATZKE, E. B. (1932) Flower variation and symmetry patterns in *Stellaria media*, and their underlying significance. *Amer. J. Bot.*, **19**, 477.

MAYER, L. (1956) Wachstum und Organbildung an *in vitro* kultivierten Segmenten von *Pelargonium zonale* und *Cyclamen persicum. Planta*, **47**, 401–46.

MAYR, E. (1954) Change of genetic environment and evolution: in *Evolution as a Process*, ed. Huxley, Hardy and Ford, 157–80.

MAZIA, D. (1961) How cells divide. *Scientific American*, **205**, 3, 101–20.

MCCLINTOCK, B. (1950) The origin and behaviour of mutable loci in maize. *Proc. nat. Acad. Sci., Wash.*, **36**, 344–55.

MCCLINTOCK, B. (1951) Chromosome organization and genic expression. *Cold Spring Harbor Symp. Quant. Biol.*, **16**, 13–47.

MELVILLE, R. (1957) Some taxonomic implications of Turing's reaction-diffusion theory of morphogenesis. *Bull. du Jardin Botanique de l'État Bruxelles*, **27**, 289–300.

MERCER, F. (1960) The Submicroscopic structure of the cell. *Ann. Rev. Plant Physiol.*, **11**, 1–24.

METCALFE, C. R. (1954) An anatomist's views on angiosperm classification. *Kew Bull.*, No. 3, 427–40.

METCALFE, C. R. and CHALK, L. (1950) *Anatomy of the Dicotyledons.* Oxford Univ. Press.

MICHIE, D. (1958) The third stage in genetics: in *A Century of Darwin*, ed. S. A. Barnett, Heinemann, London, 56–84.

MICHNIEWICZ, M. and LANG, A. (1962a) Effect of gibberellins A₁ through A₉ on flower formation in *Myosotis alpestris* L. *Naturwissenschaften*, **49**, 211–2.

MICHNIEWICZ, M. and LANG, A. (1962b) Effect of nine different gibberellins on stem elongation and flower formation in cold-requiring and photoperiodic plants grown under non-inductive conditions. *Planta*, **58**, 549–63.

MIETTINEN, J. K. and WARIS, H. (1958) A chemical study of the neomorphosis induced by glycine in *Oenanthe aquatica. Physiol. Plant.*, **11**, 193–9.

MILLER, C. O. and SKOOG, F. (1953) Chemical control of bud formation in tobacco stem segments. *Amer. J. Bot.*, **40**, 768–73.

MILLER, C. O., SKOOG, F., OKUMURA, F. S., SALTZA, M. H. VON and STRONG F. M. (1956) Isolation, structure and synthesis of kinetin, a substance promoting cell division. *J. Amer. chem. Soc.*, **78**, 1375–80.

MILLER, S. L. (1953) A production of amino acids under possible primitive earth conditions. *Science*, **117**, 528.

MILLICH, F. and CALVIN, M. (1961) Coacervation of salts of polyvinylsulfonic acid induced by heavy metal ions. Univ. California Radiation Laboratory Rept., UCRL, 9519, 4.

MOEWUS, F. (1949) Zur biochemischen Genetik des Rutins. *Port. Acta Biol.*, (A) Goldschmidt Vol., 161–99.

MOEWUS, F. (1950) Zur Physiologie und Biochemie der Selbststerilität bei *Forsythia. Biol. Zentralbl.*, **69**, 181–97.

MOHAN RAM, H. Y. (1963) *In vitro* modification of regeneration in foliar embryos of *Bryophyllum calycinum* Salisb: in *Plant Tissue and Organ Culture*, ed. P. Maheshwari and N. S. Ranga Swamy, Univ. of Delhi, 159–67.

MOOG, F. (1952) Enzymes in the development of the chick embryo. *Ann. N.Y. Acad. Sci.*, 55–7.

MOORE, B. (1912) *The Origin and Nature of Life.* Home Univ. Press, London.

MOORE, B. and WEBSTER, T. A. (1913–4) Synthesis by sunlight in relationship to the origin of life. *Proc. Roy. Soc.* B, **87**, 163–76.

MOORE, T. C. and BONDE, E. K. (1962) Physiology of flowering in peas. *Plant Physiol.*, **37**, 149–53.

MOREL, G. (1963) Leaf regeneration in *Adiantum pedatum. J. Linn. Soc. Lond. (Bot.)*, **58**, 381–3.

MORGAN, L. (1922) *Emergent Evolution.* Gifford Lectures, 1922. Henry Holt, New York.

MORGAN, T. H. (1925) *Evolution and Genetics.* Princeton.

MORGAN, T. H. (1932) *The Scientific Basis of Evolution*. London.

MORITZ, O. (1959) Serologie als Methode der Botanischen Verwandtschafts-forschung. *Recent Advances in Botany, IX* Internat. Bot. Congr., Montreal, **1**, 77–82.

MÜHLETHALER, K. and FREY-WYSSLING (1959) Entwicklung und Struk-ture der Proplastiden. *J. Biophys. and Biochem. Cytol.*, **6**, 507–12.

MULLER H. J. (1951) The development of the gene theory. *Genetics in the 20th Century*, ed. L. C. Dunn, New York, 77–99.

MURNEEK, A. F. (1927) Physiology of reproduction in horticultural plants, II: The physiological basis of intermittent sterility with special reference to the spider flower. *Res. Bull. Univ. Mo. Agric. Exp. Sta.*, **106**, 1.

NAGEL, E. (1953) Teleological explanations and teleological systems: in *Vision and Action*, ed. S. Ratner. Rutgers University Press.

NARAYANASWAMI, S. (1963) Studies on growth of excised grass embryos in culture: in *Plant Tissue and Organ Culture—A Symposium*, ed. P. Mahesh-wari and N. S. Ranga Swamy, Univ. of Delhi, 302–313.

NEEDHAM, J. (1942) *Biochemistry and Morphogenesis*. Cambridge Univ. Press.

NEEDHAM, J. (1944) Matter, Form, Evolution and us: in *This Changing World*, ed. J. R. M. Brumwell, Routledge, London, 27–38.

NORTHROP, F. S. C. and BURR, H. S. (1937) Experimental findings con-cerning the electro-dynamic theory of life and an analysis of their physical meaning. *Growth*, **1**, 78–88.

OPARIN, A. I. (1938, 1953) *The Origin of Life*, trans. S. Margulis. Second edn., Dover, New York.

OPARIN, A. I. (1957) *The Origin of Life on the Earth*, trans. A. Synge. Third edn., London.

OPARIN, A. I. (1961) *Life, Its Nature, Origin and Development*, Eng. trans. A. Synge, Oliver and Boyd, Edinburgh and London.

OPPENHEIMER, J. M. (1955) Problems, concepts and their history. *Analysis of Development:* ed. Willier *et al.*, 1–24.

PALM, C. and CALVIN, M. (1961) Irradiation of methane, ammonia, hydro-gen and water. *Univ. California Radiation Laboratory Rept.*, *UCRL*, 9519, 30.

PARPART, A. K. (1949) *The Chemistry and Physiology of Growth*. Princeton Univ. Press.

PATAU, K., DAS, N. K. and SKOOG, F. (1957) Induction of DNA synthesis by kinetin and indoleacetic acid in excised tobacco pith tissue. *Physiol. Plantarum (Cph.)*, **10**, 949–66.

PAULET, P. and NITSCH, J. P. (1959) Stimulation chimique de bourgeonne-ment chez *Cardamine pratensis* L. *Bull. Soc. bot. France*, **106**, 426–41.

PERRET, J. (1952) Biochemistry and bacteria. *New Biol.*, **12**, 68–96.

PICKEN, L. (1960) *The Organization of Cells*. The Clarendon Press, Oxford.

PEIRCE, J. G. (1926) *The Physiology of Plants*. New York.

466 *Organization and Evolution in Plants*

PIRIE, N. W. (1952) Vital blarney. *New Biol.*, **12**, 106–12.

PIRIE, N. W. (1953) Ideas and assumptions about the origin of life. *Discovery*, **14**, 238.

PIRIE, N. W. (1954) On making and recognizing life. *New Biol.*, **16**, 41–53.

PIRIE, N. W. (1960) Biological replication considered in the general context of scientific illusion: in *Biological Replication, New Biol.*, **31**, 117–35.

PISSAREV, W. E. and VINOGRADOVA, N. M. (1944) Hybrids between wheat, and *Elymus*. *C.R. Dokl. Acad. Sci. U.S.S.R.*, **45**, 129–32.

PLANTEFOL, L. (1948) L'ontogénie de la fleur. *Ann. Sci. Nat., Bot.*, *XI*, **9**, 33.

PLATT, J. R. (1961) Properties of large molecules that go beyond the properties of their chemical sub-groups. *J. Theoret. Biol.*, **1**, 342–58.

PLUNKETT, C. R. (1944) The primary physicochemical basis of organic evolution. In J. Alexander's *Colloid Chemistry*, Reinhold, New York, **5**, 1173–97.

POLANYI, M. (1957) Scientific outlook: its sickness and cure. *Science*, **125**, 480–4.

POLANYI, M. (1958) *Personal Knowledge*. Routledge, London.

PONTECORVO, G. (1959) Trends in genetic analysis. *Columbia Biol. Ser.* 18. New York.

POSTLETHWAIT, S. N. and NELSON, O. E. JR. (1957) A chronically wilted mutant of maize. *Amer. J. Bot.*, **44**, 628–33.

POTONIÉ, H. (1902) Die Pericaulome-Theorie. *Ber. deut. bot. Ges.*, **20**, 501. (In Arber, 1930.)

POTONIÉ, H. (1912) *Grundlinien der Pflanzen-Morphologie im Lichte der Palaeontologie.* Jena.

PRAT, H. (1945) Les gradients histo-physiologiques et l'organogènese végétale. *Contr. Inst. bot. Univ. Montreal*, **58**, 1–151.

PRAT, H. (1948) Histo-physiological gradients and plant organogenesis. *Bot. Rev.*, **14**, 603.

PRAT, H. (1954) Symposium on Gradients. *Rept. Internat. Bot. Congress, Paris.*

PRIESTLEY, J. H. (1928) The meristematic tissue of the plant. *Biol. Rev.*, **3**, 1.

PRIESTLEY, J. H. and SWINGLE, C. F. (1929) Vegetative propagation from the standpoint of plant anatomy. *U.S. Dept. Agric., Tech. Bull.*, 151.

PRINGLE, J. W. S. (1953) The Origin of Life. *Symp. Soc. exp. Biol.*, **7**, 1.

PRINGLE, J. W. S. (1954) The evolution of living matter. *New Biol.*, **16**, 54–67.

PURVES, W. K. and HILLMAN, W. S. (1958) Response of pea stem sections to indole acetic acid, giberellic acid and sucrose as affected by length and distance from apex. *Physiol. Plant*, 11–29.

RANDOLPH, L. F., ABBE, E. C. and EINSET, J. (1944) Comparison of shoot apex and leaf development and structure in diploid and tetraploid maize. *J. Agr. Res.*, **69**, 47–76.

RAPER, J. R. (1955) Some problems of specificity in the sexuality of plants. In *Biological Specificity and Growth*, 119–40; (Ed. E. G. Butler). Princeton University Press, New Jersey.

REECE, P. R., FURR, J. F. and COOPER, W. C. (1946) The inhibiting effect of the terminal bud on flower formation in the axillary buds of the Haden mango. *Amer. J. Bot.*, **33**, 209.

REEVE, E. C. R. and HUXLEY, J. S. (1945) Some problems in the study of allometric growth. *Essays on growth and form.* Oxford Univ. Press.

REINERT, J. (1962) Morphogenesis in plant tissue cultures. *Endeavour*, **21**, 85.

REINERT, J. (1963) Experimental modification of organogenesis in plant tissue cultures: in *Plant Tissue and Organ Culture—A Symposium*, ed. P. Maheshwari and N. S. Ranga Swamy, Univ. of Delhi. 168–77.

RENSCH, B. (1959) *Evolution above the Species Level.* Methuen, London.

RHOADES, M. M. and MCCLINTOCK, B. (1935) The cytogenetics of maize. *Bot. Rev.* **1**, 292–325.

RICHARDS, F. J. (1948) The geometry of phyllotaxis and its origin. *Symp. Soc. exp. Biol.*, **2**, 217–45.

RICHARDS, F. J. (1951) Phyllotaxis: its quantitative expression and relation to growth in the apex. *Phil. Trans. Roy. Soc.*, B, **235**, 509–63.

RICHARDS, F. J. (1956) Spatial and temporal correlations involved in leaf pattern production at the apex: in *The growth of leaves*, ed. F. L. Milthorpe, Butterworth Scientif. Public., London, 66–75.

RICKETT, H. W. (1944) The classification of inflorescences. *Bot. Rev.*, **10**, 187.

RIJVEN, A. H. G. C. (1952) *In vitro* studies on the embryo of *Capsella bursa-pastoris. Acta bot. neerl.*, **1**, 157–200.

RIS, H. and SINGH, R. N. (1961) *Biophys. Biochem. Cytol.*, **9**, 63–80.

ROPER, J. A. (1958) *Cold Spring Harbour Symp. Quant. Biol.*, **23**, 141.

ROTH, I. (1957) Relation between the histogenesis of the leaf and its external shape. *Bot. Gaz.*, **118**, 237–45.

ROUX, W. (1895) The problem, methods and scope of developmental mechanics. trans. W. M. Wheeler from *Archiv fur Entwicklungsmechanik der Organismen.* Wood's Hole Biol. Lectures, 1894.

RUSSELL, E. S. (1930) *The Interpretation of Development and Heredity.* Oxford Univ. Press.

SACHS, J. (1875) *Textbook of Botany.* Oxford Univ. Press.

SACHS, J. (1887) *Lectures on the Physiology of Plants*, trans. H. Marshall Ward, Clarendon Press, Oxford.

SACHS, R. M. and LANG, A. (1957) Effect of gibberellin upon cell division in *Hyoscyamus. Science*, **125**, 1144–5.

SACHS, R. M. and LANG, A. (1961) Shoot histogenesis and the subapical meristem; the action of gibberellic acid, Amo-1618, and maleic hydrazide:

Q

in *Fourth Internat. Conf. on Plant Growth Regulation*, Yonkers, N.Y., Aug. 1959, Ames, Iowa State Univ. Press, 567.

SACHS, R. M., BRETZ, C. F. and LANG, A. (1959) Shoot histogenesis: the early effect of gibberellin upon stem elongation in two rosette plants. *Amer. J. Bot.*, **46**, 376–84.

SACHS, R. M., LANG, A., BRETZ, C. F. and ROACH, J. (1960) Shoot histogenesis: subapical meristematic activity in a caulescent plant and the action of gibberellic acid and Amo-1618. *Amer. J. Bot.*, **47**, 260–6.

ST HILAIRE, G. (1837) *Lectures*. Résumé in *Rev. et Mag. de Zool.*, 1 Jan., 1837.

SALISBURY, F. B. and BONNER, J. (1958) Effects of uracil derivatives on flowering in *Xanthium*. *Plant Physiol.*, Suppl., **33**, 25.

SALISBURY, F. B. and BONNER, J. (1960) Inhibition of photoperiodic induction by 5-fluorouracil. *Plant Physiol.*, **35**, 173–7.

SANDERS, M. E. (1950) Development of self and hybrid embryos in artificial culture. *Amer. J. Bot.*, **37**, 6–15.

SANDERS, M. E. and BURKHOLDER, P. R. (1948) Influence of amino acids on growth of *Datura* embryos in culture. *Proc. nat. Acad. Sci., Wash.*, **34**, 516.

SATINA, S., BLAKESLEE, A. F. and AVERY, A. G. (1940) Demonstration of the three germ layers in the shoot apex of *Datura* by means of induced polyploidy in periclinal chimeras. *Amer. J. Bot.*, **27**, 895–905.

SATINA, S., BLAKESLEE, A. F. and AVERY, A. G. (1941) Periclinal chimeras in *Datura stramonium* in relation to development of leaf and flowers. *Amer. J. Bot.*, **28**, 862–71.

SATINA, S., BLAKESLEE, A. F. and AVERY, A. G. (1943) Periclinal chimeras in *Datura* in relation to the development of the carpel. *Amer. J. Bot.*, **30**, 453–62.

SCHECHTMAN, A. M. (1955) Ontogeny of the blood and related antigens and their significance for the theory of differentiation: in *Biological Specificity and Growth*, ed. E. G. Butler, Princeton Univ. Press, 3–31.

SCHINDEWOLF, O. H. (1950) *Grundfragen der Paläontologie*. Stuttgart.

SCHLEIP, W. (1929) *Die Determination der primitiv Entwicklung*. Akad. Verlag. Leipzig.

SCHMITT, F. O. (1955) Cell constitution: in *Analysis of Development*, ed. Willier *et al.*, 39–69.

SCHMUCKER, T. (1934) Über den Einfluss von Borsäure auf Pflanzen, inbesondere keimende Pollenkörner. *Planta*, **23**, 264–83.

SCHOPFER, W. H. (1940) Recherches sur la phénologie de *Melandrium album* (Miller) Gke. parasité par *Ustilago violacea* (Pers.) Fck. *C.R. Acad. Sci. Paris*, **210**, 703.

SCHOUTE, J. C. (1913) Beiträge zur Blattstellungslehre. *Réc. trav. bot. neerl.*, **10**, 153–339.

SCHOUTE, J. C. (1936) Fasciation and dichotomy. *Réc. trav. bot. neerl.*, **33**, 649–69.

SCHRAUDOLF, H. and REINERT, J. (1959) Interaction of plant growth regulators in regeneration processes. *Nature, Lond.*, **184**, 465–6.

SCHRÖEDINGER, E. (1944) *What is Life?* Cambridge Univ. Press.

SCHÜEPP, O. (1926) Meristeme. Linsbauer's *Handbuch der Planzenanatomie*, Berlin, 4.

SCHÜEPP, O. (1929) Untersuchungen zur Beschreibenden und experimentellen Entwicklungsgeschichte von *Acer pseudoplatanus. J.B. Wiss. bot.*, **70**, 743.

SEIFRIZ, W. (1935) The structure of protoplasm. *Bot. Rev.*, **1**, 18–36.

SEIFRIZ, W. (1936) *Protoplasm*. New York.

SEIFRIZ, W. (1938) Recent contributions to the theory of protoplasmic structure. *Science*, **88**, 21–5.

SEYMOUR SEWELL, R. B. (1931) The problem of evolution. *J. Bombay Nat. Hist. Soc.*, **35**, 2.

SHEN, S. C. (1955) Enzyme development as ontogeny of specific proteins: in *Biological Specificity and Growth*, ed. E. G. Butler, Princeton Univ. Press 73–92.

SIMON, E. W. and CHAPMAN, J. A. (1961) The development of mitochondria in *Arum* spadix. *J. Exp. Bot.*, **12**, 414–20.

SIMPSON, G. G. (1950) *The Meaning of Evolution*. Oxford Univ. Press.

SIMPSON, G. G. (1953) *Major Features of Evolution*. Columbia Univ. Press.

SINNOTT. E. W. (1931) The independence of genetic factors governing size and shape. *J. Hered.*, **22**, 381.

SINNOTT, E. W. (1935) Evidence for the existence of genes controlling shape. *Genetics*, **20**, 12.

SINNOTT, E. W. (1936) A developmental analysis of inherited shape differences in cucurbit fruits. *Amer. Nat.*, **70**, 245.

SINNOTT, E. W. (1942) An analysis of the comparative rates of cell division in various parts of the developing cucurbit ovary. *Amer. J. Bot.*, **29**, 317–23.

SINNOTT, E. W. (1946) Substance or system: the riddle of morphogenesis. *Amer. Nat.*, **80**, 497–505.

SINNOTT, E. W. (1954) Biology and teleology. *Bios*, **25**, 35–43.

SINNOTT, E. W. (1958) The genetic basis of organic form, *In* Genetic Concept for the Origin of Cancer. *Ann. New York Acad. Sci.*, **71**, 1223–33.

SINNOTT, E. W. (1960) *Plant Morphogenesis*, New York and London.

SINNOTT, E. W. and BLOCH, R. (1944) Visible expression of cytoplasmic patterns in the differentiation of xylem strands. *Proc. nat. Acad. Sci., Wash.*, **30**, 388–92.

SINNOTT, E. W. and BLOCH, R. (1945) The cytoplasmic basis of intercellular patterns in vascular differentiation. *Amer. J. Bot.*, **32**, 151–6.

Q*

SINNOTT, E. W., DUNN, L. C. and DOBZHANSKY, TH. (1950) *Principles of Genetics*, Fourth edn., New York.

SKOOG, F. (1944) Growth and organ formation in tobacco tissue cultures. *Amer. J. Bot.*, **31**, 19–24.

SKOOG, F. (1950) Chemical control of growth and organ formation in plant tissues. *Année biol.* **54**, III, **26**, 545–62.

SKOOG, F. (1954a) Substances involved in normal growth and differentiation. Abnormal and pathological plant growth. *Brookhaven Symp. Biol.* **6**, 1–21.

SKOOG, F. (1954b) Chemical regulation of growth in plants: in *Dynamics of Growth Processes* ed. E. F. Boell, Princeton: Univ. Press, 148–82.

SKOOG, F. and MILLER, C. O. (1957) Chemical regulation of growth and organ formation in plant tissue cultures *in vitro.*—The Biological Action of Growth Substances. *Symp. Soc. exp. Biol.*, **11**, 118.

SKOOG, F. and TSUI, C. (1948) Chemical control of growth and bud formation in tobacco stem segments and callus cultured *in vitro*. *Amer. J. Bot.*, **35**, 782–7.

SKOOG, F. and TSUI, C. (1951) Growth substances and the formation of buds in plant tissues: in *Plant Growth Substances*, ed. F. Skoog, Madison: Univ. of Wisconsin Press, 263–87.

SKOOG, F., SCHNEIDER, C. L. and MALAN, P. (1942) Interactions of auxin in growth and inhibition. *Amer. J. Bot.*, **29**, 568.

SMUTS, J. (1922) *Holism and Evolution*. London.

SNOW, M. and SNOW, R. (1931) Experiments on phyllotaxis. I. The effect of isolating a primordium. *Phil. Trans. Roy. Soc.*, B, **221**, 1–43.

SNOW, M. and SNOW, R. (1935) Experiments on phyllotaxis. III. Diagonal splits through decussate apices. *Phil. Trans. Roy. Soc.*, B, **225**, 63–94.

SNOW, M. and SNOW, R. (1937) Auxin and leaf formation. *New Phytol.*, **36**, 1–18.

SNOW, M. and SNOW, R. (1942) The determination of axillary buds. *New Phytol.*, **41**, 13–22.

SNOW, M. and SNOW, R. (1948) On the determination of leaves. *Symp. Soc. exp. Biol.*, **2**, 263–75.

SNOW, M. and SNOW, R. (1952) Minimum areas and leaf determination. *Proc. Roy. Soc.*, B, **139**, 545.

SNOW, M. and SNOW, R. (1953) Regeneration of the potato shoot apex. *Nature, Lond.*, **171**, 224.

SNOW, M. and SNOW, R. (1955) Regulation of sizes of leaf primordia by growing-point of stem apex. *Proc. Roy. Soc.*, B, **144**, 222–9.

SNOW, M. and SNOW, R. (1959) Regulation of sizes of leaf primordia by older leaves. *Proc. Roy. Soc.*, B, **151**, 39–47.

SNOW, R. (1936) Upward effect of auxin in coleoptiles and stems. *New Phytol.*, **35**, 292–304.

SNOW, R. (1955) Problems of phyllotaxis and leaf determination. *Endeavour*, 14, 190–9.

SNOW, R. and SNOW, M. (1954) Experiments on the cause of dorsiventrality in leaves. *Nature, Lond.*, 173, 644; 174, 352–3.

SÖDING, H. (1952) *Die Wuchsstofflehre, Ergebnisse und Probleme der Wuchsstoff-forschung.* Thieme, Stuttgart.

SOMMERHOFF, G. (1950) *Analytical Biology.* Oxford Univ. Press.

SONNEBORN, T. M. (1963) Implication of the new genetics for biology and man. *AIBS bull.*, 13, 2, 22–26.

SOSSOUNTZOV, I. (1954) Le développement in vitro de colonies prothalliennes de *Gymnogramme calomelanos* en présence des acides aspartiques et glutamiques et leurs amides (asparagine et glutamine). *Physiol. Plant.*, 7, 726.

SPEMANN, H. (1921) Die Erzeugung tierischer Chimären durch heteroplastische embryonale Transplantation zwischen *Triton cristatus* und *taeniatus. Roux' Arch.*, 48, 533.

SPEMANN, H. (1938) *Embryonic Development and Induction.* Yale Univ. Press.

SPENCER, H. (1898) *Principles of Biology.* Second edn., New York.

SPIEGELMAN, S. (1948) Differentiation as the controlled production of unique enzymatic patterns. *Symp. Soc. exp. Biol.*, II, *Growth*, 286–325.

SPURWAY, H. (1949) *La Ricerca Scientifica*, 19, (*see* Haldane, 1952).

STADLER, W. J. (1954) The gene. *Science*, 120, 811–9.

STANIER, R. Y. and VAN NIEL, C. B. (1962) *Arch. Mikrobiol.* 42, 17–35.

STEBBINS, G. L. (1950) *Variation and Evolution in Plants.* Oxford Univ. Press.

STEBBINS, G. W. and SHAH, S. S. (1960) Developmental studies of cell differentiation in the epidermis of monocotyledons. II. Cytological features of stomatal development in the Gramineae. *Develop. Biol.*, 2, 477–500.

STEEVES, T. A. (1959) The development of leaves in sterile nutrient culture. *IX Intern. Bot. Cong. Proc.*, 2, 380.

STEEVES, T. A. and WETMORE, R. H. (1953) Morphogenetic studies on *Osmunda cinnamomea* L.: Some aspects of the general morphology. *Phytomorph.* 3, 339–54.

STEEVES, T. A. and SUSSEX, I. M. (1957) Studies on the development of excised leaves in sterile culture. *Amer. J. Bot.*, 44, 665–73.

STEEVES, T. A. and BRIGGS, W. R. (1958) Morphogenetic studies on *Osmunda cinnamomea* L.: The origin and early development of vegetative fronds. *Phytomorph.*, 8, 60–72.

STEEVES, T. A. and BRIGGS, W. R. (1960) Morphogenetic studies on *Osmunda cinnamomea* L. The auxin relationships of expanding fronds. *J. Exp. Bot.*, 11, 45–67.

STEEVES, T. A., GABRIEL, H. P. and STEEVES, M. W. (1957) Growth in sterile culture of excised leaves of flowering plants. *Science*, 126, 350–1.

STEIN, O. L. (1955) Rates of leaf initiation in two mutants of *Zea mais*. *Amer. J. Bot.*, **42**, 885–92.

STEIN, O. L. and KROMAN, R. A. (1954) An analysis of growth rates in substage A of plastochron nine in *Zea mays* L. *Minnesota Acad. Sci.*, **22**, 104–8.

STEINBACH, H. B. and MOOG, F. (1955) Cellular metabolism. *Analysis of Development*, ed. Willier *et al.*, 70–90.

STEINBERG, R. A. (1947) Growth response to organic compounds by tobacco seedlings in aseptic culture. *J. Agric. Research*, **75**, 81.

STEINBERG, R. A. (1949) Symptoms of amino acid action on tobacco seedlings in aseptic culture. *J. Agric. Research*, **78**, 733.

STEINBERG, R. A. (1952) Frenching symptoms produced in *Nicotiana tabacum* and *Nicotiana rustica* with optical isomers of isoleucine and leucine and with *Bacillus cereus* toxin. *Plant Physiol.*, **27**, 302.

STEINBERG, R. A., BOWLING, J. D. and MCMURTREY, J. E. JR. (1950) Accumulation of free amino acids as a chemical basis for morphological symptoms manifesting frenching and mineral deficiency symptoms. *Plant Physiol.*, **25**, 279.

STENLID, C. (1959) Species differences between plant roots in the reaction to inhibitory sugars. *Physiol. Plant.*, **12**, 218.

STERN, C. (1955) Gene action. *Analysis of Development*, ed. Willier *et al.*, 39–69.

STERN, H. (1960) Biochemical sequences in mitosis: in *Developing Cell Systems and their Control*; ed. D. Rudnick, Ronald Press Co., New York, 135–65.

STEWARD, F. C. (1961a) Vistas in plant physiology: Problems of organization, growth and morphogenesis. *Can. J. Bot.*, **39**, 441–60.

STEWARD, F. C. (1961b) Organization and integration: Plant cell growth and nutrition: in *Growth in Living Systems*, ed. M. X. Zarrow. Proc. Internat. Symp. on Growth, Purdue Univ., 1960. 453–90.

STEWARD, F. C. and POLLARD, J. K. (1957) Nitrogen metabolism in plants: ten years in retrospect. *Ann. Rev. Plant Physiol.*, **8**, 65–114.

STEWARD, F. C. and POLLARD, J. K. (1958) ^{14}C-Proline and hydroxyproline in the metabolism of plants. An episode in the relation of metabolism to cell growth and morphogenesis. *Nature, Lond.*, **182**, 828.

STEWARD, F. C. and MOHAN RAM, H. Y. (1961) Determining factors in cell growth: some implications for morphogenesis in plants. *Advances in Morphogenesis*, ed. J. Brachet and M. Abercrombie, Academic Press Inc., New York and London. 190–265.

STEWARD, F. C., WETMORE, R. H. and POLLARD, J. K. (1955) Nitrogenous components of the shoot apex of *Adiantum pedatum*. *Amer. J. Bot.*, **42**, 936–8.

STEWARD, F. C., MAPES, M. O. and SMITH, J. (1958) Growth and organized development of cultured cells. *Amer. J. Bot.*, **45**, 693.

STEWARD, F. C., WETMORE, R. H., THOMPSON, J. F. and NITSCH, J. P. (1954) The nitrogen components of certain shoot apical growing regions. *Amer. J. Bot.*, **41**, 123–34.

STEWART, W. N. (1959) The origin of vascular plants: monophyletic or polyphyletic? *Recent Advances in Botany*, IX Internat. Bot. Congr. Montreal, II, 960–3.

STICHEL, E. (1959) Gleichzeitige Induktion von Sprossen und Wurzeln an *in vitro* kultivierten Gewebestücken von *Cyclamen persicum*. *Planta*, **53**, 293–317.

STINGL, G. (1907) Experimentelle Studie über die Ernährung von pflanzlichen Embryonen. *Flora, Jena*, **97**, 308–31.

STOWE, B. B. and YAMAKI, T. (1957) The history and physiological action of the gibberellins. *Ann. Rev. Plant Physiol.*, **8**, 181–216.

STREET, H. E. (1957) Nutrition and metabolism of plant tissue cultures. *J. Nat. Cancer Inst.*, **19**, 467.

STREET, H. E., HUGHES, J. G. and LEWIS, S. (1960) Studies on the growth of excised roots. X. Individual amino acids and acid-hydrolysed casein as nitrogen sources for the growth of excised tomato roots. *New Phytol.*, **59**, 273.

STRONG, F. M. (1958) *Topics in Microbial Chemistry*. Wiley, New York; Chapman and Hall, London.

STURTEVANT, A. H. (1918) An analysis of the effects of selection. *Publ. Carneg. Instn.*, No. 264.

STURTEVANT, A. H. (1921) The North American species of *Drosophila*. *Publ. Carneg. Instn.*, No. 301.

STURTEVANT, A. H. (1951) The relation of genes and chromosomes: in *Genetics in the 20th Century*, New York, 101–10.

SUBRAMANYAM, K. (1962) *Aquatic Angiosperms*. C.S.I.R., New Delhi.

SUSSEX, I. M. (1951) Experiments on the cause of dorsiventrality in leaves. *Nature, Lond.*, **167**, 651–4.

SUSSEX, I. M. (1953) Regeneration of the potato shoot apex. *Nature, Lond.*, **171**, 224.

SUSSEX, I. M. (1954) Experiments on the cause of dorsiventrality in leaves. *Nature, Lond.*, **174**, 351–2.

SUSSEX, I. M. (1955a) Morphogenesis in *Solanum tuberosum* L.: Apical structure and developmental pattern of the juvenile shoot. *Phytomorph.*, **5**, 253–73.

SUSSEX, I. M. (1955b) Morphogenesis in *Solanum tuberosum* L.: Experimental investigation of leaf dorsiventrality and orientation in the juvenile shoot. *Phytomorph.*, **5**, 286–300.

SUSSEX, I. M. (1958) A morphological and experimental study of leaf development in *Leptopteris hymenophylloides* (A. Rich.) Presl. *Phytomorph.*, **8**, 97–107.

474   *Organization and Evolution in Plants*

SUSSEX, I. M. and STEEVES, T. A. (1953) Growth of excised fern leaves in sterile conditions. *Nature, Lond.*, **172**, 624–7.

SUSSEX, I. M. and STEEVES, T. A. (1958) Experiments on the control of fertility of fern leaves in sterile culture. *Bot. Gaz.*, **119**, 203–8.

SUSSEX, I. M. and CLUTTER, M. E. (1960) A study of the effect of externally supplied sucrose on the morphology of excised fern leaves *in vitro*. *Phytomorph.*, **10**, 87–99.

SUTTON, D., SCOTT, E. G. and STREET, H. E. (1961) Studies on the growth in culture of excised wheat roots. II. The growth-promoting activity of aminoacids. *Physiol. Plant.*, **14**, 712.

SWAIN, T. (1963) *Chemical Plant Taxonomy*. Academic Press, London and New York.

SWANSON, C. P. (1958) *Cytology and Cytogenetics*. London.

TEPFER, S. S. (1953) Floral anatomy and ontogeny in *Aquilegia formosa* var. *truncata* and *Ranunculus repens*. *Univ. Calif. Publ. Bot.*, **25**, 513.

TEPFER, S. S., GREYSON, R. I., CRAIG, W. R. and HINDMAN, J. L. (1963) In vitro culture of floral buds of *Aquilegia*. *Amer. J. Bot.*, **50**, 1035–45.

THIMANN, K. V. and BONNER, W. D. (1948) The action of triiodobenzoic acid on growth. *Plant Physiol.*, **23**, 158.

THODAY, D. (1933) Some physiological aspects of differentiation. *New Phytol.* **32**, 274–87.

THODAY, D. (1939) The interpretation of plant structure. Presidential Address, Sect. K, Brit. Ass. Adv. Sci., 1–21.

THODAY, J. M. (1958) Natural selection and biological progress: in *A Century of Darwin*, ed. S. A. Barnett, Heinemann, London, 313–33.

THOMAS, M. (1961) Physiology, in *Contemporary Botanical Thought*, Oliver and Boyd, Edinburgh and London, 149–70.

THOMAS, M., RANSON, S. L. and RICHARDSON, J. A. (1956) *Plant physiology*. Fourth edn. Churchill, London.

THOMPSON, D'ARCY W. (1917, 1942) *On Growth and Form*. Cambridge Univ. Press.

THOMPSON, J. MCL. (1937) On the place of ontogeny in floral inquiry. *Publ. Hartley Bot. Labs. Liverpool Univ.*, **17**, 3.

TORREY, J. G. (1958) Endogenous bud and root formation by isolated roots of *Convolvulus* grown *in vitro*. *Plant. Physiol.*, **33**, 258–63.

TORREY, J. G. (1963) Cellular pattern in developing roots. Symposium on cell differentiation; ed. G. E. Fogg, 1962. *Soc. Exp. Biol.* (In press.)

TROLL, W. (1928) *Organization und Gestalt im Bereich der Blüte*. Springer, Berlin.

TROLL, W. (1935, 1937, 1938) *Vergleichende Morphologie der höheren Pflanzen*. Borntraeger, Berlin.

TURRILL, W. B. (1938) The expansion of taxonomy with special reference to the spermatophyta. *Biol. Rev.*, **13**, 342.

TURING, A. M. (1952) The chemical basis of morphogenesis. *Phil. Trans. Roy. Soc.*, B, **237**, 37–72.

TYLER, A. (1947) *Growth*, 10, Suppl. 7–19.

UPCOTT, M. (1936) The parents and progeny of *Aesculus carnea. J. Genet.*, 33, 135–49.

VALENTINE, D. H. (1961) Evolution in the genus *Primula:* in *A Darwin Centenary*; ed. P. J. Wanstall, Buncle, Arbroath.

VAN FLEET, D. S. (1959) Analysis of the histochemical localisation of peroxidase related to the differentiation of plant tissues. *Canad. J. Bot.* **37**, 449–58.

VAVILOV, N. I. (1922) The law of homologous series in variation. *J. Genet.*, **12**, 47.

VERNON, C. (1962) The origin of life. *The Listener*, 3 May, 768–9; 10 May, 814–7.

VIRTANEN, A. I. and LINKOLA, H. (1946) Organic nitrogen compounds as nitrogen nutrition for higher plants. *Nature, Lond.*, **158**, 515.

VIRTANEN, A. I. and LINKOLA, H. (1957) On the effect of aminoacids and amines on the growth and the form of the pea plant. *Suomen Kemistilehti*, 30 B, 220.

VÖCHTING, H. (1877) Uber Theilbarkeit im Pflanzenreich und die Wirkung innerer und ausserer Krafte und Organbildung an Pflanzentheilen. *Pflugers Arch. ges. Physiol.* **15**, 153–90.

VÖCHTING, H. (1878, 1884) *Über Organbildung in Pflanzenreich.*

VÖCHTING, H. (1892) *Über Transplantation am Pflanzenkörper.* Tubingen.

VÖCHTING, H. (1908) *Untersuchungen zur experimentellen Anatomie und Pathologie des Pflanzenkörpers.* Tubingen.

VOELLER, B. R. and CUTTER, E. G. (1959) Experimental and analytical studies of pteridophytes, XXXVIII: Some observations on spiral and bijugate phyllotaxis in *Dryopteris aristata* Druce. *Ann. Bot., Lond.*, N.S. **23**, 391.

WAARD, J. DE and FLORSCHÜTZ, P. A. (1948) On the interaction of 2,3,5-triiodobenzoic acid and indole-3-acetic acid in growth processes. *Proc. Acad. Sci. Amst.*, **51**, 1317.

WAARD, J. DE and ROODENBURG, J. W. M. (1948) Premature flowerbud initiation in tomato seedlings caused by 2,3,5-triiodobenzoic acid. *Proc. Acad. Sci. Amst.*, **51**, 248.

WADDINGTON, C. H. (1939) *An Introduction to Modern Genetics.* London.

WADDINGTON, C. H. (1940) *Organisers and Genes.* Cambridge Univ. Press.

WADDINGTON, C. H. (1942a) The canalization of development and the inheritance of acquired characters. *Nature, Lond.*, **149**, 264.

WADDINGTON, C. H. (1942b) Canalization of development and the inheritance of acquired characters. *Nature, Lond.*, **150**, 363.

WADDINGTON, C. H. (1944) Life from a new angle: in *This Changing World*, ed. J. R. M. Brumwell, Routledge, London, 39–48.

WADDINGTON, C. H. (1948) The genic control of development. Symp. *Soc. exp. Biol.* **2**, *Growth*, 145–76.

WADDINGTON, C. H. (1952) How do adaptations occur? *The Listener*, **48**, 805.

WADDINGTON, C. H. (1953a) The origin of biological pattern. *New Biol.*, **15**, 117–25.

WADDINGTON, C. H. (1953b) The genetic assimilation of an acquired character. *Evolution*, **7**, 118.

WADDINGTON, C. H. (1957) *The Strategy of the Genes.* London

WADDINGTON, C. H. (1958) Theories of evolution: in *A Century of Darwin*, ed. S. A. Barnett, Heinemann, London, 1–18.

WADDINGTON, C. H. (1959) *Biological Organization.* Pergamon Press, London.

WADDINGTON, C. H. (1961) *The Nature of Life.* Allen and Unwin, London.

WADDINGTON, C. H. (1962) *New Patterns in Genetics and Development.* Columbia Univ. Press, New York.

WALD, G. (1954) The origin of life. *Scientific American*, Aug. 1954.

WARD, M. (1963) Developmental patterns of adventitious sporophytes in *Phlebodium aureum* J. Sm. *J. Linn. Soc. Lond.* (Bot.), **58**, 377–80.

WARD, M. and WETMORE, R. H. (1954) Experimental control of development in the embryo of the fern, *Phlebodium aureum. Amer. J. Bot.*, **41**, 428–34.

WARDLAW, C. W. (1924) Size in relation to internal morphology. 1. Distribution of the vascular system in *Psilotum, Tmesipteris* and *Lycopodium. Trans. Roy. Soc. Edinb.*, **53**, 503–32.

WARDLAW, C. W. (1925) Size in relation to internal morphology. 2. The vascular system of *Selaginella. Trans. Roy. Soc. Edinb.*, **54**, 281–308.

WARDLAW, C. W. (1928) Size in relation to internal morphology. 3. The vascular system of roots. *Trans. Roy. Soc. Edinb.*, **56**, 19–55.

WARDLAW, C. W. (1943) Experimental and analytical studies of pteridophytes. I. Preliminary observations on the development of buds on the rhizome of the ostrich fern (*Matteuccia struthiopteris* Tod.). *Ann. Bot., Lond.*, N.S., **7**, 171–84.

WARDLAW, C. W. (1948) Experimental and analytical studies of pteridophytes. XIII. On the shoot apex in a tree fern, *Cyathea Manniana* Hooker. *Ann. Bot., Lond.*, N.S., **12**, 371–84.

WARDLAW, C. W. (1949) Experiments on organogenesis in ferns. Ninth Growth Symp., *Growth*, Suppl., **13**, 93–113.

WARDLAW, C. W. (1951) Organisation in plants. *Phytomorph.*, **1**, 22–9.

WARDLAW, C. W. (1952a) Experimental and analytical studies of Pteridophytes. XVIII. The nutritional status of the apex and morphogenesis. *Ann. Bot., Lond.*, N.S., **16**, 207–17.

WARDLAW, C. W. (1952b) *Phylogeny and Morphogenesis.* London.

WARDLAW, C. W. (1953a) Comparative observations on the shoot apices of vascular plants. *New Phytol.*, **52**, 195–208.

WARDLAW, C. W. (1953b) A commentary on Turing's diffusion reaction theory of morphogenesis. *New Phytol.*, **52**, 40–7.

WARDLAW. C. W. (1955a) *Embryogenesis in Plants.* London and New York.

WARDLAW, C. W. (1955b) Experimental and analytical studies of pteridophytes. XXVIII. Leaf symmetry and orientation in ferns. *Ann. Bot., Lond.*, N.S., **19**, 389–99.

WARDLAW, C. W. (1955c) Evidence relating to the diffusion-reaction theory of morphogenesis. *New Phytol.*, **54**, 39–48.

WARDLAW, C. W. (1955d) The chemical concept of organization in plants. *New Phytol.*, **54**, 302–10.

WARDLAW, C. W. (1956a) A note on the effect of isolating the fern shoot apex by shallow incisions. *Phytomorph.*, **6**, 55–63.

WARDLAW, C. W. (1956b) Experimental and analytical studies of pteridophytes. XXXIV. On the shoot apex of the Bird's Nest fern, *Asplenium nidus* L. *Ann. Bot., Lond.*, N.S., **20**, 363–73.

WARDLAW, C. W. (1956c) Generalizations on the apical meristem. *Nature, Lond.*, **178**, 1427–9.

WARDLAW, C. W. (1956d) The inception of leaf primordia: in *The Growth of Leaves*, ed. F. L. Milthorpe. Butterworth Scient. Publns., London, 53–64.

WARDLAW, C. W. (1957a) Experimental and analytical studies of pteridophytes. XXXV. The effects of direct applications of various substances to the shoot apex of *Dryopteris austriaca* (*D. aristata*). *Ann. Bot., Lond.*, N.S., **21**, 85–120.

WARDLAW, C. W. (1957b) Experimental and analytical studies of pteridophytes. XXXVII. A note on the inception of microphylls and macrophylls. *Ann. Bot., Lond.*, N.S., **21**, 427–37.

WARDLAW, C. W. (1957c) On the organization and reactivity of the shoot apex in vascular plants. *Amer. J. Bot.*, **44**, 176–85.

WARDLAW, C. W. (1957d) The reactivity of the apical meristem as ascertained by cytological and other techniques. *New Phytol.*, **56**, 221–9.

WARDLAW, C. W. (1957e) The floral meristem as a reaction system. *Proc. Roy. Soc. Edinb.*, **66**, 394–408.

WARDLAW, C. W. (1958) Reflections on the unity of the embryonic tissues in ferns. *Phytomorph.*, **8**, 323–7.

WARDLAW, C. W. (1959) Methods in plant morphogenesis. *J. Linn. Soc. Lond.* (Bot.), **56**, 154.

WARDLAW, C. W. (1960a) Some preliminary observations on the inception of the inflorescence. *Proc. Linn. Soc. Lond.*, **172**, 90.

WARDLAW, C. W. (1960b) The inception of shoot organization. *Phytomorph.*, **10**, 107–10.

WARDLAW, C. W. (1961a) Morphology: in *Contemporary Botanical Thought*, Oliver and Boyd, Edinburgh and London, 1–26.

Q**

WARDLAW, C. W. (1961b) Growth and development of the inflorescence and flower: in *Growth in Living Systems*, ed. M. X. Zarrow. Basic Book Inc., New York, 491–523.

WARDLAW, C. W. (1963a) Apical organization and differential growth in ferns. Symp. on *Growth and Development of Archegoniate Plants*, J. Linn. Soc., (Bot.) London, 58, 385–400.

WARDLAW, C. W. (1963b) Experimental investigations of floral morphogenesis in *Petasites hybridus*. *Nature, Lond.*, **198**, 560–1.

WARDLAW, C. W. (1963c) A surfeit of species. *Trans. Bot. Soc. Edinb.*, **39**, 361–72.

WARDLAW, C. W. (1964) (a) General physiological problems of embryogenesis in plants. (b) Physiology of embryonic development in cormophytes. (c) The morphogenetic role of apical meristems: fundamental aspects. (d) The organization of the shoot apex. *Handbuch der Pflanzenphysiologie*, Vol. XVI, Springer-Verlag, Heidelberg.

WARDLAW, C. W. and CUTTER, E. G. (1955) Experimental and analytical studies of pteridophytes. XXX. Further investigations of the formation of buds and leaves in *Dryopteris aristata* Druce. *Ann. Bot., Lond.*, N.S., **19**, 515–26.

WARDLAW, C. W. and CUTTER, E. G. (1956) XXXI. The effect of shallow incisions on organogenesis in *Dryopteris aristata* Druce. *Ann. Bot., Lond.*, N.S., **20**, 39–56.

WARDLAW. C. W. and MITRA, G. C. (1958) The response of the shoot apex of *Dryopteris aristata* (Vill.) Druce and of detached meristems of *Onoclea sensibilis* L. and *Matteuccia struthiopteris* Tod. to physiologically-active substances. *Bull. Bot. Soc. Bengal*, **12**, 63–84.

WARDLAW, C. W. and SHARMA, D. N. (1961) Experimental and analytical studies of Pteridophytes. XXXIX. Morphogenetic investigations of sori in leptosporangiate ferns. *Ann. Bot., Lond.*, N.S., **25**, 477–90.

WARIS, H. (1957) A striking morphogenetic effect of amino acid in seed plants. Proc. Soc. Biochemica, Biophysica et Microbiologica Fenniae. *Suomen Kemistilehti*, **30**, 121.

WARIS, H. (1959) Neomorphosis induced in seed plants by amino acids. I. *Oenanthe aquatica. Physiol. Plant.*, **12**, 753–66.

WARIS, H. (1962) Neomorphosis in seed plants induced by amino acids. II. *Oenanthe lachenalii* Physiol. Plant. **15**, 736–52.

WATSON, D. M. S. (1926) The evolution and origin of the amphibia. *Phil. Trans. Roy. Soc.*, B, **214**, 189.

WEBER, A. V. and STEIN, O. L. (1954) A comparison of the rates of leaf initiation in seedlings of *Zea mays* L. under field and growth chamber conditions. *Minnesota Acad. Sci.*, **22**, 94–8.

WEBSTER, B. D. and STEEVES, T. A. (1958) Morphogenesis in *Pteridium aquilinum* (L.) Kuhn. General morphology and growth habit. *Phytomorph.*, **8**, 30–41.

WEIER, T. E. (1963) Changes in the fine structure of chloroplasts and mitochondria during phylogenetic and ontogenetic development. *Amer. J. Bot.*, **50**, 604–11.

WEINSTEIN, L. H., NICKELL, L. G., LAURENCOT, H. J. and TULECKE, W. (1959) Biochemical and physiological studies of tissue cultures and the plant parts from which they are derived. I. *Agave toumeyana* Trel. *Contrib. Boyce Thompson Inst.*, **20**, 239.

WEISS, P. (1939) *Principles of Development.* New York.

WEISS, P. (1947) The problem of specificity in growth and development. *Yale J. Biol. and Med.*, **19**, 235–78.

WEISS, P. (1949a) Differential growth: in *The Chemistry and Physiology of Growth*, ed. A. K. Parpart, Princeton Univ. Press, 135–86.

WEISS, P. (1949b) Growth and differentiation on the cellular and molecular levels. *Exp. Cell Research*, Suppl. 1. *Proc. Internat. Congr. Exp. Cytol.*, 475–82.

WEISS, P. (1950) Perspectives in the field of morphogenesis. *Quart. Rev. Biol.*, **25**, 177–98.

WEISS, P. (1955) Specificity in growth control: in *Biological Specificity and Growth*, Princeton Univ. Press, 195–206.

WEISS, P. (1956) The compounding of complex macromolecular and cellular units into tissue fabrics. *Proc. Nat. Acad. Sci., Wash.*, **42**, 819–30.

WENT, F. W. (1938a) Specific factors other than auxin affecting growth and root formation. *Plant Physiol.*, **13**, 55–80.

WENT, F. W. (1936) Allgemeine Betrachtungen über das Auxin-Problem. *Biol. Zentralbt.* **56**, 449.

WETMORE, R. H. (1950, 1953a) Tissue and organ culture as a tool for studies in development. *Proc. Seventh Internat. Bot. Congr., Stockholm*, 369–70.

WETMORE, R. H. (1953b) Carbohydrate supply and leaf development in sporeling ferns. *Science*, **118**, 578.

WETMORE, R. H. (1954) The use of *in vitro* cultures in the investigation of growth and differentiation in vascular plants. *Brookhaven Symp. Biol.*, **6**, 22–40.

WETMORE, R. H. (1955) Differentiation of xylem in plants. *Science*, **121**, 626–7.

WETMORE, R. H. (1956) Growth and development in the shoot system of plants: in *Cellular mechanisms in differentiation and growth*, Princeton Univ. Press, 173–90.

WETMORE, R. H. (1959) Morphogenesis in plants—a new approach. *American Scientist*, **47**, 326–40.

WETMORE, R. H. and MOREL, G. (1949) Growth and development of *Adiantum pedatum* L. on nutrient agar. (Abstr.). *Amer. J. Bot.*, **36**, 805–6.

WETMORE, R. H. and RIER, J. P. (1963) Experimental induction of vascular tissues in callus of angiosperms. *Amer. J. Bot.*, **50**, 418–30.

WETMORE, R. H. and SOROKIN, S. (1955) On the differentiation of xylem. *J. Arnold Arboret.*, **36**, 305–17.

WETMORE, R. H. and WARDLAW, C. W. (1951) Experimental morphogenesis in vascular plants. *Ann. Rev. Plant Physiol.*, **2**, 269–92.

WETTER, R. and WETTER, C. (1954) Studien über das Erstarkungswachstum und das primare Dickenwachstum bei leptosporangiaten Farnen. *Flora, Jena*, **141**, 598–631.

WHALEY, W. G. H., MOLLENHAUER, H. H. and LEECH, J. H. (1960a) Some observations on the nuclear envelope. *J. Biophys. Biochem. Cytol*, **8**, 233.

WHALEY, W. G., MOLLENHAUER, H. H. and LEECH, J. H. (1960b) The ultrastructure of the meristematic cell. *Amer. J. Bot.*, **47**, 401–49.

WHITE, P. R. (1939) Controlled differentiation in a plant tissue culture. *Bull. Torrey Bot. Club*, **66**, 507–13.

WHITE, P. R. (1957) *Proceedings of the Decennial Review Conference on Tissue Culture*, ed. P. R. White. *J. Nat. Cancer Inst.*, 19. no. 4.

WHITEHEAD, A. N. (1926; 1938) *Science and the Modern World*. Cambridge Univ. Press.

WILDON, D. C. and MERCER, F. V. (1963) The ultrastructure of the vegetative cell of blue-green algae. *Aust. J. Biol. Sci.*, **16**, 585–96.

WILKIE, D. (1963) Genetic analysis of variation in the bracken prothallus. *Jour. Linn. Soc. Lond. (Bot.)*, **58**, 333–6.

WILLIAMS, S. (1937) Correlation phenomena and hormones in *Selaginella*. *Nature*, **139**, 966.

WILLIAMS, W. (1962) The impact of genetics. Inaugural Lecture, Univ. of Durham, 1–18.

WILLIER, B. H., WEISS, P. A. and HAMBURGER, V. (1955) *Analysis of Development*. Philadelphia and London.

WILLIS, J. C. (1914) On the lack of adaptation in the Tristichaceae and Podostemaceae. *Proc. Roy. Soc.* B, **87**, 532–50.

WILLIS, J. C. (1922) *Age and Area*. Cambridge Univ. Press.

WILLIS, J. C. (1940) *The Course of Evolution*. Cambridge Univ. Press.

WILSON, E. B. (1925) *The Cell in Development and Heredity*. Third edn., Macmillan, New York.

WINCHELL, A. (1870) *Sketches of Creation*. Harper, New York.

WIRTH, K. (1959) Beeinflussung von Stoffleitung und Organneubildung an Blattstücken. *Naturwissenschaften*, **46**, 236.

WIRWILLE, J. W. and MITCHELL, J. W. (1950) Six new plant growth inhibiting compounds. *Bot. Gaz.*, **111**, 491–4.

WOERDEMAN, M. W. (1955) Immunobiological approach to some problems of induction and differentiation: in *Biological Specificity and Growth*, ed. E. G. Butler, Princeton Univ. Press, 33–58.

WOLF, F. T. (1952) The production of indoleacetic acid by *Ustilago zeae*, and its possible significance in tumor formation. *Proc. Nat. Acad. Sci., Wash.,* **38**, 106.

WOLFF, K. C. F. (1759) *Teoria Generationis.*

WOODGER, J. H. (1929) *Biological Principles.* Kegan Paul, London.

WOODGER, J. H. (1930, 1931) The 'concept of organism' and the relation between embryology and genetics. *Quart. Rev. Biol.,* **5**, 1;6, 178.

WOODGER, J. H. (1945) On biological transformations. *Essays on growth and form.* Oxford Univ. Press.

WOODGER, J. H. (1948) Observations on the present state of embryology. *Symp. Soc. Exp. Biol.,* **2**, 351. Cambridge Univ. Press.

WORSDELL, W. C. (1916) *The Principles of Plant Teratology.* London.

WRIGHT, S. (1929) The evolution of dominance. *Amer. Nat.,* **63**, 556.

WRIGHT, S. (1934) Physiological and evolutionary theories of dominance. *Amer. Nat.,* **68**, 24.

WRIGHT, S. (1945) Genes as physiological agents. *Amer. Nat.,* **79**, 289–303.

ZACHARIUS, R. M., CATHEY, H. M. and STEWARD, F. C. (1957) Nitrogenous compounds and nitrogen metabolism in the Liliaceae. III. Changes in the soluble nitrogen compounds of the tulip and their relation to flower formation in the bulb. *Ann. Bot., Lond.,* N.S., **21**, 193–201.

ZEEVAART, J. A. D. (1962) DNA multiplication as a requirement for expression of floral stimulus in *Pharbitis nil. Plant Physiol.,* **37**, 296–304.

ZEEVAART, J. A. D. and LANG, A. (1962) The relationship between gibberellin and floral stimulus in *Bryophyllum daigremontianum. Planta,* **58**, 531–42.

ZIMMERMANN, W. (1930a) *Phylogenie der Pflanzen.* Jena.

ZIMMERMANN, W. (1930b) Main results of the Telome Theory. *Palaeobotanist,* **1**, 456.

ZIMMERMANN, W. (1938) Die Telomtheorie. *Der Biologe.* Seventh Yr. **12**, 385.

ZIMMERMAN, P. W. and HITCHCOCK, A. E. (1942) Flowering habit and correlation of organs modified by triiodobenzoic acid. *Contr. Boyce Thompson Inst.,* **12**, 491.

ZIMMERMAN, P. W. and HITCHCOCK, A. E. (1949) Triiodobenzoic acid influences flower formation of tomatoes. *Contr. Boyce Thompson Inst.,* **15**, 353.

ZIMMERMAN, P. W. and HITCHCOCK, A. E. (1951) Growth-regulating effects of chlorosubstituted derivatives of benzoic acid. *Contr. Boyce Thompson Inst.,* **16**, 209.

Index